MAN AND IMPACT
IN THE AMERICAS

E.P. Grondine

Man and Impact in the Americas
© 1998, 1999, 2000, 2001, 2002, 2003, 2004, 2005
E. P. Grondine

TABLE OF CONTENTS

And as He sat upon the Mount of Olives,
His disciples came unto him privately, saying,

"Tell us, when shall these things be?
And what shall be the sign of your coming,
and of the end of the world?"

And Jesus answered…

"Immediately after the tribulation of those days
shall the Sun be darkened,
and the Moon shall not give her light,
and the Stars shall fall from Heaven,
and the powers of the heavens shall be shaken."

Matthew 24

"A Delta Air Lines jet was traversing Arizona on a clear day. The copilot was bombarding passengers with remarks about landmarks over the PA system.

"Coming up on the right side of our cabin, you can see Meteor Crater. A major tourist attraction in northern Arizona, it was formed when a lump of nickel and iron weighing 300,000 tons, 150 feet across, struck the earth at 40,000 miles an hour, scattering white-hot debris for miles in every direction. The hole measures nearly a mile across and is 570 feet deep."

From the cabin, a passenger was heard to exclaim: "Wow! It just missed the highway!"

Reported by *Short Final*, AVweb

FORWARD

Famine, pestilence, and plague; drought and flood, freezing, hurricane and hail; volcano, earthquake, tsunami, the shaking of the waters – these are but a few of the natural afflictions which have been visited upon man in his ancient past. And their power has been acknowledged by our historians and anthropologists since the very beginnings of their crafts.

From February 1997 to March 2003 it was my privilege to investigate the effects on mankind of a newly recognized natural force, that of the impact with the Earth of small pieces of asteroids and comets.[1] The work which lays before you is the first volume of the results of those investigations, encompassing to some extent the effects of asteroid and comet impacts in recent times upon man in the Americas; it is intended for its companion volumes to cover those effects in the ancient Near East and Europe. The tasks of investigating those effects in Asia and Africa will be the responsibilities of others.

In truth this work started as nothing more than a simple op-ed piece for an industry paper, an effort originally intended to take in total no more than two days' time. In February 1997 the National Broadcasting Company televised a science fiction movie, "*Asteroid*", which attempted to portray the effects of an asteroid impact on the United States. And in her review of the movie, the Washington Post's lead space correspondent, Kathy Sawyer, had written that no one had ever been killed by an impact. However, I seemed to remember from my readings that a group of Russian researchers had recently determined that several people had been killed by the impact of a piece of a comet that occurred in 1908 at Tunguska in Siberia. My plan was to simply take one day to dig out that report and write it up, and to spend another day in transmitting that piece and taking care of its placement.

To save time, rather than go through my clip files of Russian materials to find the report, or go through the paper collection at the Library of Congress, I thought it might be more efficient to use the new tool, the internet. This turned out to be a terrible mistake…

Instead of the Russian researchers' Tunguska report, what turned up in my internet search were the first postings of those people who might be called the "neo-catastrophists". While many of the internet items available were the works of Immanuel Velikovksy[2] adherents espousing a wandering Venus with the use of imaginary planetary dynamics, and many others were the works of followers of Otto Muck[3], making abysmal anthropological claims in support of their arguments about the end of Plato's Atlantis, there was yet a third group of people who were doing serious work, which seemed to show that not only had several nomads in Siberia been killed by impact, but that impacts in ancient times had killed extremely large numbers of people.

Before this point in time I had always presumptuously dismissed the warnings of Dr. Edward Teller[4] and his associates about the danger of cosmic impacts to the Earth as being little more than the ravings of unemployed weapons makers looking for work.

2

While Luis and Walter Alvarez[5] and their associates had pretty well shown by 1980 that the dinosaurs had been completely killed off by an impactor which hit at Chicxulub, surely impacts of this type were large and very infrequent – surely the risk was too small to worry about, or too small to spend any money on. Given the forces involved, what could anyone do about it anyway?

But now this new group of researchers was seriously and coherently arguing that multiple smaller impacts had killed large numbers of people in the recent past, say the last 5,000 years or so. I later learned that in Western Europe these researchers had been inspired by two books, *The Cosmic Serpent* (1982) and *The Cosmic Winter*(1990), the works of two professional British astronomers, Bill Napier and Victor Clube. Clube and Napier had argued that extinctions were caused by the impact of comets, not asteroids, and that extinctions were periodic on a roughly 26-million-year basis. More importantly for the work at hand, Clube and Napier also claimed that in the recent past the Earth and man had been pounded by the chunks of, and shadowed by the dust of, one Comet Enke.

These people were not the only group of serious researchers working on this problem. In Eastern Europe, travel writer and later President of Estonia Lennart Meri had stumbled upon the impact crater at Kali, Estonia which had been researched by Ivan Reinvald (1878-1941, published 1928), and Agu Aaloe (1927-1980, working from 1955-1980). Meri had realized that the impact there was rather recent, and had written the books *Hõbevalge* ("Silverwhite" or "Silvery White") in 1976 and Hõbevalgem ("More Silvery White") in 1984, to great success. Many were now following in his footsteps.

So my op-ed piece was now going to take two weeks, rather than the two days I had initially planned on. I had long been fascinated with the Minoans, and of particular interest to me was the Joshua impact, by which the Minoan forces allied with the Hittite King Hantilish had been destroyed; and along with this was the mention by Pliny of destruction by impact of the Etruscan city of Volsinii. The idea raised itself that not only the mystery of the end of the dinosaurs, but several major historical mysteries might finally be solved, if only the possibility of fatal cosmic impacts was taken into account. On a more fundamental level, such impacts could easily explain the extraordinary amount of resources ancient peoples had spent supporting their "astronomers", building their "observatories", and engaging in all sorts of bizarre magic concerning the heavens.

Holding to the two-week limit, I gathered together the scant materials available on the best researched of the fatal impacts, and composed a jaunty short op-ed piece in which I argued that recent deaths by impact had indeed occurred. It was rejected, an altogether not surprising result, when one considers the reluctance of the human mind to accept that one's world and everything and everyone in it can in an instant be blown from the face of the Earth at any moment completely without warning.

While I realize that now, suffice it to say that at the time I was stunned by the rejection. This first rejection was followed by multiple succeeding rejections, received from the participants in various internet historical discussion groups, usually with words such as "absurd". But I was certain, d*** it, as there were ancient writings which described these hits, and these accounts accompanied the disappearances of large numbers of people.

I continued on in this state for some months. Seeking some kind of affirmation, I attended the annual meeting of the American Anthropology Association, which luckily was being held in Washington that year, and met up with an old acquaintance of mine. I described my recent research to him and one of his colleagues over dinner at a local Greek restaurant. Imagine my amazement when he informed me that a prominent researcher in the field was not only attending that very same meeting, but actually would be giving a talk on it!

Thus began my involvement with Liverpool's John Moore's University's Benny Peiser. One can scarcely imagine my relief at finding out that not only were there other relatively sane researchers who were seriously working in this area, but that they had actually held a conference at Cambridge University just slightly earlier (July 11-13, 1997). Benny provided me with a copy of that meeting's papers, and further invited me to join an e-mail group which he had set up to keep the meeting's participants abreast of the news and in touch with each other's work.

At last I had found a place where I could share my very own little bits of research without being treated as being absolutely insane. I can assure anyone that the feeling arising from being considered sane by one's contemporaries is a very gratifying feeling indeed.

As this relationship evolved, I ended up more or less becoming the Washington stringer for the Cambridge Conference group. Certainly the money the United States government spent on this problem was too little to rate any coverage in the usual space industry publications, and as the aerospace industry was in a recession then, advertising sales were down as well, along with outside article purchases. In the face of no placement through regular outlets, simply making my fellow scriveners aware of the tremendous resource the Cambridge Conference represented seemed to me to be the responsible thing to do.

All has been more or less fine and dandy since that evening in Washington, and I suppose that I owe my acquaintance several drinks for his introduction, if not several bottles. The surprising thing to me since then has been the sheer amount of historical material on impacts which I have succeeded in more or less fortuitously running into. Buried among the bulk of materials surviving from mankind's past, these materials comprise but a small part, but they are to me without question the most significant part.

Which brings us to the work at hand....

(Footnotes)

[1] What are asteroids and comets? Entire books have been written about each of them, often offering conflicting views. For the purposes at hand, an easy way to think of asteroids and comets is as the bits of space stuff which were left over after the planets in our Solar System formed. That's easy enough, and the problem which this book deals with, as it were, is that the planets are still forming – still picking up bits of this space stuff, even to the present day.

[2] Immanuel Velikovsky (1895-1979), psychologist (associate of Freud) and scientific publisher (associate of Einstein). Velikovsky's fascination with the origins of monotheism led to his notice of an impact mentioned in the biblical book of Joshua, and this in turn led to an attempt by him to survey impact myths from around the Earth. His synthesis *Worlds in Collision,* Macmillan/Doubleday, 1950 and followup *Ages in Chaos,* Doubleday, 1952, featured impossible planetary dynamics including a wandering Venus and imagined histories attempting to make co-incidental entirely different historical impacts.

[3] Otto Muck (-1965), prolific German engineer who worked on the V-2 rocket at Peenemunde and invented the snorkel for the U-Boat. In his book *Atlantis gefunde* (Victoria, 1954) Muck argued that a massive asteroid strike in the Atlantic which occurred on 5 June 8498 BCE (Mayan calendar date) not only destroyed the legendary kingdom of Atlantis but also led to the end of the last ice age.

[4] Edward Teller, (1908-2003), nuclear physicist who led development of the hydrogen bomb for the United States. The beginnings of Teller's interest in asteroid and comet impact are hidden within a secure environment, but most likely were linked to the detection of high atmosphere comet and asteroid impacts by the first generation of U.S. Early Warning Satellites.

[5] Luis Walter Alvarez (1911-1988), nuclear physicist whose works included neutron accelerators, methods for generating radar waves, conventional explosive triggers for nuclear charges, and devices for the study of sub-atomic phenomena. Significantly, Alvarez worked with Teller both at Los Alamos and at the University of California, Berkeley.

In 1978 Luis accompanied his son Walter (geologist, University of California, Berkeley) on an expedition to Italy to recover samples from the geological layer which separated the dinosaurs from life. Luis then subjected the sample to detailed atomic analysis, employing Frank Asaro and Helen Michel to perform the measurements. After much work exploring the possibility that a super-nova had killed the dinosaurs, the team finally detected worldwide concentrations of iridium which could only have been delivered by the impact with the Earth of a massive body from deep space.

CHAPTER 1

THE PROBLEM DEFINED

Having already gathered together materials on some of the historical impacts that had occurred in Europe and the ancient Near East, in the year 2000 I used the opportunity provided by a trip to a Mars planning conference in Houston to conduct a survey of a number of North American archaeological sites. While my primary area of interest was and is the Bronze Age Aegean, and I had no particularly intense interest in or expertise on Native American cultures, my earlier comments to the Conference that someone surely must be already undertaking a survey like this had been met with such skepticism on Dr. Peiser's part ("you hope") that I decided to at least attempt the task myself.

The area I covered in that first survey was for the most part what I think of as the "Barbeque Zone" of south east North America, that area where Native Americans, and thus their colonial conquerors, used pepper flavored tomato sauces in their cooking. As some impacts were discovered through this trip, in the year 2001 this first survey was followed by a survey of the materials on the coastal peoples of southeast North America.

MIGRATIONS CAUSED BY IMPACT

Going into the survey in 2000, I knew what had usually happened in the Near East after a small piece of an asteroid or comet had hit: the neighboring people had usually either invaded or simply walked into the newly decimated/depopulated area.

Now as general background, the following are the possible alternative outcomes when two groups of people come into contact:

1) One population group may kill the other completely
2) One population group may kill most men, women, and children of the other group, absorbing either some skilled craftsmen, cultural leaders, translators, or some surviving children
3) One population group may kill the men and children of the other group, absorbing its fertile women
4) One population group may kill the males of the other group, absorbing its fertile women and their children
5) One population group may dominate the other group, reducing it to and keeping it in a clearly defined supportive role
6) The two population groups may occupy the same area, with each in a distinct and separate ecological niche
7) The two population groups may remain in separate adjoining areas and engage in trade
8) The two population groups may remain in separate adjoining areas and maintain strict separation
9) One population group or both may harbor diseases to which the other population group has no immunity, and contact brings decimation or

extinction to one or both groups

My task was to help to document a new case, the case where

10) One population group is blown off the face of the Earth by the impact of a small piece of an asteroid or comet, and the neighboring group simply walks into their now empty lands

MIGRATIONS AND LONG-TERM CHANGES IN CLIMATE

To identify those impact related migrations it would be necessary to separate them from migrations caused by long-term changes in climate. Ken Hsu had been putting forth evidence of a 1200-year worldwide climate cycle, in which 600 years of "good" weather was followed by 600 years of "bad". Hsu had pointed out that the period from 2400-2200 BCE[1] was marked by drought in the Middle East, cold in Europe, and the movement of Indo-European peoples into China. He had gathered evidence that the next climate maximum ended ca. 1250 BCE, with the arrivals of Urnfield peoples in Europe, and foreign invaders in China. The following climatic optimum ended around the year 0 with the arrival of the Helvetians in Europe, and the Wang Mong "hunger year" in China. Hsu saw the medieval optimum lasting from 900 CE to 1300 CE, when the Vikings, the Hanseatic League, and the Silk Road towns all thrived. What followed was a period of cold in Europe, drought in China, and invasion by northern peoples, which ended about 1800 CE.

Finnish researcher Timo Niroma had been trying to tie these long-term climatic fluctuations to the period of Jupiter's orbit, an effect which must arise either through the effect of Jupiter's gravity on the nuclear reaction of our Sun, or through Jupiter's effect on the flow of the solar stream coming off of our Sun.

Thus another part of the problem which I needed to solve was to figure out whether anything similar had occurred in North America.

MIGRATIONS AND SHORT-TERM COLLAPSES IN CLIMATE

In addition to these migrations caused by long-term cycles in the climate, we also knew that there had been migrations caused by short term climatic collapses. These climate crashes appeared to have been caused by the dust in the atmosphere blocking sunlight. Sometimes this dust had come from the eruptions of volcanoes, and this was well known, but one of Clube and Napier's central arguments was that in the recent past sometimes this dust had come from the Earth passing through the tail of Comet Encke. Evidence for these collapses in Europe and the ancient Near East had been gathered together by tree ring expert Mike Baillie and others.

Geologist Peter Schulz and anthropologist Bruce Masse had also documented a massive impact event in Rio Cuarto, Argentina, from roughly this period, and it was likely that the dust load from this impact in South America had also caused a massive climatic collapse.

8

I now needed to add short-term climate failures to my list of things to watch for, which already included both the direct effects of the blasts of impacts, and long-term climatic failures. Thus prepared, I started.

THE LIMITS OF THE SURVEYS

The work before you reflects the limits of those initial surveys, with very limited reference made to the first peoples of the arctic and western North America. Reflecting on these limits today, I think that so much of the Hopi, Navajo, Pacific Coastal, and Arctic peoples' cultures survived the European conquest, and that there are so many scientists among them far better able than your humble scribe to write on their impact lore, that I won't have to undertake that work myself. At least I hope so.

I also ask the reader to keep in mind another limit on those initial surveys, which is that at that time, to my knowledge, no one in the community of American anthropologists had ever previously considered the possibility of asteroid and comet impact as a cause for Native American beliefs and behaviors. As there are now specialists on these peoples working through the available materials looking for signs of impact events, a fuller story of man and impact in the Americas than the one you have before you should be available in the not too distant future. But until those studies come along, I suppose that the one you have before you will have to do for the time being.

(Footnotes)

[1] The new era designations of CE (Christian Era) and BCE (Before the Christian Era) are used here in place of their old equivalent abbreviations of AD (Anno Domine – Year of our Lord) and BC (Before Christ). These modern abbreviations are now commonly used in respect of the religious beliefs of those 5 billion people living on the Earth who practice religions other than Christianity. As an immediate example, while for Christians Jesus is their Lord, nearly every Native American people had prophets of their own long before the arrival of the Europeans.

MAP OF KNOWN IMPACT CRATERS ON THE E ARTH
adapted from map by Natural Resources Canada

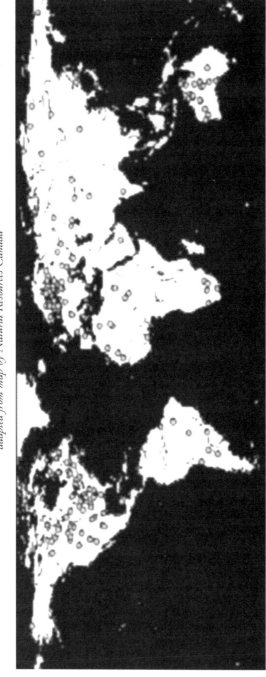

The high incidence of known impact craters in Europe and North America probably reflects the work of geologists in those areas, rather than any preference on the part of asteroids and comets to hit there.

CHAPTER 2

GETTING TO THE CROSSINGS

While asteroid and comet impacts with the Earth do not happen all that often, mankind[1] has been around in one form or another for some nearly 7 million years or so. Given this fact, I suppose that the proper place to start this work is by showing how these impacts affected man as he evolved from the other primates, both getting him ready for his crossing into the Americas, as well as getting the Americas ready for him. In doing this I will be following in the steps of Benny (Dr Peiser) and his colleague Michael Paine of Spaceguard Australia, who have long been interested in the effects of asteroid and comet impact on man's evolution.

By measuring the differences in our DNA from that of the chimpanzees, dates of around 7 millions years ago have been estimated for our divergence from our primate brethren. But despite recent fossil finds, we still have no firm evidence showing that this very early date is correct. However, we do have fossil evidence from the Great Rift Valley in Africa showing a divergence of *Ardipithecus Ramidus (Kababa)* from chimpanzees about 5.8 million years ago. The first clear evidence of this divergence is an increase in the size of molar teeth, a reduction in eye-tooth and incisor size, and the development of the bones required to occasionally walk upright.

There are many theories as to what put man on his evolutionary path to intelligence.

It used to be claimed that a climate change led to our evolution. In this theory, the closing of the Tethys Sea between Asia and Europe led to a drier environment in Africa, which in turn led to trees dying off, with the remaining trees separated by open grasslands. These grasslands were then supposed to have forced our ancestors to walk across them to get to the remaining trees for food, and this in turn was supposed to have freed our hands and minds for tool use.

The problem with this theory is that we now know that our divergence from the chimpanzees occurred well before the closing of the Tethys Sea. However, since as a general principle most theories are simply too good (at least to their originators) to abandon them, this theory has now been reworked, with the emergence of the grasslands linked with the formation of the Great Rift Valley itself some 10 to 8 million years ago.

Unfortunately, this new date is a little too early to explain our divergence from the chimpanzees. The solution to the problem of grasslands lies with the ancient elephants (*Recki and P. Deinotheres*) which were evolving at that time, and which did change their environment through the simple act of grazing. After a couple of million years these elephants provided the ecological "niche" which our ancestors exploited, and it is important to note that hominid fossils are nearly always found in close association with elephant fossils. The simple truth of the matter appears to be that the chimpanzees remained in the trees, while our ancestors moved to the margins of these elephant pastures.

That simple difference in ecological niche was the key to all that followed. Today we nearly always mentally picture our most ancient ancestors as a few individuals straggling alone across vast grasslands, when in truth they lived in bands of 50 or so individuals, hanging out on the edges of elephant pastures. The elephants offered some protection from the larger cats, and this allowed our ancestors to move down out of the trees.

This immediately brings us to the next question: what did the elephants get out of this? The answer lies in the second earlier theory for man's evolution. It used to be claimed that man was the only tool using animal, that his ability to walk upright had freed his hands to make tools. This claim was made until chimps were noted using sticks to feed at termite nests, using stones to crack nuts, and importantly, using sticks to kill attacking predators.

Anthropologists were then left in the awkward position of either having to drop the theory, or admit that chimpanzees were human, at least to some degree. Since the second alternative was what the anthropologists had been claiming all along, it is the one universally adopted today. Given our undeniable genetic similarity with the chimpanzees, it is safe to claim that even in the earliest times our ancestors probably did then the same things chimps do today: use stones to crack nuts open and use sticks to kill small cats. Indeed this is what the fossil record shows, as the teeth of the fossils of our earliest ancestors show that they were well developed for eating both nuts cracked open with stones[2] as well as roots dug up with sticks.

At this point we can now picture our earliest ancestors living in bands of 50 or so individuals in the trees around the grasslands formed by the grazing ancient elephants, which the elephants usually created around lakes and ponds. These ancient elephants (*Recki and P. Deinotheres*) not only provided protection against the larger cats, they also favored the propagation of the nuts and roots which they ate in common with our ancestors. Our ancestors took care of the smaller cats and other nuisances with their sticks and stones, and the elephants tolerated them well in return. Their troop's howlings would also have provided the elephants with warning of the approach of larger cats.

But all of this new information still leaves open the question as to why we evolved in the direction we did, while the chimps did not. Based on what we know, let's try to come up with a reasonable answer to this. Our ancestors would have "walked" with the elephants as they occasionally moved from pasture to pasture as the grass ran out, from waterhole to waterhole as the water ran dry. Now while much study has been made of changes in hip structure to accommodate these walks, little study has been made of changes in shoulder structures necessary to use stones to crack open nuts and weld sticks to dig roots and kill small cats; and yet another thing that man does well that chimpanzees do not is accurately throw things for long distances.

Another mental picture which we have today is that despite their ability to use sticks to kill small cats, our most ancient ancestors were always at the mercy of largest predatory cats. But imagine, if you will, a larger cat attacking what is actually shown in the fossil record: 50 or so individuals sitting around an elephant pasture, with stones in their hands which they are using to crack open nuts. If a large cat attacks this group, it may succeed in gaining its dinner, but at a very high risk of death, as instead of enjoying a tasty meal, it may end up being stoned to death instead. Now cats do have a certain amount of intelligence, and with so many ancient cattle (bovids), horses (equids), antelope, and deer grazing in the nearby elephant pasture, all of which were relatively defenseless compared to our ancestors, why would it have bothered with *Australopithecus*, unless it were very hungry indeed?

Moving on, the third theory which I will mention here is that of progenesis: unlike most animals, we are born in an undeveloped state, which allows us to learn behaviors such as tool use as our brains develop. This trait used to be thought to be uniquely human, but has now been noted among chimpanzees and other primates as well. Indeed, chimp mothers have to teach their offspring both how to use sticks to dig out termite nests, and more importantly how to use stones to crack open nuts. This progenesis is also seen in the human fossil record: mothers probably used their ability to walk upright occasionally to carry their children, instead of having them hang on.

Another interesting point is that sex had become more recreational and less procreational. This developmental immaturity in turn required an extended dependence upon the care of our mothers, and this in turn required that our mothers enter into lasting pair bonds with our fathers. And since like the chimpanzee the unit of survival for Australopithecus was a band of 50, not the individual and its mother, some way had to be found to keep the group together. Sex was a good way of doing this, and the physiology and neurology of the centers of mating evolved to fill this new need for sexual pleasure. The reduction in eyeteeth size is probably not only related to the reduction of fruit in our diets but also related to the lack of biting in mating.

A final point is that female chimpanzees will leave their troop and go to another one to find mates. This not only prevents inbreeding, it also leads to the spread of chimpanzee technology from troop to troop.

Not much altogether, but it was a start.

6.5 AND 6.1 MILLION YEARS AGO:
AUSTRALOPITHECUS AND THE SUPERVOLCANOES

The Great Rift Valley of Africa is called the "Great Rift" Valley because it is a great geological rift which formed between tectonic plates as they moved apart, and the entire region is volcanically active. Occasionally one of these small volcanoes would go off, and whoever was living close by would be certain to be affected by it.

But to give my vulcanological brethren their due, occasionally extremely large volcanoes would go off else where on the Earth, with eruptions so large that they would fill the air with dust and sulfur. These super volcanoes actually spewed up so much dust and sulfur that it would actually block the light of the sun from the Earth, and lead to the failure of plants both due to the lack of sunlight, as well as to their simply being frozen by the falling temperatures.

14

One of these supervolcanoes went off about 6.5 million years ago at Blacktail along the Snake River Plain in today's United States, leaving a crater measuring some 100 kilometers long by 60 kilometers wide and ejecting some 3,400,000,000,000 tons of rock.[3] Another "smaller" super-volcano erupted some 6.1 million years ago at Cerro Panizos on today's Argentinian-Bolivian border, throwing out a mere 1,600,000,000,000 tons of ejecta while leaving a crater measuring "only" 8.2 kilometers across.

While we do not currently know how severe the effects were of the eruptions of these supervolcanoes, we have recently observed in detail the effects on the Earth's climate of the eruptions of much smaller volcanoes. The eruptions of Laki in 1783 and Tambora in 1851 produced cold weather world wide which lasted for a year, knocking out crops, while the larger explosion at Krakatoa in 1883 produced cold weather which lasted for several years.

HOW *AUSTRALOPITHECUS* SURVIVED THE CLIMATE COLLAPSES

From the observed effects of these recent volcanoes we can infer that the eruptions of these super-volcanoes must have affected *Australopithecus*'s world in similar but far more severe ways. The climate collapses would have severely reduced food supplies for several years, and the cold and lack of sunlight would have finished off many plants and trees completely.

Australopithecus ate nuts and roots, and these hardy trees and plants would have been among the last foods to be affected by the cold. Competing primates who relied on fruits instead of nuts and roots would have been hit hardest by the falling temperatures. The fruit trees on which those competitors depended must surely have been knocked out first, while roots are far hardier to cold, and any animal which ate them would have had a better chance at coming through it all.

The nut and root eating animals included not only *Australopithecus* but elephants as well. During the climate collapses, it would have been necessary for the elephants to travel great distances to harvest the remaining food stocks, and the ability to walk would have been a favored survival trait. And elephants would not have been the only animal to become more mobile, as those who could keep up with the elephants as they wandered seeking out new pastures during the collapses would also have been favored to survive.

Another trait which must have favored the survival of *Australopithecus* over that of other species was that they had an entirely different supply of food near at hand. Like the chimpanzees of today, *Australopithecus* must also have killed and eaten small animals, and in climate collapses this ability to kill and eat meat would have provided them with foods to substitute for the plants which had been killed by the cold.

Finally, one can be sure that these impacts and the resulting climate collapses led to the deaths of many animals, and any species which scavenged on their remains would have had a sure food source through these winters. In the climatic downturns, meat from the killing of small animals must have been supplemented with meat scavenged from the carcasses of animals which had died due to the cold.

15

5.6–5.0 MILLION YEARS AGO:
MORE SUPER-VOLCANOES ERUPT

There were three more major volcanic eruptions which affected our early ancestors around this time, not even considering the smaller eruptions, about which we have no complete information on as of today. 5.6 million years ago there was an eruption at Blue Creek on the Snake River Plain in the United States, leaving a crater measuring some 8.1 kilometers across while ejecting 1,200,000,000,000 tons of magma. Sometime around 5.4 million years ago Cerro Galan in Argentina started to erupt, and though at the current time it's difficult to say exactly how large this eruption was, the final crater measured some 32 kilometers across. Finally, about 5 million years ago an unnamed super-volcano[4] went off in Bolivia in the Huaylillas Ignimbrite formation, leaving a crater measuring only some 10 kilometers across while ejecting some 1,300,000,000,000 tons of magma.

5 MILLION YEARS AGO:
IMPACTS AND *AUSTRALOPITHECUS* RAMIDUS

Worse was to come. Due to the detailed observations of recent volcanic eruptions, we know that the part of a volcano's molten rock which is fine enough and hot enough to actually go into the atmosphere, afterwards drops out quite quickly due to gravity, falling back to Earth nearly entirely within only one or two years. We now know that it is not this dust which blocks the sunlight, but rather the sulfur which these volcanoes eject: this sulfur forms droplets of sulfuric acid high in the upper atmosphere by combining with the water vapor there. These particles of sulfuric acid remain airborne for much longer periods of time, and play a far greater role in blocking sunlight from the Earth than the dust does; and thus they are more important than the dust in cooling things off.[5]

Now besides volcanoes, another source for particles in the atmosphere is the impact of asteroids and comets with the Earth. In these cases the effects are worse, as a good part of the rock which these things hit is turned into vapor. Not only will these fine particles of dust remain airborne longer; in the case of some impacts the asteroid which hits will actually be made of sulfur to one varying degree or another. Additionally, even the near miss of a comet can deposit large amounts of very fine dust in the Earth's upper atmosphere.

About 5 million years ago, give or take 300,000 years, something, either an asteroid or comet, hit at Bigach, Kazakhstan, and left a crater measuring some 8 kilometers across. (For those of you not versed in the metric system, see the footnote, as I am not going to convert all of this over for you.[6]) We usually think of an explosion this big in nuclear terms, but even these terms will not completely do here: the largest nuclear explosion ever set off by man was the Soviet Union's "Tsar Bomba" (King of Bombs), which was detonated on 30 October 1961 over Novaya Zemlya, producing some 50,000 kilotons of explosive force; in comparison, the Bigach impactor exploded with a force of some 2,174,151 kilotons, or roughly 40 times that.[7] And that was only a medium sized impact.

16

We have a rough time trying to imagine explosions of that size, but one way of thinking about it is in terms of "Hiroshimas", which unit of measure we all unfortunately know all too well. Thought of in these terms, the impact at Bigach was about 174,000 times the explosion at Hiroshima.[8] While something like 26,000 square kilometers were blasted by this impact, and another 223,000 square kilometers or so were directly set on fire by its explosion, all of this happened in Asia: the part that probably had the most important effect on our ancestors was the some 350,000,000 tons of vaporized rock which the Bigach impact put into the upper atmosphere. That vaporized rock, along with a part of the 350,000,000,000 tons of ejecta thrown out from the crater, must have thrown the world into a very severe winter for several years.

Again, the Bigach Impact was not even a large one. It was followed 200,000 years or so later by an asteroid or comet impact at Karla, Russia, which left a hole in the Earth measuring some 10 kilometers across. While the Bigach Impact had the force of 174,000 Hiroshimas, the impactor which hit at Karla had a force of roughly 365,000 Hiroshimas. Some 428,000 square kilometers were immediately set on fire by the heat of its explosion, and some 680,000,000 tons of vaporized rock were placed in the atmosphere.

Yet even the effects of the Bigach Impact and the Karla Impact combined do not match those of what hit at Kara-Kul, Tajikistan, only a few hundred thousand years later, a mere blink of the eye in terms of man's time here on Earth. The Kara-Kul impact left a hole measuring some 52 kilometers across, set some 38,000,000 square kilometers on fire, and threw some 95,000,000,000 tons of vaporized rock into the air. Its explosive force was roughly equivalent to some 88,000,000,000 Hiroshimas. (Yes, you read that correctly, its force was that of 88 billion Hiroshimas).

What effect did these impacts have on our ancestors? Well, aside from the climate collapses, whose effects were immediate, the fires from these impacts must also have set a good-size chunk of Northern Asia on fire - whatever trees were there originally, they were gone afterwards, and grasslands probably grew up in their place. These grasslands would survive for millions of years, and large animals would evolve to feed on them. And these animals would become very, very important to our ancestors a short few million years later.

4.3-4.0 MILLION YEARS AGO:
MORE SUPER-VOLCANOES

About 4.3 million years ago a super-volcano erupted at Kilgore, once again on the plain of the Snake River in today's United States. This eruption left a crater measuring some 80 kilometers long and 60 kilometers across, and discharged some 1,900,000,000,000 tons of rock and sulfur into the air. Only 100,000 years later, a super-volcano erupted at Cerro Galan in Argentina, leaving a crater 32 kilometers in diameter, while ejecting some 1,200,000,000,000 tons of rock.

200,000 thousand years after this, about 4 million years ago, a super-volcano went off at La Pacana, Chile, which left behind a crater measuring 60 kilometers long and 35 kilometers wide. It is estimated that some 3,900,000,000,000 tons of ejecta came out of this one.

4.0 MILLION YEARS AGO:
AUSTRALOPITHECUS STARTS TO WALK

While we can't say right now with any exactness how cold the winters were which these super volcanoes and impacts produced, or how long they lasted, we do know from later smaller historical impacts and volcanic eruptions that they must have occurred, and that they must have been severe. Based on the known historical mortality rates for these later events, we can also assert that these ancient climate collapses led to great evolutionary stresses, and that only the fittest survived.

Whatever the immediate effects of these volcanoes and impacts on Australopithecus were, afterwards we find them walking upright all the time, even though they were not fully adapted for it: *Australopithecus ramidus* became *Australopithecus amanenesis* The elephants clearly had had to move to new pastures more often during these climatic collapses, and *Australopithecus* had moved right along with them. Their earlier changes in diet, to nuts and roots and meat, were probably reinforced as well during the collapses.

MORE IMPACTS, MORE CLIMATE COLLAPSES, MORE CHANGES

Walking upright easily would take another two climate collapses, but these collapses were caused by impact, not super volcanoes. The impact of an asteroid or comet near today's Roter Kamm in Namibia "only" left a hole some 2.5 kilometers across in the ground. Coming in with a force of some 3,600 Hiroshimas, it "only" set nearly 10,000 square kilometers on fire, and "only" threw some 10,500,000 tons of vaporized rock into the atmosphere. But while the Roter Kamm impactor "only" did this much, it had hit much closer to the Great Rift Valley, *Australopithecus's* home, than the earlier Asian impactors had, and thus the direct effects of its blast were likely to have been felt more intensely there.

However, the next impactor struck again in Asia, at El'gygytgyn in Russia, and left a hole 18 kilometers across, had the power of 2,600,000 or so Hiroshimas (and that is 2.6 million Hiroshimas, in case the number slid by you), set some 2,000,000 square kilometers on fire again (see above), and threw some 4,000,000,000 (that is 4 billion) tons of vaporized rock into the air. Certainly once again there was a global climate collapse, though again how intense it was and how long it lasted no one can say today with any degree of absolute certainty.

When did these impacts occur? Right now we don't know this with any absolute certainty either. The best date that can currently be set for the Roter Kamm Impact is 3.7 million years ago, give or take 300,000 years, while the best date that can currently be set for the El'gygytgyn Impact is 3.5 million years ago, give or take 500,000 years. My guess is that there was an impactor, either an asteroid or comet, which fragmented while still in space, and the newly separated pieces of it hit the Earth a relatively short time apart on the cosmic scale of things. My best guess is that they hit together about 3.7 million years ago, and together they caused a severe enough climate collapse

18

to cause man's adaption of walking upright to become permanent: *Australopithecus amanenesis* became *Australopithecus afarensis*, and his wrist and hand changed completely, as they were now used entirely for grasping instead of walking.

Sadly, we shall probably never know much about *afarensis's* tools, as they probably used found objects the same way that chimps do – whether sticks, stones, or bones. The difference may have been that now they used them more often and carried them around for longer times with their newly freed hands.

2.7 MILLION YEARS AGO
MORE IMPACTS, MORE CLIMATE COLLAPSES:
AUSTRALOPITHECUS LEARNS HOW TO CUT: *HOMO* EMERGES

Roughly 3 million years ago, perhaps as late as 2.7 million years ago, there was another pair of impacts, again most likely caused by the impacts of separate fragments of the same parent asteroid or comet. While these impacts were smaller than the impacts mentioned above, both of these pieces hit the African continent, and their effects on our ancestors must have been more direct.

The first of these pieces hit at Aouelloul in Mauritania and left a crater measuring a mere 390 meters across. While it took only 93 kilotons or so to make this crater, the catch here is that it is most probable that this impactor exploded when it hit the atmosphere, instead of when it hit the Earth. To deliver 93 kilotons to the surface from 5 to 8 kilometers up meant that it had to explode there with a force about 1,000 times that, say 93,000 kilotons or so, around 7,500 Hiroshimas. The blast in this case would have leveled every tree for about 3,200 square kilometers and set on fire everything within about 1,700 square kilometers.

The other piece of this comet or asteroid hit at Talemzane, Algeria, and left a hole in the ground measuring some 1,750 meters across. While this explosion was a mere 13,800 kilotons, 1,100 Hiroshimas, and leveled only 900 square kilometers while setting on fire 3,600 square kilometers or so, again it had hit close to the Great Rift Valley. The blast would have thrown about 3,650,000 tons of vaporized rock into the atmosphere, alongside roughly another 3,635,000,000 tons of debris, and a good part of all of this would have landed right in the Rift.

What was the result of the climate collapse this time? In response to the reduction in plant foods, *Australopithecus* adds meat to his diet in a big way, and develops some new tools to do it. Fossils of *Australopithecus garhi* have been found alongside bones which show that he was using tools to cut and chop meat from bones, and using rocks to smash bones open to get at their marrow.

Australopithecus had learned how to cut things, and how to bang one rock against another rock to make the sharp rock edges to do this. This new technology may have come about as a simple accident incidental to cracking open nuts or bones with rocks, wherein one rock fractured into pieces and cut its user. This undoubtedly was a painful lesson, and one which must have happened quite often before, but for some reason this time the lesson was learned and put to good advantage.

PARANTHROPUS - A DEAD END

It is also interesting that about this time our hominid ancestor now evolved in two separate directions, one leading to us, the other leading to a dead end. Another adaptation to the climate collapse caused by these impacts seems to have been the development by some *Australopithecines* of robust jaws for eating the nuts and roots which they used to open with stones. These *Australopithecine* offspring are known today as *Paranthropus aethiopicus*.

If one notes that breaking open nuts is a learned behavior, carefully taught by mother chimps to their infants, then one could easily imagine that if enough of these mother *Australopithecines* were lost in a climate collapse following these major asteroid or comet impacts, the entire group's knowledge of how to use stones to break open nuts could be lost as well. If that knowledge of how to break open nuts was lost, other *Australopithecine* knowledge could possibly have been lost as well: what foods are safe, how to use sticks to fend off predators. The loss of all of this knowledge would have given evolutionary advantage to other traits among the survivors, besides nut-cracking jaws, as they would also have had less protection against predators, and traits such as the ability to flee, or brute strength would also have been favored.

And that is exactly what the fossil record shows.

2.0-1.8 MILLION YEARS AGO:
MORE SUPER-VOLCANOES AND IMPACTS

About 2 million years ago a stunning super-volcano erupted at Yellowstone in the United States. It left a crater measuring some 100 kilometers long by 50 kilometers wide, from which it ejected some 5,500,000,000,000 tons of molten rock and sulfur. (That's 5,500 billion tons with a b.)

This massive volcano was followed by two "small" impacts. About 1.88 million years ago either an asteroid or comet hit at Karikkoselkä, Finland, with the force of 660 Hiroshimas, throwing into the atmosphere around 2,300,000 tons of vaporized rock and another 2,300,000,000 tons of pulverized rock, from a "small" crater measuring only a kilometer and a half across. The next impactor was even smaller than that, but it hit close to the Great Rift at Kalkkop, South Africa, around 1.8 million years ago. As this impactor left a crater measuring only 640 meters across on the ground, most likely it burst in the air with the force of some 38,000 Hiroshimas, setting on fire around 4,700 square kilometers while leveling 9,700 square kilometers: anything living in that blast area was most likely killed outright by the impact.

THE AXE: *HOMO ERECTUS* EMERGES

Whatever the effects of these climatic collapses, *Australopithecus's* ability to butcher meat by using sharp edges to cut it off of bones had led to substantial change. The sharp edges had become knives, and they had begun to hunt the animals of the elephant pastures. Their brains grew larger, and *Australopithecus* evolved into *Homo habilis*. *Homo habilis* had begun to spread, and it has recently been discovered that by about 1.8

million years ago he had even made it as far as the elephant pastures of Southern Europe.

But it appears to have been the next big invention, the axe, which turned *Homo habilis* into *Homo erectus*[9]. While due to the lack of preservation of organic remains it is impossible to know with certainty if *Homo erectus* used his axes with his hands, or whether he attached them to sticks, given the difficulty in holding the sharp edges of an axe in ones hands, the second alternative appears to be the only viable one. An axe attached to a stick provides leverage, and can be thrown for some distance with accuracy.

Homo erectus was now the top predator of the elephant pastures, and he quickly spread along the elephant pastures of not only Africa, but on into the elephant pastures of today's India, and farther onward into the elephant pastures of Southeast Asia, and then north along the east coast of Asia.

1.4 MILLION YEARS AGO:
MORE MAJOR IMPACTS

About 1.4 million years ago there were two more major impacts which caused major climatic collapses. About 1.4 million years ago either an asteroid or a comet hit at New Quebec, Canada, and left a hole in the ground measuring 3.4 kilometers across. This impact must have placed around 27.7 million tons of vaporized rock in the atmosphere, while throwing out another 27.7 million tons or so of pulverized rock. Everything within about 4,000 square kilometers was blown down, while roughly some 23,000 square kilometers was set on fire. This newly created grassland undoubtedly provided great pasturage for the North American "elephants", the mammoth.

The dating of the next impact presents an interesting problem. About 1.3 million years ago, give or take 210 thousand years, something, either asteroid or comet, hit at Bosumtwi in Ghana and left a hole in the ground measuring some 10.5 kilometers across. The Bosumtwi impactor hit with a force of roughly 10,400 Hiroshimas, threw some 27,700,000 tons of vaporized rock in the air, alongside another 27,600,000,000 tons or so of pulverized rock. Everything within about 500,000 square kilometers was set on fire. As this piece of space stuff hit relatively close to the Great Rift, anything living nearby would have been severely affected by it, and the dating here is important.

THE BOSUMTWI IMPACT AND *PARANTHROPUS*

Paranthropus, the Australopithecines who perhaps may have lost the use of tools through catastrophic events (above), had by now evolved into two separate species, Paranthropus Bosei and Paranthropus Robustus. It appears that the effects of the Bosumtwi Impact caused the extinction of *Paranthropus boisei*, which was living in East Africa at the time, while *Paranthropus robustus*, living in Southern Africa to the south of *Paranthropus boisei*, would manage to survive the effects of the Bosumtwi Impact.

HOMO ERECTUS BEGINS TO HUNT ELEPHANT:
THE SPEAR, THE PIT TRAP, AND AMBUSH

A great deal of argument is taking place today within the anthropological community as to what occurred next, as to whether *Homo erectus* further evolved in Africa, or whether his next big evolutions occurred in Asia. It should be noted in this regard that academics will usually argue amongst themselves whenever there is a lack of data which allows them to do so: this appears to be a learned behavior, though what useful role it plays among them is unclear at this time.

What is clear is that somewhere around this time at some place *Homo erectus* invented the spear, a sharp stone placed on the end of a stick. While both sticks and sharp stones had been known for some time, today's laws do say that a combination of known technologies in a new way qualifies as a new invention, and this was certainly a major one. Spears have much greater range than axes, and thus allow larger game to be safely and reliably taken from greater distances.

Everything in the elephant pastures was now fair game, except for the very largest animals, including the elephants themselves, whose size meant that individual spear wounds would only make them mad and a very real threat to the hunters' lives. However, all primates have an exceptional spatial sense, and a good ability to remember locations within that space. *Homo* now used their excellent spatial sense to place themselves in safe locations along the routes which they knew these largest animals, the megafauna, would soon be traveling. A final tactic they developed was digging holes along these routes and covering them over, and then waiting for their victim to fall in.

Man turned on the "elephants"; in using this term here I include particularly the mammoth. If one is looking for the place where these new technologies were developed, one must remember that much of north Asia had been turned into grasslands some 3.5 million years previous to this point in time by the Bigach, Karla, and Kara-Kul impacts, and had been kept that way by the El'gygytgyn impact of some 2.3 million years previous.

Using this elephant-killing technology, *Homo erectus* would evolve into a new species, *Homo heidelbergensis*[10], whose fossils have been found as of today in Europe, East Asia, and Africa. Given all of this, I have little doubt that the *Homo heidelbergensis* (nee *erectus*) fossils will be found in Central Asia when excavations begin there.

1 MILLION YEARS AGO:
THE ZHAMANSHIN IMPACT

About 1 million years ago two small impacts took place, which would not be worth mentioning here, except that they may have involved pieces of the Zhamanshin Impactor. One of these pieces most likely hit at Veveers in Western Australia, exploding in the air with a force of some 475 kilotons, and leaving a crater of only 80 meters diameter in the ground, while the other, larger piece hit at Monturaqui, Chile. Again this most likely exploded in the air, this time with a force of some 12,800 Hiroshimas, leaving a hole some 469 meters across in the ground.

22

While both of these impacts undoubtedly had climatic effects which affected *Homo* throughout his range, these effects were minor compared to the effects of the impact which took place at Zhamanshin in today's Kazakhstan. This impactor left a hole measuring some 14 kilometers across. Its explosive force was equal to 1,100,000 Hiroshimas, and it placed some 1.8 billion tons of vaporized rock into the atmosphere, alongside another 1,800 billion tons of pulverized rock.

PARANTHROPUS COMES TO AN END

Though *Paranthropus robustus* had managed to survive the Bosumtwi Impact, it did not survive the climate collapse caused by the Zhamanshin Impact. *Paranthropus* now disappear from the fossil record, leaving proof that intelligence was a more effective survival trait than raw strength.

HOMO HEIDELBERGENSIS SPLIT IN TWO

The Zhamanshin impactor had hit right in the middle of *Homo heidelbergensis*'s Eurasian range, and it split the species into two widely separated groups which would now evolve along widely divergent paths.

HOMO HEIDELBERGENSIS IN EUROPE

The group of *Homo heidelbergensis* which survived in Eurasia to the west of the Zhamanshin Impact appears to have continued in the specialized spear-hunting of large animals, including the mammoth, and as they did so they later evolved into Neanderthal man, Homo neanderthalis (below).

HOMO HEIDELBERGENSIS IN EAST ASIA AND AFRICA:
MAN LEARNS TO FISH

The group of *Homo heidelbergensis*[11] which survived to the east of the Zhamanshin Impact appear to have taken a different path. While due to the relative lack of fossil record it is impossible to state the following with any certainty, it appears that the group to the east of Zhamanshin Impact had moved into a new niche: instead of relying on "elephants" and elephant pastures, it appears that they may have begun to use their spears as harpoons, moving out of the elephant pastures and into river environments.

As all the coastal sites of Asia from this period are now under several hundred meters of water, due to water released by melting glaciers at the end of the most recent Ice Age, we can't say today with any certainty how and where man's move into these river environments progressed. Some would claim that the move progressed in East Asia, others in Southeast Asia, and yet others would vehemently insist that this move made its farthest gains along the rivers of East Central Africa. The one thing that is certain is that in the other areas of the world besides Europe, man was now moving out of the elephant pastures, and on to the rivers.

800,000 YEARS AGO:
CLIMATIC COLLAPSES AND ANOTHER SPLIT

When a large impactor hits the Earth, a part of the vaporized rock which it throws up into the atmosphere will condense there in the form of tektites, spheres of glass which are then deformed by their fight through the Earth's atmosphere. We know from tektites found in Southeast Asia that a large impactor hit somewhere in northern Indo-China around 800,000 years ago, even though the crater that threw them out has not been found yet.

This was not the only event which produced climatic collapse around this time. A super-volcano went off at Posea, Indonesia, which left behind an opening in the Earth's crust measuring 100 kilometers long by 30 kilometers wide, while throwing out some 2,000,000,000,000 tons of rock and sulfur into the air. As both of the events took place right in the middle of *Homo's* range in Southeast Asia, they must have had severe effects on them, though at the present time it is impossible to say how severe these effects were.

There were two more super-volcanoes which went off around this time, but both of these erupted in North America. Around 700,000 years ago a super-volcano erupted at today's Long Valley, California, leaving behind a crater some 35 kilometers in length and 20 kilometers wide, while 600,000 years ago the Yellowstone complex once again erupted in a really super massive way, this time leaving behind a crater some 85 kilometers long and 45 kilometers wide. The first of these super-eruptions threw about 1,200,000,000,000 tons of rock and sulfur into the atmosphere, while the second of them threw up an astounding 2,200,000,000,000 tons.

Both the Northern Indo-China impact and the Posea super-volcanic eruption had occurred right in the middle of *Homo heidelbergensis's*[12] eastern range, isolating the northern groups from the southern groups.[13] It is likely that at this point the northern group moved onto the plains, and returned to mammoth hunting as a key food source.

70,000 YEARS AGO:
NEANDERTHALS IN THE ICE AGE

In Europe, *Homo heidelbergensis* would continue to focus of the hunting of large animals: mammoth, wooly rhino, bison, wild cattle, reindeer, wild horses and red deer. He would evolve the traits useful to these hunts, brute strength and a high tolerance for pain.

There was a snag with this survival strategy. While the river valleys formed the routes for the migrations of these large animals, Neanderthals ignored both the resources of the rivers themselves, as well as those presented by smaller animals. As the Earth's climate entered its next ice age, the populations of the large animals fell, and *Homo neanderthalensis* went extinct

THE LATER CLIMATE COLLPASES

Around 300,000 years ago two minor impactors hit in Australia, with one at Wolfe Creek leaving behind a 875 meter diameter crater, and one at Dlagaranga leaving behind a crater of only 27 meters across, and the effects of these upon man were probably quite small on the cosmic scale of things. However, the next impactor hit right in the middle of *Homo*'s range in today's South Africa at Tswaing (Pretoria Saltpan), and it left a hole in the ground measuring some 1,130 meters across. It must have hit with the force of around 257 Hiroshimas, throwing some 980,000 tons of vaporized rock in the air along with another 980,000,000 tons of pulverized rock. Everything for about 1,113 square kilometers would have been set on fire by the heat of the explosion, with an even greater area set on fire by the vaporized rock.

The next impactor was also small, but again it hit in the middle of *Homo*'s range. About 100,000 years ago a small impactor hit at Amguid, in today's Algeria, and since it left behind a crater measuring only 450 meters across, it likely exploded in the air. In this case everything for some 4,500 square kilometers was likely blown down, and everything within 2,300 square kilometers was set on fire.

About 52,000 years ago another impactor hit in the middle of *Homo*'s range, this time at Lonar in today's India. The explosion had a force of some 1,280 Hiroshimas, and threw out 4,000,000 tons of vaporized rock and another 4,000,000,000 tons of pulverized rock from the 1,183 meters crater it left behind. Everything with 1,000 square kilometers or so was blown down, and everything within about 4,100 square kilometers was set on fire from the blast, with an unknown area set on fire by the vaporized rock as it fell back to Earth.

While the next impactor did not land in the middle of *Homo*'s range, as it did a great deal to prepare the area for man's later arrival there, it needs to be mentioned here. An iron impactor hit some 50,000 years ago near today's Barringer, Arizona, and it left a crater some 1,186 meters across. This must have hit with nearly 302 Hiroshimas of force, throwing out some 1.1 million tons of vaporized rock, alongside another 1.1 billion tons of pulverized rock. While only 400 or so square kilometers would have been flattened by this hit, another 1,270 square kilometers were undoubtedly set on fire by it, along with an unknown area set on fire by the vaporized rock. Perhaps this impact played a role in creating the grasslands which fed the large animals which man would soon be hunting there.[14]

HOMO SAPIENS APPEARS

Homo neanderthalis would be replaced in Europe by the descendants of *Homo heidelbergensis* who had moved into the river valleys and learned to use their marine resources. However you name it, by now this branch of man's family tree had evolved into *Homo sapiens*, and they used these marine resources in a big way: their diet included not only fish and shellfish, but also the water fowl which fed and nested in marshes.

Not only had *Homo sapiens* learned how to fish, they had developed another key technology, boats, and they had reached Australia by some 50,000 years ago.

25

The stage was now set for man to move into the Americas.

(Footnotes)

[1] My apologies to the ladies, but in this chapter I will use the old terms "man" and "mankind" when speaking about our ancestors. In doing so I suppose I will just have to own up to my sexism, instead of than admitting to my age by mentioning my discomfort in using the newer terms.

[2] While I am unsure as to any fossil record of this, it would also seem that this ability to use stones to crack open nuts would also have allowed our most primitive ancestors to crack open the shells of turtles. Because of their shells adult turtles have few natural predators, and they may have provided our early ancestors with readily available easy meals.

[3] All data here on super volcanoes comes from the Cambridge Volcanic Database. A more complete compilation, which will give a detailed listing of volcanoes to 7 magnitude, as well as those in Africa, should be available shortly.

[4] With all of the names available, it is remarkable that the vulcanologists have not come up with one yet from amongst their community - one might wonder if perhaps their rivalries have prevented them from doing so. In all humility, if they are really so stuck for a name, may I suggest that they could always name it after me.

[5] The effects of this sulfuric acid on the ozone layer are still not known. It is possible that the ozone layer plays a key role in climate by moderating the amount of our Sun's energy which is retained by the Earth, but it is currently unknown if these increases in ozone merely accompany the increases in temperature, or are responsible for it.

[6] The easy way to remember the conversion from kilometers to miles is to remember that the speed limit in Canada is often 100 kilometers per hour. Sorry, but all of you who enjoy driving fast will have to visit elsewhere, as this is only about 60 miles per hour, U.S. Oh well – Montana is still wide open! For the rest, a metric ton is about the same mass as an English ton, while a meter is about as long as a yard. Given the staggeringly large sizes mentioned here, these kind of very rough equivalents will get you through okay.

[7] Entire books have been written on the problem of scaling nuclear and other large explosions. The best of them are classified. The scaling used here is from J.A. Northrup, editor, *Handbook of Nuclear Weapons Effects, Calculational Tools Abstracted from the DSWA's Effects Manual 1 (EM-1)*, Defense Special Weapons Agency, Washington, D.C., 1996, cited by Robert Nelson, "Nuclear "Bunker Busters" Would More Likely Disperse Than Destroy Buried Stockpiles of Biological and Chemical Weapons", *Science and Global Security*, v.12, p.69-89, Taylor and Francis Group Inc, 2004. Blast and thermal effects scaling were done using nuclear models, which clearly have different specific energies from impacts, but the results are close enough for the problem at hand. Similarly, given crater ages and erosional constraints on Earth, no adjustment was made to crater diameters; as gravitational regime scaling adjustments and some of the early material adjustments also tend to obscure the occurrence of cometary impact; those who may wish to pursue these issues further in greater detail already know how to do so.

[8] Using for the size of the Hiroshima explosion the widely accepted estimate of 12.5 kilotons.

[9] The classing of hominid fossils into species and subspecies is hotly debated with

nearly every paleoanthropologist having his or her own. Here the distinctions between *Homo ergaster* and *Homo erectus* have been dropped.

[10] Once again, the taxonomy of hominid fossils is a hotly debated issue. The key technology here is the spear.

[11] For some reason we lost our fur somplace as we evolved, and the waters of the marine environment of coastal Asia seems a very likely candidate. The key technology here is the spear, whether used for larger game or as a harpoon.

[12] While some would lump *Homo heidelbergensis* with *erectus*, my intent here is solely to point out certain catastrophes which most certainly affected the evolution of modern man. Although this is another area under intense study and debate, my guess is that all *erectus* descendants were still able to interbreed by this time, and likely continued to be able to do so for some time afterwards.

[13] These events may be reflected in the Asian distribution of the D haplogroup of mitochondrial DNA.

[14] For those working in the field I would be remiss not to mention the Tenoumer Mauritania Impact of some 21,500 years ago which left behind a 1,900 meter crater. This exploded with a force 305 Hiroshimas, threw 1.14 million tons of vaporized rock in the air, alongside another 1,140 tons of pulverized rock, blew down about 400 square kilometers, and set on fire around 1,200 square kilometers. But then this occurred later than the time being discussed here.

MAP OF THE EARTH'S MAJOR OCEAN CURRENTS

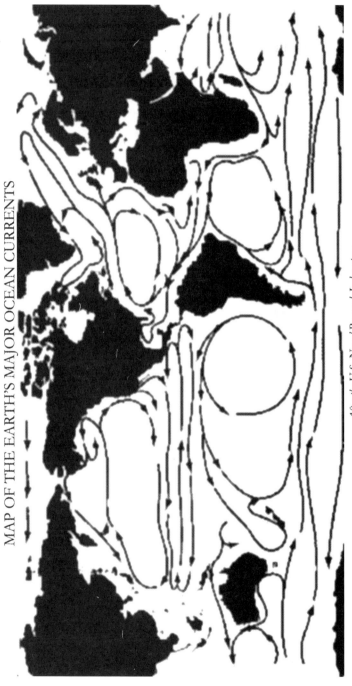

After the U.S. Naval Research Laboratory

CHAPTER 3

THE FIRST PEOPLES CROSS TO THE AMERICAS

THE DEBATE OVER MAN'S ARRIVAL IN THE AMERICAS

It is popularly "known" that there was "a" Siberian land bridge which allowed man to cross into the Americas. Unfortunately for this theory, hard evidence keeps showing up that man actually arrived in the Americas well before this. Indeed, the DNA of the mitochondria of Native Americans shows that there were something like 5 distinct crossings involved.

Before discussing this DNA evidence, an important point needs to be emphasized, which is this: modern scholars who argue about Native American origins nearly always refer to the peoples who occupy the different continents today, rather than to their ancient populations. For example, we usually think of Europe, or Siberia, or Africa in modern terms, but it is actually impossible that ancient man thought of these areas in the same way we do: tens of thousands of years ago, not only were the landscapes much different, the peoples who were living in them were much different from those living there now. For example, the very idea of an Asia separate from North America was probably not among the concepts of those who came across by this route; the same goes for those who crossed over to the Americas by water.

THE ROLE OF LARGE OCEAN GOING WATERCRAFT IN THE PEOPLING OF THE AMERICAS

In recent years new data have become available which show that large boats played a role in the initial movement of people into North America, and this at a time far earlier than suspected. As was seen in Chapter 1, man had large watercraft at a very early period in time, roughly at about the time of the peopling of Australia, and while the dates are hotly contested, rough dates of about 50,000 BCE are most likely. The extent of man's occupation in the Sahara of Africa 50,000 years ago, during this period of the first use of boats, along the coast of the South Atlantic, is completely unknown today.

But once you have man in boats, the rest follows naturally. The plain fact is that due to natural currents and the weather, both trans-Pacific and trans-Atlantic contacts were inevitable, if not by design, then certainly by accident.[1] In the 100 year period from 1775 to 1875 at least 20 Japanese junks were involuntarily driven by storms and currents to landing points in the Americas ranging from the Aleutian Islands to Mexico, an average of 1 boat every 5 years.[2] Further, in the last century some 600 African craft have washed up on the coast of South America, a rough average of 1 watercraft every 2 months.[3]

What we can reasonably conclude from this relatively contemporary evidence is that once ancient fishermen showed up in coastal areas some 50,000 years ago, they would regularly have been driven between continents. A few of these fishermen would have survived, and fewer still would have returned to their homes – after all, try to return they would, as it was unlikely that early fishermen took their wives out to fish with them. But even though very few of these reluctant explorers would have survived, these processes would have taken place for many millennia, and the tales of the survivors would have been cultural treasures indeed – knowledge of new environments completely unexploited by man – treasures which these ancient peoples would have hoarded for thousands of years.

Undoubtedly the watercraft primitive man used for ocean travel were very large dugout canoes, made by felling and hollowing out simply enormous trees. The largest of these dugout canoes would have been the size of European ocean-going vessels, measuring 80 feet or so in length, and some 10 to 12 feet wide. Nonetheless, the prospect of a voyage across the open ocean even in these large dugouts must have presented a gloomy view indeed. Certainly at this point in man's development these trips would not have been undertaken readily, unless there were some compelling reason which drove some people to risk it: getting caught with another man's wife, for example, or getting thrown out of the family, or being fed up with the village's leaders, or starvation caused by a short term climatic downturn. Whatever the cause, some made the trip.

THE SOUTH ATLANTIC CROSSINGS

While much of the heated anthropological discussion has focused on Pacific crossings, the evidence for early crossings from Africa has been ignored for the most part. Furthermore, the participants in these discussions have usually referred to Africa in modern terms, though its reality tens of thousands of years ago was quite entirely different. At this time, the area south of the Atlas Mountains was a well watered area, not the Sahara Desert of today. The ancient peoples who occupied what is now the Sahara Desert left us abundant art showing them engaged in their pursuits.

The deltas at the mouths of the rivers which ran south of the Atlas Mountains and on into the Atlantic Ocean must have been heavily settled as well, but unfortunately we have little way of knowing much about these settlements, as they are under several hundred feet of water now. When the last Ice Age ended, its ice melted and released its water into the world's oceans, drowning these ancient shorelines.

At the rock shelter at Pedra Furada (Perforated Rock), situated along the Rio Piaui River in northeast Brazil, artifacts dating to at least 32,000 BCE have been found.[4] Today a desert, in these earlier times this area of multiple rock shelters was forest bordering on grasslands, resembling the Sahara during this period. And as in the Sahara, extensive murals have been found which were produced by these early people.

While these murals have been compared to those in Spain, it seems far more likely that they were produced by people from the Sahara. From the historical record we know that accidental crossings from Africa to Brazil were far more common than accidental crossings from Spain to Brazil, and if one takes a look at the chart of ocean currents, the reasons for this are clear.

THE PACIFIC CROSSINGS

At Quebrada Jaguay in Peru, a team led by Daniel H. Sandweiss of the University of Maine, Orono, recovered bits of knotted cordage, possibly the remains of fishing nets, abundant bones of fish, primarily drum, and shells of mollusks and crustaceans dated to between 11,924-10,774 BCE. At Quebrada Tacahuay in Peru, researchers led by David K. Keefer of the U.S. Geological Survey found a hearth, tools and obsidian flakes, as well as the bones of numerous fish--mostly anchovy, whose small size implies the use of nets rather than hook and line--and seabirds, including cormorants, booby, and pelican, remains radio carbon dated to about 10,789 BCE.

 While the remains recovered from South America so far do not confirm the existence of large watercraft at this very early period in time, the remains from the Arlington Springs site on Santa Rosa Island off the coast of California most certainly do. Here the 11,000-year-old skeleton of a woman was found; that is from 9,000 BCE or so, and Santa Rosa was an island at that time.[5]

More telling than these physical remains is the high coincidence of both Coastal Asian as well as Polynesian DNA markers seen in some Native American peoples who share the D and B mitochondrial DNA haplogroups. Since the B haplogroup is found among nearly the entire population of Polynesia, and not in Coastal Asia, it is nearly impossible that this bit of genetic history could have arrived in the Americas by any other means than the use of large boats. In addition to this Polynesian gene, the geographic distribution of the D haplogroup in the Americas and Asia indicates that the same thing was true for some of the early peoples of Coastal Asia: they must have used boats to get here.[6]

THE PALEOLITHIC HUNTERS CROSS THE ANCIENT SIBERIAN LAND BRIDGE(S)

It is popularly believed that there was "an" ancient Siberian land bridge, called Beringia, which allowed man to cross into the Americas; this land bridge ran inland of the western coastal mountain ridge, and connected to the plains of North America. But clearly there were other "bridges" which ran along the Pacific coast. Again, most Pacific coastal sites are most certainly under water now, due to the rise in sea levels which occurred as the glaciers of the last Ice Age melted.

There were at least two openings of these corridors, as the mitochondrial DNA evidence shows two distinct crossings. Native American peoples living at the southern tip of South America possess the C mitochondrial DNA haplogroup in common with peoples living in North Central Asia; they must have crossed to the Americas well before the A mitochondrial DNA haplogroup peoples moved into the area of the land bridges, as the C peoples are not found there later.

This last crossing, of the A mitochondrial DNA haplogroup people, is the only crossing which the majority of the anthropological community used to acknowledge, and as a result it is the crossing which we always picture in our mind's eye. However, as the genetic evidence for an earlier crossing is undeniable, our mind's eye will simply have to refocus itself.[7]

MASTODONS, MAMMOTHS, AND THEIR HUNTERS

It is also commonly believed that this land bridge was extremely cold, because of the glaciers found immediately to the north of it - this was the Ice Age, after all. From the pollen remains of the trees which were growing then there is no denying that it was cold there during the winter. But it is also clear that the glaciers held a large amount of the Earth's water, so much water, in fact, that during the summer this corridor would actually resemble a dry warm savannah.

The fur of the "Wooly" Mammoth is dry, not oily, and it protected the mammoth from the heat, rather than insulating it from the cold. This fact about the mammoth's fur goes against what most of us "know", as when we try to put together a mental picture of a mammoth, it usually features one of them in a snowy landscape swaying its tusk about, furiously facing off against some fur clad hunters threatening it with spears.

Again, one of the most interesting things about mammoths is that their fur is the type of fur seen on camels, designed for insulation against heat. What this means is that the mammoth were migrating animals which only moved to the north during the warmest summer months, and then moved south again as winter set in. These migrations must have been over ranges of several thousands of kilometers (that's hundreds of miles, for you non-metric folk), and early man must have followed them as they migrated with the seasons.

Having gotten rid of the snow, let's move on to the spears. I once saw a remarkable film showing a group of Pygmies armed with poisoned spears attacking an African elephant: they attacked this elephant in a heavily wooded area, using the trees for cover while they snuck up on it, and then ran away after delivering the initial spear strike. They then tracked the elephant for several days, and finally dispatched it after it was already down. This hunt was viewed by them as a very dangerous undertaking, as these hunts often resulted in the hunters' deaths, and the hunt was accompanied by a great deal of ceremony at both its start and its finish

Clearly, if one were to undertake the killing of large animals as a way of earning a regular living, instead of as an occasional hunt, as the modern Pygmies now do, methods other than direct attack with spears would have had to have been used. It is known that later Native American peoples would intentionally set fires, both as a way of hunting bison, as well as a way to provide pasturage for deer, and it seems that the same technique might have been used by the ancient hunters for hunting mammoth and other megafauna (large animals). Besides stampeding game off of cliffs with fire, some sites show early Native Americans trapping mammoth in bogs, and the intentional digging of pit traps certainly seems a possible development of this technique.

A final point in all of this is that man has a very highly developed sense of spatial awareness, a brain function that he does not share with any other animal, including his nearby relatives among the great apes. [8] What this sense of spatial awareness does is allow man to plan, to know both where he and other things will be far in the future, and to position himself accordingly. This brain function allowed man to ambush large game: he would have known their migratory routes, and by placing himself auspicious locations along them beforehand, say on overhanging cliffs, or near bogs, or even up trees, he could ambush large game which would have presented a threat to him if he had attempted to take it head on.

So we can keep the spears, but we have to picture ancient man using them to finish off animals which he had already trapped.

MAN ENTERS THE EAST COAST OF NORTH AMERICA:
LET'S NOT HUNT ANYTHING WHICH CAN KILL US, EH?

If you stop to consider it, it immediately seems reasonable that it would have been far easier for ancient man to have made a living by harvesting fish and shell fish and killing peaceful coastal browsing deer, rather than by killing large angry mammoth and mastodons. Indeed, judging from the remains found to date, ancient man himself seems to have reached this very same conclusion rather quickly.

The earliest evidence found so far of ancient man in Virginia comes from the Cactus Hill site, which lies near the interior of southeastern Virginia's coastal plain, on the floodplain of the Nottoway River, a small river that drains a relatively moist region before it joins with two other rivers to ultimately discharge into the Albemarle Sound in North Carolina. Along the Nottoway River blades made from the local quartzite have been found in pre-Clovis levels dating back to ca. 14,990 BCE. Current faunal remains from the Cactus Hill site include deer bones and mud turtle shells.

Archaeologists surveying the route for the widening of the State Highway 20 in Virginia stumbled across an ancient jasper quarry at Brook Run which was used ca. 9,500 BCE. Little occupational debris has been found at the Brook Run site, and this is little surprise. These Clovis hunters probably continued down the Rappahannock River to what would then have been the Chesapeake River (instead of the Chesapeake Bay), on down the stream to the land of easy living. They then would have returned to Brook Run only to gather the stones they needed to make their tools.

The switch in diet is more clearly seen at the Saltville River site located in the Shenandoah Valley, which lies to the west of the coastal area, between ridges of the Appalachian Mountains. The animals were attracted here by the salt licks (it is after all called the "Saltville River"), and man in turn was attracted by the animals, particularly the ones which became bogged down in the mud near the salt licks. The remains of mastodon, ground sloth, bison, musk ox, caribou (it was still cold), wild horses, and deer have been found here, including the worked bones of mastodon and musk ox dated to around 12,000 BCE.

Nearby the excavators found large shell middens (mounds of freshwater shells) which incorporated the butchered remains of fish and amphibians and which dated to around the same time. While the ages of both the Cactus Hill site and the Saltville site are hotly contested, it is extremely unlikely that these shells just piled themselves up, conveniently including butchered remains.

Clovis technologies, usually thought to be some of the earliest stone tool technologies, do not show up at Cactus Hill until the relatively late date of 8,970 BCE. It is currently impossible to know whether this change in tool types was simply the introduction of new technologies, or whether it represented a new migration into the area; this is due in part to the lack of excavations, and in part due to the looting of the site by arrowhead hunters.[9]

Strangely, the quarry at Brooks Run was abandoned after what is estimated at only a few hundred years of use. Strangely, at the Cactus Hill site, the early pre-Clovis and Clovis levels are separated by several meters of sterile sand from the occupation levels left there by the later Archaic peoples. The date of these discontinuities is shortly before 8,300 BCE. What caused these peoples to abandon these sites?

THE EARLY HUNTERS OF FLORIDA AND THE SOUTH

The range of the megafauna on which early man dined was not limited to northern regions. If you remember, the wool of the "Wooly" Mammoth cooled it: as has been pointed out elsewhere repeatedly, elephants live today in Africa, India, and South-east Asia, and they are not restricted to eating grass in grasslands, but will eat the bark off trees if necessary.

Remains of early man have been found at the Coats-Hines site in Tennessee, at the Topper site in South Carolina, and at the Little Salt Spring site and Page Ladson site in Florida. In particular, worked bone and ivory from a number of extinct mammals have been found at a number of places in Florida.

WHAT KILLED THE MAMMOTH?

While many suspect that early man hunted these large animals into extinction, the changes in total game populations as well as the environment are not completely understood today. It is known that in Africa large herds of elephant have converted forested areas to grassland, and that later Native Americans would intentionally set fires both as a way of hunting bison as well as to provide pasturage for deer. The use of fire for hunting may have resulted in the deaths of more game than that needed for immediate use, and perhaps in the future evidence for the use of fire for hunting may show up in pollen samples.

Whatever the results of these pollen studies, while the megafauna may have survived the early hunters, it is certain that they did not survive the sudden change in climate which soon occurred.

HARD EVIDENCE OF A MAJOR CATASTROPHE

Frank Hibbens was one of the first archaeologists to excavate Folsom and Clovis remains, and in 1933 and 1941 he traveled to Alaska trying to find remains of early man along the "Siberian Land Bridge". Hibbens' account of the work of the pioneering archaeologists makes for a fine read, and his description of what he found in Alaska, and where he found it, makes for particularly fascinating reading....

"Frozen in the muck walls, or beaten out beneath the insistent pounding of the streams of water {from the hydraulic jets], were logs and twisted trees and branches and stumps. Here and there were layers of moss and peat; but nowhere in the muck could we find a layer of charcoal, or a fire pit, or any of those other indications that we had come to associate with the campsites of the ancient hunters.

"Mammals there were in abundance, dumped in all attitudes of death. Most of them were pulled apart by some unexplained prehistoric catastrophic disturbance. Legs and torsos and heads and fragments were found together in piles or scattered separately. But nowhere could we find any definite evidence that humans had ever walked among these trumpeting herds or had ever seen their final end.

"On one particular rainy, dark afternoon, we were assisting one of the paleontologists in excavating the remains of an Alaskan lion - a great, striped beast with long fangs, slightly reminiscent of a Bengal tiger. He looked like a nasty customer in death, even though he was represented only by scattered bones in the black muck. As we sought for the lower jaw of the lion in a newly revealed surface of muck, we found our evidence of man-a flint point still frozen solid in the muck bank.

"Its position was about ninety feet below the original surface. We photographed it in place, then removed it from the frozen ground, eagerly held it up, and turned it over for inspection. We washed the clinging muck from it in the muddy water beneath our feet. It was of pink stone, finely chipped and gracefully shaped, and undoubtedly made by the hand of man."[10]

Hibbens concluded that the massive slaughter which he had seen in the muck had been caused by worldwide volcanic eruptions:

"One of the most interesting of the theories of the Pleistocene end is that which explains this ancient tragedy by world-wide, earthshaking volcanic eruptions of catastrophic violence. This bizarre idea, queerly enough, has considerable support, especially in the Alaskan and Siberian regions.

"Interspersed in the muck depths and sometimes through the very piles of bones and tusks themselves are layers of volcanic ash. There is no doubt that coincidental with the end of the Pleistocene animals, at least in Alaska, there were volcanic eruptions of tremendous proportions. It stands to reason that animals whose flesh is still preserved must have been killed and buried quickly to be preserved at all. Bodies that die and lie on the surface soon disintegrate and the bones are scattered. A volcanic eruption would explain the end of the Alaskan animals all at one time, and in a manner that would satisfy the evidences there as we know them. The herds would be killed in their tracks either by the blanket of volcanic ash covering them and causing death by heat or suffocation, or indirectly by the volcanic gases. Toxic clouds of gas from volcanic upheavals could well cause death on a gigantic scale. If every individual, old and young, were killed, extinction would naturally follow."[11]

Alaska is a seismically active area with many volcanoes, some of which Hibbens himself had seen erupting, and it seems not unnatural that Hibbens assumed that the ash which he saw in the muck came from volcanoes. One problem with this explanation is that the known volcanoes did not massively erupt worldwide around this time. Another problem with this explanation is that several Native American peoples clearly remember that the dust which Hibbens saw came from a comet.

THE ASTRONOMICAL SYSTEMS OF THE NORTHERN PEOPLES: THE HORNED SNAKES AND THE THUNDERBIRDS

In fact, several Native American peoples preserved memories of Holocene Start Impacts and the comet which caused them, and its dust, and a few of their memories will be set out below. But in order to understand these legends, it is necessary first to understand the astronomical systems in which they are expressed, i.l, these peoples' cosmologies.

The northern peoples' cosmological theories were widely held, with variants. In these astronomical systems asteroids and comets are viewed as "horned snakes", which were known by various names: by the Cherokee as Unktena and on the Plains as Unkteni or Uncegila, for example. The "horns" of these snakes are extremely hard, and are of extreme value: they are meteorites, and they still have great value today. Sometimes the "horned snakes" are grouped together with "spitting snakes", which are comets, and sometimes not. As in Middle Eastern societies, there is no differentiation between asteroid and cometary impact and lightning, which is simply seen as a smaller snake.

One of the key facts which generally eludes modern mythologists is that Native Americans often saw space as a cold dark lake, and the "water" aspect of these "snake" myths is a complete bafflement to them. But this is really a minor quibble, as most modern Native American anthropologists have no idea of impact events, and have never considered that they might have played a key role in the formation of Native American cosmologies.

Either the "thunders" or the "thunderbirds", the second known as Tlanuwa to the Cherokee, were man's protectors against the cosmic snakes, the comets and asteroids. Naturally, when either the "thunders" or the "thunderbirds" defeated a "horned snake", lightning and the sound of thunder would be heard, coming from where the asteroid or comet hit the Earth. Similarly, thunder was heard after lightning strikes, and this was viewed as a sign of the thunders' or thunderbirds' defeat of the lightening "serpent" or "snake".

A MENOMINI TALE OF THE THUNDERBIRDS[12] SHOWING THEIR ASTRONOMICAL SYSTEM

"Far, far away in the west where Sun sets, there floats a great mountain in the sky: above Earth the rocks lie tier on tier. These cliffs are too lofty to be reached by any earthly bird: even the Great War Eagle can not soar so high.

"But on the summit of this mountain dwell the Thunderbirds. They have control over the rain and hail. They are messengers of the Great Sun himself, and their influence induced Sun and Morning Star to give the Great War-Bundles to our race. They delight in fighting and great deeds, (and) they are mighty enemies of the horned snakes, the Misikinubik. Were it not for the Thunderers, these Snakes would overwhelm the earth and devour mankind.

"When the weather is fair, then watch as you travel abroad, for the snakes come out to bask in the sun; but when the weather is cloudy, you need fear nothing, for the Thunderers come searching from behind the clouds for their enemies, the Misikinubik [the horned snakes]."

A MOHAWK TALE OF THE THUNDERS AND SERPENTS
SHOWING THEIR ASTRONOMICAL SYSTEM

In this Mohawk legend the Good Mind appoints the thunders to protect the people from the Bad Mind's serpents (comets). It is adapted to modern usage from the Mohawk version of the creation myth given by Seth Newhouse to J.N.B. Hewitt.[13]

"Then, truly, during that time when the Good Mind was traveling again to inspect again the things which he had finished on this Earth, then he saw another man.

"And the Good Mind addressed the man, saying, "What are you doing as you go on your way?" The other said, "It seemed that it became necessary for me to see you." The Good Mind replied, "That is undoubtedly true."

"The other person answered and said, "I desire that you should allow me to live. If you will consent to my request, I will give assistance to you: I will watch over the peoples' bodies, and I will also give them life and support, and moreover I will continue to defend the people who you created."

"The Good Mind said: "Let me see what kind of power you have." Thereupon the man, whose name of old is Hi'non' [Thunder], started upon a run and went up into the clouds. Now, truly, rumblings were heard: it thundered in the clouds, and lightning was also sent out, and moreover so many flashes shot forth that they seemed as though only one from their rapidity.

"So then the man descended to where the Good Mind was standing, and he said: "Now assuredly you saw what kind of power I have." The Good Mind said: "It is indeed true that you are able to do just as you told me. Are you also able to regularly throw water on this earth as the summers come?" The man answered, saying: "I am able to do so." Then the Good Mind said: "So then let me see how you will do this," and the man replied: "Yo'; so be it."

"Now again he ascended on high to where the clouds are present. Now again it thundered and the lightning flashed, but besides this the clouds became thick and black, and then the rain came forward. From the sea the rain came over the dry land, and it was marvelous as it came along.

"Then of course the rain passed, and the man again returned to the place where the Good Mind was. The Good Mind then spoke to him, saying: "What you are able to do is satisfactory. It will indeed come to pass, following closely the course pointed out by you in your request. Indeed, from now on it will be your duty to travel continually, for it was you yourself who requested this. Do not then ever fail to do your duty.

"You must, of course, be ever vigilant; if at whatever time there come dangers to the lives of men because of Great Serpents [comets] moving from place to place in the depths of this Earth and the Sea [space]; if it comes to pass that at some time these Great Serpents desire to seize the people as they travel together from place to place, you must at once kill such Serpents, and when you kill them, they will be that on which you will feed. Other animals also, equal in evil power to these, all such shall fare like the Serpents. You will have to watch these forever, and have them as your adversaries.

"Now then, of course, I have finished this matter. Such is the office which you have assumed. People will name you "Our Grandfather whose voice is customarily uttered in diverse places.""

"Then, indeed, the two parted company."

A LENAPE ACCOUNT OF THE HOLOCENE START IMPACT EVENT

Suitably equipped with this knowledge of the thunders and thunderbirds, and their enemies the snakes, we can now begin to understand some of the Native American accounts of the Holocene Start impacts. The following account has been adapted to modern usage from the one preserved in the Walum Olum, the ancient history of the Lenape people.[14]

> 1. Long ago there was a Mighty Snake [comet], and beings evil to men.
> 2. This Mighty Snake [comet] hated those who were there,
> (and) he greatly disquieted those whom he hated.
> 3. He harmed all things, he injured all things,
> and all were not in peace.
> 4. Driven from their homes, the men fought with this murderer.
> 5. The Mighty Snake [comet] firmly resolved to harm the men.
> 6. The Mighty Snake [comet] brought three persons [fragments?],
> he brought a monster [impact],
> he brought rushing water [an impact mega-tsunami].
> 7. Between the hills the water rushed and rushed,
> dashing through and through, destroying much.
> 8. Nanabush, the Strong White One, Grandfather of beings,
> Grandfather of men, was on Turtle Island.

While "Turtle Island" has certain allegorical aspects[15], it is strange to see the turtle play such an essential role in Lenape legend. Turtles are reptiles, and for the most part are unable to generate internal heat to warm their bodies, which limits their range to temperate climates; there are and were none of these in the far north of the Lenape people's original homeland. The only possible exception here may have been sea turtles,

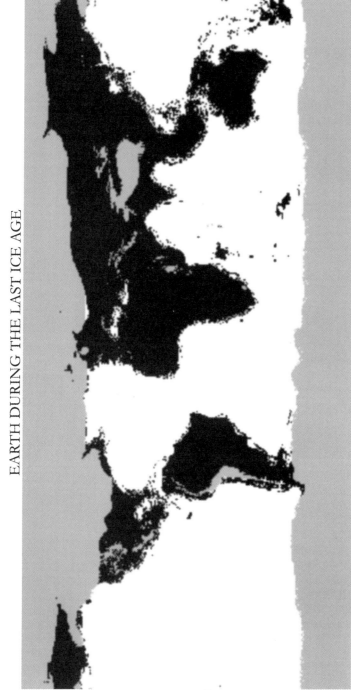

EARTH DURING THE LAST ICE AGE

After United States Geological Survey

which thrive in warm water: perhaps the Japanese Current provided warm water to coastal Alaska, and "Turtle Island" refers to coastal Alaska before the end of the last Ice Age.

9. There he was walking and creating:
and as he passed by,
he created the turtle [skin boats?].
10. Beings and men all went forth,
they walked in the floods and shallow waters,
down stream there in the turtle [skin boats?].
11. There were many monster fishes, which ate some of them.
12. The Great Mind's daughter came,
and helped with her canoe [wooden boat]:
she helped all, as they came and came.
13. Thus Nanabush, Nanabush, the Grandfather of all,
the Grandfather of beings, the Grandfather of men,
became the Grandfather of the turtle [skin boats?].
14. The men were then together on the Great Turtle [the Earth],
like turtles.
15. Frightened on the Great Turtle [the Earth],
they prayed that what was spoiled should be restored.
16. The water ran off, the earth dried, the lakes were at rest,
all was silent, and the Mighty Snake [comet] departed.

THE HOLOCENE CLIMATE COLLAPSE:
THE LENAPE MIGRATE EAST, THEN SOUTH

Whether these impacts were the cause of the end of the Ice Age or just coincidental to it is a hotly debated topic. Whatever the cause, the climate did begin to change.

Part III
1. After the rushing waters [had finished],
 the Lenape of the [Sea] Turtle were close together,
living together there in hollow houses..
2. It froze where they lived, it snowed where they lived,
it stormed where they lived, it was cold where they lived.
3. At this northern place they spoke favorably
of mild, cool (lands), with many deer and buffaloes.
4. As they journeyed, some being strong, and others rich,
they separated into house-builders and hunters;
5. The strongest, the most united, the purest, were the hunters.
6. The hunters showed themselves at the north, at the east,
at the south, at the west.

ATTACK ON THE SNAKES [MISSASAUGA]

7. In that ancient country, in that northern country,
in that [Sea] Turtle Country,

41

the best of the Lenape were the men of the Turtle Clan.

Perhaps the Turtle Clan were the boat builders.

"8. All the cabin fires of that land were disquieted,
and all said to their priest, "Let us go."
9. They went forth to the Snake [Missasauga] Land to the east,
going away earnestly grieving."

Snakes, like turtles, are also reptiles, and for the most part are also unable to generate
internal heat to warm their bodies. This also limits their range to temperate climates,
and there are and were none of these in the far north. The northernmost range of
snakes, and in particular of the poisonous Missasauga rattlesnake, would appear to be
along the Saint Lawrence at its junction with Lake Erie.

"10. Split asunder, weak, trembling, their land burned,
they went, torn and broken, to the Snake [Missasauga] Land."

A MOHAWK ACCOUNT OF THE END OF THE ICE AGE,
SHORTLY BEFORE Ca. 8,350 BCE
                                    10,900,
The following passage is adapted from a Mohawk version of the creation myth given by
Seth Newhouse to J.N.B. Hewitt.[16]

"It came to pass that the Good Mind, as he traveled from place to place, after a
while went along the shore of the lake (Lake Ontario). There, not far away, he
saw the Bad Mind making for himself a bridge of ice across the lake, a bridge
which already extended far out on the water.

Thereupon the Good Mind went to the place where the Bad Mind was working,
and when he arrived there, he said: "Tawi'skaron, what is this that you are
doing for yourself?" The Bad Mind replied, saying: "I am making a pathway
for myself." And then, pointing in the direction toward which he was building
the bridge, he added: "In that direction there is a land where dwell great animals
of fierce dispositions. As soon as I complete my pathway to that other land,
thereafter they will habitually come over. Along this pathway they will be in the
habit of coming across the lake to eat the flesh of human beings who are about
to dwell on the earth."

So then the Good Mind said to the Bad Mind: "You should stop the work which
you are doing. Surely the intention of your mind is not good." The Bad Mind
replied, saying: "I will not cease from what I am doing, for, of course, it is good
that these great animals shall be in the habit of coming here to eat the flesh of
human beings who will dwell here."

So of course the Bad Mind did not obey and cease from building the bridge for
himself, and thereupon the Good Mind turned back and reached dry land. Now
along the shore of the sea grew shrubs, and he saw a bird sitting on a limb of
one. The bird belonged to the class of birds which we call the bluebirds. And the

Good Mind then said to this Bluebird: "You shall kill a cricket. You shall remove one hind leg from it, and you shall hold it in your mouth, and you shall go there to the very place where the Bad Mind is working. You shall land very near to the place where he is working, and you shall cry out."

"And the Bluebird replied, saying, "Yo". Thereupon the Bluebird truly did seek for a cricket, and after a while it found one, and it killed it, too. Then it pulled out one of the cricket's hind legs and put it into its mouth to hold, and then it flew, winging its way to the place where the Bad Mind was at work making his ice bridge.

There it landed, near to him at his task. And of course it then shouted, "Kwe', kwe', kwe', kwe', kwe'." At which the Bad Mind raised up his head and looked, and he saw the bluebird sitting there. He believed from what he saw that the bluebird held in its mouth the thigh of a man, and also that its mouth was wholly covered with blood.

It was then that the Bad Mind sprang up at once and fled. As fast as he ran the bridge of ice which he was making dissipated."

What was this Bluebird with its mouth covered with blood, whose appearance caused the ice to melt? Was it a comet passing through space all too near to the Earth?

A TUSCARORA ACCOUNT OF A HOLOCENE START IMPACT ON THE SAINT LAWRENCE RIVER

The following passage has been adapted to modern usage from an account given by Tuscaroran Chief Elias Johnson.[17]

A Great Horned Serpent also next appeared on Lake Ontario who, by means of his poisonous breath, caused disease, and caused the death of many.

At length the old women congregated, with one accord, and prayed to the Great Spirit that he would send their grandfather, the Thunder, who would get to their relief in this, their sore time of trouble, while at the same time burning tobacco as burned offerings. And so finally the monster was compelled to retire in the deeps of the lake by thunderbolts.

Before this calamity was forgotten another happened. A blazing star fell into their fort, situated on the banks of the St. Lawrence, and destroyed the people. Such a phenomenon caused a great panic and consternation and dread, which they regarded as ominous of their entire destruction. Not long after this prediction of the blazing star it was verified.

These tribes, who were held together by feeble ties, fell into dispute and wars among themselves, which were pursued through a long period, until they had utterly destroyed each other, and so reduced their numbers that the lands were again overrun with wild beasts.

At this period there were six families who took refuge in a large cave in a mountain, where they dwelled for a long time. The men would come out occasionally to hunt for food. This great cave was situated at or near the falls of the Oswego River.

The Holder of the Heavens then came and extricated these six families from the subterraneous bowels and confines of the mountain. The people always looked to this divine messenger, who had power to assume various shapes as emergency demanded, as the friend and patron of their nation.

This company were a particular body, which called themselves of One Household. Of these there were six families, and they entered into an agreement to preserve the chain of alliance which should not be extinguished under any circumstance.

(Footnotes)

[1] For an overview of the early work on accidental ocean crossings, see Gerard Fowke, *Archaeological History of Ohio*, Ohio State Archaeological and Historical Society, Columbus, Ohio, 1902, p. 36, in particular Fowke's citations of both Bancroft's and Schoolcraft's specific observations on the phenomenon and its relation to the peopling of the Americas.

[2] Robert Heine-Geldern, "The Problem of Transpacific Influences in Mesoamerica", *The Handbook of Middle American Indians*, Volume 4, University of Texas Press, citing Brooks, 1875.

[3] John L. Sorenson and Martin H. Raish, *Pre-Columbian Contact with the Americas Across the Oceans: An Annotated Bibliography*, Vol II, p. 106, entry M-143

[4] Cyclone Covey has assembled a bibliography of materials relating to this work, and given the difficulty in finding these materials, I repeat a part of it here. Niede Guidon & G. Delabrias, "Carbon-14 Dates Point to Man in the Americas 32,000 Years Ago," *Nature* CCCXXI/6072 (19 June 1986), 769-71; Guidon, "Les Premières Occupations Humaines de l'Aire Archéologique de São Raimundo Nonato-Piauí-Brasil," *L'Anthropologie* XXXXVIII/2 (May 1984), 263-71, "On Stratigraphy & Chronology at Pedra Furada," *Current Anthropology* XXX/1 (Dec. 1989), 641-42, "Las Unidades Culturales de São Raimundo Nonato—Sudeste des Estado de Piauí—Brasil," in *New Evidence for the Peopling of the Americas*, ed. Bryan, 157-71; "The First Americans: Cliff Notes," *Natural History* XCVI/8 (Aug. 1987), 6, 8, 10, 12; Robert G. Bednarik, "On the Pleistocene Settlement of South America," *Antiquity* LXIII/2 (March 1989), 101-07; Paul Bahn, "Dating the First American," *New Scientist* CXXXI (22 July 1991), 26-28; Warwick Bray, "Finding the Earliest Americans," *Nature* CCCXXI/6071 (19-25 June 1986), 726; Fiedel, "The Peopling of the New World," 51, & *Prehistory of the Americas* (Cambridge University 1987), 79; Meltzer, Adovasio, & Dillehay, "On a Pleistocene Human Occupation at Pedra Furada, Brazil," *Antiquity* LXVIII/261 (Dec. 1994), 695-714; Guidon, A.-M. Pessis, Fabio Parenti, Michel Fontugue, & Claude Guérin, "Nature & Age of the Deposits in Pedra Furada, Brazil: Reply to Meltzer, Adovasio & Dillehay," ibid. LXX/268 (June 1996), 408-21; Guidon & B. Arnaud, "The Chronology of the New World," 167-78

[5] Current field work in this area of study is always covered in both *The Mammoth Trumpet* and the journal *Current Research in the Pleistocene*, both from the Center for the Study of the First Americans, Department of Anthropology, Texas A&M University,

College Station, Texas.

[6] J.D. McDonald, Maps of World Haplogroups, 2004, the McDonald Institute For Archaeological Research, Cambridge University. McDonald cites more principal researchers as contributors to the maps than can be listed here. The analysis here is my own.

[7] McDonald, ibid.

[8] Ernest W. Kent, *The Brains of Men and Machines*, Byte Books, McGraw Hill, Peterborough, New Hampshire, 1981

[9] Past and current excavation reports are available via *The Mammoth Trumpet*, cited above..

[10] Frank C. Hibbens, *The Lost Americans*, Thomas Y. Cromwell Company, New York, 1969, p. 123-127

[11] Hibbens, ibid., p. 161-167

[12] George E. Lankford, compiler and editor, *Native American Legends*, August House, Little Rock, Arkansas, 1987, p 76, citing Stith Thompson, Tales of the North American Indians, Indiana University Press, Bloomington, Indiana, 1929, p. 318

[13] J.N.B. Hewitt, *Iroquoian Cosmology*, Annual Report of the Bureau of Ethnology, v 21, 1903, Government Printing Office, Washington, D.C.

[14] *The Walum Olun*, Appendix E here. Line numbers following the usage of Brinton's Part II

[15] The "turtle" referring to the penis of the Creator.

[16] J.N.B. Hewitt, ibid..

[17] Elias Johnson, *Legends, Traditions, And Laws of The Iroquois, or Six Nations, and History of the Tuscarora Indian*, Union Printing and Publishing Company, Lockport, New York, 1881

CHAPTER 4

THE NEW PEOPLES EMERGE

MAN DISAPPEARS FROM THE ATLANTIC COAST

Given the spread of sites over such a wide area of Atlantic North America where pre-Clovis and Clovis tools are found, some may wonder why these peoples did not adopt or evolve new tool technologies, and why evidence of that evolution in tool use has not been found.[1] Of course, it may be that the reason these peoples did not adopt these technologies is simply that they were dead, killed by a Holocene Start impact in the Atlantic, caused when another fragment of the impactor that hit in the northern Pacific Ocean[2] hit in the Atlantic.

Indeed, an Atlantic Holocene Start impact may have not only killed all humans living in this area, it may also have completely destroyed all the herds of game animals that lived there. With no game to hunt, there would have been no reason for man to move back into the area until game herds had recovered. This scenario agrees with what is found in the areas along the Atlantic coast: the slow introduction of archaic tools by the migrations of archaic tool users from other areas.

THE RED PAINT PEOPLE APPEAR ALONG THE NORTHERN ATLANTIC COAST

About 6,000 BCE a new people appear on the Atlantic coast of Canada. Known to archaeologists as the Maritime Archaic people, they are more commonly known as the Red Paint People for their habit of covering the bodies of their dead with crushed oxidized iron, red ochre. This seagoing people had a most amazing tool kit, and most distinctive are their polished stone tools. Even given that these were a marine people who constantly saw water polished stones, their adaptation of sand/water abrasion for tool making is distinct. Continuing with the wonder, found alongside the polished stone tools are even more remarkable chipped points. These people had also developed the technique of using bone antler tips to chip serrated edges onto their points, making them far sharper than points simply knapped with the ordinary technique of using rock on rock.

Not only are they far sharper than anything seen before, the stone points came in various sizes to tip various weapons, including not only harpoons, but also atlatls, spears thrown with levers. It took anthropologists many years of research to understand how these atlatls work, but it is clear now that the atlatl provides enormous force, so much force that Spanish conquistadors were afraid of them because their projectiles could penetrate their armor. Able to penetrate the thickest hide when used by a skilled thrower, the atlatl also provided added range against smaller game.[3]

The harpoons of the Red Paint People featured detachable imbedding bone points, which would have held to game as it tried to swim away. Finally, these people also had drills, which they must have developed both to create clothing to stand up to the cold,

47

as well as to create skin boats.

Where did this final group of Native Americans originally evolve? Right now, no one knows with much certainty, but subglacial Eurasia seems the best bet. This group most likely provided the final haplogroup seen in Native Americans, the X mitochondrial DNA haplogroup, which is found not only along the northern Atlantic coast of North America and down the Saint Lawrence River, but also in Europe.

THE RED PAINT PEOPLE'S MIGRATIONS BEGIN

About 4,000 BCE people appeared along Lake Superior who had a technology identical to that of the Red Paint People of the Atlantic coast. These people are informally known as the Red Ochre People[4] by the regional archaeologists, and it is not known whether they were the Red Paint People, or simply a people who were already there who adopted the Red Paint People's technologies and culture. Polished stone tools have been found in sub-glacial Canada which may indicate the adoption of the Red Paint People's culture by those already living in that area, but the finds of these artifacts have been so rare that nothing very definitive can be said about the matter one way or the other.[5]

One thing that can be said with some certainty is that these Red Ochre People escaped the cold of Lake Superior's winters by using their boats to travel down to the Door Peninsula of Wisconsin. This peninsula is much warmer than the surrounding area, and if one finds refuge from the icy winds among its dunes, it is positively tropical in comparison with the −30 temperatures of the surrounding areas. Not only is the Door Peninsula much warmer than the surrounding areas, it provides an abundance of sea food throughout the winter, and the shore area across Green Bay from the Door provides birds and deer in abundance.

RED PAINT CULTURE SPREADS DOWN THE MISSISSIPPI RIVER

The Door Peninsula was still not warm enough. The Red Paint Culture spread down the Mississippi River, where it evolved along the large lakes formed by the Mississippi as it hit various obstacles on its path to the Gulf of Mexico. The key type site for the development of this southern variant of the Red Paint Culture is the Modoc[6] rock shelter in Illinois, just to the southeast of the present day city of Saint Louis. Yet further to the south, in the Tennessee River Valley, a continuous uninterrupted line of development is seen from Folsom times to around 4,000 BCE. Then the new Red Paint technologies suddenly appear, undoubtedly adopted by the peoples already living along the river.[7]

This seems as good a place as any to bring up the subject of fish traps. Fording a stream was usually accomplished by throwing trees or stones into it until a dry passage could be made across it. It is a short step from building a ford like this to the building of a fish trap, where migrating fish are herded by means of a stone gate into a basket seine. Two of the interesting things about both the Watson Break and the Poverty Point archaeological sites, which will be discussed below, appear to be both the lack of fishhooks and the lack of the use of shellfish such as clams and mussels as food sources.

ARBOREAL TECHNIQUES: THE USE OF NUTS AND FRUITS FROM TREES

As the Red Paint Culture spread south, it encountered nut harvesting peoples. Just as wild deer played something of the same role for Native Americans as domesticated cattle did for Europeans, nuts such as acorn, hickory, pecan and walnut played the same role for Native Americans as grains did for the Europeans.[8] The first settled Native American societies depended on nuts for their starches and oils. Of particular note is the role of the pecan, which though very small at first, grew in importance. It is worth noting that acorns, which also played a large role in these peoples' diets, must be processed to remove their tannin before they can be eaten by humans, while pecans and walnut do not.

Along with the management of nut trees, these peoples also began to manage fruit trees such as persimmon, and fruit bushes such as wild grape and hackberry. In some areas these peoples' ancient groves survived the rigors of climatic change and the environment through the ages, and first colonists would often note a "Hickory Hill" or "Cherry Hill" or some such.[9] While at this time it is not clear exactly how they managed these trees, it is clear that manage them they did. As will be seen a little later below, contact period informants described tree grafting, but this most likely was a fairly late technique.

THE FIRST CULTIGENS

As will be seen in Chapter 9, corn (maize) actually made a late appearance in North America. Instead, at this early time these people were collecting seeds from honey locust, goosefoot, knotweed, and doveweed, and they made some use of squash. Crops such as squash, pumpkins, sunflower root, and these seeds would be cultivated in North America long before corn (maize) was.

THE FIRST RIVER SOCIETIES AND THE FIRST "MOUNDS"

Ancient Native Americans now had sufficient food technologies to enable them to live in one place, or at least in the same area, for long periods of time, provided there was an environment where all of these food technologies could be utilized at the same time. There were several such environments, but the ones we're interested in were not directly ON the two branches of the Mississippi River. These two branches of the Mississippi River itself were simply too large, too liable to flood, and their banks not dry enough for trees.

The place where this environment occurred was on the smaller tributaries of the East and West Mississippi, roughly from north Louisiana south, and the use of earth as a building material starts around 4,000 BCE in these areas. Given a flat and marshy environment prone to flooding, the desire for housing elevated above it is obvious.

These food technologies allowed a fairly dense settlement of these areas, and this led to the need to organize larger social units. This was accomplished by holding periodic meetings of nearby groups, and the first structure to enable this type of meeting which is known of is Watson Break, Louisiana, dated to 3,400 BCE. While 11 mounds are counted altogether at Watson Break, it looks to me to be rather more like 6 major mounds connected by an embankment to form a circle with a gate. The number 6 is significant in later constructions in the area, as will be seen.

NATCHEZ AND YAZOO MEMORIES OF THE RED PAINT CULTURE

"When the Natchez retired to this part of America where I saw them, they there found several nations, or rather the remains of several nations, some on the east, others on the west of the Missisippi [River]. These were the people who are distinguished among the natives by the name of Red Men, and their origin is so much the more obscure, as they have not so distinct a tradition, as the Natchez, nor arts and sciences like the Mexicans, from whence we might draw some satisfactory inferences. All that I could learn from them [the Natchez] was that they came from between the north and the sun-setting; and this account they uniformly adhered to whenever they gave any account of their origin." – Simon Le Page du Pratz, in his *History of Louisiana*, most likely taken from his conversations with the Natchez Chief of the Guardians of the Temple.

"This journey [northeast to the lands of the Shawnee, the Five Nations, the Abenakes, and finally the Atlantic Ocean], instead of satisfying, only served to excite my curiousity. Our old men, for several years, had told me that the Ancient Word informed them that the Red Men of the north came originally much higher and much farther than the source of the Missouri River; and as I had longed to see, with my own eyes, the land from whence our first fathers came, I took my precautions for my journey westwards." - The Yazoo explorer Moncacht-apé to Simon Le Page du Pratz.

EVENTS ALONG THE EAST COAST:
THE DUGOUT CANOE APPEARS ON THE CHESAPEAKE BAY

In the Chesapeake Bay area we find evidence of new additions to the Archaic peoples' diets of deer, bear, and small mammals: the remains of American oysters, hard clams, soft clams, Bay shad, and sturgeon.[10] The sure signs of a maritime adaption of these archaic peoples are the appearance of fishing net weights along with axes and adzes. While nets can be cast from shore to catch some varieties of both birds and fish, they are more effective for fish if they are used from a canoe. And while dugout canoes can be manufactured by burning out the center of naturally downed trees, better watercraft can be had if a good tree is selected, ringed with an axe, coals set into this ring until the tree is downed, the tree trunk's center burned out, and then the rough form finished into a hull with an adze.

The remains of very few of these dugouts have been recovered, but the preferred wood in later times appears to have been that of the poplar tree because of its light weight. Lips were left at both ends of the craft so that it could be grabbed up and beached or portaged easily. Some later Native American illustrations show two man dugouts in use, but these may have been used for communication only. From the dugouts recovered, a three man craft seems to have been used for trade, since while portaging two men could carry the craft while the third man carried the trade goods. Other illustrations from the contact period show three man watercraft craft used as workboats, with two people controlling the boat while the third gathers food. Combined with the weighted net, these dugouts made it possible to reliably harvest fish and waterfowl.

WHERE DID THIS DUGOUT TECHNOLOGY COME FROM?

A problem with attributing this dugout technology to the Red Paint People is that at these middle Atlantic sites the remains of cultivated hickory nuts and walnuts appear, along with the stone tools for working the nuts, at the same time that these watercraft construction technologies do. (The maypop fruit was also cultivated by these peoples.) Further, soapstone cooking bowls and soapstone baking tools also appear at the same time.

While it is possible that these technologies could have spread by inland contact from the north, down from Lake Erie along the Shenango River and Coniango River (Beaver) to today's Pittsburgh, and from there up the Monangahela River and down the Potomac River to the Chesapeake Bay, these peoples' source for their arboriculture [tree-based] technology appears to have been the river peoples whose remains have been found at the Sara's Ridge site, the Paris Island, South Carolina, site and the Rocky River, North Carolina, site. One problem here is that these river peoples did not live along the coast, and at these river sites there is no indication of their construction of large watercraft.

ENTIRELY NEW TECHNOLOGIES APPEAR:
THE STALLINGS ISLAND COMPLEX

But a short time later these river dwelling peoples adopted an entirely new technology, and this may be clearly seen at Stallings Island, Georgia, where the Mill Branch riverine culture existed for several hundred years before being replaced by a Shell Ring culture around 1,700 BCE. Here have been found levels containing soapstone artifacts overlain by levels containing fiber-tempered pottery, another entirely new technology.

THE PROBLEM: THE SPREAD OF DUGOUT WATERCRAFT TECHNOLOGIES

Given the area and time period being surveyed here, the problems of when these watercraft were developed, how they were used, and how they spread become central.

Many in the anthropological community decry any suggestion of trans-Pacific or trans-Atlantic contact, as though the adoption by Native Americans of "foreign" technology would somehow take something away from them. The plain fact is that due to natural currents, both trans-Pacific and trans-Atlantic contacts were inevitable, if not by design, with certainty by accident. Once again, in the one century from 1775 to 1875 at least 20 Japanese junks were involuntarily driven by storms and currents to landing points from the Aleutian Islands to Mexico, an average of 1 watercraft every 5 years.[11] Further, in the last century some 600 African craft have washed up on the coast of South America, a rough average of 1 watercraft every 2 months.[12]

Given these rates of accidental trans-oceanic crossings, it is a slur on the Native American peoples to insist that either 1) they were so cruel that they immediately dispatched every mariner who had the misfortune to be ship wrecked, and then the good luck to be stranded on their shores alive, or 2) they were too stupid to take advantage of the new technologies which either these mariners or their crew-less watercraft would have provided.   Those who blindly dismiss trans-oceanic contact also fail to consider that technologies may have spread from Native Americans in the other direction – and this is well evidenced as well. Plants with trans-oceanic distribution include cocoanut, various edible palm, pineapple, banana, cotton, the grain amaranth, and hennequin, a type of hemp.[13]

LATER WATERCRAFT IN THE CARIBBEAN SEA AND ATLANTIC OCEAN

When we think of dugout watercraft, the first image that comes to mind is that of the dugout canoes used today on the rivers of many parts of the world. This smallness in size reflects not only the uses for which these craft were and are constructed, which are those of production and trade on rivers, but also reflects the current scarcity of large diameter trees. It must be remembered that during the times of the first migrations into North America, and indeed even up to the time of European contact, trees with diameters of 3 meters and more were common. Indeed, satisfying the need for timbers for the British Navy was one of the first reasons that that government had for placing its settlers in North America. I don't think it can be excluded that this need for large trees may also have played a role in early trans-Atlantic contacts, those contacts which may have occurred as Europe was deforested, while the peoples of coastal Europe still depended on large watercraft built from large single trees.

Fernando Colon, Columbus's second son, provided us with an account of one oceangoing large dugout which his father encountered during his fourth voyage, and it is worth repeating part of it in full here:

> "Having come to the island of Guanaja, the Admiral sent ashore his brother Bartholomew with two boats. They encountered people who resembled those of the other islands, but had narrower foreheads. They also saw many pine trees and pieces of earth called calcide which the Indians use to cast copper; some of the sailors thought it was gold....by good fortune there arrived at that time A CANOE AS LONG AS A GALLEY AND EIGHT FEET WIDE, MADE OF A SINGLE TREE TRUNK (m.c.) like the other Indian canoes; it was freighted with merchandise from the western regions around New Spain. Amidships it had a palm-leaf awning like that on Venetian gondolas; this gave complete protection against the rain and waves. Underneath were women and children, and all the baggage and merchandise. There were twenty-five paddlers aboard, but they offered no resistance when our boats drew up to them."

The "other Indian canoes" which Fernando refers to were those which Columbus and his men had seen earlier, those of the Taino (Arawak) and Carib of the islands, and these dugouts were probably not as large as those of the Choton traders of Central America, which Fernando was describing here. The Spanish colonial historian Orvieda[14] recorded the use of sail by the Taino, but not by the Carib, who relied on paddles for propulsion. Given the trade which existed along the east coasts of Central America and South America, the Taino (Arawak) likely used sails at a much earlier period. Orvieda also recorded the Choton's use of sails on their watercraft, and the Choton's conduct of regular trade along the east coast of Central America for a long period of time is fairly well evidenced by the distribution of the remains of trade goods.

It seems likely that all of the Caribbean watercraft did not use centerboards or sideboards, and thus the prevailing winds and currents must have played a large role in determining the movements of peoples and goods through the region.[15]   As might reasonably be expected, and as will be seen, these watercraft played a significant role both in the conduct of trade, and in the spread of peoples as well.

LATER WATERCRAFT ALONG THE PACIFIC COAST

In his book *The Pyramids of Tucume*, Thor Heyerdahl[16] described the watercraft used by Native Americans along the Pacific Coast at the time of European contact. These were ocean-going rafts equipped with sails and a superstructure to keep their goods and passengers dry, which were called "balsas", a term related to the balsa wood logs which were tied together to construct them. These watercraft were very large, and they had capacities of up to 60 to 70 European tons.

The use of these balsas along the Pacific coast of South America dates at least to what anthropologists call the "Early Intermediate Period", around 200 BC, as both the Chimu and Moche foundation myths have their founders arriving from the south on balsa rafts.[17]

The bindings which tied their logs together were of hennequin, a type of hemp, and the distribution of this plant is important for the understanding of ocean trade. The balsas used two types of masts, with one type of mast mounted along the center line, and the other type constructed of two poles attached to the raft's sides and joined over its center to form an upside-down V shape. The balsas had two types of sails, both square and lateen (triangular), which when combined with the use of centerboards gave them the ability to travel against the wind.

These craft ranged up and down the Pacific Coast of both South and Central America, and special note should be made of the circular stone anchors which these watercraft used. Anchors of this type have been recovered at several sites along the west coast of Central America, and been identified as anchors.[18] Another artifact which must be associated with the use of these rafts are large jars for the storage of fresh water, jars which most likely replaced earlier wooden vessels used for the same purpose. A final artifact indicative of the use of balsa watercraft are non-native stones which were used for ballast.

These craft not only carried merchandise for trade, but also served as "mother-ships" for fishing expeditions. The general method used by these peoples was not line fishing, that is, fishing with hooks and lines, where the hooks would have been preserved as artifacts. They used net fishing instead, sometimes from the shore, or sometimes two fishermen would mount small three log craft and drag a net between them, then returning their catch to either the shore or to a large balsa "mother-ship".

While the designs of these balsas reflect the lack of large trees in the areas on the west coast of South America, based on the evidence of trans-Pacific contacts, in particular the mitochondrial DNA distributions, there is good reason to suspect that the first ocean-going watercraft along the Pacific coasts were large dugout boats.

WHERE DID THE STALLINGS ISLAND TECHNOLOGY COME FROM?

The Stallings Island complex was preceded by shell rings in Florida which appear to have been built almost 1,000 years earlier, around 2,700 BCE. There is little doubt that this was an ocean-going maritime technology, with very large dugout watercraft, as early shell ring sites also existed on Cuba.

PACIFIC CONTACT?

Further, even more ancient coastal shell sites have been found along the Pacific Coast of both Central America and South America. Betty Meggers has pretty well documented contacts between Jomon Japan and coastal South America at Valdivia by around 3,300 BCE.[19]

AFRICAN CONTACT?

While little is known about the archaeology of the Atlantic coast of Africa during this period, based on site distribution and late accidental crossings it is highly likely that early seafarers may have arrived from the areas at the mouths of the rivers south of the Atlas Mountains.[20]

TWO LISTS OF EARLY COASTAL SITES

The following lists started with a list given in *The Art and Archaeology of Pre-Columbian Cuba*, Ramon Dacal Moure and Manuel Rivero de la Calle[21], whicht was then added to. The Atlantic list must be used with caution, as the dates those authors gave for both Stallings Island and Poverty Point archaeological sites are wrong, and I have not verified myself that all of their sites are maritime culture sites.

ATLANTIC COASTAL SITES

It is generally held that there were two early migrations into the Caribbean Islands: the Casimiroid, which is hypothesized to have crossed a land bridge or island chain from Central America around 4,000 BCE, and the Ortoiroid, which is believed to have spread from the northeast coast of South America after 2,000 BCE. Despite the pottery found at Puerto Hormiga, these later people are generally held to have been aceramic.

Banwari Trace, Trinidad	5,500 BCE
Gulf of Paria, Venezuela	3,650 BCE
Levisa, Cuba	3,190 BCE
Puerto Hormiga, coastal Colombia	2,925 BCE Pottery
Canimar Abajo, Cuba	2,750 BCE
22 sites, Aruba	2,500 BCE-ca 1,000 BCE shells, no pottery
Cubagua, Venezuela	2,200 BCE
Sapelo, Georgia	2,150 BCE shell ring
Ossabaw Island, Georgia	2 shell rings? - late archaic ends ca 1,000 BCE
Cueva Funche, Cuba	2,050 BCE
Canapote, coastal Colombia	2,050 BCE
Madrigales, Hispaniola	2,030 BCE
St. John's River, Florida	ca 2,000 BCE East Coast, Orange Pottery, incised decoration
Gulf Coast, Florida	ca 2,000 BCE West Coast, Norwood Pottery, paddle decoration
Hilton Head Island, S. Carolina	ca 2,000 BCE 3 shell ring sites of 17 in US
Hoyo Del Todo, Hispaniola	1,940 BCE
Stallings Island, Georgia	1,850 BCE Pottery, up Savannah River from coast
Jolly Beach, Antigua	1,775 BCE no pottery
Manicuare, Aruba, off Venezuela	1,620 BCE
Barlovento, coastal Colombia	1,550 BCE
Damajayabo, Cuba	1,300 BCE
El Povenir, Hispaniola	1,185 BCE
Cueva el Purial, Cuba	1,110 BCE

PACIFIC COASTAL SITES

Siches, Peru	ca. 5,000 BCE
Cerro Mangote, West Coast Panama	4,860 BCE
Rio Chiriqui, West Coast Panama	4,610 BCE
Valdivia, Ecuador (pottery)	3,300 BCE influenced by Jomon Culture, Japan
(Meggers)	
Xoconocho, West Coast Mexico	3,000 - 2,000 BCE shell middens, no pottery
Barra, Mexico	1,800 BCE pottery, riverine, early species of maize
Machalilla, Ecuador	1,600 BCE from Columbia, headbinding

Chorrera, Ecuador   1,200 BCE from Central America

MAN DOES NOT LIVE BY FISH ALONE

As was mentioned earlier in this chapter, while in the eastern hemisphere of our planet early large scale societies depended on grains for food, in North America the early societies depended on trees. Indeed, the cultivation of trees began very early in the western hemisphere, and while the evidence recovered to date is sparse, the North American shell ring cultures almost certainly depended on the cultivation of various palm trees. Ramon nut is seen in Caribbean sites, while plantain (a banana variant) and cocoanut trees show up in differing limited Pacific coastal regions.

SOUTH AMERICA AS A SOURCE FOR DUGOUT TECHNOLOGY:
EARLY AGRICULTURE ON THE AMAZON AND ORINOCO RIVERS

The final foodstuff important to early coastal man in the Americas was manioc, and for this one must turn to its native range, what are now the jungles of South America. Given the dense vegetation that exists in this region today, it is hard to imagine this area turned into plains by foraging megafauna. It is harder still to imagine the hunters of those megafauna turning to agriculture when that megafauna died off.

Fortunately for us, some people have already been hard at work on this, including Dr. Hoopes of the University of Kansas.[22] As Dr. Hoopes points out, "The earliest evidence for New World pottery comes from the central Amazon, with dates around 7,000 BC (Roosevelt et al. 1991, Roosevelt 1995). It is present in northern Colombia by 4,000 BC (Oyuela 1995), coastal Ecuador by 3500 BC (Damp and Vargas 1995), and central Panama by 3,000 BC (Cooke 1995)." By Hoopes' account there is no need to look for the introduction of pottery technology via trans-oceanic contacts, as Native Americans had already developed the technology quite independently. And as the Amazon dwellers were river peoples, it is likely that they had developed dugout canoes as well.

THE SOUTH AMERICAN MOUND BUILDERS

In the mountains of South America, around 2,600 BCE the arboriculture of the coastal peoples was supplemented by the cultivation of beans, lima beans, and squash[23]. One of the most distinctive items of this culture is their construction of large mounds in the center of their urban complexes. In as much as their cultivation appears to have been based on the use of networks of channels for irrigation, this implies some measure of organization of labor, and thus of a hierarchical organization to their societies, a hierarchy demonstrated very convincingly by the existence of these large mounds. These cultures' aquatic roots may be seen in their heavy use of seafood, and besides their use of irrigation, it is more than likely that they may also have used some forms of aquaculture.

THE SPREAD OF MOUND BUILDING TO THE NORTH:
THE "FORMATIVE"

More to the focus here, this mound building culture appears to have spread north from South America, with these arboreal, raised field, and aquaculture technologies forming the basis for the coastal Olmec (Zoque) societies and other societies along both the eastern coast of Central America and the shores of the highland lakes of that region. That this technology transfer was water-borne is proved by the existence of large mounds on the island of Cuba, as well as by the appearance of a large mound culture first seen in North America at the mouth of the Mississippi River, particularly at Baton Rouge, Louisiana. Whether this technology transfer was done by paddle-powered dugouts or by sail-powered craft is unknown, but the cultivation of both cotton (possibly used for sails) and hennequin (possibly used for ropes for rigging) spread.

THE FIRST NORTH AMERICAN COASTAL SOCIETIES

Along the Gulf Coast, a different culture was emerging from that seen at Watson Break[24]. Up the Mississippi River from the coast, at the Baton Rouge mounds, dated to 3,000 BCE, we see evidence of a society organized in an entirely different manner than that which was emerging on the rivers further to the north. At this site we find 2 large mounds, indicating a much more centralized and stratified society than that found at Watson Break. In coastal plains hurricanes are a yearly danger, and one way of surviving hurricane flooding is simply to build your house on a very highly elevated platform.

In lower Florida, societies emerged which replaced stone technologies with shell-based tools. While some of these societies remained stable for thousands of years until European contact, they also remained outside the area of trade interaction with Native American societies to the north. What is clear from contact records is that these peoples possessed sufficient skills to control the access to their parts of the coast, and this pattern also held to the west, with important consequences, as will be seen.

THE ALABAMA MIGRATION LEGEND

"Formerly the ocean (Gulf of Mexico) was not as large as it is today, and at that time the Alabama Indians, who lived upon the other side, came westward across it in canoes. When they had gotten about halfway over they came upon an island (Cuba?) where they rested and fished. Then they resumed their journey and presently reached this land.

"At first they lived upon acorns, and they also roasted and ate cane sprouts. Later they made bows and arrows with which to kill deer, and having nothing with which to cut up the meat they used sharp rocks. They also had to learn how to kindle a fire. To accomplish this they used as a drill the stem of a weed called has-salat-po ('plant-with-which-to-make-fire'), which is like sassafras, and the wood of a tree called baksa (bass) for a base stick.

"Traveling inland, they established their village near a river and lived there for a long time.[25]

THE TSULAGI [CHILLICOTHE] MIGRATION LEGEND

Alongside the Alabama, the Tsulagi also remembered their ancestors crossing the Gulf of Meixco and migrating to the north.

Their Descent From The Heavens:

"After this the Great Spirit put the 12 men and the two old men he had created - he had created two to supply their place in the original number - in a large thing like a basket (a boat?) and told them he was going to put them on the Great Island. The old man first named [Kwikule] carried with him in a pack on his shoulders all the good things entrusted to his care for the benefit of the people...." Tenskwatawa, 'Open Door', the Shawnee Prophet[26]

The Mekoche Migration From The South - Crossing The Gulf Of Mexico:

"The first earth they saw in their journey was on the other side of the great lake [the Gulf of Mexico], and when they had arrived on the sea shore they stopped and rested. The old man [Kwikule] told them that the place where his heart was, was in a northern direction from them, and at a great distance. [But] they could see nothing but water, and knew not how they were to cross the Great Water to the Island.

"The old man [Kwikule] then took from his pack a gourd and began to sing. They sang for a period of twelve days, during which time they ate nothing but a few roots. The old man then told the people that the Great Spirit had promised to grant them all they desired, and that they must pray to him to remove the water which impeded their journey to the Island. Soon afterward the water was dried up and they saw nothing but sand..." Tenskwatawa, 'Open Door', the Shawnee Prophet

The Original Chillicothe [Tsulagi] split from the Mekoche:

"The old man [Kwikule] observed that as he was too old to lead the party he would give his pack to one of the others, and he appointed Chilicothe [Tsulagi] to be the leader and bearer of the pack, and told him that he would remain behind.

"So Kwikule seated himself on that which was the shore, and the young leader Chillicothe went forward with the band, which by this time had become quite numerous. When they had arrived on the opposite shore they encamped and remained for the period of twelve days employed in singing, during which time, as before, they abstained from eating. They then sent the waiting servant [messenger] to Kwikule, who had remained behind, to find out [tell him] what course they had come, but the waiting servant returned, and told them that the waters had returned to their place, and that he could see nothing else.

"Then Mekwikla made a speech to the people and told them he was satisfied of the power and justness of the Great Spirit, and that they must remove farther to the north, but that he would remain on the shore to look back to his friend Kwikule who remained on the opposite side of the sea [the Gulf of Mexico].

"These two old men have since turned into rocks and sit in their respective positions at this day, where they will remain so long as this Great Island stands..." Tenskwatawa, 'Open Door', the Shawnee Prophet[27]

The Tsulagi March Up The Mississippi River:

"When Chilicothe had arrived with his warriors on this side of the ocean [the Gulf of Mexico], they were one day traversing the borders of the sea, and they found a large animal (a crocodile) lying dead upon the shore.

"They immediately cut him open and took out his heart, which, along with a piece of his flesh, they deposited carefully in a bag and carried it with them on their journey.

"Upon their arrival at the Shawnee River [Ohio/Mississippi River] they began to encounter difficulties. Opposition was made to their progress by those who inhabited the adjacent country, and they were compelled to send out scouting parties and war parties in order to maintain their possessions...." Unknown, via Trowbridge[28]

(Footnotes)

[1] For paleolithic–archaic discontinuities in the Chesapeake Bay area, see *Bay, Plain, and Piedmont, A Landscape History of the Chesapeake Heartland from 1.3 Billion Years Ago to the Year 2000*,The Chesapeake Bay Heritage Project, September 2000, The National Park Service, Chesapeake Bay Program, Annapolis, Maryland, available via the Internet. For paleolithic-archaic discontinuities in other Atlantic coastal regions, refer to the site reports.

[2] Chapter 3 here.

[3] One of the most common remains found in excavations are parts of atlatl kits, which were often earlier mislabeled as being personal ornaments, as no one understood at the time of the excavations exactly how the atlatl worked. They often remain mislabeled as personal ornaments to this day.

[4] Gathered from conversations with local archaeologists. These antecedent people are not to be confused with the formal Red Ochre Culture proper, which appears much later.

[5] William A. Fox, "The Lakehead Complex, New Insights", *Archaeological Research Report* 13, Historical Planning and Research Branch, Ontario Ministry of Culture and Recreation, 1980, p. 127-154

[6] "Mounds, Modoc, and Mesoamerica", *Papers in Honor of Melvin L. Fowler*, Illinois State

Museum Scientific Papers, Volume XXVIIII, Illinois State Museum, Springfield, Illinois, 2000

[7] A very nice collection of local lithics can be viewed in the museum at the mound in Florence, Alabama. While some archaeologists view the Glacial Kame peoples as descendents of the Old Copper Peoples, it seems more likely to me that they developed in this region. For their remains, see Robert N. Converse, *The Glacial Kame Indians*, The Archaeological Society of Ohio, 1979. While it is true that the Glacial Kame peoples used red ochre, the type artifact for their culture is the sandal soled gorget, large ellipses made from conch shell which were worn strapped to the head. These conch shells are only available on the Atlantic and Gulf coasts of Florida. Though their copper artifacts have never been put to spectral analysis, given this trade with the south, their source for sheet copper may have been the deposits of the Tennessee River area, and not those of Isle Royale. Unfortunately, the radio-carbon dates for the Glacial Kame are too poor to determine whether they moved into north-west Ohio due to the migration of the Mekoche or Adena into their original range, and it is possible that they migrated into that area at these two different times. Their practice of periodic mass re-internment may indicate an Iroquoian people, and it may be that they were partially ancestral to the later Wyandot/Wendat people, and on this I differ here with Converse, who sees them as ancestral to the Hopewell. Unfortunately a large part of the contact period Huron/Wendat/Wyandot ethnographic materials were largely unavailable to me at the time this survey was conducted, including in particular their own histories. This work will be extended to include them if resources become available to do so, and help in this regard will be appreciated.

[8] For food use at the Poverty Point site, including specifically intensive use of nuts see Jon L. Gibson, *Poverty Point,* Department of Culture, Recreation and Tourism, Louisiana Archaeological Survey and Antiquities Commission, second edition, 1999

[9] To my knowledge there is no overall database of these clusters of cultivated trees, as well as no ready to hand information on the original ranges of these species.

[10] For the appearance of maritime archaic technologies in the Chesapeake Bay area, see *Bay, Plain, and Piedmont, A Landscape History of the Chesapeake Heartland from 1.3 Billion Years Ago to the Year 2000,*The Chesapeake Bay Heritage Project, September 2000, The National Park Service, Chesapeake Bay Program, Annapolis, Maryland. Available via the Internet.

[11] Robert Heine-Geldern, "The Problem of Transpacific Influences in Mesoamerica", *The Handbook of Middle American Indians*, Volume 4, University of Texas Press, citing Brooks, 1875.

[12] John L. Sorenson and Martin H. Raish, *Pre-Columbian Contact with the Americas Across the Oceans: An Annotated Bibliography,* Vol II, p. 106, entry M-143

[13] Those who are more interested in trans-oceanic contact than in the peopling of the coastal areas of South-East North America, the Caribbean, and coastal Central America, and the effect of cometary and asteroidal impact on these peoples, I direct to: Robert Heine-Geldern, "The Problem of Transpacific Influences in Mesoamerica"; and Philip Philips, "The Role of TransPacific Contact in the Development of New World Pre-Columbian Cultures", both in *The Handbook of Middle American Indians*, Volume 4, University of Texas Press; Geoffrey Ashe, Thor Heyerdahl, Helge Ingstad, J.V. Luce, Betty Meggars and Brigitta Wallace, *The Quest for America*, Pall Mall Press, London, 1971; and Andrew Collins, *Gateway to Atlantis*, Carroll and Graff, New York, 2000

[14] Gonzalo Fernandez de Orvieda y Valdez , *Historia General y Natural de las Indias* , 1535
[15] Seasonal current and wind charts for the Caribbean may be found in *Art and Archaeology of Pre-Columbian Cuba*, Ramon Dacal Moure and Manual Riviero de la Calle, University of Pittsburgh Press, Pittsburgh, 1996.
[16] Thor Heyerdahl, Daniel H. Sandweiss, and Alfredo Navarez, *The Pyramids of Tucume*, Thames and Hudson, New York, 1995
[17] Gary Burton, *Inca Myths*, British Museum Press and University of Texas Press, 1999, p. 59-62, citing Cabello Balbao for the Chimu myths, Moche myth source uncited
[18] So much for the mysterious "stone rings" found in some excavations.
[19] Megger's direct demonstration of this using original artifacts used to be viewable on the second floor of the Smithsonian's Natural History Museum in Washington. I hope that it still is.
[20] Ivan Van Sertima's *They Came Before Columbus*, Random House, New York, 1976 is an excellent accessible introduction to the material on likely later African contacts with the Americas; specialists dealing with these earliest contacts will probably find themselves working with primary materials.
[21] Ramon Dacal Moure and Manuel Rivero de la Calle, ibid.
[22] http://www.ukans.edu/~hoopes/nature.html. See also, *The Emergence of Pottery: Technology and Innovation in Prehistoric Societies*, William Barnett and John Hoopes, editors, Smithsonian Institution Press, Washington, 1995
[23] A nice overview of Caral may be seen at http://www.archaeologychannel.org/caralint.html
[24] One problem we now run into is the lack of preserved sites. Due to rising sea levels, many early coastal areas between Louisiana and Florida are now submerged. To the west hurricanes have also certainly washed away at least one site, and most likely nearly all the rest. One important coastal site remains unexcavated in Louisiana, which is alluded to in the site list.
[25] John R. Swanton, *Myths and Tales of the Southwestern Indians*, Bureau of Ethnology Bulletin 88, Smithsonian Institution, United States Government Printing Office, 1929, Alabama Story Number 2
[26] The Ancient History of the Shawnee, Appendix C here
[27] ibid.
[28] ibid.

The Sasques= ahanougs
are a Gvant like peo= ple &
thus a =tyred

Uttowig

Attack   Tesiniah

S   I.   S   Q V E

CHAPTER 5

COPPER TRADING GIANTS[1]

EUROPE AS A SOURCE FOR DUGOUT TECHNOLOGY

In the previous chapter, the possibilities of African, Asian, and South American contacts were considered as sources for the dug out canoe technology which appeared in the Chesapeake Bay Region as it was repopulated following the Holocene Start impacts.

Aside from the human remains which have been found in Australia, which place the use of dugouts there at some 50,000 BCE, some of the earliest evidence of large boat building comes from Franchti cave in Greece, and is dated to around 7,000 BCE. The idea presents itself that dug out technology may have survived the Holocene Start impact events near to this area, and then spread from these survivals back along the Mediterranean Sea into coastal Europe. Continuing along this path, it is possible that from coastal Europe the technology for building dugout boats may have spread back into North America. In this chapter Native American accounts of their contacts with Europe ca. 3,000 BCE will be examined, as well as excavation reports of the archaeological remains associated with these contacts.

COPPER MINING BEGINS ON ISLE ROYALE ca. 3,000 BCE

About 3,000 BCE a new culture appears on Isle Royale and in the wintering areas of the Red Paint People on the Door Peninsula. These people came to Isle Royale to mine copper, and over the next two millennia, until about 1,000 BCE, they would mine tens of millions of pounds of copper both from this island as well as from the copper deposits along the shores of Lake Superior. Out of these tens of millions of pounds of copper, to my knowledge less than 6,000 pounds have ever been recovered from the excavations of Native American archaeological sites.

While many popular books have been written about a European copper trade with North America, to my knowledge all of them have focused on Europeans coming to North America, and none have considered the possibility that this trade was conducted by Native Americans who were descended from the Red Paint People. To argue on what may be at best a few isolated trade goods or mementoes recovered from wrecked ships and possibly two inscriptions that there was an extensive European presence in North America which conducted this trade, and implying that the First Peoples were incapable of working copper or trading it, is racist in the extreme.

This chapter, Chapter 7 and Chapter 9 will set out evidence indicating that Native Americans were trading copper to Europe using sail-powered dugout canoes.

THE GIANTS

The first European colonists to enter the Valley of the Ohio River settled in the same prime locations which Native American peoples had used for millennia, and they were intrigued by the large mounds which they found at these spots. Upon opening them, they were astounded by the discovery of the skeletons of large individuals, and these finds were combined with an account from a Moravian missionary to produce a mythical people, the Mound Builders, who had built all of the mounds. Continuing on with this European colonists' myth, these Mound Builders were supposed to have been an advanced race which had been conquered by the Native Americans who currently occupied the lands, and since these Native peoples had a weak claim based on conquest, dispossessing those peoples of their lands was morally justified.

First off, there were no "Mound Builders". Different Native American peoples, including the "Giants", used earth to construct different structures at different times and for different purposes: as a material for the burial of kings and other high status individuals, as a material for the construction of the bases of temples and palaces, as a material for the erection of group burials, as a material for the construction of forts, and as a material for the construction of observatories. "Mounds" are the remains of these structures after the passage of anywhere from several hundred years to several millennia.

About 90 years after these first speculations by the colonists, the archaeologists and anthropologists had actually recorded Native Americans using earth to build these structures, and they were appalled by the use which the earlier colonists had made of this "Mound Builder" myth to dispossess the peoples of their lands. This led them to an absolute denial not only of this myth, but also to a denial of the existence of "Giants" until the late 1950s. At that time, archaeologist George K. Neuman discovered the remains of a giant while excavating at Steubenville, just down the Ohio River from Pittsburgh, and shortly afterwards archaeologist Don W. Dragoo discovered similar remains while excavating Cresap Mound in West Virginia.[2]

THE FIVE NATIONS ACCOUNT OF THE APPEARANCE OF THE GIANTS

The European colonists ignored the Native American accounts which described these "Giants" as being Native Americans, such as the following one from the Five Nations:

> "In the ancient days, after the Great Island had appeared upon the big waters, and after the Earth had brought forth trees, herbs, vegetables, and all else, and after the creation of the land animals, then the Eagwehoewe people, the Real People, were created too, and they resided in the north regions. And after a time, some of those people became Giants, and they committed outrages upon the inhabitants.

> "Now after many years a body of the Eagwehoewe people, the Real People, encamped on the bank of a majestic stream, and was then named the Kanawage, now called the St Lawrence River."[3]

EUROPEAN CONTACT ACCOUNTS OF THE GIANTS

Besides ignoring these native accounts., the later European colonists also ignored the accounts of the first European colonists, which also described these "Giants" as being Native Americans. Indeed, the Andastes, an Iroquoian people closely related to the Five Nations, and who lived immediately to the south of them, had men of giant stature ruling them, as John Smith's Viriginia colonists related:

"... 60 of those Susquehannocks (Andastes) came to us . . . such great and well proportioned men are seldom seen, for they seemed like giants to the English . . . These are the strangest people of all those countries both in language and attire. As for their language, it well matched their proportions, sounding from them like a voice in a vault. Their attire is the skins of bears and wolves, some have cassocks made of bears' heads and skins . . . The half sleeves coming to the elbows were the heads of bears, with their arms coming through the open mouth . . . for a jewel, one had the head of a wolf hanging from a chain . . . with a club suitable to his greatness sufficient to beat out one's brains. Five of their chief wereowances (leading chiefs) came aboard us . . . (of) the greatest of them his hair, the one side was long and the other shorn close with a ridge over his crown like a cock's comb . . . The calf of whose leg was ¾ of a yard around, and all the rest of his limbs so comparable to that proportion that he seemed the goodliest man we ever beheld!" [4]

HOW TO MAKE GIANTS:
ACCOUNTS OF A NATIVE AMERICAN TECHNOLOGY

While it is fascinating to speculate on a hypothetical race of Giants, in point of fact Native Americans had technologies for increasing the stature of their leaders, and the usage of these techniques extended from the Old Copper Culture through the Red Ochre cultures into "Adena" times, and then on into the times of the Southern Ceremonial peoples. The first Spanish explorers in North America also observed "giants" ruling the coastal peoples of South Carolina, these most likely southern Iroquoian peoples who had adopted Mississippian culture, and Peter Martyr[5] investigated their technologies for creating Giants in some detail. As Martyr's account is for the most part unknown, I include it here to end much idle speculation.

"I now come to a fact which will appear incredible to your Excellency. You already know that the ruler of this region is a tyrant of gigantic size. How does it happen that only he and his wife have attained this extraordinary size? No one of their subjects has explained it to me, but I have questioned the above-mentioned licenciate Ayllon [licensed by the King of Spain to conquer and secure Florida, which was all of south eastern North America], a serious and responsible man, who had his information from those who had shared with him the cost of the expedition. I likewise questioned the servant Francisco [a Native American from Chicora], to whom the neighbors [neighboring peoples] had spoken.

"Neither nature nor birth has given these princes the advantage of size as a hereditary gift: they have acquired it by artifice. While they are still in their cradles and in [the] charge of their nurses, experts in the matter are called, who by the application of certain herbs, soften their young bones. During a period of several days they rub the limbs of the child with these herbs, until the bones become as soft as wax. Then they rapidly bend them in such wise [ways] that the infant is almost killed. Afterwards they feed the nurse on foods of a special virtue. The child is wrapped in warm covers, the nurse gives it her breast and revives it with her milk, thus gifted with strengthening properties. After some days rest the lamentable task of stretching the bones is begun anew. Such is the explanation given by the servant Francisco Chicorana.

"The Dean [Captain] of La Concepcion [a ship], whom I have mentioned, received from the Indians [who had] stolen on the vessel {actually, they had been lured on the ship and then abducted by the Spaniards for the slave trade] that was saved [the other slaving ship was lost], explanations differing from those furnished to Ayllon and his associates. These explanations dealt with medicaments and other means used for increasing the size. There was no torturing of bones, but a very stimulating diet composed of crushed herbs was used. This diet was given principally at the age of puberty, when it is nature's tendency to develop and substance is converted into flesh and bones. Certainly it is an extraordinary fact, but we must remember what is told about these herbs, and if their hidden virtues could be learned I would willingly believe in their efficacy." [Perhaps a steroid or growth hormone precursor was involved.]

"We understand that only the kings are allowed to use them, for if anyone else dared taste them, or obtain the recipe of this diet, he would be guilty of treason, for he would appear to equal the king. It is considered, after a fashion, that the king should not be the size of everyone else, for he should look down upon and dominate those who approach him. Such is the story told to me, and I repeat it for what it is worth. Your excellency may believe it or not."

Whether or not one believes Peter Martyr's informants, it is a fact that the first Europeans to contact both these Southern Ceremonial Cult societies and the Andaste people reported that their leaders were of extraordinary height. The possibility exists that this increase in height may have been accomplished by the technologies Martyr describes, or perhaps not.

NURTURE OR NATURE?

One problem with this explanation is that the existence of such technologies does not explain the deaths in childbirth following interbreeding which Native Americans remembered in their legends of the Giants. Similar accounts of death in childbirth following breeding with Giants are found in the Near East, and they have been collected together by Andrew Collins in his book *From the Ashes of Angels*, along with other legendary and archaeological materials from the Near East relating to giants.[6]

Collins argues in his book that a distinct species of giant *Homo sapiens* evolved in ancient Egypt, and then migrated to the Lake Van region of what is now modern Turkey, and that then this technologically advanced sea-going people spread from that area. It seems far more likely to me that a technologically advanced people may have evolved not in Egypt, but instead along the coasts of the Black Sea, in the period before the Straits of the Dardenelles opened up and the Black Sea flooded. I also think it far more likely that the lake around which this people may have later evolved was probably not Lake Van, but instead Lake Urmiah in modern Iran, the biblical Garden of Eden, as this area would have been in contact with the rivers which carried not only towards Turkey and Mesopotamia but also with rivers which carried towards China and India.

Alongside the legends of death in childbirth caused by interbreeding with these giants, Collins notes the legends, figurines, and human remains which show these peoples' extraordinary height, their long faces, and their snake-like eyes. Among the identifying aspects of their culture which Collins catalogues in his book are a shaman class which uses the wings of large birds as a costume, and their practice of excarnation, which is to say, leaving the corpses of the dead exposed on platforms for their consumption by large birds.

Collins posits a re-migration back to Egypt of these people, and ties them in with the appearance of the seagoing Amratian and Gerzian peoples along the shores of the Mediterranean Sea, along with their pottery, lead and silver from Southwest Asia, lapis lazuli from Afghanistan, and copper. Collins cites noted Egyptologist Walter Bryan Emery's report of the recovery of "anatomical remains of a people whose skulls were of a greater size and whose bodies were larger than those of the natives."[7] Here again I'll differ with Collins, as it seems far more likely to me that this people were related to the appearance and distribution of Cardiod Pottery westward along the Mediterranean Sea to the Straits of Gibraltar, their emergence into the Atlantic Ocean, and a subsequent contact with the Red Paint People.

Altogether Collins' *From the Ashes of Angels* is a fine and fascinating read, if while doing so one keeps in mind that visitors to the Sphinx peed on it for millennia, and that the ensuing "water erosion" does not date it to 10,000 BCE.

A WENDAT (HURON) ACCOUNT OF THE GIANTS

"On the shores of the Lake of the Woods (at the east end of Lake Huron, south of Georgian Bay, in Ontario, Canada) stood an Indian village. One summer day, after a heavy rain had passed over the country, a Giant suddenly appeared in the village. He was as tall as the tallest hemlock, and he carried in his hand a club which was longer than the longest canoe.

"'I come from a country in the far north,' he said to the people of the village,'and I am tired and hungry. You must bring me all the wild rice and game that you have. Even that may not be enough to satisfy me.' His orders were obeyed, and all the people of the village gathered to see him enjoy the food that was brought.

"But when he had eaten every morsel, the Giant said that he was still hungry. With one blow of his huge club he killed all the people who had treated him with kindness. Only one person escaped - a little boy who happened to be sick in one of the wigwams.

"During the night, the Giant ate a number of the dead bodies, and then he disappeared. He had not discovered the little boy. In a few days the child was well enough to move about, and as he went from one lodge to another, he was made unhappy by their emptiness. He remembered all his relatives and friends, and thought bitterly of the Giant Cannibal.

"For many years he lived alone. First he lived largely on such birds as the partridge. But as he grew older, he became a successful hunter who often feasted on deer and buffalo. He grew to be a strong man, but a very lonely one. Every time he thought of the Giant who had destroyed his people, he thirsted for revenge.

"As time passed, the hunter became more and more lonely and discontented. He decided to fast and to ask the Spirits to give him power to find and destroy the Giant Cannibal. Taking pity on him, the Spirits sent to his aid a troop of one hundred men, FROM WHOSE BACKS GREW THE MOST BEAUTIFUL WINGS [m.c.] he had ever seen.

"'We know all about the Giant,' they said, 'and we will help you find him and kill him. He is very fond of the meat of the white [polar] bear. If you will give a [polar] bear feast, the Giant will come and ask you for some of the choicest parts.' They agreed that the feast should take place in a large natural wigwam, formed by the locked branches of many trees.

"As soon as they had decided upon the day for the feasting, the hundred strangers disappeared, and the hunter started toward the north in search of a [white] bear. He killed a bear, prepared the feast, and at the time agreed upon, the strange people with wings [growing from their backs] returned. First, all danced and sang, for the feast was a joyous one. When the bear soup was filling the wigwam with a pleasant odor, all heard a heavy tramp in the woods. In a short time the Giant appeared, attracted to the place by the smell of the food. He rushed in like one who knew nothing about fear, but when he saw the winged people he became quiet.

"'May I join you in your feast?' he asked the hunter. 'You may join us if you will go to the nearest stream emptying into the lake and bring back a large rock that you will find there.' The Giant was angry at the request, but the people with wings made him afraid to disobey. He did as he was bidden, although the thong he used to hold the rock on his back cut a deep gash in his forehead.

"Not yet satisfied, the hunter now said to the Giant, 'Before we admit you to the feast, you must bring to the wigwam a gill-net that will reach across the widest stream.' So the Giant obtained a huge net from a mammoth spider that lived in a cave, and brought it to the hunter.

"Pleased but still not satisfied, the hunter said, 'One more thing is necessary before we can admit you to the feast. You must come dressed in a robe of weasel skins which still have on them all the teeth and claws.' In due time the Giant obtained the weasel skins, made the robe, and appeared at the wigwam wearing it.

"The feast then began, and it lasted for several days and nights. The hunter, the strange people with the wings, and the Giant danced and caroused together as if they were the best of friends. The Giant was delighted with the singers and praised them before all of the company. He did not know that in his bowl of soup the hunter had placed a bitter root that would deprive him of all his strength.

"On the last night of the feast, the Giant became so tired and stupid that he asked permission to sleep awhile. That was just what the hunter wished. In the center of the lodge the strangers spread the weasel-skin robe, and the Giant lay down upon it. He rested his head on the stone he had brought from the river, and over him was spread the net he had brought from the mammoth spider.

"Quickly the Giant fell into a deep sleep, while the others continued their revelry. Each of the one hundred men with wings seized his war-club, and all formed a ring round the sleeping Giant. Together they danced the dance of revenge. At a signal from the hunter, everyone gave the sleeping figure a heavy blow with his war-club.

"Then the spirit-men disappeared into the air, and the weasel skin was transformed into a host of small animals. Hungrily they feasted upon the body of the Giant, and by morning there was nothing left of him but his bones. These bones the hunter gathered into a heap and burned to ashes. Then he threw the ashes into the air. Immediately he was surrounded by all the beautiful birds that now fill the world. In this way the Giant Cannibal was destroyed, and his body was turned into birds, some of which are used as the food of man."[8]

THE ARCHAEOLOGICAL REMAINS OF THE COPPER TRADING GIANTS

Old Copper Culture sites found in the same areas where Red Paint Culture remains are found, and the copper tools of the Old Copper Culture find their closest parallels in the stone tools of the Red Paint People. However, the Red Paint peoples appear to have been an arctic people with compact bodies which conserved body heat, while the copper artifacts are associated with the skeletal remains of (Iroquoian) "giants", as will be seen below.

My guess is that copper tools and copper mining first evolved in the area around the copper deposits at Mamainse in Ontario on the north shore of Lake Superior, and that this culture then spread from there to Isle Royale. During the period of time being discussed in this chapter, ca 3,000 BCE, the Copper Trading Giants did not or could not land on the south shore of Lake Superior, nor exploit the copper deposits there. The copper deposits along the Keweenaw Peninsula on the south shore of Lake Superior first became accessible to them after ca 2,360 BCE. The remains which have been found on Isle Royale are associated solely with sites found on the north shore of Lake Superior.[9]

Their principal copper workings on Isle Royale seem to have been around McCargoe Cove on its north coast, and it seems that during this period they used simple hand mauls to free the copper from the rock. Modern experiments at mining copper with these ancient simple hand mauls have resulted in broken fingers, and later mauls have one or two circles around them. I suspect that these later mauls may have been tied onto hide ropes and then swung against the rock faces to get at the copper seams.

The large house mentioned in the Menomini legend given below may be a reference to the large houses of the Copper Trading Giants. Years ago, on an elevated slope overlooking Lake Superior, near a small dockage on the south side of Isle Royale, where a stream about forty feet in width had cut a channel through the island's rock, a series of shallow circular excavations ranging from 10 to 30 feet in diameter and about 4 feet in depth were found.[10] These may have been the foundation for circular houses, for as will be seen, the use of circular house structures by these people occurred in later periods. It seems likely that these people's fundamental social unit was the boat and its captain, and the house was built to provide shelter for all of them together.

Fish of different species were so plentiful at the time that enough of them could be caught by one person in a few hours to feed an entire group for days. Caribou, moose, and rabbit abounded. Wild strawberries remained at McCargoe's Cove thousands of years later, and blueberries, blackberries, and raspberries were found, along with an unidentified plant with a two-inch edible fruit. So many berries remained on the Isle Royale at the time of European contact that the first peoples called it "Berry" (Minong) Island. Game, fish, and fruit alone would have been a limited diet; in the island's small lakes, flag and wild rice grew. The earlier existence of nut trees on the island was also reported, but I don't think that their distribution was ever recorded. Given wintergreen's use in the northern Atlantic coastal regions, its existence on Isle Royale is particularly interesting.[11]

In the winter the people who worked the copper deposits on Isle Royale most probably headed south to the Door Peninsula and the adjacent shoreline across Green Bay. As the Door Peninsula is surrounded by water on three sides, this helps to raise its temperature in winter, and if one shelters from the winds in its dunes, it is positively balmy in winter, particularly when compared with the 12-foot-deep snows on the south shore of Lake Superior. Due to the changing water levels of the Great Lakes it is difficult to locate Old Copper Culture sites[12], and no early one has been found yet on the Door, although an early site was accidentally discovered just across Green Bay from the Door Peninsula at the town of Oconto. Radiocarbon dates for the cemetery which was stumbled onto here date it to around 4,000-3,500 BCE.[13]

71

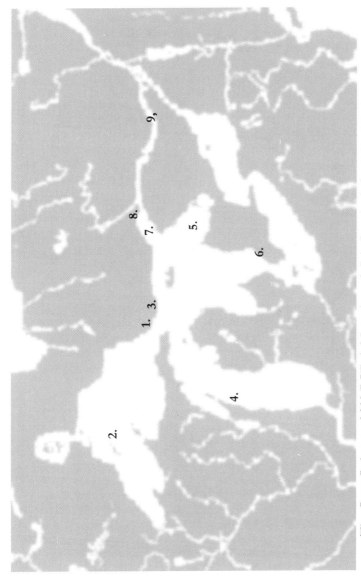

The Great Lakes ca 6,000 BCE 1. Mamainse 2. Isle Royale 3. Sault Ste. Marie 4. The Door Peninsula 5. Georgian Bay 6. Kettle Point 7. Lake Nippising 8. Porte d'Enfer 9. The Ottawa River

THEIR ROUTE TO THE ATLANTIC

We know with certainty that these people were in contact with the Atlantic Ocean, either directly or indirectly, from the recovery from their graves of shells from the Atlantic Ocean.[14] Given their lack of access to the south shore of Lake Superior, their trade route from Isle Royale to the Atlantic Ocean must have taken these people along the north shore of Lake Superior[15] to the portage between Lake Superior and Lake Huron at Sault Sainte Marie, the Rapids of St Marie.

That Sault Sainte Marie, or the "Soo" as the local people call it, was always an important location is beyond doubt. One of the earliest hoards of copper tools was found here in 1893, and displayed at the Chicago World's Fair held that year.[16] Life was good at the Soo, and the food plentiful – fish, game, birds, plants. In the times of European contact peoples from throughout the region would gather there for trade festivals. Just to the west of the Soo are the copper deposits at Mamainse, mentioned earlier, the only copper deposits on the north shore of Lake Superior, and the remains of the early copper miners have been found there, though never professionally excavated.

From the Falls at Sainte Marie the traders must have proceeded to the east along the north shore of Lake Huron, but their route is unclear at this time. The Ice Age had just ended, and the entire region of the lakes was much different than it is today; just where the north shore of Lake Huron was during this time is poorly known.

Once in the east, two water routes appear to have been used to get around Niagara Falls. The most northern of these routes passes from Georgian Bay into Lake Nipissing and then down the Ottawa River to meet the Saint Lawrence at Montreal, and this northern route to the east was extensively used during the later times of the European fur trade. This northern route would have taken these people near to Porte de L'Enfer on the Mattawan River. The "Gates of Hell", which was given this name by the European colonists because of its spiritual significance for the First Peoples, may have been a source for their iron oxide, the red paint which these people used for decoration and in ritual.

One of the most important archaeological sites evidencing the use of this northern route by about 2,750 BCE is that at Morrison Island 6, located on the Ottawa River between the Canadian provinces of Quebec and Ottawa. The markings on tools found there match exactly those found on tools from the Old Copper Culture of Wisconsin.[17] An important item to note here is that the dates found on Isle Royale and across from the Door Peninsula are much earlier than the eastern dates, and they probably indicate a spread of copper technology from that area.

The southern water route to the east appears to have been to Georgian Bay, and then via the Trent River portage to Lake Ontario at Picton.[18] Key remains along the Copper Trading Giant's southern route were found at Penetanguishene on the south side of Georgian Bay.[19] From Picton, their course would have been along the north shore of Lake Ontario and then up the Saint Lawrence River. Their remains were found at Les Galops Rapids, near modern Cardinal, Ontario: "All of these relics [a copper adze, a large copper knife, a small copper knife, a copper spearhead, stone chisels, stone gouges, a red pipe-stone tube, flint projectile points, and a miniature clay mask] were found at a depth of about fourteen or fifteen feet below the surface, in a soil composed of sand and clay. The shore at this point of land, which is considerably washed by the action of a rapid stream, presents a face of large granite boulders with quartz conglomerate – a fitting resting place for the stalwart forms of a score (20) of skeletons, which were found inhumed in a circular space [perhaps the bottom of a large burial mound- e.p.] with their feet towards the center. Some of the skeletons were of gigantic proportions. The lower jaw of one is in my possession, and is sufficiently large to surround the corresponding bone [the jaw] of an adult of our present generation..." By the way, these people were hierarchical, as "A few yards distant from this spot, and at about the same depth from the surface, another circular place of sepulture was exposed to view; but here the organic remains [the bodies] had been subjected to the action of fire [cremated]...."[20]

My guess is that in the east these people moved south in the fall to escape the harshness of the northern winters, as they did in the west, where they moved from the north shore of Lake Superior to the winter warmth of the Door Peninsula. The southern lands of the eastern group may have spanned through Port Edwards/Kettle Point (a source for chert), on through London/Hind[21], and on to Lake Huron at Hamilton.

Whether they traveled via the northern route or the southern route, the Saint Lawrence River must have then provided the traders with their access to goods from the Atlantic Ocean.

MENOMINI ACOUNTS OF THE COPPER TRADING GIANTS:
ME'NAPUS KILLS FLINT-ROCK

The following passages come from variants of the Menomini legends of Me'napus' (Big Rabbit's) killing of Flint Rock, and recall events which occurred some 5,000 years before they were written down. Taken as a whole, the fragments appear to remember an earlier complete historical cycle which started at the end of creation, when Me'napus' mother first gave birth to all the animals, and then to the spirit animals of the Menomini clans, and then to Me'napus and Flint Rock. It appears that in the original creation cycle, after Me'napus' birth, he attacked the Spirit Rock people living to the south on the prairie, then turned himself into a small rabbit to steal fire from the Red Paint People, and finally killed the Giant Flint Rock.

Despite the variations among the preserved fragments, they explicitly agree that Flint Rock lived across the Atlantic Ocean. Further, they all agree that the death of Me'napus' mother was caused by her interbreeding with Giants, as either Flint Rock, Me'napus, or one of his brothers was so large that his birth tore her open and she subsequently bled to death.

In reading the following variants it must be realized that in later times the Menomini relied on birch-bark canoes for water transportation, and unlike many northern Native American peoples, did not use sails. These legends are the only place where the

Menomini mention the use of large dugout canoes and sails, and some variants of Me'napus' theft of fire and killing of Flint Rock have him crossing the Great Sea to Europe in birch bark canoes instead. [22]

THE EUROPEAN FLINT ROCK

"Once upon a time a certain old woman had a daughter. Now, he [she?] who was born first, him the old woman took up. The old woman had a wooden bowl; into it she set him {her?] down [upon the Earth]. And then were born all kinds of animals.

"And then she used to warn her never to stand facing the north. Well, could you expect a maiden always to keep it in mind? ~ There came a time when by chance she stood facing the north. Truly, of a sudden her belly swelled. And then at one time she became ill. But at the very last the Flint-Rock came into the world. And in its passage it entirely cut up the mother, breaking her with the force of its body. So now that woman died.

"Then, in time, Me'napus grew up, dwelling always with his grandmother. Then he said to her: 'Why, Grandmother, I haven't any mother at all!' 'Oh,' his grandmother answered him; 'Across the sea he stays who killed your mother; Flint-Rock he is called.' - Lawe

"Then, at one time, Me'uapus questioned his grandmother. Thereupon she told him the tale: 'The Flint-Rock is he who killed your mother. Indeed, not here dwells he who killed your mother: over yonder he dwells, on the far shore of this Great Sea, whence the white man is to emerge, across the Great Sea.' "'Well then, I shall go to the far shore there, to kill him who slew my mother. Yes, I shall go there, I shall cross the water,' said Me'napus. "'You speak foolishly; you cannot make out to cross the water.'" - Kisewatohseh

"Then once, by chance as it were, he questioned his grandmother, 'Now, Grandmother, how does it happen, this thing, that there is no fire?', he asked his grandmother.

"'Oh, Grandchild, Grandchild, what a pitiful question! Your mother, when all of you were born - that was when our fire was flushed out with the flow [of blood].'

"'So that is it!' Me'napus answered his grandmother; 'In that case, Grandmother, I shall look for it, to see if somewhere or other there be not fire', he told his grandmother.

"'Oh, Grandchild, on the other shore of this Great Sea there is a land: there dwell some people, they possess fire,' his grandmother told him; 'You cannot possibly get there.'"

"'So that is it! Why, Grandmother, it is not far; I shall go fetch it. It is I, Me'napus I am called, Grandmother; there is nothing I cannot do; I shall bring it,' he said to his grandmother. 'Well, Grandson, it will be well enough, if you bring it!' the little old woman answered her grandson.

"'Oh, but Grandmother, how will my uncles continue to fare as long as the Earth shall endure, if through the course of time there is to be no fire?' As a matter of fact, the Creator of all things had planned all this, and that Me'napus should continue to set things right, being his firstborn child. - Nehtsiwihtuk

ME'NAPUS' DUGOUT CANOE

"Thereupon he set out and began seeking his father. He did not find him. Then he questioned his grandmother.

"This is what his grandmother told him: 'He is not a good creature, your father.'
"'Oh, Grandmother, please tell me about him!'
"Then this is what his grandmother told him: 'Over in this direction, they say, dwells your father. You cannot possibly kill him.'
"'Very well, I shall go there,' said Me'napus.

"Then he built his dug-out canoe; then also he took some grease with him. Then he set out paddling, to go to his father. Now, when he had got quite near the place, he was unable to make his boat go: his dug-out hung as if glued fast there in the water. That was when he used that grease, greasing his dug-out. So now he was able to paddle on.

"Then he reached his father. He saw where his father was. Then Me'napus took thought as to what he should do to kill his father.

"Off went Me'napus, up into the air; Me'napus turned into plantdown to go to his father. There was his father; there he lay extended. Then Me'napus drifted around in the breeze. - Kimewan

"So then the boy set out. When he reached the sea, why, off without end it extended beyond the reach of sight. 'Now then, how am I to do this thing?' reflected the lad. Then he saw some of those things, - on little oak-trees they hang; round things as big as this: oak-galls they are called. Little Me'napus broke one off; he hollowed it out.

"When he had entirely hollowed it out, 'Now then, let me be small!' he said. Lo, a tiny little boy, as big as this, he was! Then he went inside the oak-gall. After going inside, he closed up the place by which he had entered.

"'Now then, from the west let the wind blow, and let there be a mighty wind!' said little Me'napus. At the edge of the water lay the oak-gall. In a little while the breeze came blowing. Truly then that oak-gall simply bounded along over the water.

'Now then, at the landing place of him who possesses the fire let me be blown ashore!' said little Me'napus. Oh, how the wind sped! In very short order he was blown ashore on the other side of the water, where that great land must be.

"Then, in due time, he thought, 'There, it really seems that this thing in which I am is no longer moving,' He made a little hole in it, and when he looked out from there, why he saw sky. So now he made larger the hole in his oak-gall; sure enough, he beheld land.

"Then little Me'napus crawled out. When he looked upshore, there stood a large house." - Nehtsiwihtuk

"Well then, when he had got all the way there, in that place a rock towered, like this, to a peak; there it stood, at its work of chopping flakes. He went and stood up close as this, to the creature that had slain his mother. He kept going closer to it, and from as nearby as this, he truly took a close shot at it. The arrow would simply bound back from the hard surface.

"When he had used up nearly all his arrows, suddenly...the little woodpecker that is as long as this - it has a red head... called out from somewhere: 'You can not kill him that way; shoot at his head-gear!'

"So then he shot at the head-gear of the rock; truly, 'Sah! sounded the Flint Rock as it fell. So now he had slain it; now had Me'napus made his first killing. In every direction spread that rock as it fell. Then he scattered the pieces of rock in every direction. "The human people shall use it when they make fire."

"And I myself used to see them, the old-time folk of yore; in their tobacco-pouches it used to be, this flint-rock. - Kisewatoseh

FLINT ROCK'S METAL KNIFE

"Then the other [Flint Rock] called him: 'Come hither, Me'napus, my son.' he said to him. Then he went there.

"'Why, you cannot kill me this way! Here, use my knife!', he told him. It was a chinaware knife. [The reference here to the "chinaware knife" is to a metal, copper, knife.] This, then, Me'napus used to kill his father; he severed his throat with the knife.

"Then he returned home. 'There, Grandmother, I've gone and killed him whom you called an evil spirit.'" - Kimewan

(Footnotes)

[1] This chapter, Chapter 7, and Chapter 9 roughly outline the effects of impact and climate collapses on the northern extent and spread of the Illinid/Archaic Lenid peoples first defined by George K. Neuman in *Origins of the Indians of the Middle Mississippi Area*, Proceedings of the Indiana Academy of Science, v. 69, Indianapolis, Indiana, 1960, and further expanded on by Don W. Dragoo, *Mounds for the Dead*, Annals of the Carnegie Museum, v. 37, The Carnegie Museum of Natural History, Pittsburgh, Pennsylvania, 1963

[2] *Mounds for the Dead*, Annals of the Carnegie Museum, v. 37, The Carnegie Museum of Natural History, Pittsburgh, Pennsylvania, 1963

[3] David Cusick's *Ancient History of the Six Nations*, Appendix A here. It is interesting to note that the name of the Kanawa River of West Virginia, which led to Tuscarora lands, also preserves this early Iroquoian word.

[4] Alanson D. Skinner, in William K. Moorehead, Roland B. Hill, Alanson D. Skinner, Thomas B. Stewart, and William B. Marye, *A Report of the Susquehanna River Expedition* (1916), Andover Press, Andover, Massachusetts, p. 46 citing John Smith, *The General History of Virginia, New England, and the Summer Isles*, most likely the 1694 edition. This work was later used by Donald N. Kudzow in *Archaeological Studies of the Susquehannock Indians of Pennsylvania*, Pennsylvania Historical Commission, Harrisburg, Pennsylvania, 1936, which repeated John Smith's report. I am most indebted to Deb Twigg of Sayre, Pennsylvania, who recovered this very significant bit of information during her investigations of the Spanish Hill site, which work she has presented on her Internet site, including Kudzow's work in full.

[5] Peter Martyr, Vatican diplomat and leading Spanish intellectual, was responsible for reporting the Spanish discoveries to the Vatican; he published this report in his Seventh "*Decade*" of 1525. His witnesses were Lucas Vasquez de Ayllon, the Captain of Ayllon's ship, and Francisco de Chicora. Francisco of the town of Chicora had been captured during a slave raid in 1521 and taken by Ayllon to Spain, as by his testimony Ayllon hoped to gain royal support for further ventures on the mainland. Ayllon succeeded in this and returned to North America, where Francisco would escape from him in 1526. The translation used here is that commissioned by John R. Swanton for his *Early History of the Creek Indians and their Neighbors*, Bureau of Ethnology Bulletin n. 72, 1922, p. 42-46. A new reprint of this work is now available from the University Press of Florida. As a brief warning, it is now known that Swanton's linguistic analysis was faulty. Chicora was a town on a river somewhere along the coasts of the Carolinas. Robert J. Salzer and Grace Rajnovich, in their book on *The Gottschall Rockshelter* (p. 67), recovered DeSoto expedition member Garscilo de la Vega's (1988, p. 258) account of Mississippian giants: "The physical measurements of Tascaluza (Tuscaloosa) were like those of his son, for both were more than half a yard taller than the others. He appeared to be a giant, or rather was one, and his limbs and face were in proportion to the height of his body." (p. 349) "In sum, he was the tallest and most handsomely shaped Indian that the Castilians saw during all their travels in Florida."

[6] *From the Ashes of Angels: The Forbidden Legacy of a Fallen Race*, Andrew Collins, Bear and Company, Rochester, Vermont, 2001

[7] From the Ashes of Angels, p. 314, citing *Ancient Egypt*, Walter Bryan Emery, Penguin Books, Harmondsworth, 1961

[8] Compiled by Ella Elizabeth Clark, *Indian Legends of Canada*, McClelland and Stewart Limited, Toronto, Canada, 1960, p. 120-121. While Clark did not specifically cite

her original source documents, her working papers, giving the initial accounts from which she compiled this telling, are held by the Washington State University Libraries, Manuscript, Archives and Special Collections, Pullman, Washington.
[9] *Wonderful Power*, Susan R. Martin, Wayne State University Press, Detroit, Michigan, 1999, p. 164 mentions "cultural groups distinct from those of the south shore" citing Peter Clark, *Archaeological Survey and Testing*, Isle Royale National Park, 1987-1990, National Park Service, Midwest Archaeological Center, Lincoln, Nebraska, 1995.

Perhaps this is just a case of misplaced expectations, but I found M.'s book frustrating, given what I had hoped for. The problem being considered in this book is man and impact, and its scope is the Americas, and it touches on the copper trade only so far as is necessary. I expected far more help from M.'s book, and quite frankly I did not receive it. M. asserts (p. 152-153) on the basis of absolutely no evidence at all that the earlier hunters in this region, who used float copper to manufacture small projectile points, adapted to an entirely maritime culture exclusively on their own, and then suddenly began trade with the Atlantic coastal regions, which claims I frankly find incredible. M.'s failure to acquaint her readers with the earlier introduction and/or adaptation of the new stone and bone tool technologies in these areas is matched by a failure to elsewhere adequately describe the cultural affiliations of the tools adapted to manufacture in copper at different sites at different times. M.'s unstated definition of a contiguous area is limited to areas connected by land, which is hardly likely to have been the case for what are demonstrably and usually considered to be maritime peoples. While I can appreciate M.'s intention to show a continuous local development of material culture, in my opinion her work as is stands does no favor to the Menomini, Dakota, HoChunk or Ojibwa peoples. M.'s failure to note the geographic extent of earlier trading networks evolves into a failure to describe the eastern distribution of early large utilitarian copper tools (p. 160, considered entirely separate from the material of p. 187-190), and further clouds the Paleolithic-Archaic transition. M. fails to describe the materials found along the trade routes in depth, at one point (p. 189) glossing over the work of Baugh and Erickson, Bourque, Donaldson and Wormer, Heckenberger, Peterson, and Basa, Smith, Varney and Pfeiffer, and Wright with one sentence, which is particularly frustrating, given the difficulty in obtaining these materials in a timely manner for the study at hand. Earlier finds by non-professionals are ignored, and finally, there is little consideration made of other North American copper sources, including significantly those in the eastern piedmont of the Appalachians and North Carolina. M. clouds defining characteristics of the Old Copper Culture or the Red Ochre Culture (p. 156). For these reasons, I found myself frustrated, and I hope that perhaps either she or some other professional archaeologist will write a work addressing these problems, or at least assemble all of the relevant materials together in one volume, or at one site on the Internet. Despite all of these complaints, in this survey I used secondary citations to Martin's work because it contains summaries and comprehensive bibliographies of materials which were otherwise unavailable to me in a timely and economic manner.
[10] Henry Gillman, Smithsonian Report, 1873, reprinted in *Prehistoric Copper Mining in the Lake Superior Region*, Roy W. Drier and Octave J. DuTemple, private publication, 1961
[11] George R. Fox, *The Ancient Copper Workings on Isle Royale*, ca. 1911, private, reprinted Drier and DuTemple, ibid.

[2] Perhaps the Whitefish River from AuTrain on Lake Superior may have been a route south, depending on water levels.

[13] For an excellent discussion of dating see Martin, ibid., p. 144-145, and for the site itself, p. 158. Perhaps the lake water levels may have made it possible during this period for the copper miners to have traveled to the Door Peninsula via Au Train and the Whitefish River instead of via Sault Sainte Marie.

[14] Martin, ibid., page 158 "whelk shell of Atlantic coast origin", citing Robert Ritzenthaler and Warren Wittry, "The Oconto Site, An Old Copper Manifestation", *Wisconsin Archaeologist*, v. 38 n. 4, 1957, p. 222-244.

[15] James B. Griffin, "Copper Artifacts from Manitoba", *Lake Superior Copper and the Indians*, ed. Griffin, Anthropological Papers n17, Museum of Anthropology, University of Michigan, Ann Arbor, 1961, p. 124, and Map 5; also "The McCullom Site", James B. Griffin and George I. Quimby, ibid., p. 91

[16] "Was the Sault a Community 8,000 Years Ago?", Woodie Jarvis, *Sault Daily Star*, 18 October, 1963, p. 17.

[17] Martin, ibid., page 188, citing Clyde Kennedy, "Preliminary Report on the Morris Island-6 Site", *National Museum of Canada Bulletin* 206, 1966, p. 100-125.

[18] Martin, ibid., p. 188, citing Wilfrid Jury, "Copper Artifacts from Western Ontario", *Wisconsin Archaeologist*, v. 46 n. 4, 1965, p. 223-246, and "Copper Cache at Penetanguishene, Ontario, Canada", *Wisconsin Archaeologist*, v. 54 n. 2, 1973, p. 84-106.

[19] Griffin, "Old Copper Artifacts from near Brockville, Ontario", Griffin, ibid., p. 118, citing Thomas Reynolds, 1856

[20] Griffin, "Old Copper Artifacts from near Brockville, Ontario", p. 118, citing Thomas Reynolds, 1856 See also Reynold's earlier and heavily edited account and illustrations of implements in Ephraim G. Squire and Edwin Hamilton Davis, *Ancient Monuments of the Mississippi Valley*, Smithsonian Contributions to Knowledge, Bartlett & Welford, New York, 1848, p. 201-202

[21] Martin, ibid., p. 189, citing William S. Donaldson and Stabley Wortner, "The Hind Site and the Glacial Kame Burial Complexes in Ontario", *Ontario Archaeology*, n. 59, 1995 and Tamara L. Varney and Susan Pfeiffer, "The People of the Hind Site", *Ontario Archaeology*, n. 59, 1995

[22] The following extracts from the Menomini legends come from *Menomini Texts*, Leonard Bloomfield, Publications of the American Ethnological Society, Volume XII, 1928, ed. Franz Boas, pub. G.E. Stechert & Co., New York

nature

INTERNATIONAL WEEKLY JOURNAL OF SCIENCE

TRAIL
OF A
BOUNCING
METEORITE

Tit for tat in
animal populations

'Muscles' from
polymer gel

BIOTECHNOLOGY
product review

Nature Magazine reports
on the research at Rio Cuarto

CHAPTER 6

COMET ENCKE IN MAYAN RECORDS

THE DIFFERENT ASRONOMICAL CONCEPTS
OF THE SOUTHERN PEOPLES AND THE NOTHERN PEOPLES

In Chapter 3 the astronomical concepts of the Northern peoples were briefly described. These concepts centered around the "thunders" or "thunderbirds" who protected the people from the "horned snakes", which is to say impactors.

During the earliest periods there appears to have been a clear early division between the astronomical concepts of the peoples of the north and the peoples of the south. The astronomical concepts of the southern peoples, to be set out more fully below in this chapter, focused on "holders of the heavens", who were to keep an impact from occurring by "holding the heavens" off of the Earth, in other words, keeping the heavens and the Earth separated.

As will be seen in Chapters 12 and 14, following the migrations north of some of these southern peoples, these two astronomical conceptions would merge to form the backbone of the astronomy of the Mississippian (Southern Ceremonial Cult) peoples.

THE ASTRONOMICAL CONCEPTS OF THE SOUTHERN PEOPLES:
THE COUNT OF DAYS

The earliest written records of man which have been found to date are counts of the days of the Moon which man inscribed on bones in Europe some 27,000 years ago. Indeed, it is likely that *Homo sapiens* brought a Count of Days along with him when he first arrived in Europe.[1]

The value of these lunar records to ancient man in planning his activities should be obvious. It must be remembered that *Homo sapiens* had developed even earlier along river systems, and was using boats along the coast of Asia by 50,000 BCE[2]. For boat using peoples, knowing when the tides would be high or low would help in the planning of fishing, and allow some ability to predict when annual storms would arrive.

The count had value for hunting peoples as well. Clearly, it is of great use when planning for hunting at night to be able to predict which nights of the month will be illuminated by the Moon. Knowing where you were in the cycle of the seasons would greatly aid in planning the hunting of migrating game, and in planning for the harvest of fruits and nuts. Lastly, I suppose that all of our ancient ancestors must also have found it extremely useful to have some idea of where their mate's hormonal cycles would be in a few days time.

Based on what we know of their later astronomies, the peoples who came over to the Americas from Asia must have brought some similar astronomy over with them. The development of this astronomy would progress and reach its fullest development in the

Mayan Count of Days, an incredibly intricate technology for keeping track of the sky and time.

THE FOUR HOLDERS OF THE HEAVENS,
THE TZUK, THE "PARTITIONING" EVENT,
AND THE CREATIONS

In order to understand the southern peoples' astronomy, it is very important to understand their idea of "partitioning". What a "partitioning" was for them was a separation of the heavens from the Earth, such as occurred during the first creation. The southern peoples also held that this separation of the heavens from the Earth was maintained by four "holders of the heavens", who kept the heavens separate from the Earth. Usually there were four of these holders of the heavens, and they were seen as being situated on the cardinal points.

The holders of the heavens themselves appear to have been conceptualized as four tornados at the cardinal points, each one of which held in check a "serpent", a cometary impactor, called "itzam" in Mayan. Besides providing this protective function, these tornados also appear to have been seen as being responsible to some degree for ordinary winds and rains. In a very distant way this southern concept of the holders of the heavens as causers of weather must be related to the northern concept of the thunders as causers of the weather, but the point of this divergence in astronomical systems is lost in the mists of time.

The southern peoples also held that occasionally these "holders of the heavens" would drop the ball, so to speak, and the result would be an asteroid or comet impact. If the impact was massive enough, it would result in a new "separation" of the heavens from the Earth, a new "creation". In this case the impacting "serpent", "itzam" in Mayan, would be promoted in rank to become a "partitioner", or the Mayan "tzuk".

One Mayan hieroglyphic sign for "tzuk" was a mirror affixed to the head. This association makes sense in that the Maya considered both asteroids and comets as being the same, and meteoritic iron was used to make some of their mirrors.[3]

These concepts were carried to North America as early as 4,000 BCE by emigrants from Central America, and they survived into later times in Mississipian (Southern Ceremonial Cult), Cherokee, and Shawnee religion.

SOUTH AMERICAN VARIANTS OF MULTIPLE CREATIONS:
THE QUECHUA AND AYMARA WARI

In his book *Inca Myths*, Gary Urton provides this outline of the Quechua and Aumara variant multiple creations, working from Guaman Poma de Ayala's account. The story is preserved in a very fragmentary form, not surprising given its suppression by both the Inca and the Spanish.[4] In this version of the multiple creation system, each age is known as a "wari", while the partitioning events are known as "pachachuti", or "turning overs".

Their first creation was Wari Wiracocharuna, or the Creation of the Llama/Alpaca People. The Llama was long considered a divine animal in South American mythology. While Gauman Poma stated that these people dressed in leaves, and had only rudimentary technologies, this undoubtedly was not true, as they had domesticated both the llama and alpaca by this time. Poma gives their gods as being Ticci Viracocha, who seems to me to be most likely the god of Tocay, an eastern kingdom; Caylla Viracocha, most likely the god of Cholla, around Lake Titicaca; and Pachamac, who was most likely the god of the area north of this. What caused the end of the first age is lost.

The people of the second creation, Wari Runa, the Creation of Men, used animal skins for clothing, had agriculture, and worshipped Viracocha, the southern god. The people lived together peacefully, and were destroyed by a massive flood.

The third age was that of Wari Purun Runa, the Creation of the Wild Men, who used spun alpaca and llama wool for clothing, practiced agriculture, and developed basic metalworking. Each town had its own king, and they worshipped Pachamac, the god of the northern areas. While this creation may represent an insertion which occurred during the alliding together of the southern and northern cosmologies, more likely it represents the shift in power from south to north which occurred following the Rio Cuarto impacts, described below.

The fourth creation was the Wari Auca Runa, the Creation of the Warlike Men. The Inca had arisen as a distinct nation around Cuzco, and during this time the world was divided into the four kingdoms, Colla-suyu (south, Lake Titicaca), Cunti-suyu (Inca-Cuzco), Chincu-suyu (north coastal), and Anti-suyu (north valley). Warfare increased, and people lived on fortified mountaintops.

The fifth creation was that of Inca rule.

THE HOLDERS OF THE HEAVENS IN OLMEC (ZOQUE) RITUAL

Some researchers are arguing today that the Zoque (Olmec) were influenced by contacts from Africa, and other researchers are arguing that they were influenced by contacts with Asia. While forming an adequate comment on either of these hypotheses lies well beyond what can be accomplished here, it appears to me that while proponents have strong pieces of evidence pointing to both trans-Atlantic as well as trans-Pacific influences, often they overstate their cases. This being the case, I suppose that what I will have to do is let both camps fight it out, and in the meantime refer to the archaeological evidence we absolutely know about the Olmec (Zoque).

While little of Olmec (Zoque) legend or writing survived, for reasons which will become apparent in Chapter 8, those Olmec (Zoque) artifacts which did survive and have been found testify clearly that they too held these southern astronomical concepts. I need to briefly describe here some of the early key cultural remains of the Olmec (Zoque), which indicate astronomical concepts which they shared with the Maya who later occupied their areas.

The first of these cultural remains are the large mounds found in Olmec (Zoque) ritual centers. The construction of these mounds indicates a highly stratified society, as they were built for the use of kings and priests/astronomers.

The second of these cultural practices shown by their remains is the Olmec (Zoque) practice of deforming the heads of their leaders, a practice which they shared with the Maya. This head deformation appears to have been helped along by the use of a small axe, known to the Maya as k'awil, and images of Olmec (Zoque) leaders commonly feature a cleft head. Combined with a city totem, the cleft head and city sign indicated rulership over a city for the Olmec (Zoque). Similar skull deformation was also practiced by the Machalilla people, who moved from Colombia into Ecuador around 1,600 BCE.

The third of shared cultural element is an annual ceremony raising a pole (later a stone) to keep the heavens and sky separate, in other words, to prevent impact events. The symbol of this safeguarding ceremony for the Olmec (Zoque) is a rectangle crossed by diagonal linear bands, where the diagonals lead to the four gods which hold up the heavens. Later Mayan versions of this annual ceremony will be described in detail below. For the time being, it is enough to point out that among the Maya this ceremony is known as the "seating" of the "tun" and "katun" periods of time, and similar practices are also attested at a later date by the people living along Lake Nicaragua. The time for the performance of these rituals was determined from the count of days.

The fourth shared cultural element is a detailed astronomy, and it is symbolized among the Olmec (Zoque) by the sign of a tri-lobe E with circles between the lobes. This symbol is the later Mayan "star" sign.

The fifth shared cultural element is the use of a celestial jaguar symbol by both the priesthood, who it may be safely assumed oversaw the detailed work of items three and four above, and by the king, whose divine intercession with the sky gods was needed.

The sixth shared cultural element is their use of celestial "dragon" imagery. The Maya used the word "itzam"(lizard), to refer to both the "crocodile" which symbolized the appearance of the Milky Way at night, as well as to name impactors, the "partitioners", the "tzukob".

The seventh shared cultural element is a ball game. Ritual stone spheres have a wide distribution throughout Central America and the Caribbean.

The eighth Olmec (Zoque) cultural element is the use of hallucinogens from water lilies and toads – the Maya themselves seem to have preferred the use of hallucinogens derived from other plants.

The ninth Olmec (Zoque) cultural element is a ceremonial cylinder, an implement of office carried by kings.

The tenth shared cultural element is the use of writing. While we have many Mayan inscriptions, only as few examples of Olmec (Zoque) writing have survived. The most likely reason for this will also be set out in Chapter 8.

A MAYAN DESCRIPTION OF THE HOLDERS OF THE HEAVENS, THE BACAB

The following passage comes from Ralph E. Roys' translation of *The Book of [The] Chilam Balam of Chumayel*.[5]

"There would be a sudden rush of water when the theft of the insignia occurred. Then the sky would fall, it would fall down upon the earth, when the four gods, the four Bacabs, were set up, who brought about the destruction of the world.

"Then, after the destruction of the world was completed, they placed [a tree] to set up in its order the yellow cock oriole. Then the white tree of abundance was set up. [This] pillar of the sky was set up, a sign of the destruction of the world; that was the White Tree of Abundance in the north. Then the Black Tree of Abundance was set up [in the west] for the black-breasted piçoy to sit upon. Then the Yellow Tree of Abundance was set up [in the south], as a symbol of the destruction of the world, for the yellow-breasted piçoy to sit upon, for the yellow cock oriole to sit upon, the yellow timid mut. Then the Green Tree of Abundance was set up in the center [of the world] as a record of the destruction of the world.

The reason why the east tree is not mentioned in this account is because it was the holder of the heavens which had just failed, causing the "sky to fall".

THE HOLDERS OF THE HEAVENS IN A TSULAGI (CHILLICOTHE, SHAWNEE) CREATION MYTH

"When the Great Spirit had accomplished the formation of this Island, he made some very large animals and placed them upon it, at the four cardinal points of the compass, to keep it steady." - Blackhoof[6]

When the Algonquin conquered the Chilicothe, who were seen in Chapter 4 to have migrated from the south coast to the north at a much earlier time, they absorbed their astronomical concepts. Thus these "very large animals" of the Shawnee are directly related to the Mayan concepts of bacabs, who kept the sky and the Earth separate.

THE HOLDERS OF THE HEAVENS AS MISSISSIPPIAN GODS

"They had a temple with a sacred fire, and according to Father Gravier, had nine principal gods, viz.: the Sun, Thunder, Fire, THE GODS OF THE FOUR CARDINAL POINTS [m.c.], the Sky, and the Earth."[7]

THE EARLIEST SURVIVING DOCUMENTS IN THE AMERICAS:
THE SURVIVAL OF MAYAN RECORDS -
INTERPRETERS, OCCUPATION, LITERACY, AND SURVIVAL

Since we've already made use of them, this is as good a place as any to explain the
survival of the records of the peoples of Central America. Indeed, the only reason why
we can speak with some certainty about the southern peoples' astronomies is because
many of their records survived the Spanish conquest.

It is well known that the Spanish Catholic priests burned most of the books of the
conquest period "Maya", as well as the books of the other Native American peoples
in Central America, in their efforts to stamp out the religions of the Native American
peoples. Thus it is also widely concluded that the Spanish priests managed to destroy
nearly all of these records, except for those few Mayan hieroglyphic documents which
somehow managed to escape destruction. Fortunately, this is not what happened.

Unlike the European immigration into North America, where relatively low-density
Native American populations were nearly completely finished off by contact with the
European diseases and large numbers of colonists then settled in the newly vacant
lands, the Spanish exploiters of Central America faced a much different situation. In
Central America there were very large Native American populations, populations so
large that fairly large populations still remained even after the European diseases had
taken their toll.

This is one factor in the survival of the written records, but an even more significant
factor in the survival of the Native American cultures and their records was the
difference between the Northern European countries and Spain in their strategies
for exploiting the newly discovered lands. France, England, and the Dutch were all
latecomers in their settlement of the New World; their primary goal in settlement
was conducting raids on Spanish ships and stealing Spanish gold, which the Spanish
in their turn had just stolen from the Native American peoples. To satisfy this goal
these Northern European countries focused their very first efforts on the permanent
settlement of ports capable of hosting their fleets for the interception of the Spanish
ships.

The Spanish conquest itself preceded these northern European efforts by some 200
years. As Spain had very few people involved in their exploitation of the lands which
they had discovered, in order for them to exploit these lands it had been necessary for
them to make use of the Native American peoples already living in those areas. In
Cuba, their first conquest, the Spanish quickly discovered that if they attempted to
enslave a people, they would fight them to the death. In the future the Spanish would
largely leave the Native American societies in place, as long as their leaders served
them, and provided them both with the labor they needed and with the goods which
they desired to send back to Spain.

What do you need to conquer a land densely populated by people who do not speak
your language? First among all things, you need interpreters capable of understanding
the language of the peoples already living in that land. These interpreters are of

incredible historical significance, and their role has been little studied to date. The usual Spanish technique for obtaining these interpreters was to kidnap speakers of the desired language, and then to learn the language from them. In the case of Central America, people with mastery of two languages were available from among the captives of warfare and from those peoples engaged in the coastal trade. Another source of interpreters for the Spanish was their recovery of shipwrecked Spanish crewmen who had not been killed by their Native American "hosts".

Other key items of intelligence which could be learned from these individuals were descriptions of the lands, the resources available for exploitation, the military strength of the people living there, any cultural myths which could be used during their conquest, and most importantly, knowledge of conflicts between the different Native American peoples, conflicts which the Spanish could then use to enlist allies for their battles.

As pointed out above, the Spanish goal during the conquest was to kill off only the very top levels of Native American governments and to take their role, leaving the subservient political leadership in place to run local affairs for the benefit of both the Spanish and as well as themselves. These local leaders had intellectuals in their employ, and thus these intellectuals survived as well, at least until the Catholic priests arrived later and began their co-optation, by conversion, or their elimination, by auto-da-fe, which is to say religious murder.

WHO WERE THE CHILAM BALAM'S?

Classic Mayan (Chol and Yucatec) creation myths feature two characters known as the "Paddler Gods". These Classic Mayan (Chol and Yucatec) language and rites were also absorbed by later Toltec and Itza immigrants into the Yucatan. One of these "Paddler Gods" has been firmly identified as the primal version of the Classic Mayan Lord, the Ahau, by the stingray spine shown placed through his nose. The other Paddler God is the primal version of the Classic Mayan Lords' intellectual advisor, the Chilam Balam, who may be identified by the jaguar (balam) skin cap which he wears.

The title "Chilam Balam" has caused much confusion, and it has been quite common for some to confuse this title with the existence of some one person, and for others to confuse "chilamob", interpreters, of which there were many, with the "Chilam Balam", of which each Lord had only one.

What does the title "Chilam Balam" mean in English? On a primitive level, it means "Interpreter Jaguar", but this does not do the title justice. The Mayan Lords are referred to as jaguars; and at the same time the Maya also referred to both the sun, spotted with sunspots, and the night sky, spotted with stars, as jaguar; and the jaguar also had astronomical significance for South Americas peoples. The best translation of the "Chilam Balam" that I can come up with is "The Lord's Celestial Interpreter", which still does not fully do the title justice.

WHAT DID THE CHILAM BALAM DO?

What were the duties of a Lord's Celestial Interpreter? He was the intellectual advisor to a Mayan Lord, the intellectual leader of a city -state, and as such his duties were all-encompassing, as can be seen from this description by Bishop Diego de Landa[8]:

> "The people of Yucatan were as diligent in matters of religion as they were in those of government. They had a high priest whom they called Achkinmai, and by another name Ahaucanmai, which means the Priest Mai or the High Priest Mai."

Landa's Mayan is known to be bad, and this is a good example of it. The first title is "Ah Kin May", which means "The Sun-Priest of the (Sun) Cycle", and the second title is "Ahua Can May", which means "Lord of the Heavens' Cycle". These titles are in addition to that of Chilam Balam. Continuing with Landa's account:

> "This person was greatly revered by the Lords, and had no repartiamento (a Spanish colonial term for an allocation of serfs) of Indians, but in addition to the offerings, the Lords made him gifts, and all the priests of the town made contributions. He was succeeded in office by his sons or closest relative, and in this lay the key to their learning.

> "And indeed it was in such matters that these priests worked most, giving advice to the Lords and answering their questions. The High Priest rarely participated in matters of sacrifice, unless they concerned major feasts or important affairs. He provided priests for the towns when they were needed, examined them in the knowledge of their sciences and ceremonies, charged them with all the duties of their office, and urged them to be a good example to the people; and he provided them with their books, and sent them out.

> "He also looked after the temples, as well as teaching Indian sciences and writing books about them. He also taught the children of the other priests and the second sons of the Lords who were reared for the office from infancy if they showed any inclination to it."

This is a major exception to Landa's earlier statement on the passage of the office of Chilam Balam by inheritance.

WHAT MATERIALS DID THE BOOKS OF THE CHILAM BALAM'S COVER?

de Landa's account continues:

> "The sciences which they taught were the reckoning of the years, months, and days, and of their feasts and ceremonies; the administration of their sacraments, and of the fateful days and seasons; their manner of divination; and their prophecies, incidents, and cures for sickness; as well as their antiquities, and method of reading and writing, where by means of their letters and characters they wrote in glyphs which represented the meanings of their

writings."

HOW DID THE CHILAM BALAM'S WRITE THEIR BOOKS?

"They wrote their books on a large sheet doubled over several times, this closed together between two boards which were highly decorated. They wrote on both sides of the sheet in columns, following the folds. And the paper they made from the roots of a tree, giving it a white gloss on which it was easy to write."

THE LORDS' KNOWLEDGE OF THE SCIENCES

"Some of the principal Lords out of diligence had also acquired these sciences, and although they never used them in public, they were held in great esteem for having done so."

THE CHILAM BALAMS' ADOPTION OF THE EUROPEAN ALPHABET

When the Spanish conquered the peoples of Central America, they usually killed only the Lords who were the rulers of the leading city-states. Those Lords who ruled lesser city-states usually escaped death, at least for a while, and these lesser leaders' Chilam Balams escaped death as well. These Chilam Balam were of especial use to the Spanish, as among the other items of knowledge which they kept, they wrote detailed records of the tribute their Lords had received, as well as the lands which they ruled. This information was vital to Spanish exploitation, and copies into the Latin alphabet of many of these land-holding records survive in the Spanish archives.

The detailed study of the conquest period is still in its infancy, and while it is known that the Latin alphabet was adopted in several variations, where these adoptions took place, as well as when and by whom, are currently unknown, as is exactly who were the Chilam Balams during the conquest period, or even the Lords of the local ruling dynasties, for that matter.

What is clear is that the different Chilam Balams made local transliterations into the Latin alphabet of the hieroglyphic records available to them, and some of these survive in collections of their records, which are usually called "The Chilam Balam of X", where X is the town in which the collection was recovered. Some nine manuscripts of these collections have been preserved, usually in later copies, while some nine more collections were known to have existed but have since disappeared. The location and recovery of these manuscripts is very much desired, but it has not been funded in any systematic way.

THE DECIPHERMENT OF MAYAN HIEROGLYPHIC WRITING
AND THE UNDERSTANDING OF MAYAN LANGUAGE

These books are not our sole source of Mayan records.

Due to the efforts of many people working for many years, it has at last become possible for the scholars working on Mayan Hieroglyphic to read parts of it. About 140 glyphs out of 287 which the Maya used are currently read[9], and the number capable of being read is slowly increasing. This reading has been accomplished in spite of the fact that due to both the nature of the writing, and the language of the Mayan script, it is not amenable to decipherment by techniques of phonetic loading.[10]

One of the key figures in this decipherment was the late Linda Schele, key both for her own personal contribution, as well as for her technique of annually assembling together most of the Mayan scholars for sessions of joint work. Another technique which Schele encouraged was fieldwork among modern Maya, and by these two techniques, along with her keen artist's eye, many words in Mayan Hieroglyphic were at last understood.

The reading of Mayan hieroglyphic texts from codices, stelae, and painted polychrome pottery has fundamentally changed the understanding of the Chilam Balams' collections of texts. The worldview which has emerged is very significantly different from those of Europe.

WHAT BOOKS DID THE CHILAM BALAMS HAVE?

As some two volumes of the *Handbook of Middle American Indians* are devoted to the manuscripts of the Native American peoples, no comprehensive listing of their writings is possible here. Mention will only be made of some of the key titles which were commonly in the Chilam Balams' collections of writings; it must be remembered that these have hieroglyphic antecedents. For an introduction to the codices which underlay some chapters of the Books of the Chilam Balam, I highly recommend *The Paris Codex, Handbook for a Mayan Priest* by Bruce Love.[11]

THE STORIES OF THE CREATIONS

The first of these writings was a creation tale, and in the Popul Vuh we have a pretty full copy of the Quiche adaptation and variation of the Maya tale. Other peoples' adaptations of the Mayan version are different, and influenced by their own histories. Fragments of this tale also remain in the Chilam Balams' collections. These creation tales contain information on the items under study here: the impact events, the multiple creations of the world and their subsequent destruction, the "partitioning" events, and the Mayan "tzuk".

One of the interesting things about the Mayan sciences is that they form a cohesive body of knowledge. An example of this may be seen in another of their books which survived, a book of medical cures. In this book the same gods which ruled over the parts of creation which included the patient's diseased part were invoked, alongside a listing of the cures for the diseases, and thus the Mayan physicians actually repeated a part of their creation story within a medical text.

In the codices themselves the creation myths appear usually to have been followed by a history of each people. While many other peoples seem to have used a sequential record, the Maya themselves appear to have extended their inductive method of science to their history. Among the Chilam Balam of the conquest period there was a book known as "The Book of Seven Generations", where the "Generations" in question seem to have been turnings of either baktuns or mays, time periods of roughly 400 and 256 years respectively. (My completely amateur guess is that baktuns were used.) It appears that the Maya organized historical events along cyclical temporal lines, instead of along a straight temporal line, so that they could bring to bear the predictive power of earlier periods as a means of handling current events. We have fragments of history in both forms preserved in the Chilam Balams' works.

Aside from the fragments of these historical works found in the Chilam Balams' collections, we have a fairly long version of one given by Landa, and this was undoubtedly provided to him by his own Native American Interpreter and Chilam Balam, Gaspar Antonio Chi (Xiu). Gaspar Antonio Chi was the son of a Xiu nobleman slain by the Cocom people[12], and the Xiu people of Merida (Tiho) apparently thought that the Spanish would be good allies against the Cocom.

After the creation story, and then the historical records of each separate people, there seem to have been a series of astrological works, whereby the goodness and badness of days, months, years, and katuns (20 years) seem to have been forecast.

Parts of different versions of these astrological works also remain in various adaptations by other peoples. These astrological works are reflective both of the inductive nature of Mayan science and of their worldview. Sadly, the Chilam Balams had learned of the genocide which the Spanish were engaged in in Cuba, undoubtedly through their peoples' trade networks, and not surprisingly many of their "prophecies" which advised surrender have been preserved. Definitely more amusing than these is one Mayan book of astrology wherein an individual's entire life and fortunes, including his marriage, number of children, illnesses, and date of death, was predicted based entirely on his date of birth.

Since these peoples had been pounded by the Sky Gods pretty severely not just once, but several times, their obsession with astronomy is perfectly understandable. The books on creation, history, and astrology appear to have been followed by books which were astronomical ephemerides, used to predict solar cycles, the cycles of Venus, and those of other planets, along with tables for the easy computation of significant dates. (It is not only modern scholars who had difficulty with Mayan dates!) Copies of these astronomical works have been recovered in the hieroglyphic, and work on reading these extremely difficult texts is proceeding.[13]

The timing of the rituals was determined on an astronomical basis, and parts of those books which gave detailed descriptions of how these rites were to be performed survived. Fragments of quiz books for the testing of both astronomers, the *Theodora*, and public officials, *The Language of Zuyua* (Zoque?) have survived as well.

Two other books, one for the instruction of sons, another for daughters, have survived in a fairly complete but Christianized form.

THE CHRISTIAN APOTHEOSIS

While little of the hieroglyphic astronomical works appear to be seen in the Chilam Balams' collections in Latin letters which we now have, we do find multiple attempts to reconcile the Mayan and Spanish calendars, as well as accounts of European astronomy.

Amazingly, the Maya had stylized their Ceiba tree, the source of their MAO hallucinogen intensifier, into a cross long before Spanish contact. The identification of this Ceiba cross with the Christian cross was almost immediate; that the Spanish should kill the Mayan Lords as a sacrifice to their God, while the Mayan Lords only sacrificed prisoners of war and the underclass, was more of a display of the power of the Spaniards' God than anything else. It is only among those Chilam Balams who were of peoples who were not the Spaniards' allies that the Mayan literature survived, and that survival continued only for a short time. Slowly their writings become more and more Christianized, and knowledge of the glyphs faded.

CORE SOUTHERN RELIGIOUS RITUALS:
HALLUCINOGENS AS A RELIGIOUS TECHNOLOGY

The first thing which must be understood about Native American religions from Central America is that they were based on the use of hallucinogens. For instance, the Mayan shamans used hallucinogens, and while specific identification of plant species is difficult, particular note must be taken of their references to what they called the "Sac Nicte", or "White Flower".

One well-known effect of hallucinogens is the inability of their users to differentiate themselves from their environment. For instance, Mayan shamans would become the gods themselves by taking on their "way", or channeling the god's spiritual force, in their way of thinking. Another effect of the stronger hallucinogens is the hallucination of objects which are not there, and this can include the hallucination of people who have been dispatched to the gods.

THE SEATING OF THE KATUN

The shamans conducted one fundamental rite to ensure that an impact event would not take place; among the Maya, this rite was known as the "Seating of the Katun". Fundamentally, what occurred was that the rite's participants would assume the roles, the "ways", of the "bacabs", those gods who kept the heavens separate from the Earth, and by their performance of the bacabs' tasks the shamans would thus magically ensure that no impact would take place during a katun's period of time.

In Mayan ritual, the shaman-bacabs would erect poles in the east, north, west, and south (some say in the Northeast, Northwest, Southwest, and Southeast) of the city-state's lands, and finally in the center of the city-state. While sometimes the "poles" were stones, at other times the Maya raised trees, and the one raised in the center of the city-state was the Ceiba tree, source of a MAO-DMT inhibitor. Given the terrible nature of the impact event which prompted the adoption of this rite, its sacrifices were severe as well, and included human sacrifice.

The rituals to ensure the separation of the heavens from the Earth of the peoples of North America are for the most part lost to us now, as are the rituals of the earlier Olmec (Zoque) people of Central America. The mentions of them which remain will be given in their contexts later in this work.

THE MAYAN "STAR WARS"

The journey of the shaman-bacabs to the four corners of a city-state's territory also provided a means for the city-states to affirm their control over a territory. Thus the seating ceremony, which ensured the separation of the Earth from the Heavens, also served to separate a polity's lands from that of its neighbors, and it was accompanied by a journey through all of a polity's lands and villages. This ritual need is a key reason why so many itineraries have survived from Central America.

Throughout Mayan history, and even before it, the territorial conflicts brought on by the need "to seat a katun" brought on regular conflict on a 20-year basis. By the conquest period the city-states were entering into larger confederations, and thus the competition to "seat a katun" had become even more intense, leading to warfare on a larger scale.

This "seating of a katun" rite has great antiquity, and as was mentioned earlier, the fact that it was practiced by the Pre-Formative (Zoque ("Olmec") et al.) peoples may be seen by one symbol worn by their lords, which is that of a rectangle crossed corner to corner by parallel lines with a square in the center. In the earlier rites poles were used instead of trees, and a Zoque (Olmec) image of just such a rite may be seen at: http://FAMSI.Saiph.com:80/dataSpark/schele/preview/07/IMG0049.jpg

THE RAIN FESTVALS

The Mayan shamans also conducted another fundamental rite, this one to ensure rainfall, crop yield, and fertility. When we think of Central America we think of rain forest, but in point of fact, as all the rain which falls on the Yucatan is quickly absorbed by the limestone underlying the region, the region is very arid. To ensure the crops, the shamans took on the "ways" of the "chac" rain gods, and performed rites tied to the timing of the appearance of Venus, which is strongly correlated with the times of optimal planting.

These chac-shamans were also responsible for ensuring the fertility of the people themselves, and performed their coming of age ceremonies. In order to assure fertility, the shaman-chacs would "purify" both people and land, and thus the Lords would wage war to "purify" the lands of their enemies under the symbols of the stars. When you read a reference by a specialist on the Maya to a "star war", this is what they mean.

Again, as was mentioned earlier, that the rituals of the chac-shamans are of great antiquity may be seen in another symbol worn by the Olmec (Zoque), that of an "E" on its side, kind of a "W", which is identified as a symbol for star.[14] The two troughs of this symbol may be related to the Venus cycle.[15]

THE MAYAN COUNT OF DAYS

A short aside as to the current level of the researchers' understanding of Mayan astronomy is in order here. Standard Mayan inscriptions usually give the date in four ways: first, as a count of days from an initial starting day; second, as a combination of the day count and solar year date; third, by means of a series of glyphs Morley catalogued as GFZYEDCXBA; and fourth, in a 819-day cycle. The last two are not understood[16] but are thought to be astronomical in nature. My guess is that these last two date forms were probably also generated using the information in the books contained in these parts of the hieroglyphic codices.

Now before the advent of carbon 14-dating, there were only two ways in which archaeologists could date remains: the first of these was by astronomical records which were discovered and then deciphered, and usually these pertained to eclipses; the second method which archaeologists then used was stratigraphy, placing other remains within the context of remains with astronomically established dates. Since the advent of carbon-14 dating, no archaeologist has had to master ancient astronomy in order to master dating.

If you're attempting to reconcile the dates, remember that conquest period Tultul, Xiu, and Itza peoples used different counts, and it is likely that those counts differed from those of the "Classic" Maya. For all of the following records it will require extremely detailed study to determine which calendar systems were in use in each of them, as well as any dating corruptions which may have been introduced into them over the course of the 2,000-3,000 years which it took for their transmission. In other words, it is going to be quite a task for the professionals to determine if any useful exact dating information can be recovered from them.

But…

THE EVENTS ca. 3,100 BCE IN MAYAN RECORDS:
HUN NAL YE, THE PARTITIONER

Part of the Maya story of these multiple creations, multiple impacts, has been preserved in a series of hieroglyphic panels set up around 692 CE at B'aakal (Palenque) by the Mayan Lord Kan Balam II. These are part of a general florescence of inscriptions which were written at that time, which probably reflects a crisis in dynastic legitimacy. The triggering event for this particular series of inscriptions occurred on 23 July, 690, and is usually thought to have been a planetary conjunction, but an appearance of Comet Halley in 684 CE may have likely caused these inscriptions to be written.

The texts describe Hun Nal Ye Tzuk, First Maize Revealed the Partitioner, his wife Na Sak (Lady White), and their children. In Mayan thought, the destruction of the "wooden people" (Chapter 8 here) led to the creation of the maize people, and this may account for the name, First Maize Revealed the Partitioner. But the events described here refer not to the destruction of the "wooden people", but rather to the destruction of the "mud people", and Hun Nal Ye The Partitioner apparently was associated with that as well.

The translations given here are adapted from those *Understanding Maya Inscriptions, A Hieroglyphic Handbook[17]*, with adaptations focusing on the titles of GIII, which were actually read pretty well, though the translators themselves did not believe their own readings. This book is an excellent introduction to the Mayan glyphic, and it is frank in its admission as to how many problems remain in reading these texts. The dates given in the table following these translations are very, very tentative.

TEMPLE OF THE CROSS INSCRIPTION

"12 Bak'tuns, 19 k'atuns, 13 tuns, and 4 winals after the previous era began;
on 8 Ahaw, 18 Sek,
was born Lady White.
It was 8 tuns and 5 winals since the birth,
And then the (?) event was carried out on 4 Ahaw 8 Kumuku;
13 baktuns were completed.
It was 1 tun, 9 winals, 2 kins
since the image was made visible at the Closed Sky, the First Three Stone Place,
and then First Maize Revealer the Partitioner entered the sky.
On 13 Ik' 20 Mol he prepared the Raised Up Sky Place,
Eight House Partition is its holy name,
it is the House of the North.
It was 1 bak'tun, 18 k'atuns, 3 tuns, and 12 winals
since Raised Up Sky Heart was set in motion by First Maize Revealer the Partitioner,
and then he [identified as God 1] arrived as Matawil.
He [identified as God 1] is the child of White Ox Ya Ch'okle Lady.
It was 2 bak'tuns, 1 k'atun, 7 tuns, 11 winals since her birth
and then the white headband was closed for her White on 9 Ik' 0 Sak."

TEMPLE OF THE SUN INSCRIPTION

"1.18.5.3.6, 13 Kimi 19 Keh:
He was born, The spirit of the Sun-eyed Torch,
The killer of the kings in the White House, the White Bone House,
The ?? of heaven,
Who with fire closed the eye of the Sun-eyed Lord Sun.

"1.18.5.3.6 days
[note the day count repetition, but this time as a day displacement]
since he [First Maize Revealed the Partitioner] set in motion the Raised Up Sky Heart
and then he [Sun-eyed Torch, the king killer] arrived at Matawil.
He [Sun-eyed Torch] is the child of Valley Lady White Holy Palenque Lord.

"9.12.18.5.16 days
since made visible the image at Closed Sky First Three Stone Place
on 4 Ahwa 8 Kamk'u and then happened 2 Kib 14 Mol."

TEMPLE OF THE FOLIATED CROSS INSCRIPTION

"1.18.5.4.0, 1 Ahaw 13 Mak:
The Third one was born,
the Red Dwarf(?) Partitioner,
The third born of the K'awil Man [First Maize Revealer the Partitioner],
the Divine Sprout K'awinal.

"1.14.14.0 days since he arrived,
the Sprout K'awinal, at Matawil,
and then was completed 2 baktuns.

"2 Ahaw 3 Wayeb,
She conjured up the gods, Valley Place Lady White,
Holy Matawil Ruler.
It happened at First True Mountain White Flower, Born First Tree Precious."

THE DATES

The dates, such as they have been reconstructed by the glyph scholars, and these are extremely, extremely tentative, are:

16 June,   3,122 BCE - The First Maize Revealer Partitioner is born
7 December, 3,121 BCE - Birth of Lady White (?)
13 August,   3,114 BCE - Image made visible at Closed Sky,
                the First Three Stone Place;
                Event for The First Maize Revealed Partitioner
5 February,   3,112 BCE - The First Maize Revealed Partitioner enters the sky,
                Prepared/Dedicated the Raised Up Sky Place in the North
                Set in motion the Raised Up Sky Heart
8 November, 2,360 BCE - Birth of the Red Dwarf(?) Partitioner
25 October,   2,360 BCE - Birth of Sun-eyed Torch, The Killer of the Kings,
                in the White House, the White Bone House,
                the ?? of the heavens,
                who with fire closed the eye of the Sun-eyed Lord Sun;
                "arrived" (struck) at Matawil
21 October,   2,360 BCE - Birth of G1
7 September, 2,325 BCE - A white headband was close for White?
17 February, 2,325 BCE - Lady White conjured up the gods at Matawil

23 July,   690 CE - Some significant contemporaneous event occurred,
                thought by some scholars to be a planetary conjunction.

                Is this Comet Halley's appearance, or its departure?

Most of these dates are derived from the texts of these inscriptions, and it needs to be emphasized again that the readings are very tentative. But…

THE CLIMATIC COLLAPSE OF 3,114 BCE

"Something happened 5,200 years ago that was abrupt and very large scale", explained Lonnie Thompson, professor of geological sciences at Ohio State University, and researcher with the Byrd Polar Research Center.[18] Dr. Thompson and his team had just returned from an expedition to Nevado Corapuna, but the big news concerned the radiocarbon dates they had just received for samples from the Quelccaya Glacier in Peru. These dated to roughly 3,200 BCE (the emphasis on "roughly"), and this new information agreed with earlier findings from the ice fields of Mount Kilimanjaro in Tanzania. There had been a devastating drought, but Dr. Thompson was at a loss as to what caused it.

AN EGYPTIAN LEGEND OF A COMETARY ENCOUNTER CA 3,114 BCE:
THE BOOK OF THE CELESTIAL COW, THE DESTRUCTION OF MANKIND

We do not have to rely solely on Mayan records for accounts of astronomical events during these early times, as the records of other peoples provide us with valuable corroborating evidence. The Egyptians left us records as well, and some of them also apparently describe impact events. Given the importance of this impact to the Maya, of special importance at this point is the account of a climate collapse and an impact given by the Egyptian *Book of the Celestial Cow*[19], and as will be seen below, this impact may be dated to around 3,114 BCE.

THE BOOK OF THE CELESTIAL COW

"(Here is the story of Ra [the Sun],) the one god, the god who was self-begotten and self-created, after he had assumed the sovereignty over men and women, and gods, and things."

Note that it is explicitly stated here that this event occurred well after creation.

A COMETARY DUST LOADING

"Now men and women were speaking words of complaint, saying, 'Behold, his Majesty [Ra, the Sun] (Life, Strength, and Health to him!) has grown old, and his bones have become like silver, and his members have turned into gold, and his hair is like unto real lapis-lazuli.'

The description here records a dimming of sunlight due to dust loading from this encounter with Comet Encke.

"His Majesty [Ra, the Sun] heard the words of complaint which men and women were uttering, and his Majesty (Life, Strength, and Health to him!) said unto those who were in his train, 'Cry out, and bring to me my Eye, and Shu, and Tefnut, and Geb, and Nut, and the father-gods and the mother-gods who were with me even when I was in Nun side by side with my god Nun.'"

Budge identified Shu as God of the Air, Tefnut as Goddess of Moisture, Geb as God of the Earth, and Nut as Goddess of the Sky - but Nut is better explained as the Goddess of the Heavens, or best as the Goddess of the Star Field. Budge glossed Nun as "the primal flood preceding creation, later the ocean in which the Earth rests", but did emphasize that the Egyptians understood the clarity of the emptiness of space as being due to its being a clear celestial "water", in other words "Nun". As will be seen further along in this story, the "eye of Ra" is the comet prototype. In later Egyptian zodiacs one comet is often pictured as the disk of Ra resting on the back of a bull: the Taurids, so to speak. Ra, the Sun, continues his speech...

"'Let there be brought along with my Eye [the comet prototype], his ministers, and let them be led secretly to me here, so that men and women cannot see them [coming] hither, and may not therefore take to flight with their hearts.'

"'Come you [also] with them to the Great House [Ra's tomb, first dynasty palace and burial structure], and let them declare their plans (or, arrangements) fully. For I will go from Nun [Space] into the place wherein I brought about my own existence, and let those gods be brought unto me there.'"

In other words, the sun disappears completely, most likely due to cometary dust loading. Everywhere on Earth crops would have failed due to the lack of sunlight, and game animal herds would have diminished due to the lack of food.

"[Then] the gods were drawn up on each side of Ra [the Sun], and they bowed down before his Majesty until their heads touched the ground, and the maker of men and women, the king of those who have knowledge, spoke his words in the presence of [Nun, Space] the Father of the first-born gods. And the gods spoke in the presence of his Majesty [Ra, the Sun], saying, 'Speak unto us, for we are listening to them (your words)'.

"Then Ra [the Sun] spoke unto Nun [Space], saying, 'O first-born god from whom I came into being, O you gods of ancient time' [Please note the usage here extremely carefully: there was a pantheon of gods whose "existence" preceded that of Ra.], "my ancestors, take heed to what men and women [are doing]: For behold, those who were created by my Eye' [in other words mankind, who had been given "unruly matter" by comets and meteorites] 'are uttering words of complaint against me. Tell me what you would do in the matter, and consider this thing for me, and seek out (a plan) for me, for I will not slay them until I have heard what you shall say to me concerning it.'

A FIRST IMPACT?

"Then the Majesty of Nun [Space] spoke to [his] son Ra [the Sun], saying, 'You are the god who is greater than he who made you; you are the sovereign of those who were created with you, your throne is set [established], and the fear of you is great: Let your Eye [the comet] go against those who have uttered blasphemies against you.'

"And the Majesty of Ra [the Sun] said, 'Behold, they have betaken themselves to flight into the mountain lands, for their hearts are afraid because of the words which they have uttered.'

The people's "flight into the mountain lands" referred to here most likely was a flight from both settled agriculture and the King's control, back to hunting, undertaken in response to the crop failures brought on by the comet's dust veil.

"Then the gods spoke in the presence of his Majesty, saying, 'Let your Eye [a comet] go forth and let it destroy for you those who revile you with words of evil, for there is no Eye [matter] whatsoever that can go before it and resist you and it when it [your Eye] journeys in the form of Hathor [this particular comet].'

"Thereupon this goddess [Hathor, the active comet] went forth and slew the men and the women who were on the mountain (or, desert land)."

Budge alerts us to his confusion with this passage by also giving the alternative reading of "or, desert land". Perhaps the best reading for the underlying term would simply be "wilderness", the place where the people could hunt game to substitute for the crops which had failed due to the comet induced climate collapse.

AN IMPACT AT HENSU, THE CITY OF HERAKLEOPOLIS

Wherever this first impact took place, the next impact struck the northern Egyptian city of Herakleopolis, as will be seen immediately below.

"And the Majesty of this god [Ra, the Sun] said, 'Come, come in peace, O Hathor, for the work is accomplished.' Then this goddess [Hathor, the comet] said, 'You have made me to live, for when I gained the mastery over men and women it was sweet to my heart.' And the Majesty of Ra [the Sun] said, 'I myself will be master over them as [their] king, and I will destroy them.'

In other words, after the first impact Ra, the Sun, asks Hathor, the active comet, to stop, but Hathor appeals, and Ra agrees to let her continue.]

"And it came to pass that Sekhet of the offerings [sacrifices] waded about in the night season in their blood, beginning at Su-ten/hen-en."

Other later readings have "hen-en/Su-ten", "Hensu", the Lower Egyptian (northern) city of Herakleopolis Magna. Budge explained "Sekhet" as the Eye of Ra, lion-headed goddess symbolizing the destructive power of Ra, the Sun. Sekhet was also known later as "Sekhmet", this most likely the active comet Hathor when "she" is near the Earth, one of the fragments of Comet Encke which the Maya described.

THE CONQUEST OF THE NORTH

> "Then the Majesty of Ra [the Sun], spoke, (saying), 'Cry out, and let there come to me swift and speedy messengers who shall be able to run like the wind . . . . and straightway messengers of this kind were brought unto him. And the Majesty of this god spoke (saying), 'Let these (messengers) go to Abu [Elephantine at the southern border of the country], and bring unto me mandrakes in great numbers.'

Here the King's control of the South of Egypt, the Upper Kingdom, is asserted. The "mandrakes" are a hallucinogenic atropa.

> "And [when] these mandrakes were brought unto him the Majesty of this god [either Ra, the Sun, or the King himself] gave them to Sekhet [the comet Hathor when near the Earth], the goddess who dwells in Annu [the city of Heliopolis] to crush."

It is unclear here whether the King had established control over the Lower (northern) Egyptian city of Heliopolis, or whether this refers to a later establishment to the Hathhor/Sekhet cult at Heliopolis.

> "And behold, when the maidservants were bruising the grain for [making] beer, these mandrakes were placed in the vessels which were to hold the beer, and some of the blood of the men and women (Budge adds "who had been slain"). Now they made seven thousand vessels of beer."

This appears to be a statement either that at least 7,000 people died in the impact at Herakleopolis, or that 7,000 people were sacrificed at Heliopolis to try and stem the gods' rage.

DAYLIGHT REAPPEARS

> "Now when the Majesty of Ra [the Sun], the King of the South and North, had come with the gods to look at the vessels of beer, and behold, the daylight had appeared, after the slaughter of men and women by the goddess [either by the comet Hathor near the Earth as Sekhet, or in the human sacrifice at Heliopolis] in their [the constellation's] season as she [Hathor/Sekhet] sailed up the river [of her water in space, in other words followed her orbit]."

Minimally, what this says is that "daylight", sunlight, reappeared when Comet Encke receded.

> "The Majesty of Ra [the Sun] said, 'It is good, it is good! Nevertheless I must protect men and women against her.' And Ra [the Sun] said, 'Let them take up the vases and carry them to the place where the men and women were slaughtered by her.'

"Then the Majesty of the King of the South and North in the three-fold beauty of the night,..." [This "three-fold beauty" may refer to the three-stemed plant icons seen in First Dynasty inscriptions. Perhaps it was the atropa.]"... caused to be poured out these vases of beer which make (men) to lie down [Budge glossed this as "sleep", but in sufficient dosages atropas cause death], and the meadows of the Four Heavens were filled with beer by reason of the Souls [of either the intoxicated and sedated or the dead] of the Majesty of this god."

In the preceding passage the King, who is now King of both the South and the North of Egypt, claims identity with Ra, the Sun. Despite Ra's command that the vessels be taken to "the place where the men and women were slaughtered by her", the "meadows of the Four Heavens" must be the locations of parts of the star field, as will be seen in the next passage.

"And it came to pass that when this goddess [Hathor/Sekhet] arrived at the dawn of day, she found these [the Four Heavens] flooded [with the beer souls], and she was pleased thereat; and she drank (Budge adds "of the beer and blood"), and her heart rejoiced, and she became drunk, and she gave no further attention to men and women.

"Then said the Majesty of Ra [the Sun] to this goddess [Hathor, the comet], 'Come in peace, come in peace, O Amit.'
["Amit" is most likely the comet Hathor when it is inactive.]. "And thereupon beautiful women came into being in the city of Amit (or Amem). And the Majesty of Ra [the Sun] spoke [concerning] this goddess, [saying], 'Let there be made for her vessels of the beer which produces sleep at every holy time and season of the year, and they [the beer vessels] shall be in number according to the number of my hand-maidens.'

"And [thus] from that early time until now men have been wont to make on the occasions of the festival of Hathor vessels of the beer which make them to sleep, in number according to the number of the handmaidens of Ra [either of the Sun or of the Pharaoh]."

A SECOND COMETARY DUST LOADING:
RA'S INSTRUCTIONS TO SHU AND NUT

The encounter was not over yet:

"And the Majesty of Ra [the Sun] spoke unto this goddess [Hathor/Sekhet/ Amit, the comet], (saying), 'I am smitten with the pain of the fire of sickness; whence comes to me [this] pain?' And the Majesty of Ra said, 'I live, but my heart has become exceedingly weary with existence with them [with men]; I have slain (some of) them, but there is a remnant of worthless ones, for the destruction which I wrought among them was not as great as my power.'

"Then the gods who were in his following said unto him, 'Be not overcome by your inactivity, for your might is in proportion to your will.'

"And the Majesty of this god [Ra, the Sun] said unto the Majesty of Nun [Space], 'My members are [have been] weak for the first time; I will not permit this to come upon me a second time.' [Here Ra, the Sun, asserts that he will not let the dust from the comet darken him again.]

"And the Majesty of the god Nun [Space] said, 'O son Shu [the air], be the Eye [matter of?] for your father . . . . .[and you, Tefnut(goddess of water) be a river] and avenue (?)[for] him; and you, goddess Nut [Star Field], place him [Shu, the Air, under you]. . . . [The text breaks up at this point.]

"And the goddess Nut said, 'How can this be [done] then, O my father Nun [Space]? Hail," said Nut . . .

". . . to the god Nun [Space], and the goddess straightway became (a cow), and she set the Majesty of Ra [the Sun] upon (her) back . . . . .

"And when these things had been done, men and women saw the god Ra [the Sun], upon the back (of the cow [Nut the Star Field]). Then these men and women said [to Ra, the Sun], 'Remain with us, and we will overthrow your enemies who speak words of blasphemy (against you) and (destroy them).'

"Then his Majesty (Ra)[the Sun] set out for the Great House [Ra's tomb, the first dynasty place/tomb], and...." [Budge restored: "and (the gods who were in the train of Ra remained) with them (with men) during that time the Earth was in darkness.", which is here restored: "and [Nut, and the gods who were in the train of Ra remained] with them [Ra and Nut] during that time the Earth was in darkness." However the line is restored, the reading that sunlight had disappeared completely is certain. That the other "gods", celestial bodies, would "disappear" as well seems entirely likely. This was a very heavy dust loading.]

FURTHER SLAUGHTER

"And when the Earth became light (again) and the morning had dawned, the men came forth with their bows and their (weapons), and they set their arms in motion to shoot the enemies (of Ra)[the Sun]."

Two alternatives suggest themselves here. The first of these is an attack by the Southern Kingdom against the Northern Kingdom, which had been weakened by the earlier impact event at the city of Herakleopolis. This would follow the usual pattern seen elsewhere, where peoples took advantage of neighboring peoples who have been weakened by impact events. The second alternative is a reduction in the population by a genocide conducted by the farmers against those who had abandoned agriculture and returned to hunting.

"Then said the Majesty of this god [Ra, the Sun], 'Your transgressions of violence are placed behind you, for the slaughtering of the enemies is above the slaughter... [Budge restored here "slaughter (of sacrifice)", more likely restored as "the slaughter (which I the Sun had planned)"].

"Thus came into being the slaughter..." [Here Budge restored "slaughter (of sacrifice)"; "slaughter (of enemies)" is also possible].

THE STAR FIELD REAPPEARS,
OR, THE CREATION OF THE STAR FIELD

"And the Majesty of this god [Ra the Sun] said unto Nut [the Star Field], 'I have placed myself upon my back in order to stretch myself out.'

"What then is the meaning of this? It means that he united himself with Nut. (Thus came into being) ....

The text is completely lost here.

"Then said the Majesty of this god [Ra, the sun], 'I am departing from them (from men), and he must come after (me who would see me; thus came into being ....

"Then the Majesty of this god [Ra, the sun] looked forth from its [the star field's] interior, saying, 'Gather together (men for me), and make ready for me an abode for (the) multitudes [of their star-souls];' thus came into being ....

"And his Majesty [Ra, the Sun] (life, health, and strength be to him!) said, 'Let a great field (sekhet) be produced (hetep)', (and) thereupon Sekhet-hetep came into being." [Note that "sekhet", "field", is also a name for the goddess Sekhet/Hathor mentioned above in the context of sedating/hallucinogenic/toxic mandrake use.] "(And the Majesty of this god [Ra, the Sun] said, 'I will gather herbs (aarat) [most likely "mandrake"] therein', [and] thereupon Sekhet-aaru came into being.

"(And the Majesty of this god [Ra, the Sun] said, 'I will make it to contain as dwellers things (khet) like stars of all sorts', [and] thereupon the stars (akhekha) came into being.

THE STAR FIELD GODDESS NUT TREMBLES

"Then the goddess Nut [the Star Field] trembled because of the height."

The "trembling" may actually have referred to a waving of the star field due to Comet Encke's dust train. In any case, Shu, the Air, is now told to hold Nut up, and additional "props" for the Star Field are created.

"And the Majesty of Ra [the Sun] said, 'I decree that supports [come into] be[ing] to bear (the goddess up)', [and] thereupon the props of heaven (heh) [the star field] came into being.

Bruce Masse's map
of the impactor's devastation

105

"And the Majesty of Ra [the Sun] said, 'O my son Shu [the Air], I pray you to set yourself under [my] daughter Nut [Goddess of the Star Field], and guard for me the supports (heh) of the millions [of stars] which are there, and which live in darkness. Take the goddess upon your head, and act as nurse for her.'

"Thereupon came into being (the custom) of a son nursing a daughter, and (the custom) of a father carrying a son upon his head."

DATING THE HERAKLEOPOLIS IMPACT

The mentions in *The Book of The Celestial Cow* of the "Great House", the First Dynasty palace whose form is preserved in the burial places of the First Dynasty Kings, sets it during the period of the First Dynasty of Egypt, in other words ca. 3100 BCE. The period of the First Dynasty also appears to be the only period in Egyptian history when the ancient Egyptians practiced human sacrifice, which is also prominently mentioned in *The Book of The Celestial Cow*. Finally, the period of the First Dynasty is also the time of the climatic collapse which Dr. Thompson evidenced at Mount Kilimanjaro.

A MAYAN ACCOUNT OF THE RESPONSE TO COMET ENCKE ca 3,114 BCE

The following has been freely adapted from the translation given by Schele, Friedel, and Parker of Quiriga Stela C.[20] Linda Schele interpreted the wording of the following stela inscription, which dates from the mid-first millennium, as being an astronomical parable, where the three thrones represent the sky, the earth, and the sea, but a literal reading of the words as the response of the Lords of three different kingdoms may originally have been meant, and it seems to work just as well.

"4 Ahaw, 8 Kumk'u, to say - to make appear;
Three stones were set, they planted;"

A list of three peoples perhaps now follows.

"One stone, the Jaguar Paddler (Chilam Balam)
and Stingray through nose Paddler (Lord),
it happened at First-Five-Sky (Na-ho-chan) Jaguar (Lord's) throne stone;"

Is "Na-ho-chan" the original Maya homeland at Kaminaljuyu in what is today's Guatemala?

"He planted a stone, the West-First-Rainpriest,
It happened in the land of the Serpent-Throne-Stone;"

Some north-western people, say the Teotihuacans in the Valley of Mexico?

"And then it happened a stone was set, [by] Na Itzamhi,
Waterlily-throne-stone, it happened at Lying-Down-Sky;"

106

"Na Itzamhi" appears in later contact period Yucatec accounts as a founder. As will be seen in Chapter 8, the east was where the "sky laid down". The "Waterlily-Throne- Stone" may perhaps be a reference to the people we know as "Olmecs".

"(The) First stone place were completed 13 baktuns
It was his action, Raised-up Sky Lord."

13 baktuns 4 Ahau 8 Kumuku is the same date given in Temple of the Cross Inscriptions, given above, which relate to an appearance of Comet Encke. 13 Baktuns is a year count, and translates into some 5,200 years. Moving back from 3,100 BCE, we end up with a date near 8,300 BCE, very near to the Holocene Start Impacts (Chapter 3) and quite possible the beginnings of the development of Native American astronomy.

THE RIO CUARTO IMPACT EVENT OF 2,360 BCE:
THE DESTRUCTION OF THE SECOND CREATION AND THE BEGINNING OF THE COUNT OF DAYS

From the information given in the Egyptians' *Book of the Celestial Cow* we can be fairly certain what occurred ca 3,100 BCE, but of the other event mentioned in the Temple of the Cross Inscription: exactly what happened around 2,360 BCE at "Matawil"?

In October 1989, Ruben Lianza, a captain in the Argentinian Air Force, noticed a series of curious parallel depressions while flying over the Argentine pampas near the city of Rio Cuarto. As fate would have it, Lianza was also an amateur astronomer, and he could find no other explanation for the depressions than that they might be the result of impacts. Pursuing his hunch, Lianza sent a packet of photographs to the editors of the magazine *Sky and Telescope*, and they in turn contacted Brown University geologist Peter Schultz.[21]

Schultz in turn managed to get funding from the National Science Foundation for a quick expedition to the scars, and along with William Colins, John Grant, and Ruben Lianza, recovered impact glasses from the depressions, thus confirming that they were formed by oblique impacts with the Earth of something from space. Because this impactor's fragments had come in at such a near angle to the surface of the Earth, they had left behind a series of parallel gouges on the pampas instead of the usual circular craters. The team estimated that the fragments had hit with an explosive force of some 350 megatons, and their results were reported in the science publication *Nature* in 1992.[22]

Philip Bland and his international team continued the work at Rio Cuarto, but they found that there were more depressions in the region, and they collected some new impact glasses from throughout the entire area. They dated these impact glasses in the lab and found that they dated to 36,000 to 52,000 years ago, far earlier than the radiocarbon dates Schultz's team obtained for the Rio Cuarto depressions, which radiocarbon dates not surprisingly agreed with the Mayan date of 2,360 BCE for the impact at Matawil. Based on this evidence, Bland's team concluded that the depressions at Rio Cuarto had been formed by natural processes, and merely incorporated earlier impact glasses.[23]

In response to Bland's team's work, Schultz assembled his own new expanded team, recovered more samples of impact glasses from the area, and had them all argon dated.[24] Not only were Bland's earlier impact glasses found and redated, but another 5 impact glasses were also found, including recent glasses from the Rio Cuarto impacts. The argon date for these recent impact glasses, 6,000 years ago give or take 2,000 years, say 4,000 years ago, agree with the radiocarbon dates, and with the Mayan date of 2,360 BCE for an impact at Matawil.

SOUTH AMERICAN LEGENDS OF THE RIO CUARTO IMPACTS

Anthropologist Bruce Masse was fascinated by the Schulz team's findings in 1992, and he collected a series of legends from different peoples throughout South America which him led to a surprising conclusion. As if the heat from a 350-megaton explosion was not enough, the Rio Cuarto impactor's fragments had come in at such a shallow angle to the surface of the Earth that the heat they had given off as they had passed through the Earth's atmosphere had managed to set most of South America on fire. Although Masse's work unfortunately has not been published yet, impact researcher Bob Kobres had previously identified some legends of the Toba and Pilaga peoples of South America that most likely refer to the Rio Cuarto impacts, and they are given here.[25]

THE GREAT FIRE

" The people were all sound asleep. It was midnight when an Indian noticed that the Moon was taking on a reddish hue. He awoke the others, "The Moon is about to be eaten by an animal." The animals preying on the Moon were jaguars [meteors], but these jaguars were spirits of the dead.

"The people shouted and yelled. They beat their wooden mortars like drums, they thrashed their dogs, and some shot at random with their guns [likely either a bad translation or neochronism]. They were making as much noise as they could to scare the jaguars [meteors] and force them to let go their prey.

"Fragments of the Moon fell down upon the Earth and started a big fire. From these fragments the entire Earth caught on fire.

"The fire was so large that the people could not escape. Men and women ran to the lagoons covered with bulrushes. Those who were late were overtaken by the fire. The water was boiling, but not where the bulrushes grew. Those who were in places not covered with bulrushes died. and there most of the people were burnt alive.

"After everything had been destroyed the fire stopped. Decayed corpses of children floated on the water. A big wind and a rain storm broke out. The dead were changed into birds. The large birds came out from corpses of adults, and small ones from the bodies of children."

THE GREAT FIRE (SECOND VERSION)

"Long ago Moon was attacked and wounded, and thus the Great Fire originated. As soon as people noticed blood on Moon, they started to chant and to shout and they struck their dogs to make them bark. Men discharged their rifles [again, a neochronism] in the hope that the monster which was preying on Moon would be frightened and relinquish his prey, but all this was of no avail. Moon was far away and his weapons broke because his spear and his club were carved of soft yuchan wood (*Chorisia insignis*) instead of hard palo mataco (*Achatocarpus praecox*).

"A fragment of Moon fell down and caused a fire. Everyone rushed to a lagoon where abundant bulrushes grew. As the fire was spreading over the surface of the earth burning the grass and the trees, people entered the lagoon. Those who had taken refuge among the bulrushes were saved, but those who had remained in the open places perished in the boiling water."

STAR MYTHOLOGY AND COSMOGONY
SUN AND MOON

"Sun (ahewa) is a big, fat woman who walks across the sky, and every evening [she] enters a fissure between the sky and the earth. At the time of the winter solstice she is a young swift-moving girl. As a result, days are short. At the summer solstice she is an old woman who walks slowly and with difficulty. That is why summer days are long and why the Sun disappears late.

"Moon (aworc'k) is a pot-bellied man whose bluish intestines can be seen through his skin. His enemy is a spirit of death, the celestial Jaguar. Now and then the Jaguar springs up to devour him. Moon defends himself with a spear tipped with a head carved of the soft wood of the bottletree (yuchan, *Chorisia insignis*), which breaks at the first impact. He [Moon] also has a club made of the same wood, which is too light to cause any harm. The Jaguar tears at his body, pieces of which fall on the earth. These are the meteors, which three times have caused a world fire. ["meteors' is in the original text.]

"The bloody Moon is almost entirely devoured by Jaguar. Men, however, are afraid, and they beat their drums, strike their dogs, shout, and make all possible noise to frighten the celestial Jaguar and force him to relinquish his prey. Finally, he weakens and Moon can disentangle himself from his grip. Moon seizes his weapons and puts Jaguar to flight. After a little while, Moon grows and again becomes a pot-bellied man. The eclipse is over. Jaguar also bears a grudge against Sun, but Sun's weapons are made of iron and she is fearless.

THE END OF THE MOUND BUILDERS OF THE AMAZON

Nearly the whole of Amazonia must have been set on fire about 2,360 BCE by the entry and explosion of the fragments of the Rio Cuarto impactor, and this impact event probably led to the Argentinian pampas and the Amazonian jungles which we know today. While the Rio Cuarto impact event appears to have put an end to the South American mound builders of the Amazon headwaters and the mountains, mound building cultures survived elsewhere in the west of South America, and they enjoyed dominance there until the rise of the Inca. Those few manioc cultivators who survived the Rio Cuarto blasts, those living in the far northwest of Amazonia, very gradually managed to re-establish themselves.[26]

THE CELESTIAL JAGUAR AND THE 'FELINE' CULTS OF WESTERN SOUTH AMERICA

Although little is known of the astronomical systems of these early civilizations of western South America, one thing that is known about all of these peoples is that their religions nearly universally featured the worship of what has been called a "feline" (cat) deity. Representations of this "feline god" figured in the religious artifacts of nearly all these people, and I can find no explanation for this "feline" deity and the extraordinary key role which it plays in these religions, other than in the fact that in all of these peoples' cosmologies the "jaguar" was a comet/asteroid, as it was for the Toba-Pilagi.

THE RIO CUARTO IMPACT EVENT OF 2,360 BCE IN MAYAN MYTH: THE BEGINNING OF THE COUNT OF DAYS AND THE DESTRUCTION OF THE SECOND CREATION

The Mayan creation story preserved memories of the destruction of earlier "creations'. The following Mayan account has been adapted from Munro S Edmunson's translation of *The Book of Chilam Balam of Chumayel.*[27]

> "Thus it was read by the First Sage Melchisedek, and the First Prophet, Puc Tun: the Catholic priest (sacerdote), and the First Sun Priest. This is the sermon of the occurrence of the birth of the Count of Days, which was before the awakening of the world occurred, and it began to run by itself, alone."

This appears to be a team translation: Melchisedek was the biblical name given by the padres to their Catholic sacerdote, "the Catholic priest", and Puc Tun was the "First Prophet" and "First Sun Priest" - in other words, the Chilam Balam.

Following the introduction, some kind of prime force next brings into existence his companions by "saying" them, and they then try to create and perfect man:

> "Then said his mother's mother, then said his mother's sister, then said his father's mother, then said his sister in law, 'What is to be said when a man is seen on the road?' So they said whilst going along, but no man occurred.

> "And then they arrived, there, in the east, and they began to say, 'Who is it that passed by here now? Here are his tracks, right here. Measure them with your foot, according to the word of the Planter [Creator]of the World.'

"Then they were to measure the footprint of our Father, who is the holy God. This was the beginning of saying the Count of the World by footsteps. This was 12 Oc [Foot].

"This is the account of his birth. For 13 Oc [Foot] occurred, and they matched each other's paces, and arrived there at the east.

"They said his [the Planter of the World's] name [Foot], since the days had no name(s) then. [By "saying" the days' names, the gods created them.] And he [the Planter of the World] traveled on with his mother's mother, his mother's sister, and his father's mother, and his sister-in-law. The month was born, and the day name was born, and the sky born, and the earth, the pyramid of water, and land, stone, and tree [were born]. Then were born the things of sea and land."

What follows appears to be an expansion of the first part of the preceding passage:

"On 1 Chuen [Artisan, Creator, Monkey] he manifested himself in his divinity, and created [the] Heaven[s] and [the] Earth.
"On 2 Eb [Stairway, Peak] he made his first pyramid.
"He descended,
coming from there in the heart of [the] heaven[s],
there in the heart of the water[s of space].
For there was nothing of earth, or stone, or tree."
[It seems likely that the Maya conceived of space as a cold clear lake.]
"On 3 Ben [Go about, think about] he made all things, each and every thing:
the things of [the] heaven[s],
and the things of the sea,
and the things of the land:
"On 4 Ix [Lady, Woman, mother of the Chacs, the rain gods]
there occurred the separation of [the] heaven[s] from the Earth.
[Again, the holders of the heavens were responsible
for the weather as well]
"On 5 Men [To work] occurred the working of everything.
"On 6 Cib [Light, Torch, Candle] occurred the making of the first light:
there occurred illumination,
for there was no Sun or Moon.
"On 7 Caban [Earth] there was born the Earth, which we did not have before.
"On 8 Etz'nab
He planted His hands and feet,
and made birds upon the Earth."

This appears to be the creation of the animals.

"On 9 Cauac Hell was first tasted.
[Cauac is the bearer to the south, where the first impact was recorded. The reference to Hell is a Christian description.]

"On 10 Ahau [Lord, He who calls out orders]
      occurred the going of [the] evil men to Hell,
      because the Holy God had not yet appeared.

This appears to be the destruction of the first creation, in which the animals were considered to have been a defective kind of man.

"On 11 Imix [Ceiba Tree mane] occurred the shaping of stones and trees.
      That was done on this day.
"On 12 Ik [Wind] occurred the birth of breath.
      This was the beginning of what is called breath,
      because there is no death in it.
"On 13 Akbahl occurred the taking of the water.
      Then He moistened earth, and shaped it and made man."

This is the creation of the "clay" men of the second creation. Other Native American peoples have different numbers of creations and destructions, but the Maya had three: the first, that of animals, the second, that of the clay men, who seem to have been destroyed by the floods caused by soot from the Rio Cuarto impact; and a third, that of the "wooden" men, whose destruction will be discussed in Chapter 8. The Creator now plans the destruction of the "clay" men:

"On 1 Kan [Heavens, Yellowed Sun?] he was disturbed in his (at) heart,
      by the evil that had been created. [This "evil" was the clay men.]
"On 2 Chicchan [To appear] occurred the appearance of everything evil.
      And He was it, even within the towns.
"On 3 Cimi [Death] He invented death.
      It happened that then was invented the first death,
      by Our Father who is God.
"On 4 Manik[?no holding back?] ... [Sadly, the text here is lost.]

THE RAINS FROM THE SOOT OF RIO CUARTO:

"On 5 Lamat [Flood] there was the invention
      of the Seven Floods of rain, water, and sea.
"On 6 Muluc [Bury, Muul, man-made mound of earth],
      occurred the burial of all the caves.

And this was before the awakening of the world.
[In other words, the final creation.]
This occurred by the commandment of Our Father, who is God.

"Everything that there was not, [which had been destroyed]
was then spoken in [the] heaven[s].
[In other words, everything was created again.]

"For there had been no stones and trees."

The "stones and trees" are required by the Bacabs for the separation of the heavens from the Earth.

"And they went and tested each other "

This probably refers to the astronomical quiz, the "Theodora", posed to candidates for astronomer.

"And then He spoke as follows: 'Thirteen heaps and seven make one.', He said for speech to emerge."

The Tzolkin, the religious and divinatory calendar of the Maya, combined a numbered 13 day week with a 20 day named week, and the number and the name changed daily. In the passage above, for example 5 Lamat [Flood] is not the day before 6 Lamat but rather the day before 6 Muluc [Bury, Muul, man-made mound of earth]. A count of 13 and then of 7 exhausts the 20 day names, and thse count began on 13 Oc [Foot], when the Creator measured off everything. Furthermore, the day name always corresponded to the last digit of the Long Count.[28]

"For they had no speech. Its origin was requested by the First Lord Sun-Priest (Kin), for their organs of speech were not yet opened, so that they could speak to each other.

"They went there to the Heart of the Sky,
and took each other by the hand.
And then they [the Bacabs] stood there in the middle of the country,
and [they] divided it up.

This is the Bacabs' partitioning ceremony described in the passages above.

"And they (the Bacabs) divided the Burners, the four of them:
4 Chiccan [Appearance] the Burner,
4 Oc [Foot] the Burner,
4 Men [To work] the Burner, and
4 Ahau [Lord, he who gives orders] the Burner.
These are the Lords, the four of them."

These "Burners" were not only impactors and lightning, they were also officials who kept a fire cult which was tied to the Count of Days. This is followed by a long passage untranslated from the hieroglyphic and a closing. Continuing with the last line...

"The account of all the days, through which The Beginning is counted, was in the east, as has been told."

(Footnotes)

[1] Alexander Marshack,*The Roots of Civilization: The Cognitive Beginnings of Man's First Art, Symbol, and Notation*, McGraw-Hill, New York, 1971, 1972

[2] Chapter 2 here

[3] For some examples of early use of the tzuk sign, see Schele's Maya Cosmos, p 140-141, and p. 418-419, though sadly Schele was unaware that impact events actually could and did occur in historic times.

[4] *Inca Myths*, Gary Urton, British Museum Press and University of Texas Press, Austin, 1999 p. 41-44

[5] Ralph E. Roys, *The Book of Chilam Balam of Chumayel*, Carnegie Institute, Washington, D.C., 1933.

[6] Adapted from the accounts given by Black Hoof to Governor Lewis Cass and recorded by C. C. Trowbridge, and located and preserved by Kinietz and Voegelin, S*hawanese Traditions*, University of Michigan Press, Ann Arbor, 1939. See also Cass and Trowbridge papers available at the Detroit Public Library.

[7] Father Jacques Gravier, "Journal of the Voyage of Father Gravier of the Society of Jesus, in 1700, from the Country of the Illinois to the Mouth of the Mississippi, Addressed to Father de Lamberville, and Sent from the Fort of the Mississippi, 17 Leagues from Its Mouth in the Gulf or Sea of Mexico, Feb. 16, 1701". In *Early Voyages Up and Down the Mississippi*, edited by John Gilmary Shea, 1861, p. 115-163. Reprinted 1902 by Joseph McDonough, Albany.

[8] Bishop Diego de Landa, *Relacion de las cosas de Yucatan*, A.R. Pagden translation, J. Philip O'Hara, Chicago, 1975, p. 42

[9] Michael D. Coe, *The Maya*, Thames and Hudson, London, 1999, p. 220-222

[10] For an excellent introduction to the Mayan hieroglyphic, I highly recommend John F. Harris and Stephen K. Stearns, *Understanding Maya Inscriptions, A Hieroglyphic Handbook*, The University of Pennsylvania Museum of Archaeology and Anthropology, Philadelphia, 1997.

[11] University of Texas Press, Austin, 1994

[12] Edmonson thought that the enemy were the Itza people.

[13] For a good overview of this work, see Bruce Love, *The Paris Codex, Handbook for a Mayan Priest*, University of Texas Press, Austin, 1994

[14] see Bruce Love, ibid., p. 89; Linda Schele, David Freidel and Joy Parker, *The Maya Cosmos*, Quill, William Morrow, NewYork, 1993, p. 361; and Susan Milbrath, *Star Gods of the Maya*, University of Texas Press, Austin, p. 188 for differing analyses

[15] Those further interested in Maya astronomy and time-keeping may wish to look in the direction of Linda Schele's *Mayan Cosmos*, Munro Edmonson's *Book of the Year*, Bruce Love's *The Paris Codex*, and Susan Milbrath's *Star Gods of the Maya*.

[16] John F. Harris and Stephen K. Stearns, ibid., p. 16-17

[17] John F. Harris and Stephen K. Stearns, Philadelphia, 1997

[18] an almost direct lift from, "Ice Cores May Yield Clues to 5,000 Year Old Mystery", Ohio State University press release, http://researchnews.ohio.edu/archive/quelcoro.htm

[19] Adapted to modern usage from the translation of E. A. Wallis Budge, *Legends of the Egyptian Gods*. Here Budge's notes and restorations are in parentheses, my own are in brackets.

[20] Linda Schele, David Freidel and Joy Parker, *The Maya Cosmos*, Quill, William Morrow, NewYork, 1993, p. 67

[21] "Teardrops on the Pampas", *Sky and Telescope*, April, 1992

[22] "Recent Grazing Impacts on the Earth Recorded in the Rio Cuarto Crater Field, Argentina", *Nature*, 16 January, 1992, cover and p. 234-237

[23] "A Possible Tektite Strewn Field in the Argentinian Pampa", *Science*, May 10, 2002, p. 1109-1111

[24] "Late Cenozoic Impact Record in the Argentine Pampas Sediments", *MAPS*, 2004; and "The Quartenary Impact Record from the Pampas, Argentina", Peter Schulz, Marcelo Zarate, Bill Hames, Christian Koebert, Theodore Bunch, Dieter Storzer, Paul Renne, Jams Wittke, *Earth and Planetary Science Letters*, v. 219, n. 3-4, 15 March 2004, p. 221-238

[25] Alfred Metraux , *Myths of the Toba and Pilaga Indians of the Gran Chaco*, American Folklore Society, Philadelphia , Pennsylvania, 1946

[26] A summary of the work in this region of William Penn, Clark Ericson, and Anna Roosevelt may be found in
"Earthmovers of the Amazon", *Science*, v. 287, 4 February 2000, p. 786-789 Work in this area involve ground survey and excavations on the headwaters of the Orinoco River, an area which today is largely under the control of cocaine traffickers.

[27] Munro S. Edmonson, *The Book of Chilam Balam of Chumayel: Heaven Born Merida and Its Destiny*, University of Texas Press, Austin, 1986, p. 120 et seq.

[28] I hope this clears everything up for you. I myself find it all confusing as hell. Since even the experts do not fully understand the Mayan calendar, and it takes anywhere from two to six months of dedicated study to even begin to acquire a mastery of its basic elements, and modern usage appears to differ from classical usage, if anyone tells you that the world is going to end precisely on December 21, 2012, it is highly likely that they are speaking about something which they do not know.

CHAPTER 7

AFTER THE FIRE

THE COPPER TRADING GIANTS MOVE SOUTH

After the impacts at Rio Cuarto ca. 2,360 BCE, the Copper Traders began to mine the copper deposits on the south shore of Lake Superior which were located on the Keweenaw Peninsula. There is no really good explanation available to explain this move to the south, and this being the case, I suppose that one is allowed to make a reasonable guess as to what occurred. Given the hostility of the earlier local peoples to the Copper Traders, my guess is that the local peoples were so weakened by the climatic effects of the Rio Cuarto blasts[1] that they were no longer able to resist the traders' advances. It may be that many were dead, with very few surviving the climatic effects of these impacts.

The Chautauqua Grounds site [2,210 BCE] across the Green Bay from the Door Peninsula likely represents this new accommodation with the local peoples.[2] From the shore, the Copper Trading Giants extended themselves along the Wisconsin River: their remains have been found at Reigh [1,660 BCE][3], and at Oceola [1,500 BCE][4], at the junction of the Wisconsin River with the Mississippi River.

They also appear to have opened two other far different routes to the south, one of which passed through the lakes to the west of Lake Superior and then down the upper Mississippi River, and the other of which passed via Chequamegon Bay and the St Croix River, to communicate with the St. Paul area. The remains of "giants" were found at today's St. Paul when the commandant's house was being constructed at Fort Snelling.[5]

Moving down the Mississippi River, the remains of giants were also found by early settlers at Prairie du Chien: "Mr. [Michael] Brisbois, who had been for a long time a resident of Prairie du Chien, informed me that he saw the skeletons of eight persons, that were found in digging a cellar near his house, lying side by side. They were of gigantic size, measuring about eight feet from head to toe. He remarked that he took a leg bone of one of them and placed it by the side of his own leg in order to compare the length of the two. The bone of the skeleton extended six inches above his knee."[6]

A HOCHUNK LEGEND OF THE COPPER TRADERS:
RED HORN KILLED BY THE GIANTS

Archaeologists Robert J. Salzer and Grace Rajnovich have done a great job in retrieving Paul Radin's recordings of the Hochunk (Winnebago) legends of the Giants[7] to explain an early Hochunk petroglyph which they have been excavating, and I highly recommend to you their book on *The Gottschall Rockshelter*. As the tale is too long to give in full here, the following has been extracted and adapted from Radin's recording of it.

"Now once again the people shouted, 'Some men are coming this way who are weeping!', so everyone went to the edge of the village to see them. The men came nearer and nearer, carrying a sacred pipe ahead of them. When the men got very near, they asked, 'Where does the chief live?' The people answered, 'In the middle of the village, in that long lodge there. This is one of the chief's friends.', they said, pointing to Turtle. ["Turtle" is likely emblematic of another people very closely allied with the Hochunk (Winnebago).] Then the suppliants went towards Turtle and directed the stem of the pipe towards his mouth. 'Ho! [Good!]', said he. They told him [Turtle] that Giants had come upon them, and they were coming to ask for his help against these Giants."

After Turtle and the villagers are defeated by the Giants, they go to ask aid from Red Horn, legendary leader of the Hochunk, and the two go off together to confront the Giants.

"The one who was helping the Giants the most was a giantess with red hair, just like Red Horn's hair. Turtle said to Red Horn, "My friend, this giantess has hair just like yours, and she is the one securing victory for her people, because she is a very fast runner. When they play ball, she does all the work. Coyote and Marten [again, probably emblematic of neighboring peoples[8]] are also married to giantesses, and these also greatly aid them."

A ball game with the Giants and Coyote and Marten follows, and Red Horn and Turtle win the game.

"Then said Turtle, 'My friends, something just occurred to me. This giantess has the same color hair as my friend Red Horn, and I think we ought to spare her life and let my friend here marry her.' 'Ho! [Good!]' they exclaimed, 'If that is your desire, then let it be as you wish.'

"Thereupon they gathered together all the Giants and placed them in four circles. [These "circles" may be the Giant's circular earthworks, or they may just be four concentric defensive circles.] Then they told the giantess that they had decided to spare her life, and she was very grateful."

A HOCHUNK MEMORY OF RIO CUARTO?

" Turtle then said, 'If kill all these at one time, we will never get through, as there are so many of them. I think we had better leave this to our friend, Storms-as-He-Walks.' Thus spoke Turtle. So Storms-as-He-Walks went towards the Giants with his club, and struck the first circle. Then it thundered, and the Thunderbirds above said, 'Storms-as-He-Walks is shooting! What can he be shooting at? He said that he liked the human beings.' Then again it thundered a second time. 'Ho-o-o! What can Storms-as-He-Walks be shooting at?', they asked a second time. Then a third and a fourth time it thundered, and the Thunderbirds said, 'Surely he has shot something.'

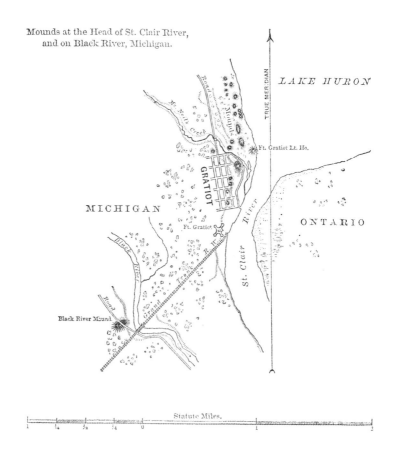

The Gratiot Works as mapped by Henry Gillman

As soon as these Giants had been killed [but not all of the Giants, as will be seen], the people left the place where the [ball] game had been played. They were living in the first village that had been attacked by the Giants. 'We are not being treated very well here, so let us go with you and live in your village.', they said. So they went home with the victors."

This "ball game" with the Giants is followed by a game of "who can shoot the farthest", a game of dice, and a game of "who can stay under water the longest" played with them. Last comes a game of wrestling, and Turtle and Red Horn are killed.

"Up to this time, they [Turtle and Red Horn] had been the only ones to play successfully. When they were killed, all those remaining in the village were also killed."

THE COPPER TRADING GIANTS' NEW ROUTE TO THE ATLANTIC OCEAN

Another phenomenon which may be related to the severe climatic effects of the Rio Cuarto impacts is that the Copper Traders added a new route between the copper deposits and the Atlantic Ocean. Again, given many of the southern peoples' hostility to them, it is likely that they were only able to adopt this route as a consequence of those peoples having been more than decimated by the climatic effects of the Rio Cuarto impacts.

Previously, the Copper Traders' range had been restricted to the areas north of the Great Lakes, and they had communicated with the Atlantic Ocean via the Saint Lawrence River. They now added a southern route, and it ran in the following manner.

Alpena, Michigan - Both the Haltimer Cache[9] and several other finds of copper artifacts have been made in the Alpena area, and can be viewed at the Jesse Besser Museum in Alpena. The Thunder Bay River's junction with Lake Huron appears to have been a favorite port of the Copper Traders.

Saginaw Bay – At the Feeheley site (1,980 BCE) burials with red ochre were found which contained copper celts, awls, beads and a gouge, and shell beads.[10] "Fifty years ago, (about 1880) I saw a mound that stood some 30 rods below on Water Street, Bay City. There was an area of about 1 ½ acres behind the mound where earth was removed to build it. At a depth of 11 ½ feet, 3 skeletons of a very large stature with large earthen pots at their heads, were found."[11]

The Saint Clair River – "In the year 1872 I made the discovery of one of the most remarkable and extensive series of tumuli [mounds] which are known to exist in this part of the lake region... I refer to the mounds situated at the head of the Saint Clair River, and which extend from a point south of Fort Gratiot for about one and one-half miles northward, along the west shore of the river and Lake Huron....The relics from the mounds, in addition to those usually found, consisted of an extraordinarily large number of broken stone hammers of the rudest kind;"[12] These hammers were identical to those found on Isle Royale[13], and polished stone tools were found[14] along with copper necklaces.

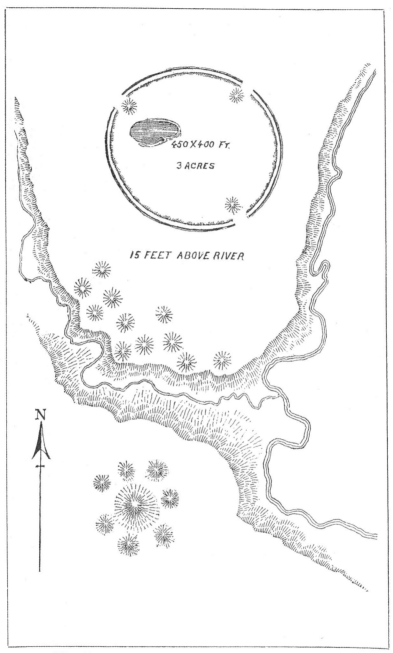

The Clinton River Works as mapped by Bela Hubbard

The Detroit River – "One of the most interesting works in this region, and which, till a few years ago, formed a member of a numerous series of mounds in the immediate vicinity, is the tumulus which I have named 'The Great Mound of the River Rouge'. This in many respects remarkable work is situated on the eastern bank of the Rouge River, a tributary of the Detroit [River], and near to the point of junction of the former with the latter river, or about four and a half miles from the city hall of Detroit...The size, shape, and well defined outlines of the monument could hardly fail to attract the attention of even the superficial observer, and impress him as to its being the work of man. With a height of 20 feet, it must originally have measured about 300 feet in length by 200 feet in width; but large quantities of sand have been removed from it from time to time, greatly reducing its proportions, and scattering or destroying a large number of interesting relics...The series of smaller mounds, extending from the great mound to the eastward, has long since been entirely removed; so has the greater number of other similar mounds which once stood immediately below the southwestern city limits...About three quarters of a mile to the north and eastward of the Great Rouge Mound, and only a few hundred feet westward of Fort Wayne, being over a third of a mile from the Detroit River, occurs the monument which I have named for distinction and from its originally circular shape 'The Great Circular Mound'. This also appears to have been one of a numerous series [of mounds], many of which have been removed for various purposes, but the present occupation of the land prevents a satisfactory examination of its character."[15] There was a ceremonial slip way which connected these mounds to the Detroit River: "In what was formerly Springwells Township, Wayne County, there was once a group of mounds, circular in form, with two parallel embankments about four feet in height leading eastward toward the Detroit River."[16]

Toledo, Ohio – The remains at Toledo appear to have been quickly lost during European settlement. One mound may survive in the Ottawa Park golf course.[17]

Sandusky, Ohio, 1876 – "Some time since, as will be remembered by the readers of the Register, a contractor from Cleveland employed a number of men and teams to fill up the trestle work of the Lake Shore and Michigan Southern railroad across Mill's Creek on the Castalia Road. In order to do this the contractor was obliged to procure considerable earth from places in that immediate vicinity, and as his eye fell upon this mound he concluded that he would level it off to correspond with the surrounding land. Accordingly he gave orders for his men to begin the work of grading the mound and hauling away the earth. His employees had only been engaged on the mound a short time when they found pieces of the skeletons of human beings.... At this point the work of grading the mound and removing the earth was discontinued...Judging from some of the bones which were found, it is thought that the persons they belonged to in life were almost giants in stature and strength.[18] - 1887: "Indian Skeletons Exhumed – On Saturday while some men were engaged in making excavations on the farm of Arden Storrs in Perkins [T]ownship they exhumed three complete skeletons of Indians, all in a fair state of preservation. At the head of one of them, supposed to have been that of a chief, was found a piece of pottery of queer design, the edges being ornamented in a rude but symmetrical manner, giving evidence of very skillful handiwork. The skull of this supposed chief was of extraordinary size. Some implements of war were also found near the skeletons."[19] – 1889: "On the

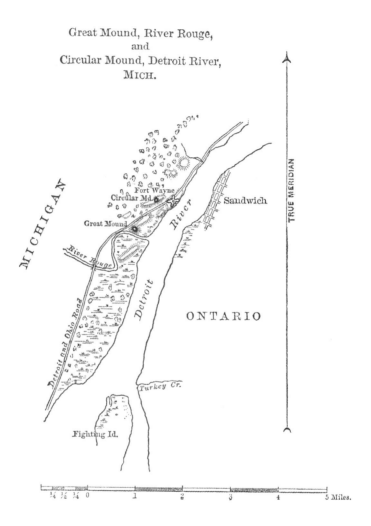

Great Mound, River Rouge,
and
Circular Mound, Detroit River,
MICH.

The Detroit River Works as mapped by Henry Gilman

highest points and some distance back from the creek banks, in fields of light, sandy soil, are found circular deposits of extremely black earth, varying in depth from one to three feet, in which are found skeletons of a 'race' – not Indians. [Though as was seen above, these remains did indeed belong to "Indians".] The skull is well developed, being full in the forehead, broad, with good height above the ears, and in all respects different from the Indians. The skeletons of adults are above the average size and some of them are gigantic. The writer, along with Dr. Charles Stroud and Mr. T.L. Williams, have dug up a number in different localities, and always, with one exception, with the same results."[20] - 1957: The skeleton of a man more than six feet, nearly seven feet in height was found near the Sunnyendland Mound at Pipe Creek Marsh.[21] The marsh was likely created by sediment choking an earlier harbor. - The Sandusky ring structure: "On Plum Brook, beginning at a point near where it empties into the marsh, is a line of mounds, or rather their remains, extending in almost a straight line to Bogart's Corners, crossing the creek in one instance, but always on the highest elevations. On one of them is a large ring, fifty feet in diameter, four feet wide, and being of black earth is plainly discernible on the yellow sandy soil. In this ring have been found several fine specimens, highly polished."[22] This last phrase is a reference to polished stone tools.

Cleveland – There were several mounds in the area of today's Cleveland at the time of European settlement, of which only the one at Woodland Cemetery survives. Most seem to have contained polished stone tools.[23] The largest of these was leveled at the time of the first settlement: "On Ontario Street, a little south of the old cemetery, was a large mound, supposed to be the work of the Mound Builders [this referred to the "giants"] of prehistoric times. It stood several years after we came, before it was made level with the surrounding earth."[24]

Ashtabula – "It was the most beautiful and lovely spot I ever beheld. It embraced some seven or eight acres; its east side was formed by the semi-circular bank of the creek, and the west by a curved embankment and ditch about twelve feet in depth. The character of the soil and timber of the exterior was totally different from that which comprised the interior. The soil outside was a hard unyielding yellow clay, covered with oak, white maple, and dwarf hemlock, with other scraggy underwood and green briers; while the soil here was the most beautiful and yielding imaginable, with a level surface as smooth as a palace walk. It was shaded by an irregular orchard, composed of black walnut, cherry, and mulberry, with no underbrush, and was overspread with a rich carpet of fine grass...In the vicinity of the village, opposite this plat of ground, in the direction of the east village, where now the white stones of the [Edgewood] cemetery may be seen, was another ancient place. It was a place of burial then as now. On the spot where lie the bodies of those who have died from the present race, there were also found the remains of bodies that belonged to a people who have passed away. The places of their graves were formerly indicated by hollows or sinks indented in the soil, and it is said that nearly a thousand of these were discovered in regular rows close together. In cultivating the soil in the vicinity implements have been found, and in excavating the ground for [modern] graves it is said that bones have been exhumed which seemed to have belonged to a race of giants. This land at one time belonged to Mr. Peleg Sweet, who was a man of large size and full features; and it is narrated that at one time he, in digging, came upon a skull and jaw which were of such size that the skull would cover his head, and the jaw could be easily slipped over his face, as though the head of the giant were enveloping his... On the west bank of the stream, a short distance from the lake [Erie], on the summit of Plum Point, has been discovered a massive mound or burial heap thirty-five feet in diameter and seven feet in height."[25] This last had a ready source of fresh water from Hubbard Run.

THE SHENANGO RIVER ROUTE

Conneaut, Pennsylvania – "There is on the bank opposite this work [a Native American fort], but further down the stream, a large burial mound,...This mound is beautifully situated on the very summit of the point of land where the river turns to the northward, and commands, as does the fort itself, an extensive view up and down the beautiful valley. The location of the mound was favorable for a lookout, and connected with defense. The defense itself might have served as a signal station, to warn against the approach of an enemy from the lake below... There were other small mounds in this neighborhood, though they are of comparatively small size. They were situated in the eastern part of the village[26].... "The mounds that were situated in the eastern part of what is now the village of Conneaut, and the extensive burying ground near the Presbyterian Church, appear to have had no connection with the burying places of the Indians. {Again, as is shown in this work, these were "Indians", just extremely tall and large ones.] They doubtless refer to a more remote period, and are the relics of an extinct race, of whom the Indians had no knowledge. [As is shown in this work, the truth is that our author simply had no knowledge of the Indians' knowledge of these people.] These mounds were of comparatively small size, and of the same general character of those that are widely scattered over the country... What is remarkable concerning them, is that among the quantity of human bones they contain, there are found specimens belonging to me of large stature, and who must have been nearly allied to a race of giants.... The ancient burying ground referred to, situated a little west of the site of where the brick [Presbyterian] Church now stands, presents an object of deeper interest perhaps than any other relic remaining in the neighborhood. It occupied an area of about four acres of land, extending northward from the bank of the creek near the brick church, to Main Street, and westward to the present residence of Mr. Horatio Thurber, and presenting, with the exception of an angle in the south line in compliance with the course of the [creek's] bank, the form of an oblong square. It appeared to have been accurately surveyed into lots running from north to south, and exhibited all the order and propriety of arrangement deemed requisite to constitute Christian burial[27]... The graves, disposed in straight rows with intervening spaces and alleys, covered the whole area, and were estimated to have been two or three thousand in number. They were examined as early as 1800, and were found to contain human bones, some of which were of large size...[28]   Aaron Wright, who examined both the graves and the mounds around 1800, wrote that the graves contained charcoal, earthenware, and human bones, "some of which were of a large size." "Skulls", Wright wrote," were taken from the mounds, the cavities of which were sufficient to admit the head of an ordinary man, and jawbones that might be fitted over the face with equal facility. The bones of the upper and lower extremities were of corresponding size."[29]

Springfield, Pennsylvania – "There are also remains of an Indian fort between Girard and Springfield. From a grave in this vicinity, some years ago, a thigh bone was exhumed which measured four inches longer than that of a man with which it was compared."[30]

Cranesville, Pennsylvania – "An ancient fortification, inclosing about two acres, upon the Pomeroy farm, a mile or two northwest of Cranesville, has been pretty much farmed over. On the top of the bank, in 1830, oak trees four or five feet in diameter were growing. [This was an early technique for estimating age, but the artifacts spoken of here are far earlier.] Skinning stones, arrow heads, an enormous skeleton and many other relics were found within the fort. A bed of coals a foot and a half below the surface appeared to be the remains of the fire of the occupants.[31] [Most likely the remains of cremations are being described.]

Pymatuning, Pennsylvania – "The fish in the stream, the wild animals in the forest, the fruits of the wildwood, consisting of chestnuts and hickory nuts growing upon the hillside, the cranberry and blueberry in the swamps, furnished food in abundance for the inhabitants, while the scenery around was pleasing to the eye, and yet the location was a safe one for defense....Professor M.C. Reed, Assistant State Geologist, mentions the fact that there is a mound on this stream, north of these works, which he designates either as a burial mound or a lookout mound....[32] "The works" south of this mound was a small circular earthwork: "One of the most interesting prehistoric inclosures in Ohio is in Wayne Township, Ashtabula County, on the west bank of the Pymatuning River. It is in the form of a circular earthwork encircled by a horseshoe shaped wall with an outer ditch. This earthwork is about two hundred feet from the banks of the Pymatuning... The north and south diameter, measured from the crests of the outer walls, is 294 feet."[33]

Greenville, Pennsylvania - "It has always been believed that a mound which formerly stood between the two Shenangos, within the borough of Greenville, was a prehistoric earthwork. The elevation, which measured some seventy-five feet in diameter across the base and twenty feet in height, was graded down some three or four years ago by Mr. Packard. The round condition of the pebbles still remaining in the base, and the general structure of the valley about it, would seem to indicate to the geologist that the foundation of the mound, at least, was produced by the action of the water from the two streams forming an eddy, rather than by the dusky tribes, though the latter may have built an earthwork upon this foundation in ages long ago."[34]

THE VENANGO RIVER OIL FIELDS

There is no question that the Copper Trading Giants used the Shenango River to travel south to the Ohio River, and not the Venango [French Broad] River further to the east.[35] Still, one finds mentions of the earlier existence of their remains at Erie, Pennsylvania, at their portage from Lake Erie to the Venango River, and even further east, in the far southwest of today's state of New York. My guess is that even though the Five Nations tolerated their presence, as the Copper Trading Giants used Onondaga chert to make some of their tools, relations between the two peoples were "uneasy" during these times.

126

Given the Copper Trading Giants' goal of reaching the Atlantic Ocean, and the ready availability of suitable places to live along that route, places far warmer than the shores of Lake Erie, why did they settle so far to the east along the lake? The answer may have been oil. Oil was available from surface seeps in western Pennsylvania; in recent centuries, these same oil deposits gave birth to the United States' oil industry. While oil can be placed in clay pots and fired to make them more waterproof, and can be used as a lubricant and as a medicine, it is the tar that held the real value for ancient peoples. The tar was used for shipbuilding, both for caulking and as a hull and rope preservative. While it is interesting to note the ancient Egyptians' use of tar to manufacture their mummies, and the finding of tobacco[36] in the drugs with which these mummies were packed, tar's ordinary industrial use was sufficient enough to give it a great value, comparable to that of copper itself.

Erie, Pennsylvania – "An ancient graveyard was discovered in 1820, on the land now known as the Drs. Carter and Dickinson places in Erie, which created quite a sensation at the time. Dr. Albert Thayer dug up some of the bones, and all indicated a race of beings of immense size."[37] – a laborer's report: "At a later date [after the construction of the link connecting the Erie and Pennsylvania railroad with the dock], when the roadway of the Philadelphia and Erie road, where it passes at the Warfel farm, was being widened, another deposit of bones was dug up and summarily disposed of as before [thrown into an embankment further along]. Amongst the skeletons was one of a giant, side by side with a smaller one, probably that of his wife. The arm and leg bones of this [N]ative American Goliath were about one-half longer than those of the tallest man among the laborers; the skull was immensely large; the lower jawbone easily slipped over the face and whiskers of a full faced man, and the teeth were in a perfect state of preservation."[38] – "In Scouler's woods, east of Erie, is an Indian burying ground. Mr. Frederick Zimmerman described a very large skeleton which was found there; with it were two copper bowls perforated at the edges and laced together with a buckskin thong, which fell to dust soon after being exposed to the air. The bowls, which would contain about a pint each, were found filled with beads."[39] These last items were probably leg rattles.

Titusville – "A short distance from Titusville in this county, and on the west side of Oil Creek, there are perhaps 2,000 pits, scattered over a level plain not exceeding 500 acres. Some of these pits are very close together, as close as the vats in a tan yard, which they somewhat resemble, each having been about seven or eight feet long, four wide, and six deep. [In their layout the oil field works somewhat resemble the graveyards found along Lake Erie.] These pits or vats had nearly all been filled, some of them entirely so, by vegetable deposit, perhaps the accumulation of ages. The mounds raised at the side of each pit by excavation of the earth from it are distinctly visible... Another thing affording an index to the time when these vats may have been made, is the fact that the inhabitants now in their vicinity first discovered the pits from their regularity in size, and the order of their location, and the indentation of the surface and the general appearance of the mounds [of dirt next to them from their excavation]; they were induced to open them. On doing so they discovered that each pit was of the size mentioned before, and walled with logs regularly cut and halved at the ends so that they could lie close together, thus preventing the caving in of the earth. [These cribs imply fairly good wood-working tools and skills.]....On visiting the pits a day or two after excavation, it was ascertained that the water in them was covered with oil to a depth of one-third to one-half an inch...".[40]

Cattaraugus River – The Cattaraugus River seems to have formed the eastern limit of the Copper Trading Giants' extent along Lake Erie, and their outposts here most likely guarded their oil works from the peoples of the Five Nations. Local historian Mason C. Winfield has looked at the early settlers' accounts of their discovery of the remains of Giants in this area, and has written the following account -   "T. Apoleon Cheney notes (in *Illustrations of the Ancient Monuments of Western New York*) that a twelve-foot high elliptical mound above Cattaraugus County's Conewango Valley held eight big skeletons. Most crumbled, but a thigh bone was found to be 28" long. Exquisite stone points, enamelwork, and jewelry (like that of Mexico or Peru) were also unearthed in the area. The mound looked like those of the Old World. Cheney also mentions a skeleton seven-foot-five (with an unusually thick skull) from a Chautauqua County site near Cassadaga Creek... Inside a very old mound near Cassadaga Lake were some large skeletons that were examined by medical gentlemen." One measured nearly nine feet. (In 1938 Charles Hunnington of Randolph was so inspired by Doc Cheney's finds that he made two giant "wooden Indian" statues, probably still at the museum in Little Valley.)...The *History of Cattaraugus County* notes the town of Carrollton's "Fort Limestone," whose rough figure-eight enclosed five acres. In 1851 the removal of a stump turned up a mass of human bones. Some were enormous. Franklinville's Marvin Older virtually gamboled about the site with them: a skull fit over his size seven-and-a-half head; a rib curved all the way around him, a shinbone went from his ankle to above his knee, and a jaw - with bodacious molars - went over his own. Its first owner had probably stood eight feet tall...Stafford Cleveland's *History and Directory of Yates County* refers to skeletons from a conical burial mound by Keuka Lake in the early 1800's. A Penn Yan doctor found that many were seven footers. (Tales of ghosts and buried treasure cling to this vicinity as well.)...Turner's *History of the Holland Purchase* reports an ancient three-acre earth fort in Orleans county (about one and a half miles west of Shelby Center) that covered seven- and eight-foot skeletons. Their skulls were well developed in front, broad between the ears, and flattened on top. Also, Turner notes that, upon digging a cellar on his town of Aurora farm, Charles P. Pierson found a giant of his own...The 1879 *History of Allegany County* noted a circular mound between Philip's Creek and the Genesee in the village of Belmont. Several feet high and fifteen or so in diameter, it disgorged human bones, some very large, when the railroad was made in 1849 and 1850."[41]

THE PITTSBURGH AREA

Pittsburgh, where the Venango-Allegheny River meets with the Ohio River, and just upstream from the junction of the Shenango-Coniango [Beaver] River with the Ohio, was a major center for the Copper Trading Giants, as it had been for the very first paleolithic hunters to arrive in the region, and would continue to be for all who would follow. There were so many of the Giants' remains found in this area that it is difficult to decide where to start with a description of them, but a graveyard at Pittsburgh similar to those found at Conneaut and Ashtabula seems as good a place as any.

McKee's Rock Mound

"Within the last few weeks quite a number of human skeletons, some of them in a tolerably fair state of preservation have been dug up from the old Indian burying ground in the Ninth Ward (present Sixth Ward). In the old history of this neighborhood, and when the red man had almost exclusive control of west of the mountains, that portion of the Ninth Ward lying in the vicinity [direction] of the Lake Superior copper works was a favorite burial ground with the Indian tribes. [Note the mention of copper here.] The tract so used extends over an area of several acres and appears to be thickly underlaid with human remains... In sinking the foundations and manufacturing establishments lately erected in this neighborhood, a large number of human bones [and] skulls were discovered, but the only perfect skeletons yet found were those disinterred while the foundations of Park and Brothers new steel works were being excavated. At a point here near the river bank, two skeletons were discovered, one of which appeared to be that of an Indian chief, and the other that of a young girl, who was perhaps the warrior's daughter. The man, judging from his remains, must have been of herculean proportions... [The girl's burial held European contact period goods.]...Some thirty feet away from the remains mentioned, were found skeletons of a warrior standing erect with face towards the Allegheny [River]. The size of the bones indicated that the man had been of immense proportions...."[42]

There were many mounds in the Pittsburgh area, those at Grant's Hill, Burgwin Park, and the Puckety Road mound[43] among them, but the most well known mound was that at McKee's Rock, excavated in 1887 and 1896. As might be expected, when this mound was excavated, it was found to contain skeletons of giants: "The next day another (skeleton) was taken out – that of a man 6 feet 4 inches in height."...."The skeleton indicated a woman of good size... The bones of the male skeleton were much decayed. They revealed that they were the framework of a large man."..."In life, this man measured seven feet in height."... "The skeleton was in the roots of a tree, and indicated a man of extraordinary size."[44]

A complete list of some of the larger enclosures which existed to the south of Pittsburgh, in a band stretching from the Yeogehenny River to the Ohio River at the time of European contact, may be found in Judge James Veech's *The Monongahela of Old*[45]. Unfortunately, it is impossible to know whether these were constructed by the Copper Trading Giants or by later inhabitants of the area.[46] However, Veech also mentions stone graves which may with certainty be ascribed to them: "Piles of stones, called Indian Graves, were numerous in many places in Fayette (County), generally near the sites of Indian villages. They were generally on stony ridges, often twenty or thirty of them in a row. In many of them have been found human bones indicating a stature of from six to seven feet."[47]

One site of particular importance to the Copper Trading Giants seems to have been around the area of today's Brownsville on the Monongahela River, which was known to the European colonists as "Redstone Old Fort". Sulfur leaching from coal deposits gave Redstone Creek its distinctive color, and there were excellent coal deposits nearby at Coal Creek which most likely provided the "canal coal" which this people worked into small pieces of artwork and jewelry. A nearby land route to the south, later known as the "Catawba Trail", may have served as a land route to the north for these river traders – by using it, there was no need for them to fight the Ohio River's current on

The remains at Moundsville, West Virginia

their return trip north. While it is difficult to sort out the European records which were made during the confusion of the inappropriately named "French and Indian" Wars, there appears to have been a burial mound at the site of today's Nemacolin's Castle, and a small ring structure located at the cemetery situated on the hill above it.[48]

INGOTS FOR THE COPPER TRADE AND THE FIRST GORGETS

At this point along the Copper Trading Giants' route to the Atlantic Ocean, the number of large copper tools which have been found drops off. It has long been noted that beaten copper tools which have been tempered in a fire will not hold their edge as long as stone tools, and many have even wondered why Native Americans ever used copper for their tools. Tthe precision of the copper tool's cut is seldom considered in these ruminations.

It has also been speculated that the number of large copper tools should drop off the further one gets from the copper sources of Lake Superior. This later speculation ignores the increasing number of rectangular copper "gorgets" which are now found along the route to the Atlantic Ocean. Interestingly, some of these early rectangular "gorgets" have no holes through which strings could be passed in order to suspend them. Given the inefficiencies of copper tools, and the increasing value of copper in trade as it neared the ocean, perhaps when copper tools reached this area they were beaten into ingots for the copper trade: perhaps instead of being "gorgets", these copper plates without holes were ingots for the copper trade.

Ingots such as these were discovered near Pittsburgh: "Local traditions and an early manuscript (Schooley, n.d.) relate that a large earth mound once stood at the mouth of Peters Creek in Allegheny County, Pennsylvania, a spot which is now completely covered by the Clairton Works of the United States Steel Company. Two copper plates reported to have come from an 1890 excavation are illustrated on [fig.].
The excavation, as described by Schooley, indicates that a primary mound covered with a layer of ashes contained at least two burials accompanied by three stone celts, one [stone?] axe, 28 large and 60 small shell beads, a stone cone, two areas of red ochre each containing a copper plate, a perforated jaw of a bear, two bear canines, one of which was sheathed in copper, a copper sheath for a canine tooth, and three pieces of folded copper. The primary mound was covered by with clay to make a mound originally about 8 feet high and 40 feet in diameter."[49]

What seems to have happened was that these copper ingots were later pierced so that they could be worn suspended from the neck as a sign of wealth and power. As time progressed, these valuable rectangular copper badges of office were later emulated by rectangular polished stone emblems worn in the same way, thus giving rise to the "gorgets", as they are known today.

THE OHIO RIVER

Grave Creek Mounds - "Near Wheeling in Virginia, on Grave Creek on the lands of Mr. Tomlins, is one mound of a conical form, 75 feet high. In the interior of this mound human bones were found of uncommonly large size. [Our source, Haywood,

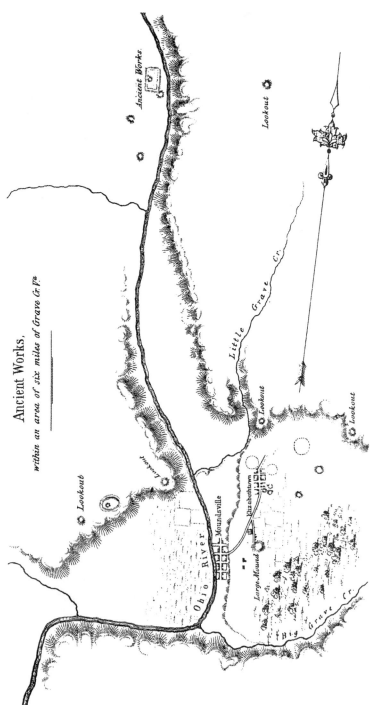

Henry Schoolcraft's map of the Moundsville works. Note the observatory on the ridge between the "Lookouts". A trade path to the east ran along Big Grave Creek.

was mistaken here, as the main mound was not opened until later.] The mounds are a mile and a half from the Ohio [River]. Here also were found mixed with bones two or three plates of brass, with characters inscribed upon them resembling letters, but of what alphabet no one could tell."[50].... "In one of the tumuli on Grave Creek below Wheeling, near to the Ohio, were found about 20 years since {ca. 1802 CE] sixty copper beads, made of a coarse wire hammered out and not drawn and cut off at unequal lengths. They were soldered together in an awkward manner, the center of some of them uniting with the edges of others. They were incrusted with verdigris, but the inside of them was pure copper.[51]

As elsewhere, these mounds were accompanied by a small circular structure built on a nearby overlook, and Henry Rowe Schoolcraft mentioned it: "Three miles back from the Grave Creek mound, [is] a rude tower of stone standing on an elevated point, which commands a view of the whole plain, and which appears to have been constructed as a watch tower, or lookout, from which to descry an approaching enemy,... About six or seven feet of the wall is still entire. It is circular, and composed of rough stones, laid without mortar or the mark of a hammer. A heavy mass of fallen wall lies around, covering an area of some forty feet in diameter. Two similar points of observation occupied by dilapidated towers, are [on the near-by river hills.]"[52]

Marietta, Ohio - Dr. S. P. Hildreth described various relics found by Governor R. J. Meigs in a 10 foot high, 30 foot diameter mound at Marietta in 1819.[53] "Lying immediately over, or on the forehead of the body, were found three large circular bosses, or ornaments for a sword belt, or a buckler; they are composed of copper overlaid with a thick plate of silver ... Two small pieces of the leather were found lying between the plates of one of the bosses; they resemble the skin of an old mummy." [Hildreth was right about the mummy skin. These bosses were later identified by F.W. Putnam[54] as being earspools. The source of the silver which Hildreth reported could only have been inclusions in copper from Isle Royale. There was no other source.] "... Around the rivet of one of them is a small quantity of flax or hemp. Near the side of the body was found a plate of silver which appears to have been the upper part of a sword scabbard; it is six inches in length and two inches in breadth, and weighs one ounce; it has no ornaments or figures, but has three longitudinal ridges. ... It seems to have been fastened to the scabbard by three or four rivets, the holes of which yet remain in the silver." [This appears to be a somewhat optimistic description of what is unusually thought of today as being an "Adena" tablet.] "...Two or three broken pieces of a copper tube, were also found, filled with iron rust [red ochre or rusted meteorite]. These pieces, from their appearance, composed the lower end of the scabbard near the point of the sword. No sign of the sword itself was discovered, except the appearance of rust above mentioned....Near the feet was found a piece of copper two inches and a half in length, an inch in diameter at the center, and half an inch at each end. It had probably been used as a plummet, or an ornament, as near one of the ends there was a crease, or groove for tying a thread. A piece of red ochre, or paint, and a piece of iron ore, which had the appearance of being partially vitrified, or melted, were also found. The ore had about the same specific gravity as pure iron." [This use of iron oxide is a distinguishing feature of the Red Paint and Red Ochre peoples.]

The mound at Marietta. Note the ditch which encircles it. A rectangular enclosure also survives nearby.

Remains at Buffington Island

The Remains at South Charleston

As elsewhere, the Marietta works were accompanied by stone graves built on nearby overlooks: "On the hills overlooking the works at Portsmouth and Marietta mounds of stone are situated."[55] The Marietta works also featured what appears to have been a ceremonial slipway, parallel banks extending to the river, as was seen at Detroit [above] and at Grave Creek.[56]

THE KANAWA RIVER

Charleston, West Virginia - There were multiple large mounds located on the Kanawa River at today's city of Charleston, West Virginia, and as may be expected, they contained the remains of "giants". Thomas mentions "a mound near Charleston, West Virginia, conical in form, about 175 feet in diameter at the base and 35 feet high. It consists of two mounds, one built on the other, the lower or original one 20 feet, and the upper 15 feet high. Near the top was a stone vault 7 feet long and 4 feet deep, in the bottom of which was found a large and much decayed skeleton, but wanting the head, which the most careful examination failed to discover. At a depth of six feet was another skeleton, and at nine feet a third...Below this were the remains of a timber vault about 12 feet square and 7 or 8 feet high. Some of the walnut timbers of this vault were 12 inches in diameter. A skeleton found lying on the floor in the middle of this vault, 19 feet below the top of the mound, measured 7 feet 6 inches in length, and 19 inches between the shoulder sockets. There were four other skeletons in this vault, which, from the positions in which they were found, were supposed to have been placed standing in the four corners. The relics found are entirely similar to those of Ohio mounds."[57]

Bishop Madison of Virginia, a very early visitor to the Charleston remains, noted that the mounds there, most of which were from ten to twenty five feet in height, were connected in a direct line to the openings of nearby small ring structures.[58]

THE SMALL RING STRUCTURES

To say the least, it is always difficult to make any kind of comment on structures which no longer exist; and the task becomes even more difficult when the areas in which the structures were located were later occupied at many different times by many different peoples. With that proviso, it is interesting to note that the Copper Trading Giants central burial mounds were often accompanied by small "circular" enclosures, enclosures whose size and location made them completely unsuitable for use as forts. Given these facts, it could be offered with some degree of certainty that the most likely use of these enclosures was to demark ritual meeting places, locations where the surrounding peoples might meet at certain times of the year.

As a further consideration along these lines, meetings held at certain times of the year entail a certain knowledge of the passage of time, which is to say, a certain astronomical knowledge. For example, the later Hopewell Hopewell circular structures have been shown by analysis to be astronomically oriented; in contrast, there is no evidence (at least no evidence that I am aware of) for earlier circular structures designed for astronomical use in the southern regions of North America. Thus the possibility presents itself that these enclosures of the Copper Trading Giants may have played a similar role as the later circular enclosures of the Hopewell. That a maritime trading people would find astronomy to be of use in navigating is a given, and that they may have passed on this knowledge through group ritual is certainly possible. This said, I suppose, given the state of the sites which exists today, any thoughts along these lines will have to remain the slimmest of conjectures....

THE ROANOKE RIVER TO THE ATLANTIC OCEAN

Traveling up the Kanawa River and the New River, it is an easy ford at today's town of Blacksburg to the Roanoke River, and then down the Roanoke River to Albemarle Sound and the Atlantic Ocean. While no mounds remain in the Blacksburg area today, they were there at the time of European settlement: "Mounds are very frequent in that neighborhood, and many curious articles of antiquity have been found there."[59] Not only did the first European settlers in the area open the mounds to retrieve these "curious articles", it appears that they destroyed the mounds as soon as possible to discourage Native American peoples from returning to visit them. Thus while early ceremonial centers have not been found yet along the Roanoke River, the polished stone tools which the Copper Trading Giants used to construct their dugout canoes have been found in profusion along its banks.[60]

Reaching the mouth of the Roanoke River, the traders traveled along Albemarle Sound, which is separated from the Atlantic Ocean by the sand bank of the Carolina Banks. The soapstone for the soapstone bowls of the Stallings Island peoples, who lived further to the south along the Atlantic Coast, came from Galax[61], near the source of the Roanoke River, and the site at Ridgeway along this river's course.[62] This was two-way trade, as fiber-tempered pottery from Stallings Island has shown up at the headwaters of the Roanoke River.[63]

How did the copper get to Europe from this point? No one knows right now, and the likely reasons for this will be set out in some detail in Chapter 8.

EVENTS ALONG THE MISSISSIPPI RIVER:
THE SECOND GENERATION OF RIVER SOCIETIES:
THE CLAN SYSTEM AND POVERTY POINT

Leaving behind our Copper Trading Giants in peace in their new homes for the time being, let us return to the other peoples who were living to the south along the Mississippi River, and their development. In human social groups a method must be found to prevent interbreeding and genetic defect, and one method of doing this is by a matrilineal clan system, wherein marriage with members of the mother's clan is forbidden. At the Poverty Point site, built around 1,730 BCE just downriver from the Watson Break site, we see evidence of a clan system which was extended far beyond the immediate area, and which enabled their peaceful contact with other groups of humans over a geographic area spanning thousands of miles.[64]

The Poverty Point site is composed of 6 half rings facing the river, with each ring further divided into 6 segments. It was first thought that these rings were defensive structures, and then observatories; but excavation has shown that they are simply the bases for houses. As the nearby Poverty Point area would not be sufficient to support the permanent year round occupation of a population of the size indicated by the house remains, it is clear that this structure was used for periodic, and most likely annual, meetings. The presence of clearly ceremonial mounds at Poverty Point, as well as the recovery of tokens showing participation in ceremonies, indicate this as well.

The social system indicated by these remains then is that the people of each nearby area, whose ritual area at Poverty Point comprised 6 ring segments, organized themselves into 6 clans. Dozens of major sites are located within a 25-mile radius of the Poverty Point ceremonial center, and Poverty Point type ceremonial centers were surrounded by villages and seasonal camps, which varied in size from 1 to 100 acres.

This culture spread. Sites have been found at Jaketown, on what was then the eastern branch of the Mississippi River, and near its mouth at Cedarland and Claiborne. Immediately to the west of Poverty Point, sites have been found on the Ouachita River and the Vermillion River. This clan system had implications for trade, as a member of any one clan who visited another village would be certain to find there a member of his clan who would help him. That the clan system enabled trade is shown by the fact that items from the modern states of Michigan, Illinois, Indiana, Ohio, Arkansas, Mississippi, and Alabama have all been found at Poverty Point.

An obvious flaw in the determination of how far Poverty Point culture spread is in the analysis of its trading network. The source of crystal quartz found at Poverty Point has not been identified, but it almost certainly comes from Mitchell County, North Carolina. It has also been assumed that all Native American copper found at Poverty Point comes from the Upper Peninsula of Michigan, without any spectral tests being performed on it. Copperhill, Tennessee, near to the North Carolina quartz source, is an obvious candidate, and based on far later remains, it is probably the most likely one. Again, without spectral tests, it has been assumed that the source for the galena lead mineral found at Poverty Point is in Wisconsin, while colonial records show a lead mine on the Wabash River in Ohio, near the junction of the Tennessee River with the Ohio River.[65]

THE THUNDERBIRD CULT AT POVERTY POINT:
THE THUNDERBIRD, THE HORNED SNAKE,
AND THE CLIMATE COLLAPSE OF 1628 BCE

An enormous mound at Poverty Point as well as a smaller one are both shaped like birds. These works without question reflect the northern Native American cosmological theories of "thunderbirds" and "snakes" (comets), which were described in Chapter 3. That both of these "thunderbird" mounds were also aligned to the solstices is a further indication of their astronomical function.

Why did the people of Poverty Point put so much effort into the construction of a huge "thunderbird" mound during these times? Undoubtedly their intense effort is tied to the appearance of Comet Encke in 1628 BCE. The dust load from Comet Encke combined with the dust load from the eruption of Thera to produce another severe climate collapse [66]; further, the earlier Rio Cuarto impact event and its ensuing climatic collapse must have been so intense that they were remembered over 700 years later.

Many scientists have commented on the odd use in the movies "Deep Impact" and "Armageddon" of astronauts to stop impactors, which is beyond the bounds of credence. But as seen at Poverty Point, this use of human protectors has very ancient precedents. Naturally, these ancient people did not want to feel unprotected against impact and lightning, and they needed a method to invoke the help of the "thunderbirds": this was accomplished by their priest-kings emulating the thunderbirds to the extent possible.[67] While no burials have been discovered to date at Poverty Point, less than 1% of the site has been excavated, and based on later cultural remains, it is clear that an early form of these priest-kings were functioning here on these fairly massive "thunderbird" mounds.

Contact era reports show astronomical lore being passed down through dances; for that matter, thunderbird dances are often a part of today's Native American festivals, and can often be seen by attending one. The image of some of the archeao-astronomers who I have met hoofing their way through these numbers always brings a smile to my face.

THE POVERTY POINT TRADE SYSTEM:
INTOXICANTS AND PHARMACEUTICALS

One of the continuing mysteries for the excavators of Poverty Point is why trade routes evolved as they did. This is not surprising, as to my knowledge nowhere in published North American anthropological theory is any account made for Native American trade in intoxicants and pharmaceuticals. That modern intoxicants and pharmaceuticals have extreme value is evident, as their modern prices commonly exceed the price of gold. The only intoxicants that are allowed discussion are the "black drink" and tobacco, which is probably more reflective of the current use of coffee and cigarettes by Americans than of anything else. It is always assumed that pipes are used to smoke tobacco only, and pipes are never checked for residue oils from other organic materials.

That Central American peoples used psylocibin has been established beyond doubt. Whether the use of these mushrooms spread is an open question. Different species of psylocibin also grow along the rivers in the southern United States which lead into the Gulf Coast, and while I have no detailed knowledge of the exact native ranges of these mushrooms today, I suspect that some occupation centers must have been situated in the dead center of those ranges. It must also be noted that these mushrooms are very sensitive to climate and surrounding vegetation, and that both were much different then than now.

Other Native American peoples made use of bufotonin derived from frog skins, both as an intoxicant and as a paralyzing poison for tipping blowgun darts. The frog motif is very common in Native American artifacts in this area, and modern use of frogs for intoxication ("toad licking") has been reported in recent times in the Barbeque Zone.

I had been under the impression that hemp, and thus marijuana, was an import from the Old World, but I have read scattered reports that it also occurred in North America as a native species. I do not know whether "Indian Hemp", *apocynum cannabium*, is of the same family, or if it is intoxicating; while I have no further interest, perhaps some readers may want to investigate this privately on their own.

As psylocibin, bufotonin, and marijuana can all be smoked, any claim without proof that pipes were solely used to smoke tobacco only has to be held suspect. Even then it is necessary to remember a key fact, that the variety of tobacco used by these peoples was much different than the variety of tobacco used today, and that in point of fact this variety had narcotic properties.

In historical times the Caddo area of Texas was a Native American trading center for mescal beans, which despite their name are not related to the peyote (mescaline) cactus, but rather to the beans. At a later time the use of daturas was fairly widespread among Native American peoples. They were usually used in a yearly festival known as the huskinaw, pushk, or busk, in which the young men of a tribe were "initiated" by the ingestion of massive amounts of this extraordinarily powerful hallucinogen. Hallucinations lasting weeks were common. You will often see these daturas identified as "snake roots" of one sort or another, as at low doses Native American peoples used them as antihistamines to block the effects of the venom of poisonous snakes.

That the religious use of intoxicants was overseen by the same individuals who treated disease is almost assured.

SALT

Another trade good which North American anthropologists are just beginning to track is salt. There are few mappings of the areas of natural salt deposits, and very little has been done in studying the development or use of those salt production methods which were documented at the time of European contact.

THE FIRST "POTTERY" AND "OVENS"

While paleo hunters wove baskets whose light weight allowed the storage of items for carriage, "pottery" first appears at Poverty Point. The remains of woven baskets covered with mud and then baked have been found there, as well as baked mud vessels tempered with moss. These containers must have been used for dry storage only, as it has been experimentally shown that it is impossible to cook in these vessels. It seems probable to me that this fiber-tempered pottery reflects an origin in the Amazon.

While it had been thought that the Poverty Point people cooked their food by throwing heated clay balls into these pots, it has been shown experimentally that this technique does not work. Instead the people of Poverty Point used these clay balls to cook some of their foods by throwing them into a fire, and then stirring the fire to let the ashes fall to its bottom, leaving the balls as a clean cooking surface.

CYCLIC CLIMATE COLLAPSE AND THE EARLY WOODLAND CULTURES

It is currently estimated that the Poverty Point ceremonial center was abandoned around 1350 BCE, and that the other Poverty Point type centers elsewhere were also abandoned at about the same time. This period is roughly the time of the Late Bronze Age migrations in Europe, and perhaps climate was at work in North America as well, but determining this will require a more exact dating of the remains than is currently available.

Unlike Europe and China, where migration is roughly from north to south, in North America the migration pattern is not as clear. What emerges during this collapse are more widely dispersed villages of the Early Woodland type, spreading to the Atlantic coast and well up into the valley of the Ohio River. It is certain that in some areas merely the culture changed, with the ethnic group remaining the same, but in at least one case there was clearly migration.

(Footnotes)

[1] Chapter 6 here

[2] Susan R. Martin, *Wonderful Power*, Wayne State University Press, Detroit, Michigan, 1999, p. 157, citing Robert Ritzenhaler, "The Osceola Site, an Old Copper sit near Potosi, Wisconsin", *Wisconsin Archaeologist*, v.38 n.4, 1975, p.186-203

[3] Martin, ibid., p. 159-160, citing Robert Ritzenhaler, "Reigh Site Report", *Wisconsin Archaeologist*, v.38 n.4, 1957, p.278-310

[4] Martin, ibid., p. 157-158, citing Robert Ritzenhaler, ibid., , p.186-203

[5] Heny Snelling, Memories of a Boyhood at Fort Snelling, via Stephen Osma, via David Wiggins, personal communication

[6] Robert J. Salzer and Grace Rajnovich, *The Gottschall Rockshelter*, Prairie Smoke Press, St. Paul, Minnesota, 2001, p. 67, citing Lucille M. Kane, June D. Holmquist, and Caroline Gilman, editors, *The Northern Expeditions of Stephen H. Long*, Minnesota Historical Society, St. Paul, Minnesota, 1978. .

[7] Paul Radin, *Winnebago Hero Cycles*, Indiana University Publications in Anthropology, Waverly Press, Baltimore, 1948. My placing of the Hochunk legend here differs from the placement put forth by Salzer and Rajnovich – one item of their data supporting their placement has been mentioned in Chapter 5 here, and another will be further examined in Chapter 15. Despite this difference, I still highly recommend their book.

[8] Making some guesses, Turtle=Menomini, Coyote=Dakota, Marten=northern people to the west of Lake Superior

[9] Lewis Binford, "The Haltiner Copper Cache", *Michigan Archaeologist*, v.7 n.2, p. 7-10, 1961

[10] James A. Robertson, William A. Lovis, John R. Halsey, "The Late Archaic", in *Retrieving Michigan's Past*, Cranbrook Institute of Science, Bloomfield Hills, Michigan, 1999, p. 116, citing Robert N. Converse, *The Glacial Kame Indians*, Archaeological Society of Ohio, Worthington, Ohio, 1980, p. 126-127, and James E. Fitting, *The Archaeology of Michigan*, Bulletin n. 56, Cranbrook Institute of Science, Bloomfield Hills, Michigan, 1975, p. 82

[11] W.R. McCormick, *History of the Lake Huron Shore*, H.R. Page and Co., 1877, p. 32-33

[12] Henry Gillman, *The Mound Builders and Platycnemism in Michigan*, Smithsonian Report for 1873, Washington, Government Printing Office; Gillman's hand corrected copy of

1877 reprint, Detroit Public Library, p. 371-372. It appears that Gillman was attempting to use platycnemism, flattening of the tibia, to prove that the mounds had been built by an earlier form of man as he evolved.

[13] Gillman, ibid., p. 385

[14] Gillman, ibid., p. 382

[15] Gillman, ibid., p. 367-369

[16] Clarence M. Burton, M. Agnes Burton, *History of Wayne County and the City of Detroit*, Michigan, S.J. Clarke Publishing Company, Chicago-Detroit, 1930, p. 11

[17] S.S. Knabenshue, "Mound Builder's Remains Within Toledo's Limits", *Ohio Archaeological and Historical Society Publications*, V. 10, Columbus, Ohio, 1908, p. 381-384

[18] *The Sandusky Register*, December 9, 1876, p. 4

[19] Sandusky, Ohio, *Daily Register*, August 8, 1887, p. 4 c4

[20] Letter from Charles N. Freeman incorporated by Lewis C. Aldrich in *History of Erie County, Ohio*, D. Mason and Company, Syracuse, New York, 1889, p. 16

[21] *Sandusky Register Star News*, 1/4/57, p. 5

[22] Letter from Charles N. Freeman of Sandusky, incorporated in History of Erie County, Lewis Cass Aldridge, N.Y., Mason, 1889, p. 15

[23] Samuel P. Orth, *History of Cleveland*, S.J. Clarke, Chicago-Cleveland, 1910, p. 73-74, citing Charles Whittlesey's survey, Smithsonian Contributions, Volume 3

[24] Elroy M. Avery, *A History of Cleveland*, Lewis Publishing Company, Cleveland, New York, 1918, p. 155, citing I.A. Morgan, "What I Recollect", *Annals of the Early Settlers' Association*, n.2 p.59, n.7 p 14, n.11, p 408

[25] *History of Ashtabula County*, William W. Williams, Williams Brothers, Philadelphia, 1878, p. 18-19. For detailed locations, see *Archaeological Atlas of Ohio*, William C Mills, Columbus, 1914

[26] Williams, ibid., p. 17. For detailed locations, see Mills, ibid.

[27] "Conneaut" by Harvey Nettleton, Esq, *Record of the Historical and Philosophical Society of Ashtabula County, Ohio*, 1847, manuscript, Ashtabula Main Library, p. 354

[28] Williams, ibid. p. 17. For detailed locations, see Mills, ibid.. The Aaron Wright account of 1841 is extensively cited by early local authors, but I cannot locate it, nor do I know if it survived, or if it was obtained first-hand from Wright. An eyewitness account by his adopted daughter of Solomon Spaulding's opening of some of the mounds ca. 1812, and the influence on the founding of the Mormon religion of his discovery in them of Giant's remains, may be found at Dale R. Broadhurst's http://www.solomonspaulding.com

[29] Carl E Feather, "Mystery of the Ancient Graveyard", *Conneaut Star Beacon*, 7/2/1996, p. B-1

[30] *History of Erie County*, 1894, Laura G. Sanford, pub. unknown, p. 23

[31] Sanford, ibid., p. 23

[32] Williams, ibid., p. 18

[33] Emerson F. Greenman, "Seven Prehistoric Sites in Northern Ohio", *Ohio Archaeological and Historical Quarterly*, v. 44, 1935, p. 220-237

[34] *History of Mercer County, Pennsylvania*, Brown Runk and Company, Chicago, Illinois, 1888, p. 394

[35] For cultural distribution maps, see William J. Myer-Oakes, *Prehistory of the Upper Ohio Valley*, Annals of the Carnegie Museum, v.34, 1955, Pittsburgh, Pennsylvania, p. 20, p. 17

[36] Andrew Collins, *Gateway to Atlantis*, Carroll and Graf Publishers, 2000, various

locations, citing the work of research chemists Svetlana Balabova, Franze Parsche, and Wolfgang Pirsig, "First Identification of Drugs in Egyptian Mummies", *Naturwissenschaftten*, v. 79, 1992, p. 358, and verification studies of Rosalie David, p. 118-119

[37] *History of Erie County*, 1884, Warner, Beers and Co., Chicago, p. 169

[38] ibid., p. 169

[39] Sanford, ibid., p. 23

[40] *History of Crawford County, Pennsylvania*, 1885, Warner, Beers and Company, Chicago, p. 140-141

[41] Mason C Winfield, "Tall Skeletons, New York: Land of Giants and Ancient Ruins", August 13, 2003, Internet site

[42] Joseph A. Brokowski, "Shannopinstown", manuscript, Carnegie Library, Pittsburgh, citing the *Gazette*, November 1, 1861

[43] Grant's Hill, Burgwin Park, and Puckety Road described by George T. Fleming, *History of Pittsburgh and Environs*, Volume I, American Historical Society, New York and Chicago, 1922, p. 22 et seq

[44] From contemporary newspaper accounts assembled by George T. Fleming, ibid. p. 22 et seq

[45] James Veech, *The Monongahela of Old*, Pittsburgh, Pennsylvania, 1858

[46] For "Fort Ancient" (Shawnee) occupation of the area, see Chapter 11 here

[47] Veech, ibid., p. 20

[48] I apologize to the reader for misplacing a small pamphlet purchased at Nemacolin's Castle, which described this ring structure, and led me to spend an afternoon examining the cemetery and its surviving circular layout. Given the fragmentary nature of the records, it is also difficult to cite particular documents on Brownsville, and a detailed discussion of them far exceeds the scope of the work at hand. That said, during a three-day effort to recover another copy of this particular pamphlet, I had a chance to examine many local documents, speak with local historian Will Conaway, and examine some of the other local sites, and the following summarizes the remains in the area as I understand them. There was a mound at the mouth of Redstone Creek, which was used as a base for fur trading from about 1740, and it was later leveled to form the foundations of the "Hangar", a supply depot built at the onset of the French and Indian Wars. This area was surrounded by heights, and during the conflict itself, the fort was moved a mile south of the mouth of Redstone Creek, and the mound at Nemacolin's Castle, the site of which forms the Castle's yard, was leveled to build a fort under the command of a Captain Paul. After the experiences at Fort Cumberland, it was realized that this position as well was open to enfilading fire from the heights above, and after the war another fort, Burd's Fort, was built on the heights to the north of today's Route 40, using the remains of a large Fort Ancient (Shawnee) structure which existed there. For a description and some citations on this structure, see Franklin Ellis, *History of Fayette County, Pennsylvania*, L.H. Everts and Co. Philadelphia, 1882. p. 18.   Given Brownsville's topography and a downturn in the local economy which has stopped its recent development, it most likely today retains sites of types which have long since been lost elsewhere.

[49] William J. Myer-Oakes, *Prehistory of the Upper Ohio Valley*, Annals of the Carnegie Museum, v.34, 1955, Pittsburgh, Pennsylvania, p. 92-95

[50] John Haywood, *The Natural and Aboriginal History of Tennessee*, 1823, edition of McCowat Press, Jackson, Tennessee, 1959, p. 308; here Haywood confused the mound

which was opened with the main mound

[51] Haywood, ibid p. 323. Haywood had an informant in the Grave Greek area, and also described the opening of an Adena mound on Little Grave Creek, p. 305-307

[52] Henry Rowe Schoolcraft, "Observations Respecting Grave Creek Mound", *Transactions of the American Ethnological Society*, p. 314, via Gerard Fowke, *Archaeological History of Ohio*, Ohio State Archaeological and Historical Society, Columbus, Ohio, 1902, p. 391

[53] Caleb Atwater, "A Description of the Antiquities of Ohio", *Archaeologica Americana*, Journal of the American Antiquarian Society, 1820, p. 168, via Henry Shepard, *Antiquities of the State of Ohio*, John O. Yorston, Cincinnati, Ohio, 1887, p. 69-70

[54] F.W. Putnam, "Iron from the Ohio Mounds", *Transactions of the American Antiquarian Society*, II, April 1883, via Gerard Fowke, op.cit. , p. 456-457

[55] Shepard, ibid. , p. 87

[56] Slipways at Grave Creek and Marietta noted at Grave Creek visitor's center

[57] Cyrus Thomas, *Burial Mounds of the Northern Sections of the United States*, Annual Reports of the Bureau of Ethnology, v.5, p. 51, condensed by Fowke, op.cit. p. 328-329

[58] Bishop Madison, American Philosophical Transactions, Volume 6, via Fortescue Cuming, *Sketches of a Tour to the Western Country*, Cramer, Spear and Eichbaum, 1810, via George T. Fleming, *History of Pittsburgh and Environs*, Volume I, American Historical Society, New York and Chicago, 1922, p. 45-47

[59] Caleb Atwater, *Writings of Caleb Atwater*, Scott and Wright, Columbus, Ohio, 1833, p. 81

[60] William J. Hranicky, *Prehistoric Axes, Celts, Bannerstones, and Other Large Tools in Virginia and Various States*, Special Publication n. 34, Archaeological Society of Virginia, 1995

[61] C.G. Holland, *An Archaeological Survey of Southwest Virginia*, Smithsonian Contributions to Anthropology, n.12, 1970, United States Government Printing Office, Washington, D.C., p.7

[62] Judith Parks, *A History of Henry County*, reprint of 1925 edition, Regional Publishing Company, Baltimore, 1976, p. 7

[63] The Cultural Resource Group and Louis Berger and Associates, *Ceramic Technology and Community Organization: Archaeological Data Recovery at the Hinan Site*, March 2000, Richmond, p. 87

[64] see Jon L. Gibson, *Poverty Point*, Anthropological Study Series n. 7, Department of Culture, Recreation and Tourism, Baton Rouge, Louisiana, 1999 for the following information on Poverty Point site

[65] For other galena sources, see John A. Walthall, *Galena and Aboriginal Trade in Eastern North America*, Scientific Papers Volume XVII, Illinois State Museum, Springfield, Illinois, 1981

[66] The climatic collapse associated with the eruption of Thera has been examined in some detail, detailed discussion of which is available in the volumes of the Thera conference proceedings. From its orbital mechanics we know that Comet Encke had to return at the same time as Thera erupted; this may find passing mention in Ovid's account of the myth of Deucalion. All of this ignores the fact that the people of Poverty Point had no way of knowing that Thera had erupted, while they could see Comet Encke, and they built a massive thunderbird shaped mound as a result of the climate collapse.

[67] The archaeological remains of these later Thunderbird Kings and European contact accounts of them will be set out in some detail later in this book.

CHAPTER 8

GOING INTO THE WATER:
THE GREAT ATLANTIC IMPACT MEGA-TSUNAMI ca.
1050 BCE

CULTURAL "DISCONTINUITIES"

Sometime around 1050 BCE nearly all of the Atlantic cultures suffered a tremendous setback. In Atlantic North America, the Late Archaic comes to an end, and shell ring cultures pretty much disappear from the Atlantic Coast, though survivors appear to have held on in Western Florida.

In the Caribbean Islands, the early shell cultures came to a stop, as did inter-island trade. Peoples immigrating into the islands a 1,000 years later would find a few technically primitive survivors who told tales of their ancestors surviving a great flood from the east by hiding out in caves.

Along the Gulf Coast of Central America, there are discontinuities at sites located over a large area, centered around a date of about 1050 BCE. The Olmec (Zoque) remains at La Venta are found buried under some 20 feet of marine sediment, and some multi-ton rock art sculptures of the region have been found located today in very unusual places.

What happened?

THE ALABAMA STORY OF THE GREAT ATLANTIC IMPACT MEGA-TSUNAMI

When this world was almost lost in the waters, a frog predicted it.[1]

[Frogs, which are commonly depicted in religious art throughout the Americas, are a source of the neurotoxin bufotonine, which was often used as a hallucinogen. As to bufotonin's psychedelic effects, although "toad licking" for recreational purposes has been reported recently in Australia, I most definitely warn everyone not to try it.

One day a man seized a frog and threw it into the fire, but another man said to him, "Don't do that." This man took the frog, cared for it, and healed it.

In thanks for this, the frog then said to him, "The land will almost disappear in the waters. Make a raft, and put a thick layer of grass underneath it, so that the beavers can not cut holes through the wood." So the man cut long dry sticks of wood and tied them together, and he put a quantity of grass underneath them.

When the other people saw him building his raft they asked him, "Why are you making this?" He answered, "A flood is going to cover the whole country." "Nothing like that can happen," they said, and some people stayed about laughing at him.

After some time the man finished his raft, and then the flood came. When the flood arrived fish came with it, and some of the people killed them, and said "We are having a good time." [In a tsunami the water at first recedes from the shore, leaving fish stranded.]

The man and his family then got upon the raft along with the frog. When the water rose, the raft went up also, and then some of the people said, "We want to get on!," but no one could get on. When the water rose higher all of the other people were drowned, but those on the raft floated up with it.

The flying things flew up to the sky and took hold of it, with their tails half in the water. The ends of their tails got wet. The red-headed woodpecker was flat against the sky and said, "My tail is half in the water."

This "red-headed woodpecker" is an Alabama description of a fragment of Comet Encke.

A MAYAN DEPICTION OF THE IMPACT MEGA-TSUNAMI

The cover of this book is taken from the Codex Dresden, page 74, which is now believed to have been the first page of this codex. It is a highly stylized picture of the Great Atlantic Impact Mega-Tsunami with a star sign.

THE BOOK OF THE THIRTEEN GODS:
MAYAN ACCOUNTS OF THE GREAT ATLANTIC MEGA-TSUNAMI,
AND THE END OF THE SECOND CREATION

Reading the following translations of the late Mayan accounts of the Great Atlantic Mega-Tsunami is pretty rough going – parts of these accounts are not understood fully by even the top Mayan experts. Not only do modern translators freely admit that they have an imperfect understanding of the vocabulary involved, the accounts themselves are what remains of abbreviated synopses of Mayan hieroglyphic books, synopsis which were done by new Mayan converts to Catholicism at the time of the Spanish conquest.[2]

That said, what comes through in all of the accounts is the Mayan description of the mega-tsunami, which was caused by the failure of the Bacabs, the Holders of the Heavens, to keep the sky separated from the Earth. The resulting impact (tz'oc, partitioning) kills all the "wooden people" of the Maya's second creation. Additionally, all of the accounts agree that this wall of water came from the east.

THE ACCOUNT OF THE IMPACT MEGA-TSUNAMI OF
THE HIGH PRIEST OF THE TOWN OF MANI[3]

> "(In the reign of 13 Ahau and 1 Ahau were the days and nights that fell
> without order, and pain was felt throughout the land. Because of this) the
> Thirteen Gods and the Nine Gods created the world and life; there also was
> born *Itzam Cab Ain.*

The late Mayan epigrapher Linda Schele spent several years of her life establishing that
this Lizard (alligator in this case) of the Spirit of the Earth, was the Milky Way of the
Maya.[4]

> "(Ah Mesencab)[5] [?] turned the sky and the Peten upside down, and the
> Nine Gods raised up *Itzam Cab Ain* [the Milky Way - the Spirit of the Earth
> Alligator].

> "There was a great cataclysm, and the ages ended with a flood. The 18 Bak
> katun was being counted and in its 17th part.

> "The Nine Gods refused to permit *Itzam Cab Ain* [the Milky Way] to take the
> Peten and to destroy the things of the world, so he [they?] cut the throat of
> *Itzam Cab Ain* [the Spirit of the Milky Way] and with his body formed the
> surface of Peten...

> "Ah Mesencab[6] , the one who laid waste to the Earth, rose up in the Katun
> 11 Ahau and bandaged the face of the Thirteen Gods [this appears to be "put
> on the masks of the Thirteen Gods"], but they did not know his name and
> they were told he was called Father, Son, and Holy Ghost [an obvious Spanish
> Christian insertion]. When the Thirteen Gods told them [the name] fire,
> stones, and clubs came down.

> "He took the green buds, large and small gourd seeds, wrapped them up with
> the *Nine Dz'acab* [?[7]], and (...)

> "They did not know that the heart of the tubercule [tuber=manioc?] was gone.
> After[ward] the evil sons and daughters were buried, although alive [they had
> no hearts], and those who were on the beach were buried between the waves
> of the sea.

> "In this katun, on the day 3 Oc, an avalanche of water came, and on the day
> 1 Cimi, everything came to an end. It was said that [the] four gods, [the] four
> *Bacabs*, were the ones that destroyed the Earth.

The *Bacabs*, it will be remembered, are the Holders of the Heavens. They destroy
the Earth by failing to hold up the heavens.

> "After this cataclysm the *Red Imix* [Milky Way[8]] Tree was erected, for it is one
> of the supports of heaven and the sign of the dawn. This one [east] is the

Bacab who turned aside. [The tsunami came from the east.]

"Kan Xib, the father, planted the *White Imix* [Milky Way] Tree to the north, and Zac Xob Chac says that this is a sign of destruction.

The *Black Imix* [Milky Way] Tree was planted to the west of Peten for the pixoy [bird] to sit upon.

The [...] planted the *Yellow Imix* [Milky Way] Tree to the south of Peten.

The *Green Imix* [Milky Way] Tree [which is to say, the hallucinogenic ceiba tree] was planted in the middle of the earth as a record of the destruction of the world.

Since then [text lost...] has established his gourd, his bowl, and his mat."

These last three items are signs of office of a Mayan *Ahau*, or King.

THE ACCOUNT OF THE IMPACT MEGA-TSUNAMI OF
THE HIGH PRIEST OF THE TOWN OF TIZIMEN[9]

In 11 Ahau, then arose the Priest of *Muzen Cab*, and tied [on] the faces [masks] of the Thirteen Gods, but they did not know their names. "The Holy", "The Remote", these are the names they called them. And they also did not show their faces to them either. At last it dawned, and they did not know their going or their coming,"

and then spoke the Thirteen Gods to the Nine Gods: "Bring down fire, bring down the rope", [This is most likely an impact plume.], "bring down stones and trees."

Then came the pounding of sticks and stones." [This is the impact blast.]

"And then appeared the Thirteen Gods, and beat their heads and flattened their faces, and they were spat on and snatched away. [This is an account of the destruction of the Zoque ("Olmec"), who were "spat upon" with a mega-tsunami.]

"The Four Year-bearers" [Munro Edmonson later (1986) translated "*cangel*" as "four changers" instead of as "year-bearers"; but as will be seen below, the *cangel* are astronomical.]   "and 5 *Za Bac*," [Edmonson translated this as "Soot Head", an impactor reference.]

"and the Quetzals were taken, and the Bluebirds." [These seem to be totems used thoughout the surviving literature in reference to two population groups.]"

The shamans rituals are established next, with the preparation of the hallucinogens followed by the heart sacrifice.

"Crushing the *Zic*, crushing the *Top*, and wrapping the seeds of the first Nine *Tz'acab*, which went to the Thirteen Levels of Heaven.

"Then was cut the membrane, and the nose, of the skeleton. Then went the heart, on account of the Thirteen Gods. But they did not know what was going." [Another comment on the current state of religious knowledge, or to the insensibility of the drugged sacrificial victim?)]

"The heart of the Moon there is dropped flat. And the fatherless, the miserable, and those without spouses or living relatives," [Sacrificial victims came from these populations.] "and those who don't have hearts, then began to rot, by the margin of the sand, by the margin of the sea.

"One torrent of water occurred, which was released by the Year-Bearers." [Once again, the *Cangel*, something astronomical, see below.]

"That was the cleaning of heaven, and also the cleaning of the lands for the period [of time] opposite the fold [of the katun], killing the youngest sons.

"That is the fold of the katun cycle, 3 Oc is the time it arrived here. 1 Cimi is the time that ended the word of the returned katun.

"The four gods - the Four *Bacab* [Holders of the Heavens] - that is their flattening of the land."

What follows is the description of the *Bacabs*, the Sky-Bearers, interlaced with the then current Spanish execution of their five priests.

"When the lands have been flattened, then there returns the Red [East] *Imix* [Milky Way] Tree, that is proceeding to pass the four. That is the sign of the flattening of the land; that is the toppling of the Tree of the Fathers of the Land, called the East Priest Xib Yuy." [The mega-tsunami came from the east.]

"Then there returns the White *Imix* [Milky Way] Tree to the north; he is called the North Priest Xic, the sign of the flattening of the lands.

"Then also returns the Black *Imix* [Milky Way] Tree to the west country, the sign of the flattening of the lands, that is the Black Imix tree, seating the West Priest Tam Puc the Weak.

"Seating the Yellow *Imix* [Milky Way] Tree to the south of the country, the sign of the flattening of the lands, seating the South Priest Oyal Mut.

"Then is seated the Green *Imix* [Milky Way] Tree in the middle of the lands, the reminder of the flattening of the lands. Piled in its place is the whole of the existence of this katun."

THE IMPACT MEGA-TSUNAMI ACCOUNT OF
THE HIGH PRIEST OF TIZIMIN[10]

In this passage the High Priest, a Chilam Balam, a Lord's Celestial Interpreter, finishes tranlsating one account of creation from hieroglyphic to roman letters, and begins working on a copy of another part of it, which includes another version of the tale set out above.

"...This is the arrival of the end of the word of the Sun Priest of *Muzen Cab* and *Za Bac Na*,
which completes the lordship of the Thirteen Lords [Gods].

"1 Ahau is the day for it, when they will join with each other:
the rising Sun, and the Moon, and night.

"Then comes the dawn from the Thirteen Gods, for the Nine Gods, who are then born and created.

"Then is born *Itzam Can Ain* [the lizard (alligator) of the Milky Way],
cutting the Pyramid of the Sun and the World.

"Then the sky is divided [from the Earth by the four Bacabs], and the land is raised.

"And then there begins The Book of the Thirteen Gods.
"Then occurs the great flooding of the Earth.
"Then arises the great *Itzam Cab Ain* [lizard (alligator) of the Milky Way]

"The ending of the word [the book?]: the fold of the Katun: that is a flood which will be the ending of the word of the katun.

"But they did not agree, the Nine Gods; and then will be cut the throat of *Itzam Cab Ain* [the lizard (alligator) of the Milky Way] who bears the country upon his back. That is Uoh Puc [?] by name, for they didn't bear their right names - to tie the stone face [put on the masks], and return the lordship."

THE IMPACT MEGA-TSUNAMI ACCOUNT OF
THE HIGH PRIEST OF CHUMAYEL[11]

This excellent very early account is preceded by a Catholic disclaimer. The Catholic influence no doubt reflects the attempt by the rulers of Merida to enlist the Spanish as allies in their local power struggle – a fatal mistake.

"It is very necessary, the path that is the introduction to the heart. This is the tun period, when it was shaped by Our Father the Remote.

"This is the taking of the occasion: this is the bal-che [?+tree] ceremony, as we honor Him here. We, the rulers spread in many parts, worship them, the true

Gods. There they are as tuns, the established representation of the True God, our God, our Father, who is God the Father of Heaven and Earth, the true God.

"However, the first gods were leperous gods, finished is the word of their worship. They have been done in by the benediction of the Father in Heaven. Then it ends, the redemption of the *tz'oc* [the redemption of the *tz'oc*, partitioning, impact event, by human sacrifice] is over, [by] the twice born life of the true God, the true Dios. When they sweetly prayed to heaven and earth, that put an end to the gods of you Mayan people.

"Shattered is the belief in your gods then.

The High Priest now explains that he is writing this solely to explain how things used to be.

"This is the account of the land at that time. That is because it was written there, because it would not have happened at the time of the making of these books." [In other words, "We're not heretics, so please don't kill us."] "These are the thousand words here for the examination of the Mayan people here, who may know how they were born and [how they] settled the land here in this country.

"In 11 Ahau, that was when there began the *Muzen Cabs* [a kind of priests] to tie [on] the faces [masks] of the Thirteen Gods - and they did not know their true names, for their older sisters and their engendered sons, their offspring, and those who are not grown: perhaps even their faces and their voices are gone.

"The dawning of the land they did not know about either, the going and the coming.

"and then there were finished the Thirteen who are Gods, by the Nine who are Gods.

"They then brought down fire, they then brought down the rope [symbol of the impact plume], they then brought down stones and sticks, then came the beating with sticks and stones. [symbolic of the impact blast]

"And then were finished the Thirteen who are Gods; and so their heads were beaten, and their faces were flattened [by the impact blast], and then their faces were flattened, and then they were forgotten, and then they were also carried away [by the mega-tsunami's wave].

"And then were planted the four *cangel* [something astronomical, see below], together with the Soot Heads [Za Bac]. Then was created also the Quetzal and the Blue Bird.

153

"And then was created the placenta of breast plants, and the heart of breast squash, and breast pumpkin, and breast beans, the wrapping of the seed of the First Nine Steps.

"Then they went to the thirteenth [13th] level of [the] heaven[s], and so then were established his membranes, and his nose, his skeleton here in the world. So then went his heart, because of the Thirteen who are Gods. But they did not know his heart was to be a plant. [tuber? manioc?]

"And then they all arrived, even the fatherless, and the suffering poor, and the widows; the living and those without hearts." [This describes the classes of people from which sacrificial victims were selected.]

Tthe Great Atlantic Impact Mega-tsunami is described next.

"And they began to wait for it: the direction of the thatch grass, the direction of the sea. The deluge of water, a storm of water, then reached the hearts of the Four *Cangel*, who radiated in [the] heaven[s], and also radiated on the land.

"Said the Four who are Gods, the Four who are Fathers of the Land: 'This water shows them to their faces. Then let us finish the flattening of the lands.'"

The "Can" in Cangels has commonly been interpreted as "four", but perhaps given this passage reading "Can" in its sense of "heavens" might make sense: the four heaven changers, the planets, or something else? The four *Bacabs* now intercede. Mention of the east tree, the east supporter of the heavens, is omitted entirely.

"The South Priest Xib Yuy then bore
the North Alligator [Milky Way] Tree in the north.
And then he bore the Entrance to (the) Heaven(s),
the sign of the flattening of the lands.
That is the North Alligator [Milky Way] Tree, said to be carried.

"And then he bore the West Alligator [Milky Way] Tree
to the seat of the black-breasted weaver bird.

"And then he bore the South Alligator [Milky Way] Tree,
the sign of the flattening of the lands, to seat the yellow-breasted weaver bird.

"And was seated the South Priest Xib Yuy, and the South Priest Oyal Mut.
And then he bore the Center Alligator [Milky Way] Tree to the middle,
signifying the flattening of the land.

"It is seated. Its being raised established the town.
And the same when the return of the katun is fulfilled."

154

A QUICHE DESCRIPTION OF SEVEN MACAW (ITZAM YE) FROM THE
POPOL VUH

A very late and highly modified version of the Mayan mega-tsunami account survived
as part of the Quiche collection of translations known as the *Popol Vuh*, and it includes
a description of *Izam Ye* , Seven Macaw,. The English translation of the *Popol Vuh* used
here is that of Dennis Tedlock, with a few modifications to tense and punctuation. To
gain some idea of the stages of transmission which the tale had undergone by the time
it was first put to paper, see the Quiche's own migration lists given on pages 149 and
184-185 of Tedlock's translation.

While the Quiche phrase "*Izam Ye*" is translated as "Seven Macaw", given the meaning
of "*Itzam*" as "lizard, alligator, snake" in Mayan, perhaps another entirely different
meaning was originally meant.

The *Popl Vuh* includes the tale of the defeat of *Izam Ye* along side the stories of
the defeats of those two other hazards to these early people, Volcano (*Zipacna*) and
Earthquake. While from the account itself, it is clear that Seven Macaw was originally
a combined comet/asteroid, Tedlock and Schele argued that Seven Macaw was the Big
Dipper, and it seems likely that such a metamorphises was underway as memory of the
impact faded. On to the story -

"This was when there was just a trace of early dawn on the face of the Earth:
there was no Sun.
But there was one who magnified himself: Seven Macaw is his name.

"The Sky-Earth was already there,
but the face of the Sun-Moon was clouded over.
Even so, it is said that his [Seven Macaw's] light provided a sign for the people
who were flooded.
He was like a person of genius [?] in his being.

In the *Popol Vuh* version, Seven Macaw appears after the impact. Seven Macaw now
speaks.

"I am great. My place is now higher than that of the human work, the human
design. [The "wooden" people had just been created.]   "I am their Sun, I am
their light, and I am also their months.

"So be it: My light is great. I am the walkway and I am the foothold of the
people, because my eyes are of metal. My teeth just glitter with jewels, and
turquoise as well: they stand out blue(?) with stones like the face of the sky.
And this nose of mine [the comet's tail] shines white into the distance like the
Moon.

"Since my nest is of metal, it lights up the face of the Earth. [Here the comet
Seven Macaw explains that he is bright because his nest is made of metal,
meteoritic iron.] When I come forth before my nest, I am like the Sun and

(the) Moon for those who are born in the light, begotten in the light. It must be so, because my face [the comet's tail] reaches into the distance," says Seven Macaw."

The hero-protector speaks next.

"It is not true that he is the Sun, this Seven Macaw, yet he magnifies himself, his wings, his metal. But the scope of his face [the comet's tail] lies right around his own perch: his face does not reach everywhere beneath the sky. The faces of the Sun, Moon, and Stars are not yet visible, it has not dawned."

This may refer obliquely to a dimming of the sky due to cometary dust load.

"And so Seven Macaw puffs himself up as the days and the months, though the light of the Sun and Moon has not yet clarified. He only wished for surpassing greatness. This was when the flood was worked upon the mannequins, the wood carvings [the wooden people]."

This is followed by a long astronomical allegory, in which hero twins, one of whom is a blowgun hunter, the other a hunter who uses nets, defeat Seven Macaw. Again, this is a very late version, and this allegory is still not fully understood by the experts even to this day.

GOING INTO THE WATER

The Maya worldview is so absolutely different from our own that it has defied analysis for several hundred years by some of the best intellects available. Possibly the fundamental reason for this failure is that modern Europeans have not experienced impact events for a considerable period of time, and certainly have experienced nothing so devastating as the impacts which the Maya experienced twice.

One of the most interesting aspects of this difference between peoples is in their view of the afterlife. The Europeans retained but dim memories of the sky gods, and most peoples placed their afterlives either in heaven, living comfortably with the sky gods, or in hell, consumed by the dimly remembered flames of a land impact. In contrast, the Maya had experienced a massive impact produced mega-tsunami, and they placed their afterworld under the sea, describing death as "going into the water".

BIBLICAL ACCOUNTS OF
THE GREAT ATLANTIC IMPACT MEGA-TSUNAMI OF ca 1050 BCE

I suppose that the best place to start these comments is with a brief mention of the chronological problems of the Old Testament. Touching as this does on the religious beliefs and/or national sentiments of Jews, Christians, and Moslems, I need to point out that their beliefs about their chronologies have absolutely no relevance for those who practice Native American traditional religions.

156

That said, Moses' exodus from Egypt can be dated to 1,628 BCE on the basis of the absolute physical evidence of the eruption of Thera (Calliste), as can the reigns of the Egyptian Pharoah Ahmose and the Hittite King Mursili I. Joshua, and the impact event mentioned in relation to him, can be dated to 1,586 BCE on the basis of both contemporary documents and archaeological remains to the reigns of the Hittite King Hantilish, the Egyptian Pharaoh Thutmose I, and Idrimi of Alalah.[12]

A chronology based on the text of the Old Testament can be locked from this point on with the reigns and events of the Pharaohs to the Peleset invasion, the death of Eli, and the campaign of Ramses III against the Peleset in his 8th year, 1179 BCE. From Comet Encke's orbital mechanics we know that it reappeared around 1159 BCE, and that its dust caused a period of climate collapse from 1159-1141 BCE, roughly contemporaneous with I Samuel 7:10: "but the lord that day thundered with a great thunder upon the Philistines, and discomfited them"

Now things get tricky, as this was a very chaotic period in the history of the "Near East". Depending on whose biblical text you use, and how you read it, the span of time from the reign of Eli to that of Jehosaphat, which is of interest here, can be set at anywhere from 180 to 211 years, possibly lower. If one uses the short span of 180 years or so, it takes us to around 1000 BCE, which we know from the carbon dates of the Native American archaeological data to have been the time of the Great Atlantic Impact Mega-Tsunami.

Unfortunately the Mayan dates for this late impact of a fragment of Comet Encke are not much help in resolving this chronological problem, as there are many alternative absolute readings for them, so the Jewish, Christian, and Moslem religious scholars are still free to argue heatedly about their chronologies as much as they want to.

II CHRONICLES 20:34

"Now the rest of the acts of Jehoshaphat, first and last,
behold, they [are] written in the Book of Jehu the son of Hanani,
who [is] mentioned in the Book of the Kings of Israel.

And after this Jehoshaphat, the King of Judah,
joined himself with Ahaziah, the King of Israel,
who did very wickedly.
And he joined himself with him
to make ships to go to Tarshish:
and they made the ships in Eziongeber.

Then Eliezer the son of Dodavah of Mareshah
prophesied against Jehoshaphat, saying,
"Because thou hast joined thyself with Ahaziah,
the LORD hath broken thy works."

And the ships were broken, that they
were not able to go to Tarshish. "

PSALM 48:4

"For, lo, the kings were assembled, they passed by together.
They saw [it, and] so they marveled;
They were troubled, [and] hasted away.
Fear took hold upon them there;
Pain, as of a woman in labor:
Thou breakest the ships of Tarshish with an east wind."

PLATO'S TALE OF ATLANTIS:
A EUROPEAN MEMORY OF THE GREAT ATLANTIC IMPACT MEGA-TSUNAMI

It has long been known that Plato's tale of Atlantis was a construction of his, one designed to instill moral lessons. It has also been widely known that Plato incorporated into this construction two remote historical memories, one a description of the Minoan confederation, and the other a memory of the invasion of the "Sea Peoples". The mystery has been why Plato set his tale in the Atlantic.

In his book "Gateway To Atlantis", author Andrew Collins carefully assembled a large amount of material documenting very firmly early contacts by peoples from Europe and the Mediterranean with those of the Western Hemisphere. So far so good, but then Collins went on to set "Atlantis" in Cuba, and further argued that Plato's tale actually referred to events at the start of the Holocene.

From the records, both written and physical, of an impact produced mega-tsunami which occurred around 1050 BCE in the Atlantic, we can assert that it is far more likely that the last bit of ancient history which Plato incorporated into his moral fable was most likely a dim memory of the effects of that impact event, rather than the Holocene start impact event. As a matter of fact, we can prove it, from Plato's own words.

EXTRACTS FROM PLATO'S *TIMAEUS*[13]

[It is often overlooked that Timaeus was an astronomer.]

CRITIAS –

I will tell an old story of the world which I heard from an aged man:
For at the time of his telling it, Critias was, as he said, nearly ninety years of age, and I was about ten.

Now the day was that day of the Apaturia, which is called the Registration of Youth, at which, according to custom, our parents gave prizes for recitations. And the poems of several poets were recited by us boys, and many of us sang the poems of Solon, which at that time had not gone out of fashion.

One of our tribe, (one Amynander) either because he thought so or to please Critias, said that in his judgment, Solon was not only the wisest of men, but also the noblest of poets.

The old man [Critias], as I very well remember, brightened up at hearing this and said, smiling, "Yes, Amynander. If Solon had only, like other poets, made poetry the business of his life, and had completed the tale which he brought with him from Egypt, and had not been compelled by reason of the factions and troubles which he found stirring in his own country when he came home to attend to other matters, in my opinion, he would have been as famous as Homer or Hesiod, or any poet."

"And what was the tale about, Critias?", said Amynander.

"About the greatest action which the Athenians ever did, and which ought to have been the most famous; but, through the lapse of time and the destruction of the actors, it has not come down to us.

CRITIAS'S GRANDFATHER CRITIAS'S ACCOUNT OF
HOW SOLON LEARNED OF ATLANTIS

"Tell us", said the other, "the whole story, and how and from whom Solon heard this veritable tradition."

He replied, "In the Egyptian Delta, at the head of which the river Nile divides, there is a certain district which is called the district of Sais. And the great city of the district is also called Sais, and it is the city from which King Amasis came.

"The citizens have a deity for their foundress; she is called in the Egyptian tongue Neith, and she is asserted by them to be the same goddess whom the Hellenes call Athene. They are great lovers of the Athenians, and say that they are in some way related to them.

"To this city came Solon, and he was received there with great honor. He asked the priests who were most skilful in such matters, about antiquity, and he made the discovery that neither he nor any other Hellene knew anything worth mentioning about the times of old.

"On one occasion, wishing to draw them on to speak of antiquity, he [Solon] began to tell about the most ancient things in our part of the world: about Phoroneus, who is called "the first man," and about Niobe; and after the Deluge, of the survival of Deucalion and Pyrrha. And he traced the genealogy of their descendants, and reckoning up the dates, he {Solon] tried to compute how many years ago the events of which he was speaking happened.

THE PRIEST OF SAIS'S OBSERVATIONS ON CATASTROPHES
AND THEIR EFFECT ON HISTORICAL MEMORY

"Thereupon one of the priests, who was of a very great age, said,
'O Solon, Solon, You Hellenes are never anything but children,
and there is not an old man among you.'

"Solon in return asked him what he meant.

"'I mean to say', he replied, 'That in mind you are all young: there is no old
opinion handed down among you by ancient tradition, nor any science which
is hoary with age.

"'And I will tell you why. There have been, and will be again, many
destructions of mankind, arising out of many causes. The greatest have been
brought about by the agencies of fire and water, and other lesser ones by
innumerable other causes.

THE MYTH OF PHAETHON:
THE EGYPTIAN IMPACT LEGEND

"'There is a story, which even you have preserved, that once upon a time
Phaethon, the son of Helios, having yoked the steeds in his father's chariot,
burnt up all that was upon the Earth, because he was not able to drive them in
the path of his father, and was himself destroyed by a thunderbolt.

"'Now this has the form of a myth, but really it signifies a declination of the
bodies moving in the heavens around the Earth, and a great conflagration of
things upon the Earth, which recurs after long intervals.

"'At such times those who live upon the mountains and in dry and lofty
places are more liable to destruction than those who dwell by rivers or on the
seashore. And from this calamity the Nile [River], who is our never-failing
saviour, delivers and preserves us.

"'On the other hand, when the gods purge the Earth with a deluge of water,
the survivors in your country are herdsmen and shepherds who dwell on the
mountains. But those who, like you, live in cities, are carried by the rivers into
the sea. Whereas in this land, neither then nor at any other time, does the water
come down from above on the fields, having always a tendency to come up
from below [from the Nile River]; for which reason the traditions preserved
here are the most ancient.

"The fact is, that wherever the extremity of winter frost or of summer does
not prevent it, mankind exists, sometimes in greater, sometimes in lesser
numbers. And whatever happened either in your country or in ours, or in any
other region of which we are informed- If there were any actions noble or
great or in any other way remarkable, they have all been written down by us of

old, and are preserved in our temples.

"Whereas just when you and other nations are beginning to be provided with letters and the other requisites of civilized life, after the usual interval, the stream from heaven, like a pestilence, comes pouring down, and leaves [behind] only those of you who are destitute of letters and education. And so you have to begin all over again like children, and know nothing of what happened in ancient times, either among us or among yourselves.

"'As for those genealogies of yours, which you just now recounted to us, Solon, they are no better than the tales of children.

"'In the first place, you remember a single deluge only, but there were many previous ones.'"

Plato will make explicit mention of these previous deluges later on.

"'In the next place, you do not know that there formerly dwelt in your land the fairest and noblest race of men which ever lived, and that you and your whole city are descended from a small seed or remnant of them which survived.

"'And this was unknown to you, because for many generations, the survivors of that destruction died, leaving no written word.

THE PRIEST OF SAIS'S DESCRIPTION OF ANCIENT ATHENS: THE PERFECT STATE

"For there was a time, Solon, before the great deluge of all, when the city which now is Athens was first in war, and in every way the best governed of all cities; [Athens] is said to have performed the noblest deeds and to have had the fairest constitution of any of which tradition tells, under the face of heaven.'"

"Solon marveled at his words, and earnestly requested the priests to inform him exactly and in order about these former citizens.

"'You are welcome to hear about them, Solon,' said the priest, 'Both for your own sake and for that of your city. And above all, for the sake of the goddess [Athene/Neith] who is the common patron and parent and educator of both our cities.

"'She founded your city a thousand years before ours, receiving from the Earth and Hephaestus the seed of your race. And afterwards she founded ours, of which the constitution is recorded in our sacred registers to be eight thousand years old.

Plato used the Egyptian memory of the Holocene-start impacts to re-date both the eruption of Calliste (Thera), and the Great Atlantic Impact Mega-Tsunami. It served the purposes of his moral lecture.

"'As touching your citizens of nine thousand years ago, I will briefly inform you of their laws and of their most famous action. The exact particulars of the whole we will hereafter go through at our leisure in the sacred registers themselves.

"'If you compare these very laws with ours, you will find that many of ours are the counterpart of yours as they were in the olden time. In the first place, there is the caste of priests, which is separated from all the others. Next there are the artificers, who ply their several crafts by themselves, and do not intermix. And also there is the class of shepherds and of hunters, as well as that of husbandmen. And you will observe as well that the warriors in Egypt are distinct from all the other classes, and are commanded by the law to devote themselves solely to military pursuits. Moreover, the weapons which they carry are shields and spears, a style of equipment which the goddess taught first to us, of the Asiatics, as [she did] first to you in your part of the world.

"'Then as to wisdom - Do you observe how our law from the very first made a study of the whole order of things, extending even to prophecy and to medicine which gives health[14], out of these divine elements deriving what was needful for human life, and adding every sort of knowledge which was akin to them?

"'All this order and arrangement the goddess [Athena/Neith] first imparted to you when establishing your city. And she chose that spot of Earth in which you were born because she saw that the happy temperament of the seasons in that land would produce the wisest of men. Wherefore the goddess, who was a lover both of war and of wisdom, selected and settled first of all that spot which was the most likely to produce men like herself.

"'And there you dwelt, having such laws as these and still better ones, and excelled all mankind in all virtue, as became the children and disciples of the gods.

THE PRIEST OF SAIS'S ACCOUNT OF
THE WAR BETWEEN ATHENS AND ATLANTIS;
DESCRIPTION OF ATLANTIS AND ITS EMPIRE

"'Many great and wonderful deeds are recorded of your state in our histories, but one of them exceeds all the rest in greatness and valor. For these histories tell of a mighty power which unprovoked made an expedition against the whole of Europe and Asia, and to which your city put an end.

DESCRIPTION OF THE ATLANTIC OCEAN, AND NORTH
AMERICA

"'"This power came forth out of the Atlantic Ocean. For in those days the
Atlantic was navigable, and there was an island situated in front of the straits
which are by you called the Pillars of Heracles. The island was larger than
Libya and Asia put together, and was the way to other islands.

"'And from these [islands] you could pass to the whole of the opposite
continent which surrounded the true ocean. For this sea which is within the
Straits of Heracles [the Mediterranean Sea] is only a harbor, having a narrow
entrance, but that other [the Atlantic Ocean] is a real sea, and the surrounding
land may be most truly called a boundless continent.

DESCRIPTION OF THE LATE BRONZE AGE MEDITERRANEAN
TRADING EMPIRE

"'Now in this island of Atlantis there was a great and wonderful empire,
which had rule over the whole island and several others, and over parts of the
continent [North America], and furthermore, the men of Atlantis had subjected
the parts of Libya [the coast of North Africa] within the Pillars of Heracles as
far as Egypt, and the parts of Europe as far as Tyrrhenia [Italy]."

ACCOUNT OF THE WAR BETWEEN ATHENS AND ATLANTIS

"'This vast power, gathered into one, endeavored to subdue at a blow our
country and yours and the whole of the region within the straits.

As was seen above, the invasions of Egypt by the "Sea peoples" took place
shortly before the time of the Great Atlantic Impact Mega-Tsunami.

"'And then, Solon, your country shone forth, in the excellence of her virtue
and strength, among all mankind. She was pre-eminent in courage and military
skill, and was the leader of the Hellenes.

"'And when the rest fell off from her, being compelled to stand alone, after
having undergone the very extremity of danger, she defeated and triumphed
over the invaders, and preserved from slavery those who were not yet
subjugated, and generously liberated all the rest of us who dwell within the
Pillars."

The preceding passage no doubt reflects Plato's desire to have Athens take the lead
against the Persians.

163

THE END OF ATLANTIS
AND THE DESTRUCTION OF ANCIENT ATHENS

"'"But afterwards there occurred violent earthquakes and floods; and in a single day and night of misfortune all your warlike men in a body sank into the earth.

"'"And the island of Atlantis in like manner disappeared in the depths of the sea. For which reason the sea in those parts is impassable and impenetrable: Because there is a shoal of mud in the way,
and this was caused by the subsidence of the island."'"

CRITIAS'S ACCOUNT OF HIS RECOLLECTION OF THE TALE

"I have told you briefly, Socrates, what the aged Critias heard from Solon and related to us. And when you were speaking yesterday about your city and citizens, the tale which I have just been repeating to you came into my mind. And I remarked with astonishment how, by some mysterious coincidence, you agreed in almost every particular with the narrative of Solon. [There is little wonder about how this "mysterious coincidence" came about.]

"But I did not like to speak at the moment, for a long time had elapsed, and I had forgotten too much; I thought that I must first of all run over the narrative in my own mind, and then I would speak. And so I readily assented to your request yesterday, considering that in all such cases the chief difficulty is to find a tale suitable to our purpose, and that having found such a tale, we should be fairly well provided.

"And therefore, as Hermocrates has told you, on my way home yesterday I at once communicated the tale to my companions as I remembered it. And after I left them, by thinking during the night, I recovered nearly the whole it. Truly, as is often said, the lessons of our childhood make wonderful impression on our memories - For I am not sure that I could remember all the discourse of yesterday, but I should be much surprised if I forgot any of these things which I have heard very long ago.

"I listened at the time with childlike interest to the old man's narrative: he was very ready to teach it to me, and I asked him again and again to repeat his words, so that like an indelible picture they were branded into my mind. And as soon as the day broke, I rehearsed them as he spoke them to my companions, that they, as well as myself, might have something to say.

"And now, Socrates, to make an end to my preface, I am ready to tell you the whole tale. I will give you not only the general heads, but the particulars, as they were told to me.

After this teasing line, Plato has his Critias turn the floor over to the astronomer Timaeus, who uses Pythagorean mathematics to derive all of existence.

EXTRACTS FROM PLATOS'S *CRITIAS*[15]

Having used his *Timaeus* to establish existence, Plato now intended to have his *Critias* reveal man's history. It was apparently Plato's intention to have Hermocrates speak about the current situation in Athens, but he never got the chance to write that piece. Plato makes reference to a grave situation instead, and this may have been his own approaching death.

CRITIAS –

"Friend Hermocrates, you who are stationed to speak last, and who have yet another in front of you, you have not lost heart as yet; the gravity of the situation will soon be revealed to you. Meanwhile, I accept your exhortations and encouragements, but besides the gods and goddesses whom you have mentioned, I would specially invoke Mnemosyne [the Goddess of Memory]: for all the important part of my discourse is dependent on her favor; and if I can recollect and recite enough of what was said by the priests [of Egypt] and brought here by Solon, I do not doubt that I shall satisfy the requirements of this theatre.

"And now, making no more excuses, I will proceed. Let me begin by observing first of all, that nine thousand was the sum of years which had elapsed since the war which was said to have taken place between those who dwelt outside the Pillars of Heracles and all who dwelt within them. This war I am going to describe.

These wars in fact occurred shortly before ca 1050 BCE. Plato simply re-dated them to the Holocene Start impacts.

"Of the combatants on the one side, the city of Athens was reported to have been the leader and to have fought out the war; the combatants on the other side were commanded by the Kings of Atlantis, which, as I was saying, was an island greater in extent than Libya and Asia, and when afterwards sunk by an earthquake, became an impassable barrier of mud to voyagers sailing from hence to any part of the ocean.

Note that here Plato has his "Atlantis" sunk by an earthquake, instead of by the forces mentioned in the preceding book. This probably refers to the explosion of Thera.

THE DESCRIPTION OF ATHENS

"The progress of this history will set out the various nations of the barbarians and the families of Hellenes which existed then, as they successively appear on the scene. I must describe first of all Athenians of that day, and their enemies who fought with them, and then the respective powers and governments of the two kingdoms. Let us give the precedence to Athens.

"In the days of old the gods had the whole earth distributed among them by allotment. There was no quarrelling, for you cannot rightly suppose that the gods did not know what was proper for each of them to have, or that knowing this, they would seek to procure for themselves by contention that which more properly belonged to others. They all of them by just apportionment obtained what they wanted, and peopled their own districts. And when they had peopled them, they tended us, their nurslings and possessions, as shepherds tend their flocks - excepting only that they did not use blows or bodily force, as shepherds do, but governed us like pilots from the stern of the vessel, which is the easy way of guiding animals, holding our souls by the rudder of persuasion according to their own pleasure. Thus did they guide all mortal creatures.

"Now different gods had their allotments in different places, which they then set in order. Hephaestus and Athena, who were brother and sister and sprang from the same father [Zeus], having a common nature, and being also united in the love of philosophy and art, obtained as their common portion this land, which was naturally adapted for wisdom and virtue.

"And there they [Hephaestus and Athene] implanted brave children of the soil, and put into their minds the order of government; their names are preserved, but their actions have disappeared, by reason of the destruction of those who received the tradition, and the lapse of ages. For when there were any survivors [of disasters coming up from the sea], as I have already said, they were men who dwelt in the mountains, and they were ignorant of the art of writing, and had heard only the names of the chiefs of the land, but very little about their actions. They were willing enough to give the names [of the chiefs of the land – Solon's genealogies] to their children, but of the virtues and the laws of their predecessors, they knew only by obscure traditions. And as they themselves and their children for many generations lacked the necessities of life, they directed their attention to the supply of their wants, and they spoke about them, to the neglect of events that had happened in times long past. For mythology and the enquiry into antiquity are first introduced into cities when they begin to have leisure, when they see that the necessities of life have already been provided, but not before. And this is the reason why the names of the ancients have been preserved to us, but not their actions.

"This I infer because Solon said that the priests [of Egypt] in their narrative of that war mentioned most of the names which are recorded prior to the time of Theseus, such as Cecrops, and Erechtheus, and Erichthonius, and Erysichthon, and the names of the women in the same manner. Moreover, since military pursuits were then common to men and women, the men of those days, in accordance with the custom of the time, set up a figure and image of the goddess [Athene] in full armor, to be a testimony that all animals which associate together, male as well as female, may, if they please, practice in common the virtue which belongs to them, without distinction of sex.

"Now the country was inhabited in those days by various classes of citizens: there were artisans, there were husbandmen, and there was also a warrior class originally set apart by divine men. The latter [the warrior class] dwelt by themselves, and had all things suitable for nurture and education. Neither had any of them anything of their own, but they regarded all that they had as common property. Nor did they claim to receive of the other citizens anything more than their necessary food. And they practised all the pursuits which we yesterday described as those of our imaginary guardians.

THE BOUNDARIES OF ATHENS

"Concerning the country, the Egyptian priests said what is not only probable but what is manifestly true, that the boundaries were in those days fixed by the Isthmus [of Corinth], and that in the direction of the continent they extended as far as the heights of Cithaeron and Parnes. The boundary line came down in the direction of the [Corinthian] sea, having the district of Oropus on the right, and the river Asopus as the limit on the left.

EROSION

"The land was the best in the world, and was therefore able in those days to support a vast army, which was raised from the surrounding people. Even the remnant of Attica which now exists may be compared with any region in the world for the variety and excellence of its fruits, and the suitableness of its pastures to every sort of animal, and this proves what I am saying. But in those days the country was fair as now and yielded far more abundant produce.

"How shall I establish my words? And what part of it can be truly called a remnant of the land that then was?

"The whole country [Greece] is only a long promontory extending far into the sea away from the rest of the continent, and everywhere the surrounding basin of the sea is deep in the neighborhood of the shore. Many great deluges [!] have taken place during the nine thousand years, for that is the number of years which have elapsed since the time of which I am speaking. During all this time, and through so many changes, there has never been any considerable accumulation of the soil coming down from the mountains, as in other places, but instead the earth has fallen away all round and sunk out of sight. The consequence of this is that in comparison to what was then, there are remaining only the bones of the wasted body, as they may be called. And in the case of the small islands, all the richer and softer parts of the soil having fallen away, the mere skeleton of the land remains.

"But in the primitive state of the country, its mountains were high hills covered with soil, and the plains, as they are termed by us, of Phelleus were full of rich earth, and there was abundance of wood in the mountains. Of the trees the traces still remain; for although now some of the mountains only afford sustenance to bees, not so very long ago there were still to be seen roofs of timber cut from the trees growing there, roofs which were of a size sufficient to cover the largest houses; and there were many other high trees, cultivated by man, and bearing abundance of food for cattle.

167

"Moreover, the land reaped the benefit of the annual rainfall, not as now losing the water which flows off the bare earth into the sea - but having an abundant supply of rain in all places, and receiving it into herself and treasuring it up in the close clay soil, it let off into the hollows the streams which it absorbed from the heights, providing everywhere abundant fountains and rivers, of which there may still be observed sacred memorials in places where fountains once existed.

"And this proves the truth of what I am saying.

"Such was the natural state of the country, which was cultivated, as we may well believe, by true husbandmen, who made husbandry their business, and were lovers of honor, and of a noble nature, and had a soil the best in the world, and an abundance of water, and an excellently tempered climate in the heavens above.

ATHENS AND GREEK LEGENDS OF EARLIER FLOODS:

"Now the city in those days was arranged on this wise. In the first place the Acropolis was not as it is now. For the fact is that a single night of excessive rain washed away the earth and laid bare the rock; at the same time there were earthquakes, and then occurred the extraordinary inundation, which was the third before the great destruction of Deucalion."

PLATO'S DATING MISTAKES

The flood of Deucalion [T'e/U/Callion] can be dated with certainty to 1628 BCE – it was the mega-tsunami produced by the explosive eruption of the Thera volcano. From the narrow bands of growth found in tree rings, and the dust found in ice cores, the explosion of Calliste [Thera] is known to have occurred in 1628 BCE.[16] Comet Encke's orbit also brought it near the Earth at this time, and the appearance of Comet Encke in the same year is described in one version of the myth of Deucalion.[17] As Plato pointed out, the Greeks had developed a rough date for the flood of Deucalion by counting the generations which came after it, and they knew approximately when it had occurred.

On the basis of the archaeological evidence, we can place the Great Atlantic Mega-Tsunami at around ca. 1050 BCE. In point of fact, the Egyptian wars Plato mentions occurred at the time of the Great Atlantic Impact Mega-Tsunami, both occurring ca 1050 BCE.

Also on the basis of archaeological evidence, most specifically that recovered by Frank Hibben[18], we can place the Holocene Start Impacts and their "floods" to around 8,300 BCE. Plato speaks here of legends of three "floods" previous to Deucalion's, and he probably mistakenly used Egyptian legends of the Holocene start impacts to re-date his combination of the memories of the "Minoan" confederacy, and the Great Atlantic Mega-tsunami, and Egyptian accounts of their wars with the "Sea Peoples".

Perhaps Plato's dating failure was due to a failure of his health, as he would die a short time later, before completing the *Hermocrates*, the final part of his encyclopedia; perhaps Plato's dating failure was simply due to his desire to have a good story; or perhaps, what is far more likely, Plato hoped that by simply removing his account to the most remote antiquity, he would be able to remove it to a time when it would be beyond question. In any case, Aristotle did not think much of it.

THE ACROPOLIS AND THE CLASSES

"But in primitive times the hill of the Acropolis extended to the Eridanus and Ilissus, and included the Pnyx on one side, and the Lycabettus as a boundary on the opposite side to the Pnyx. And [the Acropolis] was entirely well covered with soil, and level at the top, except in one or two places.

"Outside the Acropolis and under the sides of the hill there dwelt artisans, and those of the husbandmen as were tilling the ground nearby. The warrior class dwelt by themselves around the temples of Athene and Hephaestus at the summit, which moreover they had enclosed with a single wall like the garden of a single house. On the north side the warriors had dwellings in common and had erected halls for dining in winter. And they had all the buildings which they needed for their common life, besides temples, but there was no adorning of them with gold and silver, for they made no use of these for any purpose. They took a middle course between meanness and ostentation, and built modest houses in which they and their children's children grew old, and they handed these houses down to others who were like themselves, always the same. But in the summertime they left their gardens and gymnasia and dining halls, and then the southern side of the hill was made use of by them for the same purpose.

"Where the Acropolis is now, there was a fountain, which was later choked by earthquake, and has left only the few small streams which still exist in the vicinity. But in those days the fountain gave an abundant supply of water for all, one of suitable temperature in summer and in winter.

"This is how they dwelt, those who were the guardians of their own citizens and the leaders of the Hellenes, who were their willing followers. And they took care to preserve the same number of men and women through all time, being so many as were required for warlike purposes, then as now-that is to say, about twenty thousand.

"Such were the ancient Athenians, and after this manner they righteously administered their own land and the rest of Hellas. They were renowned all over Europe and Asia for the beauty of their persons and for the many virtues of their souls, and of all men who lived in those days they were the most illustrious.

THE ATLANTEANS

"And next, if I have not forgotten what I heard when I was a child, I will impart to you the character and origin of their adversaries. For friends should not keep their stories to themselves, but have them in common.

"But before proceeding further in the narrative, I ought to warn you that you must not be surprised if you should perhaps hear Hellenic names given to the foreigners. I will tell you the reason for this: Solon, who was intending to use the tale for his poem, enquired into the meaning of the names, and found that the early Egyptians in writing them down had translated them into their own language. And he recovered the meaning of the several names, and when copying them out again, [he] translated them into our language.

"My great-grandfather, Dropides, had the original writing, which is still in my possession, and [it] was carefully studied by me when I was a child. Therefore if you hear names such as are used in this country, you must not be surprised, for I have told [you] how they came to be introduced.

THE DESCRIPTION OF CALLISTE [THERA]

"The tale, which was of great length, began as follows:

"I have remarked before while speaking of the allotments of the gods, that they distributed the whole Earth into portions differing in extent, and made for themselves temples and instituted sacrifices. And Poseidon, who received for his lot the island of Atlantis, fathered children by a mortal woman, and settled them in a part of the island, which I will describe.

"Looking towards the sea, but in the center of the whole island, there was a plain which is said to have been the fairest of all plains and very fertile. Near the plain again, and also in the center of the island at a distance of about fifty stadia[19], there was a mountain not very high on any side.

"In this mountain there dwelt one of the earth born primeval men of that country, whose name was Evenor, and he had a wife named Leucippe, and they had an only daughter who was called Cleito. [This is Calliste, the previous name of Thera.]

"The maiden [Cleito, Calliste] had already reached womanhood before her father and mother died. Poseidon fell in love with her and had intercourse with her. And breaking the ground, he inclosed all around the hill in which she dwelt, making alternate zones of sea and land larger and smaller, encircling one another. There were two [zones] of land and three [zones] of water, which he turned as with a lathe, each having its circumference equidistant every way from the center, so that no man could get to the island, for ships and voyages were not as yet. Poseidon himself, being a god, found no difficulty in making special arrangements for the center island, bringing up two springs of water from beneath the earth, one of warm water and the other of cold, and making every variety of food to spring up abundantly from the soil.

THE ATLANTIC DIVISION

"Poseidon also begat and brought up five pairs of twin male children; and dividing the island of Atlantis [which should not be confused with the island of Calliste, Cleito] into ten portions, he gave to the first-born of the eldest pair his mother's dwelling and the surrounding allotment, which was the largest and best, and made him king over the rest. The others he made princes, and gave them rule over many men, and a large territory.

"And he named them all: the eldest, who was the first king, he named Atlas, and after him the whole island and the ocean were called Atlantic. To his twin brother, who was born after him, and obtained as his lot the extremity of the island towards the Pillars of Heracles, facing the country which is now called the region of Gades in that part of the world, he gave the name which in the Hellenic language is Eumelus, in the language of the country which is named after him, Gadeirus.

These are the two kings of the two kingdoms, one on each side of the Straits of Gibraltar.

"Of the second pair of twins he called one Ampheres, and the other Evaemon. To the elder of the third pair of twins he gave the name Mneseus, and Autochthon to the one who followed him. Of the fourth pair of twins he called the elder Elasippus, and the younger Mestor. And of the fifth pair he gave to the elder the name of Azaes, and to the younger that of Diaprepes."

It is likely that these pairs follow a north-south pairing as well, but it is near useless to try and recover any information from them.

"All of these, and their descendants for many generations, were the inhabitants and rulers of the diverse islands in the open sea [Atlantic Ocean]; and also, as has been already said, they held sway in our direction over the country within the Pillars [of Heracles] as far as Egypt and Tyrrhenia [Etruscan Italy]."

Note the extent of the trade alliance within the Mediterranean.

"Now Atlas had a numerous and honorable family, and they retained the kingdom, the eldest son handing it on to his eldest for many generations; and they had such an amount of wealth as was never before possessed by kings and potentates, and is not likely ever to be again, and they were furnished with everything which they needed, both in the city and country. For because of the greatness of their empire many things were brought to them from foreign countries, and the island itself provided most of what was required by them for the uses of life.

"In the first place, they dug out of the earth whatever was to be found there, solid as well as fusile, and that which is now only a name and was then something more than a name, orichalcum [copper], was dug out of the earth in many parts of the island, being more precious in those days than anything except gold. There was an abundance of wood for carpenter's work, and sufficient maintenance for tame and wild animals.

ELEPHANTS:
TRADE WITH COASTAL AFRICA

"Moreover, there were a great number of elephants in the island; for as there was provision for all other sorts of animals, both for those which live in lakes and marshes and rivers, and also for those which live in mountains and on plains, so there was for the animal which is the largest and most voracious of all.

"Also whatever fragrant things there now are in the earth, whether roots, or herbage, or woods, or the essences which can be distilled from fruit and flower, grew and thrived in that land - Also the fruit which admits of cultivation, both the dry sort, which is given us for nourishment, and any other which we use for food - we call them all by the common name pulse - And the fruits having a hard rind, affording drinks and meats and ointments [pomegranates] - And good store of chestnuts and the like, which furnish pleasure and amusement, and are fruits which spoil with keeping - And the pleasant kinds of dessert, with which we console ourselves after dinner, when we are tired of eating - All these that sacred island which then beheld the light of the sun, brought forth fair and wondrous and in infinite abundance. With such blessings the earth freely furnished them.

DESCRIPTION OF CALLISTE (THERA)

"Meanwhile they went on constructing their temples and palaces and harbors and docks, and they arranged the whole country in the following manner.

"First of all they bridged over the zones of sea which surrounded the ancient metropolis, making a road to and from the royal palace. And at the very beginning they built the palace in the habitation of the god and of their ancestors, which they continued to ornament in successive generations, every king surpassing the one who went before him to the utmost of his power, until they made the building a marvel to behold for size and for beauty.

"And beginning from the sea they bored a canal of three hundred feet in width and one hundred feet in depth, and fifty stadia in length [Plato gives another diameter for the island below], which they carried through to the outermost zone, making a passage from the sea up to this, which became a harbor, and leaving an opening sufficient to enable the largest vessels to find ingress.

"Moreover, they divided at the bridges the zones of land which parted the zones of sea, leaving room for a single trireme to pass out of one zone into another, and they covered over the channels so as to leave a way underneath for the ships; for the banks were raised considerably above the water.

"Now the largest of the zones into which a passage was cut from the sea was three stadia in breadth, and the zone of land which came next of equal breadth; but the next two zones, the one of water, the other of land, were two stadia, and the one which surrounded the central island was a stadium only in width. The island in which the palace was situated had a diameter of five stadia. All this including the zones and the bridge, which was the sixth part of a stadium in width, they surrounded by a stone wall on every side, placing towers and gates on the bridges where the sea passed in.

"The stone which was used in the work they quarried from underneath the center island and from underneath the zones, on the outer as well as the inner side. One kind was white, another black, and a third red; and as they quarried, at the same time they hollowed out double docks having roofs formed out of the native rock.

"Some of their buildings were simple, but in others they put together different stones, varying the color to please the eye, and to be a natural source of delight.

"The entire circuit of the wall which went round the outermost zone they covered with a coating of brass, and the circuit of the next wall they coated with tin, and the third, which encompassed the citadel, flashed with the red light of orichalcum [copper].

THE MEETING PLACE OF THE LYCEAN CONFEDERATION

"The palaces in the interior of the citadel were constructed in this way.

"In the center was a holy temple dedicated to Cleito [Calliste] and Poseidon, which remained inaccessible, and was surrounded by an enclosure of gold. This was the spot where the family of the ten princes first saw the light, and there the people annually brought the fruits of the earth in their season from all the ten portions, to be an offering to each of the ten. [Note this annual festival.]

"Here was Poseidon's own temple which was a stadium in length and half a stadium in width, and of a proportionate height, having a strange barbaric appearance. All the outside of the temple, with the exception of the pinnacles, they covered with silver, and the pinnacles with gold. In the interior of the temple the roof was of ivory, curiously wrought everywhere with gold and silver and orichalcum [copper]; and all the other parts, the walls and pillars and floor, they coated with orichalcum [copper].

173

"In the temple they placed statues of gold. There was the god himself standing in a chariot: the charioteer of six winged horses, and of such a size that he touched the roof of the building with his head. Around him there were a hundred Nereids riding on dolphins, for such was thought to be the number of them by the men of those days. There were also in the interior of the temple other images which had been dedicated by private persons. And around the temple on the outside were placed statues of gold of all the descendants of the ten kings and of their wives, and there were many other great offerings of kings and of private persons, coming both from the city itself and from the foreign cities over which they held sway. There was an altar too, which in size and workmanship corresponded to this magnificence, and the palaces, in like manner, answered to the greatness of the kingdom and the glory of the temple.

THE FOUNTAINS AND WATER SYSTEM OF CALLISTE (THERA)

"In the next place, they had fountains, one of cold and another of hot water, in gracious plenty flowing, and they were wonderfully adapted for use by reason of the pleasantness and excellence of their waters. They constructed buildings about them and planted suitable trees; also they made cisterns, some open to the heavens, others roofed over, to be used in winter as warm baths; there were the kings' baths, and the baths of private persons, which were kept apart; and there were separate baths for women, and for horses and cattle, and to each of them they gave as much adornment as was suitable.

"Of the water which ran off they carried some to the grove of Poseidon, where there were growing all manner of trees of wonderful height and beauty, owing to the excellence of the soil, while the remainder was conveyed by aqueducts along the bridges to the outer circles.

HORSES

"And there were many temples built and dedicated to many gods; also gardens and places of exercise, some for men, and others for horses, in both of the two islands formed by the zones. And in the center of the larger of the two [zones] there was set apart a race-course a stadium in width, and in length allowed to extend all round the island, for horses to race in.

"Also there were guardhouses at intervals for the guards, the more trusted of whom were appointed to keep watch in the lesser zone, which was nearer the Acropolis [Note the slip here for "center"], while the most trusted of all had houses given them within the citadel, near the persons of the kings.

THE DOCKS

"The docks were full of triremes and naval stores, and all things were quite ready for use.

174

"Enough of the plan of the royal palace. Leaving the palace and passing out across the three you came to a wall which began at the sea and went all round: this was everywhere distant fifty stadia [five stadia] from the largest zone or harbour, and enclosed the whole, the ends meeting at the mouth of the channel which led to the sea. The entire area was densely crowded with habitations; and the canal and the largest of the harbours were full of vessels and merchants coming from all parts, who, from their numbers, kept up a multitudinous sound of human voices, and din and clatter of all sorts night and day. "

THE REST OF [ANOTHER] LAND

Note that Critias explicictly states that the land described in the following passage is different from the island of Calliste (Thera). Perhaps it is a description of the entire Aegean basin, perhaps it is a description of an area around Ilium (Troy), perhaps it is a description of an area in southern Spain, perhaps it is a description of Cuba, perhaps it is a description of the Yucatan Peninsula, perhaps it is a description of the valley of Mexico, perhaps it is a description of North America with a reduced scale, perhaps it is a description of someplace else – the prefect land of Plato's mind...

"I have described the city and the environs of the ancient palace nearly in the words of Solon, and I now must endeavor to represent the nature and arrangement of THE REST OF THE LAND.

"The whole country was said by him to be very lofty and precipitous on the side of the sea, but the country immediately about and surrounding the city was a level plain, itself surrounded by mountains which descended towards the sea: it was smooth and even, and of an oblong shape, extending in one direction three thousand stadia, while across the center inland it was two thousand stadia. This part of the island looked towards the south, and was sheltered from the north.

"The surrounding mountains were celebrated for their number and size and beauty, far beyond any which still exist, having in them also many wealthy villages of country folk, and rivers, and lakes, and meadows supplying food enough for every animal, wild or tame, and much wood of various sorts, abundant for each and every kind of work.

"I will now describe the plain, as it was fashioned by nature and by the labors of many generations of kings through long ages. It was for the most part rectangular and oblong, and where falling out of the straight line, it followed the circular ditch. The depth, and width, and length of this ditch were incredible, and gave the impression that a work of such extent, in addition to so many others, could never have been artificial. Nevertheless I must say what I was told. It was excavated to the depth of a hundred feet, and its breadth was a stadium everywhere; it was carried round the whole of the plain, and was ten thousand stadia in length. It received the streams which came down from the mountains, and winding round the plain and meeting at the city, was there let off into the sea."

175

What follows is a description of irrigation agriculture, but whether this was Mesoamerican or Anatolian (Ilian - Trojan) is unclear.

"Further inland, likewise, straight canals of a hundred feet in width were cut from it through the plain, and again let off into the ditch leading to the sea: these canals were at intervals of a hundred stadia, and by them they brought down the wood from the mountains to the city, and conveyed the fruits of the earth in ships, cutting transverse passages from one canal into another, and to the city. Twice in the year they gathered the fruits of the earth, in winter having the benefit of the rains of heaven, and in summer [having the benefit of] the water which the land supplied by introducing streams from the canals."

HORSES AND CALVARY

As there were no horses in Mesoamerica, this passage must either describe the Trading League, or the Lycian Confederation's method of raising troops, or be another "wish" of Plato for a "perfect" method of organizing military forces. It would be interesting to compare it with Etruscan troop levies.

"As to the population, each of the lots in the plain had to find a leader for the men who were fit for military service, and the size of a lot was a square of ten stadia each way, and the total number of all the lots was sixty thousand. And of the inhabitants of the mountains and of the rest of the country there was also a vast multitude, which was distributed among the lots and had leaders assigned to them according to their districts and villages. The leader was required to furnish for the war the sixth portion of a war-chariot, so as to make up a total of ten thousand chariots; also two horses and riders for them, and a pair of chariot-horses without a seat, accompanied by a horseman who could fight on foot carrying a small shield, and having a charioteer who stood behind the man-at-arms to guide the two horses. Also, the leader was bound to furnish two heavy armed soldiers, two slingers, three stone-shooters, and three javelin-men, who were light-armed, and four sailors to make up the complement of twelve hundred ships.

"Such was the military order of the royal city. The order of the other nine governments varied, and it would be wearisome to recount their several differences. [It would be wearisome, because they were already included in the troop count just given.]

METHOD OF LOCAL GOVERNANCE

"As to offices and honours, the following was the arrangement from the first. Each of the ten kings in his own division and in his own city had the absolute control of the citizens, and, in most cases, of the laws, punishing and slaying whomsoever he would.

LYCIAN CONFEDERATION MEETINGS ON CALLISTE (THERA)

"Now the order of precedence among them and their mutual relations were
regulated by the commands of Poseidon which the law had handed down.
These were inscribed by the first kings on a pillar of orichalcum [copper],
which was situated in the middle of the island, at the temple of Poseidon,
whither the kings were gathered together every fifth and every sixth year
alternately, thus giving equal honour to the odd and to the even number. "

This amounts to a 5+6+5+6 or 22 year cycle, which roughly corresponds to a normal
sunspot cycle.

BULL SACRIFICE

There were no bulls in the Americas, only bison, and there is no record of bison
sacrifice. There are representations of bull sacrifice on Crete, and this passage
therefore most probably refers to the Lycian ("Minoan") Confederation.

"And when they were gathered together they consulted about their common
interests, and enquired if any one had transgressed in anything, and passed
judgment. And before they passed judgment they gave their pledges to one
another on this wise: There were bulls who had the range of the temple of
Poseidon; and the ten kings, being left alone in the temple, after they had
offered prayers to the god that they might capture the victim which was
acceptable to him, hunted the bulls, without weapons but with staves and
nooses; and the bull which they caught they led up to the pillar and cut its
throat over the top of it so that the blood fell upon the sacred inscription.

"Now on the pillar, besides the laws, there was inscribed an oath invoking
mighty curses on the disobedient. When therefore, after slaying the bull in the
accustomed manner, they had burnt its limbs, they filled a bowl of wine and
cast in a clot of blood for each of them; the rest of the victim they put in the
fire, after having purified the column all round. Then they drew from the bowl
in golden cups, and pouring a libation on the fire, they swore that they would
judge according to the laws on the pillar, and would punish him who in any
point had already transgressed them, and that for the future they would not,
if they could help, offend against the writing on the pillar, and would neither
command others, nor obey any ruler who commanded them, to act otherwise
than according to the laws of their father Poseidon. This was the prayer which
each of them offered up for himself and for his descendants, at the same time
drinking and dedicating the cup out of which he drank in the temple of the
god.

"And after they had dined and satisfied their needs, when darkness came on,
and the fire about the sacrifice was cool, all of them put on most beautiful
azure robes, and sitting on the ground, at night, over the embers of the
sacrifices by which they had sworn, and extinguishing all the fire about the
temple, they received and gave judgment, if any of them had an accusation

to bring against any one; and after they had given judgment, at daybreak they wrote down their sentences on a golden tablet, and dedicated it together with their robes to be a memorial.

THE LYCIAN CONFEDERATION

"There were many special laws affecting the several kings inscribed about the temples, but the most important was the following: They were not to take up arms against one another, and they were all to come to the rescue if any one in any of their cities attempted to overthrow the royal house; like their ancestors, they were to deliberate in common about war and other matters, giving the supremacy to the descendants of Atlas. And the king was not to have the power of life and death over any of his kinsmen unless he had the assent of the majority of the ten.

THE WAR

"Such was the vast power which the god Poseidon settled in the lost island of Atlantis, and this power he afterwards directed against our land for the following reasons, as tradition tells:

"For many generations, as long as the divine nature lasted in them, they were obedient to the laws, and well-affectioned towards the god [Poseidon], whose seed they were: For they possessed true and in every way great spirits, uniting gentleness with wisdom in the various chances of life, and in their intercourse with one another. They despised everything but virtue, caring little for their present state of life, thinking lightly of the possession of gold and other property, which seemed only a burden to them. Neither were they intoxicated by luxury, nor did wealth deprive them of their self-control: but they were sober, and saw clearly that all these goods are increased by virtue and friendship with one another, whereas by too great regard and respect for them, they are lost and friendship with them.

"By such reflections and by the continuance in them of a divine nature, the qualities which we have described grew and increased among them. But when the divine portion began to fade away, and became diluted too often and too much with the mortal admixture, human nature got the upper hand. And then they, being unable to bear their fortune, behaved unseemly, and to him who had an eye to see [they] grew visibly debased, for they were losing the fairest of their precious gifts. But to those who had no eye to see the true happiness, they appeared glorious and blessed, at the very time when they were full of avarice and unrighteous power.

"Zeus, the god of gods, who rules according to law, and is able to see into such things, perceived that an honorable race was in a woeful plight, and wanting to inflict punishment on them, that they might be chastened and improve, collected all the gods into their most holy habitation, which, being placed in the center of the world, beholds all created things.

"And when he had called them together, he spoke as follows- "

The rest of the dialogue of *Critias* has been lost – or perhaps Plato never wrote it. Note that Plato acknowledges here the gods of Athens, trying to avoid the charges of blasphemy which led to Socrates' execution. It is entirely possible that Plato realized that his reconstruction of history was faulty, and with Socrates finally realized that the Greek gods were merely men made divine… There's no way of knowing, as the answers to these questions died with Plato.

THE DIFFICULTIES OF WORKING WITH NON-MAYAN MEGA-TSUNAMI ACCOUNTS: LATER POPULATION MOVEMENTS AND CULTURAL TRADITIONS IN CENTRAL AMERICA

There are abundant non-Mayan materials which preserve memory of the Great Atlantic Impact Mega-Tsunami, but they have been omitted here, and a few words of explanation are in order to explain this decision.

It must be remembered that this event occurred some 3,000 years ago, and there have been many migrations since then, some of which will be covered later in this book. Given all of these cultural overlays, the original Formative peoples' flood stories were severely modified by each succeeding people. To use these materials here, it would have been necessary to go through each of these stories in depth and strip off each cultural layer, in order to finally arrive at last at something approaching an accurate memory of events.

This has important consequences, particularly when working with the 20-some pictographic manuscripts which the Spanish conquistadors sent home from their base of conquest in the city of Texcoco. (Texcoco was a city in the Valley of Mexico which was a rival to the Mexica (Aztec) capitol city of Tenochtitlan). All that it is necessary to do to use these manuscripts historically is to firmly identify and then strip out the Mexica, Toltec, and Teotihaucan layers of them.

The same problems hold true for the flood legends from the Caribbean Islands: to use these here, we would have to go through each of the numerous flood myths from the islands, examining closely the migrations of peoples from South America and Central America into each island, the exact time and place of the recording of each myth, and through labored analysis attempt to come up with something approaching a fact.

Fortunately, the Mayan reports of this impact event survived fairly intact.

(Footnotes)

[1] Adapted (for tense and pronoun identification) from John R. Swanton, *Myths and Tales of the Southwestern Indians*, Bureau of Ethnology Bulletin 88, Smithsonian Institution, United States Government Printing Office, 1929, Alabama Story 4

[2] Covered in Chapter 6 here

[3] Adapted from *The Codex Perez and the Book of Chilam Balam of Mani*, page 118, translated to English with notes by Eugene Craine and Reginald Reindorp, University of Oklahoma Press, Norma, 1979. It is unclear from the statements of Craine and Reindorp whether the parts in parenthesis are new readings, restorations from other copies, or their own additions to the text.

[4] For this idenitification, see Linda Schele, with David Freidel and Joy Parker, *Maya Cosmos*, Quill/William Morrow, New York, 1993, in particular p. 97

[5] Glossed by Craine and Reindrop as the Four *Bacabs*, but this does not seem correct, as the *Musencabs* are shamans: See the passages given here below

[6] "musencab" reading as in footnote 5

[7] These have been identified as either gods, creators, conjurors, priests, steps, the Lord of the Nine Generations, and the Nine Doctors – see Munro, 1982, p. 46, f. 888 and Schele, 1993. Most likely they are simply the well attested Mayan hallucinogens.

[8] =alligator:Munro,1986; =Milky Way:Schele, 1993

[9] Adapted from *The Book of Chilam Balam of Tizimin: The Ancient Future of the Itza*, translated and annotated by Munro S. Edmonson, University of Texas Press, Austin, 1982, page 45 *et seq.*

[10] Adapted from *The Book of Chilam Balam of Tizimin*, Edmonson, pages 40-41.

[11] Adapted from *The Book of Chilam Balam of Chumayel: Heaven Born Merida and Its Destiny*, translated by Munro S Edmonson, University of Texas Press, Austin, 1986, page 152 et seq. I prefer Edmonson's translations where available.

[12] Extensive discussion of these identifications may be found in the Cambridge Conference Archives, maintained by Bob Kobres.

[13] Adapted from Benjamin Jowett's translation

[14] Note the use of drugs for both hallucinogenic as well as medical purposes, as is also commonly seen in the Americas.

[15] Adapted from Benjamin Jowett's translation

[16] For an overview of the archaeological investigations of the eruption of Thera, see Charles R. Pellegrino's Unearthing Atlantis: An Archaeological Odyssey to the Fabled Lost Civilization, Avon/Harpers Collins, New York, 1991. Extensive discussion of geological evidence is available in the Cambridge Conference Archive

[17] Ovid's Metamorphosis I: 244

[18] Chapter 3 here

[19] The length of a "stadia" is approximately 607 feet, and 5,280 feet are in an English mile – metric converters are available on the internet. If you wish to convert all of Plato's measurements into modern units of measurement go ahead, but remember that the resulting numbers are highly likely to be completely useless: first because they are Plato's numbers; and second because they have been transmitted for centuries, and are very likely to have been further corrupted.

CHAPTER 9

AFTER THE FLOOD

THE END OF THE EUROPEAN COPPER TRADE

The copper trade was now at an end - thanks to the impact of a fragment of Comet Encke and the resulting Great Atlantic Mega-Tsunami. There were no more copper traders: not only had the Olmec (Zoque) been crippled, and the island peoples annihilated, but the southern eastern coastal cultures had come to an abrupt end, along with the Canadian Maritime Archaic.

The local peoples, who had long resented the Copper Traders, now began to attack.

ca 1,000 BCE: THE FIVE NATIONS' ACCOUNT OF THEIR WARS WITH THE GIANTS[1]

"About the time this occurred the Eagwehoewe people lived on the Kanawagae River, or the St. Lawrence River. But they could not enjoy tranquility, as they were invaded by Giants who they called Ronnongwetowanea, who came from the north and inhabited it to a considerable degree."

That this "invasion" of the Copper Trading Giants was a real event, and not simply a myth, is evidenced by the recovery of their early copper tools in the lands of the Five Nations. During the period of colonial settlement, scattered finds of copper tools were made throughout their lands, with significant finds of copper tools made in the area of the town of Baldwinsville near Lake Onondaga.[2]

"Now the Giants' mode of attack was silly, as they never dared to fall upon an enemy without the prospect of success. They especially took advantage of the times when warriors were absent from a town. After plundering the people's houses and making captives of those who they found, they would then hastily retreat to their residence in the north. "

THE FIVE NATIONS SECOND BATTLE WITH THE GIANTS

"One instance: A family of princes lived near the river St. Lawrence, a family which contained six brothers and a sister; and their father was a noble chieftain who had fallen in an earlier contest with the enemy Giants."

The "family' referred to here must have been composed of at least 7 Iroquoian peoples, with one of them ruled by a Queen and not by a King, as were the Five Families. Note also that their "father", the ruler of the Five Families, had been killed in an earlier battle with the Giants.]

181

"One time these brothers went out on a day's hunt, and left their sister alone in the camp. Unfortunately, while they were gone, a Giant made a vigorous attack and the woman soon became prey to the invader.

"In the evening the brothers returned to camp, and they were much grieved to discover that their sister was missing. They immediately made a search of the surrounding area, but the night became too late, and the darkness prevented them from carrying their search out further.

"In the morning the eldest brother determined to pursue the enemy until he could discover something about their sister, and he promised to return in seven days if nothing should happen to him. Accordingly the Prince set out and pursued the traces of the enemy.

"After he had journeyed three days he reached the Giant's residence about sundown. At first sight he discovered his sister was gathering some sticks for fuel near the Giant's house, but as he approached his sister she retired.

"The Princess soon proved by her conduct that she had fallen in love with the Giant, and that it was impossible to gain her confidence. The Prince was now brought to the point of view of dreading the enemy; however, he was still willing to risk the dangers he knew he was about to meet."

The Princess mentioned here may safely be identified with an Iroquoian Queen formerly in control of the Shenango River watershed and adjacent areas on Lake Erie, areas shown by archaeological evidence to have been under the control of the 'Giants' by this time.

"The Prince remained outside until about dusk, and then he entered the Giant's house. He was received happily by the Giant with the most favorable words, and his fears were soon dissipated as the Giant offered him his pipe as a tribute of his respect, which the Prince accepted.

"After enjoying the evening meal, they talked together for a good while, without the least appearance of hostility. As the night was getting late, the Prince was invited to bed. But the Giant now began to act to deceive the Prince, as he commenced to amuse him for part of the night in singing songs. The Giant had determined to assassinate his visitor at his first opportunity.

"Now the Prince was so fatigued by his journey that he was soon fast asleep, and the Giant killed him there in bed. He then deposited the Prince's body in a cave near his house where he stored the carcasses. The Giant was much pleased with his conquest over the Prince, and he advised his wife to watch daily in order that he might impose on another enemy.

"The seven days during which the Prince had avowed to return elapsed. As his brother had not returned, the youngest of the brothers, Donhtonha, was greatly alarmed at his disappearance, and he resolved to pursue him.

"Now Donhtonha was a most stout and ferocious looking fellow, and after he armed himself, he commenced the journey to the Giant. Now Donhtonha also arrived at the place after the time mentioned, and he also found his sister, just as his brother had earlier. And before he had time to reconcile with her, she returned to the house, exactly as she had done before, and informed the Giant that some person was coming.

"Donhtonha entered the Giant's house appearing very angry and ready to strike, and he enquired for his brother. This alarmed the Giant, and he was prompt to pacify Prince Donhtonha. The Giant replied that he had made peace with Donhtonha's brother, who had then gone on to visit some people in the neighborhood, and that he expected that he would return at any moment.

"Upon this assurance Donhtonha's anger became somewhat abated; his sister provided some food, and he was soon enjoying their domestic felicity. But alas, the Giant was far from being friendly, and he was only taking the time to form a plan to deceive his visitor.

"The evening was growing late, and Dohhtonha was out of patience waiting for his brother to return, and he renewed his enquiries. So the Giant invited his visitor to bed, where he hoped to kill him.

"Now the Giant rose from his seat and commenced his usual custom in singing. But Prince Donhtonha perceived that some evil plan was being carried out against him, and he resolved to abandon the bed for a while. He begged leave for a few moments, and went out after various considerations from being imposed.

"There Donhtonha procured some pieces of wood which produced a faint light in the night, and he put them above his eyelids and again went back to the bed. The giant was now deceived, for while his visitor was asleep, his eyes appeared as though he was continually awake.

"As soon as daylight came, Donhtonha hurried from the bed. He was about to make a search for his deceased brother, but the Giant protested this to him, which soon excited his suspicions of the act. After a long debate Donhtonha attacked the Giant, and a severe fight ensued.

"At last Donhtonha killed the Giant, and he burnt him in the ruins of his house. But the Giant's spirit fled to the heavens and changed into one of the eastern stars.

"Now during the engagement Donhtonha's sister had become aggrieved, and she fled to the wilderness, and lamented there for her deceased husband. And she died in despair, but her spirit also became one of the stars, one of the northern stars.

"After his conquest Donhtonha took up his search for his brother again. He discovered the remains of his brother, wept over them, and burnt them to ashes."

THE FIVE NATIONS THIRD BATTLE WITH THE GIANTS

"At another time another group of Ronnongwetowanea Giants attacked a small town located on the bank of the Kanawage River (St. Lawrence.) This occurred during the season when the people went out to hunt, and there was nobody left in the town except an old chief and his attendant, who was named Yatatonwatea.

"While these two were enjoying their repose in the house, they were suddenly attacked by Ronnongwetowanea Giants. But Yatatonwatea went out the back door and escaped, deserting the aged chief to his fate.

"The enemy, however, spared no time, and the chase was soon on; this caused Yatatonwatea to retreat as fast as possible. Yatatonwatea attempted to make resistance in various places, but he was compelled to retire at the very appearance of the enemy. He endeavored to gain his retreat by traversing various creeks and hills, but it was in vain.

"Yatatonwatea then undertook a new method of making a small effect upon the progress of his enemy. After running some distance, he discovered an imposition which his enemy would promptly cherish, and he drove a flock of pigeons in their way to amuse them until he could hide himself under the bank of the river.

"Unfortunately the flattering hope was seen to fail: Yatatonwatea remained there but a short time before he saw the enemy was coming at full speed, and he was soon obliged to abandon the position and continue his flight.

"Again, Yatatonwatea tried to conceal himself among the rocks of the mountain, but in the meantime the enemy advanced every moment. At this he became dismayed, finding that nothing could resist the impetuosity of his pursuer.

"But determined not to surrender as long as he was capable of keeping out of their reach, Yatatonwatea immediately took the path which led to the hunting grounds, in search of some of his people. Fortunately at a short distance he met two warriors, and he was instantly supported, and made a vigorous resistance. During the battle the warriors conducted themselves as heroes, which ultimately gained them the triumph, notwithstanding that one of them received a severe wound by club. After terrible combat the Ronnongwetowanea were exterminated.

"Yatatonwatea hastened to the hunting encampment with an alarm whoop and advised the people of the substance of what had happened, and the dangers which the enemy presented to their now vacant towns. As soon as the people received this intelligence, they immediately returned to their settlements.

900 BCE: THE FIVE NATIONS' FINAL BATTLE AGAINST THE GIANTS

"A convention was then held by the chieftains in order to take some measures to defend their country. As the Ronnongwetowanea tribe were not numerous, the chieftains deemed it expedient to raise a large force, and therefore sent a few hundred warriors to subdue them.

"After decisive contests the warriors gained the victory, and it was supposed that the Ronnongwetowanea tribe has ever since ceased to exist.

"This fate probably befell them about 2,500 winters before the Dutch came to the lands of the Five Nations. [3]

Using a rough date of 1600 CE for the appearance of the Dutch in the lands of the Five Nations, we end up with a date of 900 BCE for this event, a date which agrees well with the date of the appearance of Adena culture along the southern Ohio River

THE ADENA:
THE COPPER TRADING GIANTS MOVE SOUTH AGAIN

The period after 1050 BCE marks the emergence of a distinctly different culture in the lower Ohio Valley and further to the south along the middle Mississippi River. With their European copper trade at an end, and under attack by the Five Nations, the Copper Traders now moved south again, this time to the warmer climes.

Somewhat bizarrely, in Ohio their culture is known by the Greek word "Adena", (sufficient), the name given to the plantation on which the type site for their culture was first excavated.[4] From the large burial mounds which the Adena built for only some individuals, it is safe to infer that their society was highly hierarchical, with Kings, nobles, and peasants. Atlatl weights, blowgun mouthpieces, and "tablets" used for the application of toxins to blowgun points are commonly found in the graves of high-ranking individuals.

These blowguns were particularly effective against small game. Usually when one travels to excavated sites, one finds blowgun mouthpieces labeled as pipes, even though the design of the object is completely inappropriate for smoking. While there were pipes, their interiors have never been checked for organic residues, and what was smoked in them is always asserted to be tobacco, while there is absolutely no hard evidence of tobacco use during very early periods. Tubes for the application of dry red ochre paint have also been found, and these also are commonly labeled as pipes.[5]

The Adena built large ditched villages, often digging their ditches in circles, squares, pentagons, or following natural edges. Many have tried to see these structures as the forerunners of "Hopewell" Hopewell observatories, but "Hopewell" Hopewell observatories show no sign of all-year occupation. Adena houses, which were circular and roofed, reached some 37 feet in diameter. As was seen in Chapter 7, this use of circular structures continued the Copper Traders' earlier practice.

Adena ritual seems to have centered on what are called "circular paired post structures", in other words four posts placed in a rectangle in the middle of unroofed circular log enclosures over 97 feet in diameter. As there has been some discussion as to what the function of these structures is, with no consensus having been reached so far, I suppose I may be forgiven for offering my guess on their use. I think the paired posts, the four posts found in the middle of these enclosures, supported platforms for the excarnation of the bodies of the dead: in other words, the corpses were placed on these platforms, and then the birds ate their flesh The circular palisades hid this "divine" process from prying eyes.

While Adena foods seem similar to those seen at Poverty Point, one of the interesting things about the Adena is their relative lack of trade goods from within the Poverty Point trade area. Another thing that is pretty clear is that so far absolutely no evidence has been found that the Adena shared the Thunderbird Cult evidenced at Poverty Point.

THE COPPER TRADING GIANTS MOVE SOUTH AND WEST:
A CHEROKEE TALE OF THE TSUNIHL'GUL[6]

This story was told by my father, and he said my grandmother told it to him:

It was in the Old Cherokee country where these Tsunihl'gul' lived. They were very tall, huge men.

There was a couple there, an old man and his wife, who had two daughters of marriageable age.

These daughters had heard many times about these tall, huge Tsunihl'gul'. These daughters were very desirous of seeing [the Tsunihl'gul'] for themselves because they had heard fantastic tales of these tall, huge men. They had heard that these men could pull up large trees with their bare hands alone. That's what they had heard, and that's what these young women desired to see.

At sunset they would hear a whooping in the west. (In the old Cherokee country there is a great mountain that begins in the east and does not end until it gets to the west.) When he [the whooper] whooped in the west, he whooped four times in traversing that mountain. His whooping ceased when he reached the end of the mountain in the east. At sunset the next evening he began whooping at the east end of the mountain. He whooped as he traversed the mountain and ceased [whooping] as he reached the west end.

This daily whooping was probably a method whereby Adena centers communicated their condition to each other. The practice of daily communal whoops at sunset would allow each center to confirm that its neighboring center was safe and had not been attacked since the last sunset.

"I wonder what we can do to see him," the young women asked themselves. So the old man [their father] called in seven conjurers." After they arrived, they decided to meet for conjuring. They determined that an intoxicating drink could be made and that they could pour it into huge cups and place them on the top of the mountain in the path where he [the Tsuhl'gul'] would be going.

"He will get drunk from these [cups], and one might be able to see him because he can't come up the hill" . . . No!" . . . "When he gets drunk, we can climb up the mountain and see him, but he won't be able to see us," said the conjurers.

This liquor that they made was called 'tsat'. They made it from corn meal and sugar in those days.

As corn did not appear until a thousand years later, this detail is clearly a later insertion. It is more likely that an early alcoholic beverage might have been made from maple sugar.

"So they made this liquor, and put it into big barrels of the sort that hold sixty-four gallons, and used six of these barrels. They put these barrels in the path where he would be going. He had a beautiful path: it was smooth and this (demonstrating) wide.

"After they had put the liquor in the middle of the path, they said, "Now let's listen for him tonight. If he is coming, we can hear him when he starts. Then we will know what he is going to do," said the old men. Then they sat in a row outside the house and looked at the top of the mountain. They watched and listened.

"Just at sundown they heard a [first] whoop. The second whoop came from the very top of the mountain. The third whoop was from right where the barrels had been put. And the fourth [whoop] they didn't hear. All was so very silent. "I wonder what he has done. He has become silent," said the men, [sitting] in a row.

"At dawn, when the roosters crowed, they heard him; but he was in the same place [at the barrels]. 'Now, they said. The last whoop came from the same place.' Then in a few minutes he whooped again. Then he whooped a third time in the same place. Several more times he whooped at the same place. He whooped many, many times.

"They said, 'He is drunk now,' because they heard him singing. 'So let's climb the mountain, and we will get there [at the barrels] just as it becomes daylight if we go now.' So they began climbing the mountain, and they took with them the [two] young women, the women who desired to see the Tsuhl'gul'.

"When they got to the top of the mountain, everything was quiet. Then they heard him whoop right behind them, just out of sight, and they heard another noise, sounding 'Daaast'!' The noise was as if he [the Tsuhl'gul] were breaking sticks. Then they saw the limbs of trees shaking.

"Then they saw the tall, huge man swaying. In his hand he had a sixty-five [gallon] barrel, drinking out of it. It had taken six men to carry one barrel up the mountain, and here he was, holding it in one hand and drinking out of it. While he was swaying, he was knocking over the smaller trees, and that is what they were hearing.

"There was a large area over which the Tsuhl'gul' had flattened the trees while he was drunk. This man that they saw there, was whooping, and every few minutes he told himself what a big man he was. When they came near him, the Tsuhl'gul' knelt down. He was still taller than they were. Then he lay down and talked with the old men.

"Then the [two] young women came up and took a look at his face. They saw that he had slanting eyes, and they fled and said, 'He has slantin eyes.'

"Then the Tsuhl'gul' asked the old men if he could have one of the young women: 'If you feel like it, will you give me one of the young women?' 'I'll give you both of them,' said one of the old men [the father], and so the Tsuhl'gul' had [the] two young women.

"The Tsuhl'gul' was very happy now, and he agreed to go with them [the two young women] to their home. They went down the mountain and went home. While going down the mountain, all observed him curiously. The Tsuhl'gul' was very friendly now.

"When they got home, the father wanted to go get some wood [firewood]. The Tsuhl'gul' said, 'I'll go get some wood.' He hunted the wood, and found it close by. He used his bare hands to cut the green trees into proper sizes. The in-laws were amazed at his strength.

"Later on, there were some neighbors. In those days Tsunihl'gul' were fond of women, and even though this Tsuhl'gul' had two wives, he wanted to marry the neighbors' daughters who lived a mile away, and he visited them often. But when he went to the neighbors' house, if it were still light, he always turned his back away from the people [who lived there].

"The Tsuhl'gul' always told funny stories when he visited these [other] young women. The young women would circle about him, trying to see his face; but the Tsuhl'gul' would always turn in another direction. The [other] young women said to each other, 'I wonder why he does that--turn away from the light? I wonder what we could do to see him?' [The two other young women had already seen him--and they were his wives!]

"So the daughters [X: the other young women] said to each other, 'Let's get some sumac tonight and make a fire because it pops [when it burns]. When he turns away, we'll put in our sumac, and the sparks from the popping might alight on him. Then he will turn toward the light.'

"So before nightfall they gathered a large pile of sumac. Early in the evening the Tsuhl'gul' arrived. When they gave him a chair by the fire, he sat down and turned away from the fire. When he did that, they put some sumac into the fire, the fire began to burn and to pop, 'Das', das', das', das', das', das'!' A spark fell upon the neck of the Tsuhl'gul' and the Tsuhl'gul' yelled, 'Ayo, yo, yo, yo!' He quickly turned around and faced the blazing fire. The young women saw his eyes: he had slanting eyes.

"'The big man has slanting eyes!' they said, and fled. When the young women fled, the Tsuhl'gul' became angry. He went far away. Then the Tsuhl'gul' began to conduct himself riotously and joined a gang of roisterers. When the Tsuhl'gul' joined this group, God permitted them all to live among people like us [of normal size]; but they were always taking all the women and wives away from ordinary-sized men until smaller men were without women. (The Tsunihl'gul' were very wicked, but women liked them.)

"So God declared that this was not the place for Tsunihl'gul'. God decided to send them all to the west, to the end of the world, and that's where they live now. Someday they may return, and we will see them, they say.

 - Siquanid

SOME ARCHAEOLOGICAL SITES

While its layout may or may not be directly related to Tsuhl'gul social organization described in this Cherokee legend, the organization of the following earthwork by four and its large central mound is interesting:

"The third group of this series [the remains near the town of Portsmouth in Ohio at the mouth of the Scioto River] is in Kentucky, near the mouth of the Tygert River. It consists of four concentric circles, placed at irregular intervals in respect to each other, and cut at right angles by four broad avenues, which conform in bearing very nearly to the four cardinal points. A large mound is placed in the center; it is truncated and terraced, and has a graded way leading to its summit."[7]

Another group of sites which seems to be related to this movement of the Copper Trading Giants are some large stone burial mounds. The following excavation report of one of them by Gerard Fowkes is of particular interest, as while Fowkes vigorously denied the existence of the Giants, nonetheless he found the remains of a giant in his own excavation, and much to his credit, he reported it: [8]

"Quite different from these [small stone graves] is a type of stone grave, once quite abundant on both sides of the Ohio River, from Manchester, Ohio, to Dover, Kentucky, a distance of twenty-five miles. A few stood at varying intervals for some miles below Dover, and as far up the river as Huntington, West Virginia; and some remain along North Fork of Licking River in Mason county, Kentucky. They were most abundant from Manchester to Ripley on the Ohio side of the river, and from Maysville to Dover on the Kentucky side. Between these points, almost, every peak, ridge, or high elevation, commanding an extensive view of the Ohio Valley, was crowned with at least one, and in many instances several of these cairns. The smallest ones contained not more than a wagon load of stones; the largest fully fifty times as much. Between these extremes was every intermediate size.

"Two miles above Aberdeen, a narrow ridge extends directly south for about 500 feet from the rolling table land. Its top is horizontal; its sides slope steeply like the roof of a house, to a gorge on either side; the end falls precipitously to the river level. A cairn on this ridge, about 300 feet from its point, was much the largest tumulus of this character yet discovered. It measured 34 feet from north to south, 37 feet from east to west, with its summit six feet above the southern margin. The surface on this side, however, is much lower than formerly, on account of careless cultivation...

"A trench reaching to the subsoil was dug entirely around the mound, and carried inward until the imbedded rocks were exposed; they covered an area: about 26 feet north and south, by 29 feet east and west... The entire area covered by these graves measured fifteen feet east and west by eleven feet north and south. The bones varied much in size; one jaw was massive and nearly two inches longer than that of anyone present at the time. Bones of children were also found. None were in condition for preservation.

"In the original soil, near the central portion of the earth mound on which these graves were made, were two small shallow holes containing some charcoal and scraps of burned animal bone; in one were two lumps of [red] ochre and a copper spool shaped object. Though much smaller, and of a slightly different pattern, the latter resembles the so-called "ear ornaments" frequently found in the large earth mounds."

THE COPPER TRADERS TAKE CONTROL OF THE UPPER MISSISSIPPI RIVER

No longer involved in trade with Europe, the Copper Traders had moved west and south, to the warmer climate of the lower Ohio River and the central Mississippi River. At this time clear evidence also appears along the western shore of Lake Michigan and along the Upper Mississippi River showing that they used this route to communicate with the Central Mississippi River Valley.

Adding to the confusion here, the remains of this culture are no longer known as the Red Paint Culture, or the Old Copper Culture, but now as the Red Ochre Culture. While this term hides the cultural continuity of these peoples, I suppose this is okay, as the use of this term indicates a site in the western lakes from around 1,000 BCE or shortly thereafter. In any case, the identifying marks are still the same as before: the use of red paint, iron oxide, in burials; the extensive tool inventory, including polished stone tools; and the emphasis on marine food sources. Additional key components are the use of large copper tools; the use of mounds for burial; and by now the production of crushed rock (grit) tempered pottery, Marion Thick pottery.

At the point where the Menominee River meets Lake Michigan, the Copper Traders shifted their habitation from the south side of the river at Chautauqua Grounds (2,260 BCE) to the north bank of the river at Riverside (1,000 BCE).[9] Marine shell from either the Atlantic Ocean or the Gulf of Mexico was found here, along with hornstone from Illinois/Indiana, and obsidian from the western United States,[10] which undoubtedly came to the Riverside site via St Paul (Chapter 7). On the Door Peninsula itself, Red Ochre remains have been found near Whitefish Bay.[11]

Further south along Lake Michigan, their remains have been found in the area of present day Milwaukee.[12]Moving still further south, their remains were also found at Antioch, near the Fox River, just to the west of Lake Michigan. "The thigh and arm bones, when measured against the side of the same bones in the men of the present day, indicate the man to have been over seven feet in height..."[13]

Along the upper Mississippi River Valley in Iowa, a key Red Ochre site was found at the junction of the Mississippi River with the Turkey River. The Turkey River Mound Group yielded a radiocarbon date sometime between 800-500 BCE.[14] Seasonal habitation sites featuring Marion Thick pottery use have been found in Iowa down the Mississippi River to Illinois.[15]

At Saint Louis, Red Ochre remains appear to have been incorporated into a later Mississippian mound. "In a very large mound [opposite St. Louis], square in shape, three hundred feet on each side and thirty feet high, there were found in contact with a number of copper implements and ornaments, a number of the teeth of the buffalo..."[16] While the "Mississipians" commonly made copper ornaments, they did not appear to use copper implements, which is to say copper tools, to any extent.

A final important observation about the distribution of the Red Ochre Culture which must be repeated here is one made by James Robertson, William Lovis, and John Halsey, which they based on the work of Mary Diddier.[17] If there is another key defining trait of the Red Ochre People besides their use of red ochre, it is their use of Turkey Tail points. These Turkey Tail points are elliptical in shape, with a pair of notches at one end which give them the appearance of a dressed turkey. They are nearly solely made from flint from Harrison County, Indiana, just north along the Ohio River from its junction with the Mississippi River, yet these Turkey Tail points are found from just to the south of Harrison County, in northern Alabama, clean up to northern Wisconsin, and eastward to the Finger Lakes region of New York.

The Copper Trading Giants had moved south.

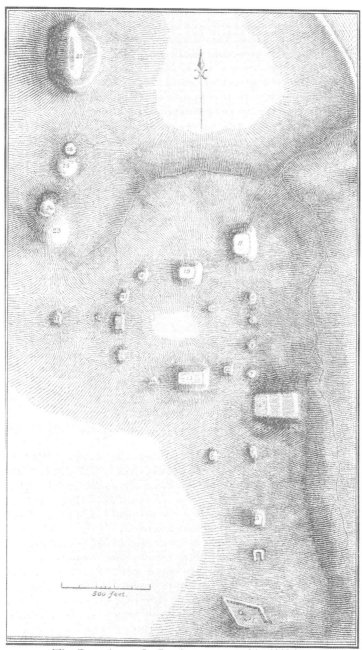

500 feet.

The Remains at St. Louis as mapped in 1819 by
Major S.H. Long of the United States Topographical Engineers. The
large mound to the north probably pre-dated the Mississippian period.

THE MENOMINI ATTACK

This state of affairs was short lived. The Copper Trading Giants were just as unloved in the west as they were in the east. Menomini accounts of their defeat of them have already been given in Chapter 5, and in this regard, the later men's graves at the Convent Knoll site in Milwaukee all showed signs of violent deaths in combat.[18]

CA. 600 BCE[19]: THE HOCHUNK ATTACK -
RED HORN'S SONS KILL THE GIANTS

With their route to the northern copper which traveled along Lake Michigan now closed to them, the Copper Trading Giants had one final route left to the north: up the Mississippi River, through the area of St Paul, and then on to the Mississippi River's northern most sources; then through the western lakes, and on to Lake Superior. The Hochunk now closed this route: [20]

"After walking for some time they came to a pleasant, level country in which a large village was situated. Then the Older Brother said, 'These are the people who killed our father.' In the middle of the village, in the chief's lodge, the scalps of their fathers were tied to a pole and used as flags. They were very much faded and Red Horn's hair had turned white.

"Then the Older Brother said, 'Brother, I hope that you are like me when you cry, for all who hear me must die.' So saying, he sang wailing songs, and the Giants in the village began to move about. 'Hee, Listen! Somebody is singing something!', and even as they spoke they jumped, head first, into the fire..."

"'Come', said the Older Brother, 'let us try to take our fathers' scalps away from these people.' [The "brotherhood" here is probably indicative of an alliance.] So they painted two of their arrows red, and two of them they painted black. Then, taking two quivers, each one of them started for the poles to which their fathers' scalps were attached... Then taking the arrows they had painted, they shot them into the throats of the [giant] guards who were looking upwards. The guards had had their bodies painted, two of them being black, and two of them being red. [This body painting is a red ochre trait. The arrows were probably not arrows, but rather atlatls.] That is why the boys had painted their arrows as they had. When those who were painted black were shot with the black arrows, they coughed up black blood until they died. The other two did the same when they were shot, except that their blood was red."

The Giants give chase, and Red Horn's two sons kill them with arrows. They finally began to kill them by clubbing them.

"Finally they came upon a little girl who was carrying her little brother on her back. These were the last of the Giants who were left. Then the Older Brother said, 'I thought I would destroy all of you, but if I did that, who will the people be able to call giants in the future? Because Earthmaker has created you, I will spare you, but you can no longer stay on this earth [land].' So saying, he threw them across the sea."

The northern copper trade of the Giants now ended.

EVENTS IN SOUTH AMERICA ca 900 BCE:
THE CANAS IMPACT

Due to the Inca imposition of a state religion, and the Spanish suppression of that religion, and the modern lack of funds for excavation or historical work, it is very difficult to work with South American myths. That said, it appears that an impact may have occurred at Canas near Cuzco, during the Early Horizon archaeological period, say around 900 BCE.

A few words of background are in order before presenting the surviving account of this impact. The Inca knew their empire as *Tahuantin-Suyu*, the four nations, *suyu*, united. These nations were *Colla-Suyu* in the south, which included Lake Titicaca, the home of an earlier empire; *Cunti-Suyu*, the nation which contained Cuzco, the Inca capitol; *Chinca-Suyu*, which contained the northern coastal region; and *Anti-Suyu*[21] in the northern mountain valley, which contained the cities of the upper Maranon River and its watershed.[22]

"*Viracocha*" appears to have been a general Incan term for any creator god, and adding to the confusion, the creator god's name also seems to have been used as part of their personal names by later Incan rulers. Viracocha, the Creator, was worshiped in the Temple of the Sun in Cuzco, along with the Sun, the Moon, the planet Venus (of the morning and evening), Thunder and Rainbow, and other lesser gods.[23] These last two major gods, Thunder and Rainbow, were the serpent gods *Yaku-mama* (Mother Water) and *Sach'a-mama* (Mother Tree), who represented primordial forces. When the snake *Yaku-mama* emerged from the underworld to the surface of the Earth, it "became" a great river, and when *Yaku-mama* emerged into the skies it "became" lightning. When the snake *Sach'a-mama* emerged into the skies it "became" rainbows.[24] My guess is that when *Yaku-mama* emerged into space it "became" comets and meteors; and my other guess is that from *Sach'a-mama*'s description as having two heads and appearing as an aged treewhich walked vertically with slowness, it may also have "been" the Milky Way.

The account given here of the Cuzco impact is adapted from that of Juan de Betanzos, *Suma y Narracion de Los Incas*, 1557.[25] Betanzos was a native of Spain who spent his adult life in Peru, became fluent in Quechua, married the niece of the last undisputed Incan King, Huayna Capac, and produced his history at the order of the Viceroy of Peru.[26]

> "And when Con Ticci Viracocha [the supreme creator] had accomplished this [the creation of men at Tihuanaco at Lake Titicaca], then he sent forth the two who had remained behind with him in Tihuanaco, to call forth the races of men in the same manner aforesaid.

These two other gods are Con Ticci Viracocha's two children, Imayana Viracocha and Tocapo Viracocha, most likely the earlier creator gods of two other kingdoms which the Inca conquered.

"One [of his sons Con Ticci Viracocha] sent through the province of Cunti-Suyu, that is to the left if one stands in Tihuanaco with one's back to the sunrise, to bring forth the people native to the province of Cunti-Suyu in the manner as aforesaid.

"The other [of his sons Con Ticci Viracocha] sent through the province of Anti-Suyu, which is on the right hand if one stands [in Tihuanaco with one's] back to the sunrise.

"When [Con Ticci Viracocha] had despatched those two, he himself left towards Cuzco, which lies between those provinces, traveling by the royal road over the sierra in the direction of Cajamarca. As he went he called forth the races of men in the manner you have heard.

"When [Con Ticci Viracocha] came to the district called Cacha, the district of the Canas [people], eighteen leagues [54 miles, 87 kilometers] from the city of Cuzco, when he called forth these Canas [people], they came forth armed. And when they saw [Con Ticci] Viracocha, not knowing him, they rushed upon him [with their] weapons in hand, intending to kill him.

"Understanding their purpose, when [Con Ticci Viracocha] saw them coming upon him thus, he suddenly made fire fall from heaven, burning a mountain peak in the direction where the [Canas] were. The people saw the fire and were terrified of being burned, so they cast their weapons on the ground and fled straight towards [Con Ticci] Viracocha.

"When they reached him they all cast themselves on the ground. And when he saw them so, he took a staff in his hand, went to where the fire was, and gave it two or three blows, whereupon it died out.

"Afterwards [Con Ticci Viracocha] told the Canas that he was their Creator, and they made a sumptuous huaca (that is, an idol or place of worship) in the place where it happened, and they and their descendants offered much gold and silver at the huaca [shrine]. And in memory of [Con Ticci] Viracocha and what happened, they set up in the huaca a huge sculpted stone figure on a large stone base about five yards long by one yard wide.

"I myself have seen the burnt mountain and the stones from it, and the burn extends for more than a quarter of a league [1207 meters]. And when I saw this marvel I called together the chief and most ancient people of the village of Cacha, and asked them about it, [and] they told me what I have recounted. The huaca [shrine] of [Con Ticci] Viracocha lies a stone's throw to the right of the burn on a level patch the other side of a stream which runs between it and the burn. Many persons have crossed the stream and have seen the huaca and the stone."

195

THE JAGUAR CULT AT CUZCO

If the location of this impact could be identified absolutely and then excavated, it would undoubtedly throw much light on the development of South American cultures. But an excavation is not necessary to show that this impact had a great effect on the local peoples.

As was observed earlier in Chapter 6, "jaguar" appears to have been a general South American term for comet/meteorite, and in connection with the Cuzco impact it is interesting to note that the city of Cuzco itself was laid out by its founders in the form of a jaguar.

THE CENTRAL AMERICAN MIGRATIONS ca 200 BCE:
MAIZE AND THE MAYA

One of the key questions archaeologists have been trying to answer for some time is the role of corn (maize) in the Americas. Where did the cultivation of corn (maize) begin, and how did the use of corn spread?

Pollen from a maize variety has been recovered at the very early date of 5100 BCE from a coastal site in Veracruz near the Zoque site of La Venta, and a more advanced version of maize shows up there only 100 years later. [27] My own guess is that this early maize was used by these early formative people simply to provide pasturage and fodder for deer herds which they then harvested. This guess is borne out to some extent by the continued cultivation of the smaller variety of maize down to around 2,500 BCE, and by these peoples' practice in later times of keeping game reserves.

More amazingly, manioc, the principle cultigen of the irrigation societies, shows up at La Venta at the very early date of 4,600 BCE, some 500 years after maize. Tracing the route of this plant from the Amazon jungle is difficult, as once again, in dealing with these early coastal cultures, one must remember that their remains may lie under the rising level of the waters of the oceans, or simply have been washed away by the Great Atlantic Impact Mega-Tsunami.

This same maize technology seen at La Venta seems to have spread elsewhere, as maize in the highlands of Mexico undergoes a marked change from 4,300 BCE to 3,500 BCE. Again, I am of the opinion that this may simply have been the development of animal forage. Why? Because the artifacts required to process the maize for human consumption have not been found.

If one is looking for the development of maize as a human foodstuff, I think one must look to the Mayan homeland of Kaminaljuyu, Guatemala. The Zoque had had control of the Atlantic to Pacific trade route which ran up the Grijalva River and then down the Izapa River to the Pacific Ocean, and they also had controlled trans-oceanic land routes which ran up the Usumacinta River, its tributary the Salinas, and then down to the Pacific. But while the Zoque had controlled the lower Montagu River from their base in Copan, the Maya at Kaminaljuyu blocked their access via this route to the Pacific.

If maize is to release its nutrients and be made sufficient to sustain human life, it requires that it be ground and soaked in lime water and then cooked, the "nixtamal" process. My guess is that this is what the Maya discovered how to do: this technology allowed the growth in their population, and their subsequent movement down the Salinas River and Belize River. The Maya were now in conflict with the Zoque, and this conflict would end with the Maya in control of nearly all of the former Zoque territory. An important factor to consider in this process is that it is entirely too likely that the Zoque population had been severely reduced around 1050 BCE by the mega-tsunami.

Besides their reliance on maize, the most distinctive thing about the Maya is their extensive use of a number of hallucinogens. This hallucinogen use is usually mentioned in passing in the literature, but it was quite central to Mayan life. The Mayan glyph for the investiture of a Lord, an Ahau, features him presenting his buttocks to the reader for a hallucinogenic enema, and scenes of this enema usage have been preserved on Mayan painted vases, and enema tubes themselves recovered from royal tombs. Even more to the point, one of the central symbols of Mayan religion, the ceiba tree, is a source for an MAO inhibitor used to amplify the effects of ayahuasca, a source of DMT. And DMT itself is described by those who have experimented with it as being like LSD, but much stronger. It's but little wonder then that some pieces of Mayan art feature scenes of self-decapitation.

ca 200 BCE: THE RISE OF TEOTIHUACAN

At about the same time as the Maya moved from their home area around Kaminaljuyu into the Zoque (Olmec) lands, another group appeared to the north in the region of the Valley of Mexico, and they established their control over the areas which the Formative peoples had previously held.

These peoples established their major city at Teotihuacan, and the cultural complex evidenced there is quite different from that of the either the Zoque or the Maya. Not only did these peoples appear on the scene without nearby cultural antecedent, their language family ,Otto-Manguean (Otomi/Mixtec/Zapotec), is different from that of Mayan.

The origin of these peoples is a problem which has vexed researchers for over a century. My guess, and let me emphasize that this is merely a guess, is that these people may have emigrated via large watercraft from the west coast of South America, and that their appearance in Mexico may be related to the disappearance of the Cupisnique people from South America around 200 BCE.

These Teotihuacanos, for lack of a better word, would go on to establish political dominance over both over most of the highlands as well as over the adjacent Mayan cities of the Usumacinta River, beginning at Mutal (Tikal) in 378 CE.[28] Wars between the group of Mayan cities under Teotihuacan influence and the group of cities not under Teotihuacan influence would continue until some 300 years later, to around the year 650 CE, when another people arrived, conquered Teotihuacan, established their control there, and began their own raids into the Mayan lands.

(Footnotes)

[1] David Cusick, *Ancient History of the Six Nations*, Appendix A here

[2] Charles C. Abbott, *Primitive Industry, or Illustrations of the Handiwork in Stone, Bone, and Clay of the Native Races of the Northern Atlantic Seaboard of America*, p. 411-422, in particular Chapter XXVIII, Copper Implements, p. 415-419. This work also contains significant material on a New Jersey copper deposit and copper work at the time of European contact, p. 412-414.

[3] Cusick, ibid

[4] Barbara Alice Mann, *Native Americans, Archaeologists, and the Mounds*, American Indian Studies, v. 14, Peter Lang pub, p. 116, following Don W. Dragoo, *Mounds for the Dead*, p. 3., and Sheltrone.

[5] For an exception to the treatment of artifacts in this way, see Robert N. Converse's treatment in *The Glacial Kame Indians*, Archaeological Society of Ohio, 1979

[6] *Friends of Thunder, Folktales of the Oklahoma Cherokees*, collected by Jack F. Kilpatrick and Anna G. Kilpatrick, Southern Methodist University Press, Dallas, p. 65-69.

[7] Ephraim Squier and Edwin Davis, *Ancient Monuments of the Mississippi Valley*, p. 78

[8] Gerard Fowke, *Archaeological History of Ohio*, Ohio State Archaeological and Historical Society, Columbus, Ohio, 1902, p. 393-402

[9] *Wonderful Power*, Susan R. Martin, Wayne State University Press, Detroit, Michigan, 1999, p. 162, citing Thomas Pleger, "A Functional and Temporal Analysis of Copper Implements from the Chautauqua Grounds Site", *Wisconsin Archaeologist*, v. 73 n. 3-4, 1992, p. 160-176, and personal communications with Pleger, including an unpublished paper on the Red Ochre Complex

[10] Martin, ibid , p. 163, citing James Griffin, "Hopewell and the Dark Black Glass", *Michigan Archaeologist*, 11, 1965, p. 115-155 for the obsidian identification. I assume Pleger made the other identifications.

[11] Victoria Dirst, *The People of the Dunes*, 1993, site report at Whitefish Bay, p. 35, citing Ronald J. Mason, *Great Lakes Archaeology*, Academic Press, New York, 1981, p. 219-224, citing accidental discovery during road building in 1905 et seq.

[12] David F. Overstreet, "The Convent Knoll Site", *Wisconsin Archaeologist*, v. 61 n.1, p. 34 –77, including a catalog of another seven "red ochre" sites in the immediate Milwaukee area. Overstreet mentions seeing a "robustness" in some of the remains, but the Waukesha County Court turned them over to a local Native American group before any analysis could be done. Whoever these people were, I hope that perhaps someday they'll lend this set of Giants' remains back to Overstreet to examine for a while.

[13] Frank R. Grover, *Some Indian Landmarks of the North Shore*, Chicago Historical Society, 1905, citing report of E.S. Ingalls, *Waukegan Chronicle*, 1852

[14] Lynn M. Alex, *Iowa'a Archaeological Past*, University of Iowa Press, Iowa City, 2000, p. 77-80.

[15] Alex, ibid., p. 88-92. Alex does not group the information on the Red Ochre Culture together in one place, viz. Table 3.

[16] William McAdams, *Records of Ancient Races in the Mississippi Valley*, via Fowke, op. cit., p. 391

[17] James Robertson, William Lovis, John Halsey, "The Late Archaic: Hunter-Gatherers in an Uncertain Environment", in *Retrieving Michigan's Bureid Past, The Archaeology of the Great Lakes State*, Cranbrook Institute of Science, Bulletin 64, 1999, Bloomfield Hills, Michigan, ed John Halsey, p. 117-118, citing Mary Ellen Didier, "A Distributional Study of the Turkey Tail Point", *Wisconsin Archaeologist*, v. 48 n. 3, 1967, p. 3-73; Noel

Justice, *Stone Age Spear and Arrow Points of the Midcontinental and Eastern United States*, Indiana University Press, Bloomington, Indiana, 1987; and William Richie, *A Typology and Nomenclature for New York Projectile Points*, Bulletin 384, New York State Museum and Science Service, Albany, 1961

[18] David F. Overstreet, "The Convent Knoll Site", *Wisconsin Archaeologist*, v. 61 n.1, p. 71

[19] For the date for Durst Phase, Robert J. Salzer and Grace Rajnovich, *The Gottschall Rockshelter*, Prairie Smoke Press, St. Paul, Minnesota, 2001, p. 74. A really impressive excavation and report – highly recommended.

[20] Paul Radin, *Winnebago Hero Cycles*, Indiana University Publications in Anthropology, Waverly Press, Baltimore, 1948, via Salzer and Rajnovich, op.cit.

[21] Keith Muscutt's *Warriors of the Clouds: A lost civilization in the Upper Amazon of Peru*, University of New Mexico Press, Albuquerque, is an excellent survey of the Chachapoya culture of the Anti-Suyu

[22] Perhaps the names of three of these quarters preserve an earlier Ch morpheme in their construction: Ch/Olla/Suyu, Ch/Unti/Suyu, Ch/Inchay/Suyu.

[23] Gary Urton, *Inca Myths*, British Museum Press and University of Texas Press, Austion, 1999, p. 10-13, no one source given

[24] Vicente Goyzeuta, *Cosqo, Inka's Sacred Capitol*. Goyzeuta has an excellent internet site at http://www.qosqo.com/qosqo/index.html.

[25] Harold Osborne, *South American Mythology*, Peter Bedrick Books, New York, 1968, 1983, p. 73-74

[26] Urton, op.cit., p. 28-29, citing R. Hamilton and D. Buchanan's translation of Betanzos, *Narrative of the Incas*, 1996. I have seen a mention of Urton's recent work on Inca astronomy, but I have not yet examined it.

[27]Economic Foundations of Olmec Civilization in the Gulf Coast Lowlands of Mexico, Mary Pohl, Reports Submitted to FAMSI, FAMSI, 2000

[28] Simon Martin and Nikolai Grube, *Chronicle of the Maya Kings and Queens*, Thames and Hudson, London, Slovenia, 2000, p. 29-31

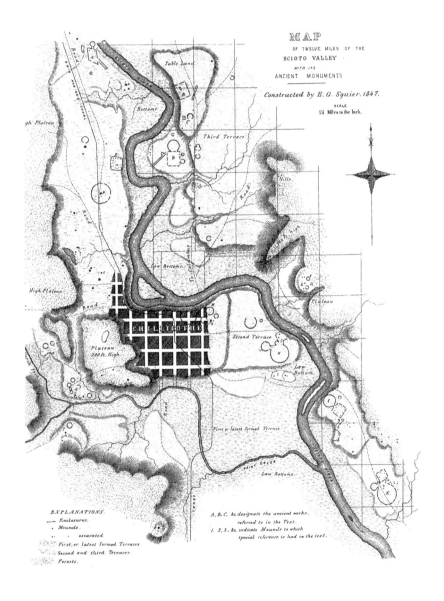

MAP
OF TWELVE MILES OF THE
SCIOTO VALLEY
WITH ITS
ANCIENT MONUMENTS

Constructed by E. G. Squier. 1847.

SCALE
1¼ Miles to the Inch.

Table Land.

Bottoms.

High Plateau.

Third Terrace.

Hills.

Road.

Low Bottoms.

High Plateau.

Road.

CHILLICOTHE

Plateau
200 ft. High.

Second Terrace.

Plateau

Low Bottom.

First or latest formed Terrace.

PAINT CREEK

Low Bottoms.

EXPLANATIONS.
— Enclosures.
• Mounds.
∴ excavated
First, or latest formed Terraces.
Second and third Terraces.
Forests.

A, B, C, &c designate the ancient works,
referred to in the Text.
1, 2, 3, &c indicate Mounds to which
special reference is had in the text.

201

CHAPTER 10

THE EMERGENCE OF "HOPEWELL" SOCIETIES

HOPEWELLIAN FORMS OF GOVERNMENT APPEAR

At about the time of the Celtic emigrations in Europe, say about 200 BCE or so, a massive revolt took place through most of the area that the descendants of the Copper Traders controlled. The classic Copper Trader single mound burials, which indicate a highly stratified society under the control of a single individual, were replaced throughout nearly the entire area by multiple mound burials, more egalitarian burials of both a diverse ruling class as well as their shamans, priests, and artisans.

Another piece of evidence of this revolt in many areas is the replacement of single-circle stand-alone astronomically oriented earthen structures with pairs of astronomically oriented rings, these paired rings nearly always accompanied by nearby paired square enclosures. As the introduction of these structures is always accompanied by great increases in trade among the regions, it may be safely inferred that these structures were used by two adjacent peoples to hold joint festivals.

Many people have been fascinated by these earthen remains and their contents, primarily because taken all together they somehow intuitively indicate freedom, peace, prosperity, and a very definite increase in technical and social knowledge. Their art, their structures, and their trade network have given the "Hopewell Hopewell" a certain mystique, and the term "Hopewell" has been adopted by other archaeologists to describe their societies. You have archaeologists talking about the "New York Hopewell" in New York, the "Goodhall Hopewell" in Michigan, the "Trempeleau Hopewell" in Wisconsin, the "Havana Hopewell" in Illinois, the "Kansas City Hopewell" in Kansas, the "Crab Orchard Hopewell" at the Ohio-Mississippi river junction, the "Cooper Hopewell" in Arkansas, the "Miller Hopewell" in Mississippi along the Mississippi River, the "Marksville Hopewell" in Louisiana, and the "Porter Hopewell" in coastal Mississippi. That there is no "Alabama Hopewell" is more reflective of the earlier lack of funds available to Alabama archaeologists than anything else.

But clearly there was something going on...

CA 100 CE: THE FIVE FAMILIES ADOPT HOPEWELLIAN FEDERATION

The following passages describing the Five Nations' adoption of the Hopewell form of government are adapted from David Cusick's Ancient History of the Six Nations[1]. The first loose confederacy of the Five Families is mentioned in Elias Johnson's account of the Holocene Start Impacts (Chapter 3), and another loose confederation is mentioned their accounts of their battles with the Giants (Chapter 9), which can be dated on archaeological grounds to shortly after the Great Atlantic Impact Mega-Tsunami, ca. 1,000 BCE. But there was also a later, more formal confederacy, which by Cusick's dating occurred around 100 CE, and this new confederation appears to have been organized based on a "Hopewellian" model. Of particular note is the introduction of extensive corn, beans, squash, potato, and tobacco agriculture.

"The Holder of the Heavens returned to the Five Families and formed their mode of confederacy, which was named Ggo-nea-seab-neh, which is to say 'The Long House', which included first, the Teakawrehhogeh people; second, the Newhawthetahgo people; third, the Seuhnaukata people; fourth, the Shoneanaweto people; and fifth, the Tehooneanyohent people.

"About this time it is supposed the Holder of the Heavens, an agent from the Superior Power, solemnly visited the families, and he instructed them in various things respecting the Infinity, matrimony, moral rules, worship, and other things. And he warned them that an Evil Spirit was in the world, and would induce the people to commit trespasses against the rules he had given them. And he offered them a favorable promise: if they remained in obedience to the rules he had given them, their souls would enter the place of happiness; but to those who were disobedient, their souls would be sent to a state of misery.

"And he gave them seeds for corn, beans, squashes, potatoes, and tobacco, along with directions on how to cultivate them. And he gave them dogs to aid them in pursuing the game, and he repeated his instruction on the game, and promised them that the great country was given to them for their maintenance.

"When he ended the interview of consolation he left."

THE FIVE NATIONS' ASTRONOMY:
LUNAR CALENDAR, THE SEASONS, AND ECLIPSE RITUALS

"The people had particular times of the moon [months] to make maple sugar, to plant corn, and to hunt deer and other animals. The seasons of the year, they are directed by the seven stars of the heavens.

"When warriors traveled in a great forest they were guided by a northern star.

"If the Sun or Moon was eclipsed, they believed that the Evil Spirit darkened it. The people assembled and made a loud noise to scare the Evil Spirit from the orb. [This function most likely accounts for the astronomical alignment of the Hopewell Hopewell observatories.]

"They believed that the clouds in the Moon were made of earth and inhabited by people."

WHERE DID THE HOPEWELLIAN SYSTEM OF GOVERNMENT EMERGE?

While we often think of "Hopewell" as being the classic "Hopewell Hopewell" of Ohio, and particularly those cultures of the Scioto River Valley trade network, in point of fact based on the archaeological evidence this revolution appears to have begun elsewhere even earlier. While the residents of the "Hopewell Hopewell" area later enthusiastically adopted the Hopewellian reforms, we know from the recent mitochondrial DNA studies performed by Lisa A. Mills[2] that the classic "Hopewell Hopewell" of Ohio display the X haplogroup of the Copper Traders[3], and it is unlikely that these reforms originated in their lands. So where did they begin?

THE CHEROKEE?

One key to the "Hopewell Hopewell"'s point of origin is that trade in mica and copper from deposits in North Carolina played a large role in their societies. The area around Copperhill, Tennessee, near the Hiwasee River, which is a tributary of the Tennessee River, was their source for sheets and nuggets of pure copper. The area of the Spruce Mountain Mineral District, in Mitchell County, North Carolina, near Holston River and French Broad River, which are tributaries of the Tennessee River, was their source for sheets of mica.

The key point here is that prior to the Hopewellian revolt, the intensive mining and trade in copper from Lake Superior seems to have come to a stop, or at least been greatly reduced. It may have been that that region was simply too cold, and since other sources of copper in warmer climates were now available, there was simply no longer any need to freeze to get copper. Or it may indicate a shift in political alliances. Cherokee resistance to the Copper Traders has been pointed out earlier[4], and their lands strike me as being as good a place as any for this revolution to have first occurred. Whatever the cause for the end of this trade, as I don't think there is any way to absolutely identify what it was, it should make good topic of conversation for anthropologists for decades to come.

Another possible indicator of an origin in the Cherokee regions is the deer horn headdresses which appear to have been used to indicate noble rank. A second class of officials show up in Hopewell Hopewell tombs, and their sign of office is a deer antler headdress. While deer often intentionally eat hallucinogens for intoxication, and thus deer antlers are regularly used by shamans as an indicator of office, antlers were also used as signs of office by lesser leaders of the Five Nations, who, as was seen above, had adopted the "Hopewell Hopewell" form of government.

A final indicator of an origin in the Cherokee regions is the "Hopewell Hopewell" remains which are well attested in Kentucky, even though among the archaeologists there made very little is made of them.

THE TENNESSEE RIVER?
THE HAMILTON, THE COPENA, AND THE HARMON CREEK CULTURES

Amazingly enough, there are no "Hopewells" in Tennessee. Instead the archaeologists there have been able to insist on 3 distinct cultures along the Tennessee River going from east to west: first is the Hamilton Culture, second the Copena Culture (from COpper and galENA), and lastly the Harmon Creek Culture. The Hamilton Culture along the Tennessee River bears a striking resemblance to the "Adena", and this is most likely one of the areas where the Adena form of government remained in power after the appearance of the Hopewell reforms. Since from the artifacts found in the

"Hopewell Hopewell" tombs it is clear that they were able to gain access to the mica and copper from North Carolina, this copper and mica must have come through the Copena area. Further down the Tennessee River were the Harmon Creek peoples, who had two important characteristics: one, they built ceremonial centers on hilltops, and two, they used stone for construction.[5]

THE SOUTHERN COASTAL REGIONS?

Conch shells from Florida have also been found in "Hopewell Hopewell" tombs. These conch shell drinking vessels were also later used by Southern Ceremonial Thunderbird Priest-Kings, and it can reasonably be inferred that they were used for drinking some kind of intoxicant. True pipes also make an appearance, which the archaeologists always assert without analysis were only used to smoke tobacco.

Given these trade goods, the possibility exists that perhaps more "democratic" forms of government had slowly emerged among the southern coastal peoples who had been devastated by the Great Atlantic Impact Mega-Tsunami.

ALONG THE LOWER MISSISSIPPI RIVER?

From what has been found in the graves of "Hopewell Hopewell" nobles, it appears that the "thunderbird" ceremonial complex was very well developed among them. Among the "Hopewell Hopewell" grave goods of particular note are the mica "bird claws" found in the nobles' graves, most likely intended to be worn by chiefs.

While the Cherokee cosmology featured cosmic thunderbirds (*tlanuwa*) and snakes (*uktena*), it appears that this thunderbird cult had earlier reached its fullest development along the southern Mississippi River, as was seen in Chapter 7. And as will be seen in the next chapter, the Kishpoko people themselves, who were the Hopewell Hopewell, would claim that they came from Weskumuisa [the Red Man, *Waaskoomisar*], a man in the south.

From the remains that were first visible at the time of European contact, clearly the junction of the Ohio River with the Mississippi River was a major "Hopewell Hopewell" trading junction. But as these remains were destroyed many years ago, many archaeologists act as though they never existed.

THE ANDASTES:
AN ADENA DISPERSION TO THE SUSQUEHANNA RIVER

Adena culture appears to have survived and evolved along the upper Ohio River from, say, Charleston, West Virginia, through Pittsburgh and then north. The region from Charleston to Pittsburgh was most likely the domain of the Pekowitha people whom the Shawnee will encounter in the next chapter (Chapter 11). The Cherokee would remember that a king of the Tsul' Kuhl, the slant-eyed or snake-eyed giants, dwelled on a great mountain in the Blue Ridge range, and viewed all the game in his district as his private property.[6]

From Pittsburgh north to Lake Erie along the Coniango-Shenango River route, and in a pocket along the upper Allegheny River, the Adena culture would evolve into what is known as Pennsylvanian Middle Woodland, which lacked the former culture's glory. No one was interested any longer in powerful kings, extremely hierarchical societies, and no one, even the surviving Adena along the Ohio, were going to continue to put up with it.

No one, that is, except for possibly those Adena who migrated east, well away from the Hopewell revolt. At the same time as a "Middle Adena" culture makes its appearance in the northern Appalachians, in the mountains of New England, the Hamilton Culture appears in eastern Tennessee. More importantly, Adena remains are now found at the mouth of the Susquehanna River, at the Saint Jones River site near Lebanon, Delaware, and the Sandy Hill site and West River sites in Maryland.[7]

Amazingly, it would appear that the Adena continued uninterrupted in this area around the head of the Chesapeake Bay clear into the times of European contact, as was seen from the account of the "giants" given by Captain John Smith's crew in Chapter 5.[8] Thus the possibility presents itself that the English, Dutch, Swedish, and French records of the Andaste (Susquehanna or Conestoga) people may preserve memories of the Copper Trading Giants, memories extending back through the Adena, through the Red Ochre, through the Old Copper, clear back to the time of the arrival of the Red Paint Peoples in North America some 8,000 years ago.

AN ENGLISH ACCOUNT OF THE COPPER TRADING GIANTS

As an example of this, consider these extracts from the account of the Andaste written by George Alsop, a London dandy who came to Maryland to work for Thomas Stockett, the province of Maryland's representative to the Andaste:[9]

> "Those Indians that I have conversed with in this province of Maryland, and have had any ocular experimental (eye witness) view of either their customs, manners, religions, and absurdities, are called by the name Susquehannocks [another European name for the Andastes], being a people looked upon by the Christian inhabitants as the most noble and heroic nation of Indians that dwell upon the confines of America; also [they] are so allowed and looked upon by the rest of the Indians, by a submissive and tributary acknowledgement: being a people cast into the mold of a most large and war-like deportment, the men being for the most part seven foot high in latitude, [with a] magnitude and bulk suitable to so high a pitch. Their voice [is] large and hollow, as ascending out of a cave, their gait and behavior straight, stately and majestic, treading upon the earth with as much pride, contempt, and disdain to so sordid a center, as can be imagined from a creature derived from the same mold and Earth."

Alsop followed this with detailed accounts of the Andaste's clothing, tattooing, government, and war regalia. He described their method of putting prisoners of war to death:

"The common and usual deaths they put their prisoners to, is to bind them
to stakes, making a fire some distance from them; then one or [the] other of
them, whose genius delights in the art of paganish dissection, with a sharp
knife or flint cuts the cutis or outermost skin of the brow so deep, until their
nails, or rather [their] talons, can fasten themselves firm and secure in [it], then
with a most rigid jerk disrobeth the head of skin and hair at one pull, leaving
the skull almost as bare as those monumental skeletons at Surgeon's Hall. But
for fear [their prisoner] should get cold by leaving so warm and customary a
cap off, they immediately apply to [their prisoner's] skull a cataplasm [plaster]
of hot embers to keep their peri-cranium warm."

Whether the European colonists invented scalping has been much debated, but
from this account it would appear that they learned the practice from the Andaste.
Continuing with Alsop's account:

"While they are thus acting this cruelty on their heads, several others are
preparing pieces of iron, and barrels of old guns, which they make red hot, to
sear each part and lineament of their [prisoners'] bodies, which they perform
and act in a most cruel and barbarous manner. And while they are thus in the
midst of their torments and excreable usage, some tearing their skin and hair
of their head off by violence, others searing their bodies with hot irons, some
are cutting their flesh off, and eating it before their eyes raw while they are
alive..."

Other Native American peoples knew well about the "cannibalism" of the "giants",
and it is remarkable that the giants survived for some millennia. The Andaste did for at
least 1600 years, and were one of the few people to survive the later Lenape and Sioux
migrations. Usually the baking of the prisoner's brain finally led to a merciful death,
its done-ness indicated when the prisoner's eyes popped out of his head. After death
the prisoner's body was distributed for general consumption, including the brain itself,
which the colonists wryly termed an "Indian Pudding".

How well did Alsop know the Andaste? Apparently, being a giant led to some
problems, which Alsop described:

"Before I bring my heathenish story to a period [end], I have one thing
worthy of your observation, for as our Grammatical Rules have it, "Non decet
quenquam mingere currentum aut mandatem", [or], "It does not become any
man to piss [while] running or eating". These pagan men naturally observe the
same rule, for they are so far from running that like a hare [rabbit] they squat
to the ground as low as they can, while the women stand bolt upright with their
arms a-kimbo..."

Alsop describes the Andaste as living in bark long-houses, and burying their dead
sitting upright facing to the west within the palisades of their villages. He also states
that once every four years they would sacrifice an infant to their Creator [Devil]. This
practice may account for the infant burials found in Adena mounds, and their method
of treating prisoners of war may account for some of the other remains which have

been found in these.

More to our topic, the Andaste apparently tried to tell Alsop of the catastrophic impacts which had befallen them:

> "The Devil, as I said before, is all the God they own or worship, and that more out of fear than any real reverence to his infernal or diabolical greatness: He forcing them to obedience by his rough and rigid dealing with them, often appearing visibly among them to their terror [as does a comet], bastinadoing [beating] them even unto death, and burning their fields of corn and houses, that the relation thereof makes them tremble themselves when they tell it."

Unfortunately, Alsop does not seem to have been much interested in their account, and that is all we have of it from him. Perhaps more of it may survive elsewhere, buried away mouldering in one colonial library or another.

THE BRENHAM, KANSAS METEORITE IMPACT AND THE "HOPEWELL HOPEWELL"

At about the time the "Hopewell Hopewell" appear in the Ohio Valley, a fairly massive pallasite fell in Kansas. The crater it left measured some 40 by 60 feet, this after some 2,000 years of weathering and 80 years of plowing. By way of comparison, the main crater at Sikote Alin measured 85 feet across, and its explosion of somewhere near 8 kilotons at 5 kilometers altitude was visible and audible for some 300 to 400 kilometers.

Fragments of worked Brenham pallasite have been found in Hopewell tombs: in the Hopewell Mounds group, with a radiocarbon date of around 47 BCE; in the Turner Mounds group; and in the Liberty Mounds Group. There was lot of this meteorite, and trade in it continued for some 500 years: goods made from it were also recovered from the Fort Ancient site.[10]

THE FIVE NATIONS' WAR WITH THE "HOPEWELL HOPEWELL"

It is not surprising that non-Hopewell burials accompanied by flints from Onondaga and Deepkill in New York have been found in burials in Hopewell mounds. The following passages are adapted from David Cusick's Ancient History of the Six Nations.[11]

> "About this time there were various nations who inhabited the southern country. These nations had descended from the families which were dispersed after the vine broke on the Ohauweyoka [Ohio] River.

> "The Holder of the Heavens visited the Five Families and instructed them in the art of war, and favored them to gain the country beyond their limits; after which he disappeared.[12]

THE TUSCARORA ACCOUNT OF THE FIVE FAMILIES WAR WITH THE
"HOPEWELL HOPEWELL"[13]

> "*Perhaps about 1,200 before the Dutch appeared in the lands of the Five
> Nations*

Cusick misplaced the following two Tuscaroran passages, setting them "Perhaps about
2,200 years before Columbus discovered America", for which read "before the Dutch
appeared in the land of the Five Nations", as explained elsewhere. Clearly these
passages belong here, as they agree with the Five Nations account of their southern
war. If either Cusick's wampum count, manuscript, or printed version is changed
to read, "Perhaps about 1,200 before the Dutch appeared in the lands of the Five
Nations," it yields a date of about 400 CE, bringing this passage into close agreement
with both the archaeological record and the date given in the Five Nations' other
account of these wars.

> "About this time the northern families formed a confederacy, and seated a great
> council fire on the Saint Lawrence River. The northern families possessed the
> bank of the Great Lakes; while in the countries in the north there were plenty
> of beavers, the hunters were often opposed there by the Big Snakes."

As was explained earlier, the 'Big Snakes" are the Mississauga (Rattlesnake) people of
Ontario.

THE FIVE NATIONS VISIT THE HOPEWELL CAPITAL[14]

> "The people living on the south side of the Big Lake (Lake Erie) made bread
> of roots, and obtained a kind of potatoes and beans found in the rich soil
> there.

> "The northern nations appointed a Prince, and they immediately journeyed to
> the south and visited the great Emperor who resided at the Golden City, the
> capital of their vast empire."

The exact location of this capital is an open question, with both the complex on the
East Fork of the Little Miami River in Ohio and the complex near Cairo, Illinois,
presenting themselves as candidates. The Hopewell-Hopewell covered their earthworks
with layers of colored clay, and the "Golden City" probably received its "golden" color
from this practice.

> "After a time the Emperor built many forts throughout his dominions, and
> almost penetrated to Lake Erie. This produced great excitement, as the people
> of the north felt that they would soon be deprived of the country on the south
> side of the Great Lakes. They determined to defend their country against any
> infringement by this foreign people.

> "A long bloody war ensued which perhaps lasted about one hundred years. The
> people of the north were too skillful in the use of bows and arrows, and could

endure hardships which proved fatal to the foreign people. At last the northern nations gained the conquest, and destroyed all the foreigners' towns and forts, and left them in a heap of ruins… "

THE HOPEWELL HOPEWELL DEFENSE

In response to the Five Nations' attacks, the Hopewell Hopewell set up signaling stations which would allow them to quickly gather together the warriors from a large area to form a defensive force: [15]

"Many of the anomalous mounds occupy prominent and elevated positions, suggesting at once the purposes to which some of the cairns or hill mounds of the Celts were applied, namely, that of signal or alarm posts. A range of these mounds extends along the eastern border of the Scioto [River] Valley between Columbus and Chillicothe, the mounds being so placed in respect to each other that signals of fire might be transmitted along the whole line in a very few minutes. Opposite Chillicothe is a hill nearly 600 feet in height, the loftiest in that entire region, upon which one of these mounds is placed. A fire on this mound would be distinctly visible for twenty miles up and the same distance down the valley, and for a long way up the valleys of the two Paint Creeks, both of which abound in remains, and seem to have been especial favorites with the Mound Builders. Similar mounds occur at intervals along the Scioto [River] below Chillicothe, and also along the Ohio [River] and the two Miami [River]s. On the hills over looking the works at Portsmouth and Marietta mounds of stone are situated.

"The great mound near Miamisburg in Montgomery County was undoubtedly used for a signal station. This mound, the largest by far in Ohio, is 68 feet in perpendicular height, and 852 feet in circumference at the base, and contains about 1,300,000 cubic feet. It stands on a high hill just east of the Great Miami [River], and has a commanding view of the broad valley of the river. It overlooks the fort on Big Twin Creek, described elsewhere, and the incomplete works at Alexandersville, as well as others still farther up the river. A fire on its summit would be visible from the large mound on section nineteen of Madison township, Butler county, and from that communication could be made to all the enclosures of that county; it could be seen from the mound near Springboro, in Warren county, and thence across the country to Fort Ancient."

While the Hopewell Hopewell were now prepared to defend themselves against attacks by the Five Nations, they had absolutely no defense against what was to befall them next…

(Footnotes)

[1] Appendix A here

[2] *Mitochondrial DNA analysis of the Ohio Hopewell of the Hopewell Mound Group,* PhD Dissertation by Lisa A. Mills, Department of Anthropology, Ohio State University, 2003.

[3] Red Paint Peoples, Copper Traders, the Glacial Kame Peoples, Red Ochre Peoples, "Adena", etc.

[4] Chapter 9, here

[5] Thomas M.N. Lewis and Madeline Kneburg, *Tribes That Slumber,* University of Tennessee Press, Knoxville, Tennessee, p. 55-70

[6] Lewis Spence, *The Myths and Legends of the North American Indians,* 1914, 1975 ed., p. 125-126

[7] For the Susquehanna River sites, Don W. Dragoo, *Mounds for the Dead,* Annals of the Carnegie Museum, v. 37, The Carnegie Museum of Natural History, Pittsburgh, Pennsylvania, 1963, p. 282 and following

[8] Chapter 5 here.

[9] George Alsop, *A Character of the Province of Maryland,* printed by TJ for Peter Dring, London, 1666, edition of 1902, Burrows Brothers Company, Cleveland, editor Newton D. Merries

[10] Here I want to thank Bernd Pauli of the meteorite list for all of the valuable information which he has so generously provided to everyone over the years, and in particular for this key information on the Brenham and Sikote Alin impacts.

[11] Appendix A here.

[12] Cusick, Appendix A here

[13] Cusick, Appendix A

[14] Cusick, Appendix A

[15] Henry Shepard, *Antiquities of the State of Ohio,* John O. Yorston, Cincinnati, Ohio, 1887, p. 87

The Chillicothe and Kishpoko peoples seek help against Comet Encke:
Thunderbird Mound in the center of the Great Observatory Circle, Newark

CHAPTER 11

COMET ENCKE AND
THE CLIMATE COLLAPSE OF 536 CE IN THE AMERICAS

In his book *Catastrophe: An Investigation into the Origin of the Modern World* [1], David Keys set out historical data which demonstrates a general collapse of the world's climate following 536 CE. As will be shown below, this climatic collapse also occurred in North America.

In his book, Keys puts forward his hypothesis that this climatic collapse occurred due to the dust created by the explosion of a massive super-volcano in Indonesia. While it is known that this volcano erupted during this period, the problem here is that no such explosion is known to have occurred at exactly that date. Instead, Keys gives a report from a late edition of the Javanese work *The Book of Ancient Kings* that the Mount Raja Basa volcano erupted ca. 416 CE,[2] and then asserts that the date of this eruption must have been misdated in this Javanese work, as no major volcanic eruptions occurred then, and moved the reported eruption to 536 CE.[3]

The problem with Keys' explanation is that there was an outbreak of a plague in Europe between 443-446 CE, and the outbreaks of plagues are known to be tied to climatic collapses, with the climatic collapses disturbing the nesting habits of plague carrying rodents. This particular plague outbreak hit especially hard in those areas and among those peoples who were in close contact with the Roman trading network – thus the Saxons were able to greatly increase their immigration into both Brittannia and Gaul, and the Burgundians were able to establish their control over the Rhone River Basin.

Was this plague of 443 CE caused by a climate collapse due to the eruption of the Mount Raja Basa volcano? My guess is that it was, though we'll have to wait for new ice cores and their layers of volcanic dust before this question can be answered definitively.

THE DUST VEIL FROM COMET ENCKE
PRODUCES A CLIMATE COLLAPSE

A different explanation for the climate collapse of 536 CE has been put forward by tree-ring specialist Mike Baillie, who argues in his book *Exodus to Arthur: Catastrophic Encounters with Comets* that the 536 CE climatic collapse was connected with the dust veil which was produced by Comet Encke. And for this encounter with Comet Encke, as for the others set out here, the records of both continents once again agree.

A EUROPEAN ACCOUNT OF CLIMATE COLLAPSE
DUE TO COMETARY DUST LOADING,
FOLLOWED IMMEDIATELY BY PLAGUE, CA. 537 CE:

From Gregory of Tours' History of the Franks:[4]

"In like manner, before the disaster in Auvergne, mighty prodigies [signs] affrighted all that region. For often three or four great splendors appeared around the sun, which the country folk described as [being] themselves suns, saying: 'Behold, three or four suns in the sky!'

"And once, on the Kalends of October, the sun appeared so darkened that not a quarter part kept its light, but it was murky and discolored as sackcloth.

"Moreover, a star, by some styled a comet, which had a projection like a sword, appeared over that region throughout the whole year, and like the heavens seemed to burn."

Gregory was working from annals, most likely those of Auvergne itself. The next passage is not clear, but may relate to plague infected birds, so I include it here.

"Many other portents were made manifest. In the church of Clermont, while matins were being celebrated at dawn on the occasion of some feast, the bird called a crested lark, which had flown in, put out with its wings all the lamps which were lit, so fast that you might have fancied them all collected in one man's hand and suddenly plunged into water. It then passed into the sacristy beneath the door hanging and there too would have put out the lamp, but it was prevented [from doing so] by the doorkeepers and killed. In the church of the blessed Andrew another bird did likewise to all the lamps that were alight."

The plague immediately followed the appearance of the fragmenting comet.

"At the coming of the disaster itself, there was made such slaughter of the people of that region that the legions of men who fell there might not even be numbered. When coffins and planks failed, ten dead or more were buried in a common pit. In the single church of Saint Peter there were counted on a certain Sunday three hundred corpses, for death came suddenly. There appeared in the groin or armpit a wound like that from a snake bite, and those who had it were [so] swiftly destroyed by the poison, that on the second or third day they breathed their last; the strength of the poison robbed men of their senses."

THE DESTRUCTION OF BAZAS, FRANCE, BY IMPACT ca 580 CE

Not only did the climate collapse due to the dust from Comet Encke, larger fragments of Encke came down as well. Gregory provides us with information on the destruction of Bazas, France by impact ca 580 BCE.[5]

215

"Villages around Bordeaux were burned by a fire sent from heaven: it took so swift a hold that homesteads and threshing floors with the grain still spread out on them were reduced to ashes. There was no other apparent cause of this fire, so it must have come from God. [6]

"The city of Bazas was burned, so that the churches and the houses belonging to them were destroyed. We learned, however, that all the sacred vessels were saved from the flames." [7]

Another account of the destruction of Bazas was preserved by Adomnan in his Life of Saint Columba: [8]

"And proceeding with greater confidence, after a slight pause, he [Lugbe] took courage to question the Saint [Columba], saying: "No fearful vision has been shown to you, has it, in this very hour?" The saint gave him this answer: 'Very terrible retribution has just now been made, in a distant part of the world.' 'What kind of retribution?', said the youth, 'And in what country has it been made?'

"Then the saint spoke thus: "In this hour, sulphurous flame has been poured down from heaven upon a city of the Roman dominion within the borders of Italy [under the domination of Rome]; and close upon three thousand men, not counting the number of women and children, have perished. And before the present year is ended, the Gallic sailors arriving from the provinces of Gaul will tell you the same."

"After some months these words were proved to have been correct. For this Lugbe went, along with the holy man to the chief place of the district; and he (Lugbe) questioned the master and sailors of a ship which arrived, and heard those things about the city and its inhabitants related by them, all precisely as the memorable man had said."

PARALLEL EVENTS IN NORTH AMERICA:
THE COLLAPSE OF THE "HOPEWELL" CULTURES CA. 537 CE

If there is one thing that is an identifying mark of "Hopewell" cultures, it is their use of nuts for food, and for most of the "Hopewell" region that nut was the pecan. The pecan remains today an ingredient in many of the favorite foods of several Native American peoples.

When the 536 AD climate collapse came it must have wiped out their nut groves nearly entirely, to the point of freezing to death both the pecan and fruit trees. Most "Hopewell" societies came to an abrupt end. In contrast, the Troyville and Coles Creek cultures in the south (to be covered in Chapter 12), with their maize base, seem to have passed through the catastrophe with not too much effect. It may simply be that they were far enough south so that their nut tree groves and fruit tree groves did not freeze to death.

THE CROSS LAKE IMPACT ENDS
THE FEDERATION OF THE FIVE NATIONS,
AND LEADS TO THE FORMATION OF THE LONG HOUSE, ca 580 CE

Pieces of Comet Encke also seem to have hit in North America, as they did in Europe. The following account of the impact of one of them been adapted from Tuscarora Chief Elias Johnson's history of Hianwatha.[9], and David Cusick dated him to about 600 CE.[10]

The literal translation of the name Hianwatha is "Wise Man", and elsewhere in his work Johnson identifies the location of Hiawatha's village as being at what is now Cross Lake, New York. From the mention of a "simple government" in the following passage, it would appear that Hiawatha led the federation of the Families. Hiawatha prominently mentions invaders from the north, who were most likely being forced south by the collapsing climate.

> "While Hiawatha was thus living in domestic life quietly among the people of the hills, and administering their simple government with wisdom, they became alarmed by the sudden news of the approach of a furious and powerful enemy from north of the great lakes.

> "As the enemy advanced, they made an indiscriminate slaughter of men, women and children. The people fled from their villages a short time before them, and there was no heart in the people to make a stand against such powerful and ruthless invaders.

> "In this emergency, they fled to Hiawatha for his advice. He counseled them to call a general council of all the tribes from the east and west. 'For,' said he, 'our strength is not in the war club and arrows alone, but in wise counsels.'

> "He appointed a place on the banks of Onondaga Lake for the meeting. It was a clear eminence from which there was a wide prospect. Runners were dispatched in every direction, and the chiefs, warriors, and headmen forthwith assembled in great numbers, bringing with them, in the general alarm, their women and children. Fleets of canoes were seen on the bosom of the lake, and every interior warpath was kept open by the foot-prints of the different tribes hurrying to obey the summons of Hiawatha.

AN IMPACT EVENT ENDS THE FEDERATION OF THE FIVE FAMILIES

The following passages in Johnson's account may describe an impact event which occurred, one which destroyed Hiawatha's ability to lead the federation of the Five Families.

> "All but the wise man himself had been there for three days, anxiously awaiting the arrival of Hiawatha, when a messenger was dispatched after him. They found him gloomy and depressed…

"The day was calm and serene. No wind ruffled the lake, and scarcely a cloud floated in the sky above. But while the wise man was measuring his steps towards the place designated for the council, and while ascending from the water's edge, a rumbling and low sound was heard, as if it were caused by the approach of a violent, rushing wind. Instantly all the eyes were turned upwards, where a small and compact mass of cloudy darkness appeared. It gathered in size and velocity as it approached, and appeared to be directed inevitably to fall in the midst of the assembly…

"…But the force of the descending body was that of a sudden storm. They had hardly taken the resolution to halt when an immense bird, with long, extended wings, came down with a swoop. This gigantic agent of the sky came with such force that the assembly felt the shock…

"…But Hiawatha was inconsolable for his loss. He grieved sorely, day and night, and wore a desponding and dejected countenance. But these were only faint indications of the feelings of his heart. He threw himself upon the ground, and refused to be comforted. He seemed dumb with melancholy, and the people were concerned of his life. He spoke nothing; he made no answers to questions put to him, and laid still as if dead.

THE COUNCIL MEETS, AND THE LONGHOUSE FEDERATION IS FORMED

"After several days the council appointed a certain merry-hearted Chief to make him a visit, and to whisper a word of consolation in his ears to arouse him from his stupor. The result was successful. He approached with ceremonies and induced him to arise, and named the time when the council would convene. Yet haggard with grief, he called for refreshments and ate. He then adjusted his wardrobe and headdress and went to the council. He drew his robe of wolf-skin gracefully around him, and walked to his seat at the head of the assembled chiefs with a majestic step.

"Stillness and the most profound attention reigned in the council while he presided, and the discussion opened and proceeded. The subject of the invasion was handled by several of the ablest counselors and the bravest warriors. Various plans were proposed to defeat the enemy.

"Hiawatha listened with silence until all had finished speaking. His opinion was then asked. After a brief allusion of the calamity which had befallen him through the descent of the great bird by the Great Spirit, he spoke to the following effect:

"'I have listened to the words of the wise men and brave chiefs, but it is not fitting that we should do a thing of so much importance in haste; it is a subject demanding calm reflection and mature deliberation.'

"'Let us postpone the decision for one day. During this time we will weigh well the words of the speakers who have already spoken. If they are good, I will then approve of them. If they are not, I will then open to you my plan. It is one which I have reflected on, and feel confident that it will insure safety.'

"When another day had expired, the council again met. Hiawatha entered the assembly with even more than ordinary attention, and every eye was fixed upon him, when he began to address the council in the following words:

"'Friends and Brothers:-You being members of many tribes, you have come from a great distance; the voice of war has aroused you up; you are afraid for your homes, your wives, and your children; you tremble for your safety.

"'Believe me, I am with you. My heart beats with your hearts. We are one. We have one common object. We come to promote our common interest, and to determine how this can be best done.

"'To oppose those hordes of northern tribes [these are the Missasauga (rattle snake people) and their allies], singly and alone, would prove certain destruction. We can make no progress in that way. We must unite ourselves into one common band of brothers. We must have but one voice. Many voices makes confusion. We must have one fire, one pipe and one war club. This will give us strength.

"'If our warriors are united they can defeat the enemy and drive them from our land; if we do this, we are safe.

"'Onondaga, you are the people sitting under the shadow of the Great Tree, whose branches spread far and wide, and whose roots sink deep into the earth. You shall be the first nation, because you are warlike and mighty.

"'Oneida, and you, the people who recline your bodies against the Everlasting Stone, that cannot be moved, shall be the second nation, because you always give good counsel.

"'Seneca, and you, the people who have your habitation at the foot of the Great Mountain, and are overshadowed by its crags, shall be the third nation, because you are all greatly gifted in speech.

"'Cayuga, you, whose dwelling is in the Dark Forest, and whose home is everywhere, shall be the fourth nation, because of your superior cunning in hunting.

"'Mohawk, and you, the people who live in the open country, and possess much wisdom, shall be the fifth nation, because you understand better the art of raising corn and beans and making cabins.

"'You five great and powerful nations, with your tribes, must unite and have one common interest, and no foes shall disturb or subdue you.

219

""And you of the different nations of the south, and you of the west, may place yourselves under our protection, and we will protect you. We earnestly desire the alliance and friendship of you all.

"'And from you, Squaw-ki-haws (being a remote branch of the Seneca Nation), being the people who are as the Feeble Bushes, shall be chosen, a Virgin, who shall be the peacemaker for all the nations of the earth, and more particularly the favored Long House, by which name this confederacy shall ever sustain.

"'If we unite in one band, the Great Spirit will smile upon us, and we shall be free, prosperous and happy; but if we shall remain as we are we shall incur his displeasure. We shall be enslaved, and perhaps annihilated forever.

"'Brothers, these are the words of Hiawatha. Let them sink deep into your hearts. I have done.'

"A deep and impressive silence followed the delivery of this speech. On the following day the council again assembled to act on it. High wisdom recommended this deliberation.

"The union of the tribes into one confederacy was discussed and unanimously adopted. To denote the character and intimacy of the union they employed the figure of a single council-house, or lodge, whose boundaries be co-extensive with their territories. Hence the name of Long House."

THE SHAWNEE MIGRATE AND CONQUER THE HOPEWELL HOPWELL PEOPLES

As was seen in Chapter 10, the Five Nations had already driven the Hopewell Hopewell from the south shore of Lake Erie. Their Long House Federation would succeed in repulsing the invaders from the north, but now Algonquin peoples driven from the north by the climate collapse moved to the west, crossed Lake Erie, and settled in southern lands along the Ohio River. Their remains are currently identified by archaeologists as being those of the "Monongahela Culture".

THE SECOND SHAWNEE MIGRATION ACCOUNT

The following passages have been adapted from the accounts given by Black Hoof to Governor Lewis Cass and recorded by C. C. Trowbridge in 1825-1828.[11]

"The Chilicothe, at present one of the nations of the confederacy, lived on the opposite side of the sea [Lake Erie]. They sent out a scout[12] to explore the country. He reached the sea coast, and discovered the island [the land], of which he informed his chiefs.

"They resolved unanimously to go to the island in search of the people who might inhabit it, and accordingly marched down to the sea shore. Many leaders were appointed to conduct them across the sea, but every one refused, until at last one of the Turtle clan accepted the appointment and led on.

"The whole party followed him and reached the shore of the island in safety, having marched all the way upon the bottom of the sea. When they arrived an encampment was immediately formed, and a fire was enkindled, the smoke of which ascended to the clouds.

"The Mekoche, whose residence was not very distant, discovered this smoke and dispatched a scout[13] to ascertain its cause. He returned and reported that a great body of people were encamped at the fire. The Chiefs directed him to go back and salute them as cousins, in the name of the whole nation.

"The Chilicothe rejected this offer, and many others which were made, but at length consented to be called grandfathers."

The Shawnee would absorb the names and traditions of the people they conquered. The Mekoche's own story of their migration from the south across the Gulf of Mexico was set out earlier in Chapter 4. The "Chilicothe" are the western branch of the Tsulagi, or Cherokee. As the Mekoche people lived in the area between the lower Ohio River and the Cumberland River, and the Chilicothe at the junction of the Scioto River with the Ohio River, the course of the Shawnee's first attack was most likely across Lake Erie and then down the Scioto River to their lands. The Shawnee migration continued from this point:

"The Chilicothe soon after came to live with their new relatives [the Mekoche]. The Kishpoko were found near the Pekowitha, and were incorporated with the Mekoche in the same manner [as the Mekoche had been]. And the Shawnee, who had previously constituted a separate nation, also joined the confederacy."

At this time the Pekowitha lived a little further up the Ohio River, and the Kishpoko lived in the area around the Ohio River's junction with the Kanawa River. [14] In his account of the Mekoche migration, Black Hoof explicitly stated that the Pekowitha were a Red Ochre people:

"The Mekoche were put upon the Great Island on the borders of Shawnee [Ohio/Mississippi] River. They had not been there long when they discovered the Pekowitha, who told them that they came from Weskumuisa [the Red Man, Waaskoomisar,], a man in the south. These two nations soon became incorporated with each other."[15]

Black Hoof's statement about the Pekowitha agrees with the X haplogroup mitochondrial DNA of the Hopewell Hopewell.[16], and the Pekowitha were related to the Red Paint peoples who had migrated millennia before to the south along the Mississippi River. Continuing with the Shawnee account of their migrations to the southern lands:

"The Confederacy's force was further augmented by the addition of the Thawikila [Thauweekeelau] who also came across the sea [Lake Erie]."

Shortly before European contact the Thawikila Nation were located on the Ohio River in the area of Sewickley Creek, just to the west of modern-day Pittsburgh. Most likely the route the Shawnee took for this part of their migration was across Lake Erie, and then down the Shenango River to the Ohio River.

THE HOPEWELL RETREAT: "EARLY" FORT ANCIENT

Under attack by their formerly peaceful neighbors to the north, the Hopewell Hopewell retreated to areas near easily defended hilltops, upon which they constructed stone fortifications. This culture is known as "Early Fort Ancient", and archaeologists regularly confuse these people with later peoples who re-used the same fortifications. The differences are so immense that they can not all be catalogued here; suffice it to say that the "Early" Fort Ancient Culture was nut-tree based, used organically tempered "pottery", and shared cultural traits with the "Hopewell Hopewell", while the "Middle" Fort Ancient Culture was corn-based, used shell tempered pottery, and shared cultural traits with the Southern Ceremonial Cult peoples.

While the retreat to hill forts is popularly thought only to have extended to the Ohio River, in point of fact there was a similar retreat to hill forts all through Kentucky, and even further south along the Tennessee River, as can be seen by a quick look at a list of the sites[17].

FORT HILL, OHIO

I want to take a few moments here to describe Fort Hill, Ohio, a truly magnificent remain. It is situated atop a 400 foot high hill - think in terms of a hill as high as the Washington Monument - and it covers some 48 acres in area. The 19th century drawings of this site do not do it justice, as some 3 levels of terracing exist inside of the fort's walls - think of it in terms of a Native American Troy.

Just as Native American remains were turned to public entertainment functions in the early 20th century, Fort Hill is now being turned to the 21st century public function of "nature reserve". Large trees entirely block the view from the fort over the surrounding countryside, and the large trees which grow immediately on top of the hill are regularly hit by lightning and then die, carrying over the hill-side parts of the Fort's stone walls, and thoroughly disrupting the levels inside of it.

Perhaps a walk through these woods while carelessly disposing of the still-lit butts of unfiltered cigarettes may be the answer here; I packed out all my cigarette butts, but I understand that Ohio has a fairly well organized archaeological society.

THE FIVE NATIONS BATTLE THE SHAWNEE:
SOHNOUREWAH THE SHAWNEE

In their march up the Ohio River, the Shawnee would finally come into contact again with the Five Nations. The following passage has been adapted from David Cusick's Ancient History of the Six Nations. Working from 50 year wampum belts, Cusick sets this event around 750 CE, shortly before the reign of Atotarho IV.[18]

"About this time the Oneidas had extended their forts down the Kaunsehwatauyea River, now known as the Susquehana River.

"At a fort situated on that river, there was a certain woman who delivered a male child of uncommon size. When he was twelve years of age, he was nearly as large as a grown person, and he would beat his playmates, which created disputes. But his mother would correct him, and afterwards she prevailed, and he promised never to injure his people.

"When grown up he became a giant and was a great hunter. His mother was provided with venison continuously, and he was so strong that when he returned from hunting he would have five or six deers and bears strung around on his belt.

"The giant was named Sohnourewah, which is to say 'Big Neck', now known as the Shawnee; he inhabited the bank of the river, and now he brought home the suits of dress and the scalps from those whom he had killed.

"The Sahwaunoo Nation [on the Hudson] sent messages to Fort Kaunasenwatayea [the Fort on the Susquehanna] to report the conduct of Soh-nou-re-wah, [the Shawnee], but the business was left to the relatives of Soh-nou-re-wah, [Shawnees], who persuaded him to reform his behavior for the future.

"But Soh-nou-re-wah, [the Shawnee] remained only two winters with out making disturbances; he went down the river and whenever he came to a town, he committed the same outrages upon the inhabitants, and plundered the people of their clothes, and skins, and other things.

"Again the Sahwaunoo [on the Hudson] sent a deputy to Fort Kaunasenwatayea [on the Susquehanna River], who reported not only their resentment, but their determination to make hostile aggressions if no satisfaction was made on their part.

"The Chief Nenauretahgo [of Fort Kaunasenwatayea] sent a belt of wampum and offered terms of peace, which were accepted. But Sohnourewah the Shawnee was not disposed to favor the treaty: he left the fort and went down and settled on the bank of the Kaunasenwatayea (Susquehanna) River, and commenced to build a fort.

(This fort was situated on the south bank of the Susquehanna River. In 1800 I [David Cusick] went over the ground myself and viewed the mound there.)

"Sohnourewah the Shawnee was frequently visited by his relatives there; and after the fortification was completed he resolved to continue to war against his enemies. As he had done before, Sohnourewah the Shawnee went from time to time and attacked the people who lived on the river: he would lay in ambush near their path, and whenever the people passed he shot them. He used a plump arrow, which was so violent that it would break a body into two parts.

"Sohnourewah the Shawnee became so mischievous to the people that his relatives were obliged to form a plan to destroy him. But Sohnourewah would not be easy to quell, as it was supposed that ten warriors were not sufficient to equal his strength.

"Now three warriors of his native people went to his fort on the Kaunasenwatayea (Susquehanna) River, bringing him his favorite dish, a mess of huckle berries and other things. Sohnourewah was pleased with their visit and the food which they gave him; but while he was eating it one of the warriors, instantly stepped on the bench where he was sitting and gave a fatal blow to the giant's head with a. club which he had concealed under his cloak.

"Sohnourewah was so distracted by this that he ran out the fort, intending to cross the river, but he sank in the mire which was near the river's bank. The three warriors prevailed and killed him on the spot. The warriors then spoiled his house and obtained a large quantity of skins, and other things, and the fort has been ruined ever since.

EVENTS IN SOUTH AMERICA:
THE FALL OF PUKARA AT LAKE TITICACA

Fragments of Comet Encke may also have impacted in South America. The account of the Pukara impact given here is that of Cristobal De Molina de Cuzco, from his Fables and Rites of the Incas, 1575.[19] Writing some 20 years after Betanzos (Chapter 9), at the request of Francisco de Toledo, the fourth Viceroy of Peru, Molina's creation account differs in many particulars from that of Betanzos. Its importance here lies in that Molina places an impact at Pucura (Pukara), which is located in the basin of Lake Titicaca.

"'The Indians also have another myth in which they say that the Creator [Con Ticci Viracocha] had two sons, one of whom they called Imaymana Viracocha, and the other Tocapo Viracocha...

"'These Indians also believed that neither the Creator [Con Ticci Viracocha] nor his sons [Imaymana Viracocha and Tocapo Viracocha] were born of woman and that they were unchanging and eternal. The various tribes of this country have many other nonsensical beliefs and fables about their origin insomuch that if we were to record them all, it would be very prolix and there would be no end to it..."

"...In the same myth they also say that at Tiahuanaco, where he [Con Ticci Viracocha] created the tribes of men, he created all the different kinds of birds, male and female of each, giving them the songs which each kind was to sing. Those that were to inhabit the forests he sent to the forests and those which were to inhabit the highlands to the highlands, each to the region proper to its kind. He also created all the different species of animals, male and female of each, and all the snakes and creeping things there are in the land and commanded each to its proper habitat. And he taught the people the names and properties of the birds and snakes and other reptiles.

"The Creator [Con Ticci Viracocha], who they say was the father of Imaymana Viracocha and Tocapo Viracocha, commanded Imaymana Viracocha, the elder of his two sons, in whose power all things are placed, to set out from that place [Pucara or Tiahuanaco ?] and traverse all the world by the road of the mountains and forested valleys. As he [Imaymana Viracocha] went he was to give names to all the trees large and small, to the flowers and fruit they were to bear, and to indicate to the people which were edible and which not, and which [of them] had medicinal properties. He [Imaymana Viracocha] also gave names to the herbs and flowers, and the time when they were to produce flowers and fruits, and taught people which could cure, and which would kill.

"His other son named Tocapo Viracocha, which in their language means "the Maker", he [Con Ticci Viracocha] ordered to go by the road of the plains, visiting the peoples, and giving names to the rivers and trees, and instructing them as to the fruits and flowers. And thus they went to the lowest parts of this land until they came to the sea, where they ascended into the sky after having finished making all that there is in the land....

"...When the Creator had fashioned the peoples and nations, giving to each their appropriate appearance and language, and had sent the Sun, the Moon, and the stars to their places in the sky from Tiahuanaco, the Creator, whom the Indians in their own language call Pachayachachic [Teacher of the World] or [Con] Ticci Viracocha, which means the Unknowable God, went along the highland road and visited the tribes to see how they had begun to multiply and to fulfill the commandments he had given them.

"Finding that some tribes had rebelled against his commands, he changed a large part of them into stones in the shape of men and women with the same costume that they had worn. The changing into stone occurred at the following places: in Tiahuanaco, in Pucara and Jauja, where they say he turned the huaca called Huarivilca into stone, and in Pachacamac, in Cajamarca, and other regions. Indeed today there are huge figures of stone in these places, some of them almost the size of giants, which must have been fashioned by human hands in times of great antiquity. And as the memory failed, and in the absence of writing, they invented this legend saying that the people were turned into stones by command of the Creator on account of disobeying his commands.

"They also say that at Pucara, which is forty leagues from Cuzco on the Collao [Collo-Suyu] road, fire came down from heaven and burnt a great part of them, while those who tried to escape were turned into stone.

With Pukara crippled, the stage was set for the rise of Tiahuanaco (Tiwanaku) in the Lake Titicaca basin and the creation of the magnificent stone structures whose remains are found there today.

COMET ENCKE AND THE MAYA:
THE INSCRIPTIONS AT PALENQUE

K'an Hoy Chitam (now read as K'an Joy Chitam) was ruling at Palenque during this appearance of Comet Encke and the catastrophic climate collapse which it produced, and the later king K'inich Ahkal Mo' Nahb' III (that's The Third) left us some account of how K'an Hoy Chitam handled the situation:

> "On Seven Ajaw, the Eighth of K'anasiy, there are seven stones.
> The *'okib'* of *Yax 'Itsam 'At*, the Tun Lord, is fashioned.
> K'an Hoy Chitam, the Holy Lord of Palenque, casts incense upon it."[20]

"*Itzam*", the cometary serpent, had once again appeared – so K'an Hoy Chitam had an "*okib*" made and dedicated, accompanied, one can be sure, with plenty of human sacrifices. While this account is brief enough, what is even more interesting is why K'inich Ahkal Mo' Nahb' III remembered the events of his predecessor of some 200 years earlier. According to account given by the historian Bede, right square in the middle of K'inich Ahkal Mo' Nahb' The Third's reign, another two comets appeared, which were scaring the hell out of everyone:

"In the year of our Lord 729, two comets appeared around the sun, striking terror into all who saw them. One comet rose early and preceded the sun, while the other followed the setting sun at evening, seeming to portend awful calamity to east and west alike. Or else, since one comet was the precursor of the day and the other of night, they indicated that mankind was menaced by evils at both times. They appeared in the month of January, and remained visible for about a fortnight, pointing their fiery torches northward as though to set the welkin aflame..."[21]

The Maya were scared as well. K'inich Ahkal Mo' Nahb' III provides us with a Mayan tale of these comets, featuring G1, the First Maize Revealer Partitioner (Impactor), G2, the Sun Eyed Torch, the Killer of Kings, and G3, the Red Dwarf Partitioner. [22]

> "No days, no winals, thirteen years, and eight k'atuns later
> Four Ajaw the Thirteenth of Yax Zihom, is the stone-seating
> It is the fifteenth K'atun,
> It is the stone-binding of K'inich Ahkal Mo' Nahb' [the third], the Holy Lord
> of Palenque.
> It is the first carrying(?) of G1, the *Zalaj B'olon*[23]

"Sixteen days, seven winals and two years later
Then Nine Kib' the Nineteenth of K'anasiy comes to pass.
The fire enters into the Eight House ..., the Fire ... House.
It is the red ... house of G1.

"Twenty-four days later
Seven Ajaw, the Third of Wayab', is the rope-taking(?).
It is his ...
It is the carrying(?) of *Zalaj B'olon.*

"Seventeen days, six winals and two years later
It is Six Kaban the Fifth of Yaxk'in[24].
It is the fire entering.
The Three-Skull Bone ... is the red ... house of G2.
The Great Sun .. House is the red ... house of G3.

"Three days and two winals later
It is Ten 'Ajaw the Eighth of Ik'-Zihom.
It is the First Five Stones.
The 'okib' of 'Aj ... (event missing)
It is in the presence of Aj Chit... G1
K'inich Ahkal Mo' Nab' [the third], the Holy Lord of Palenque, casts upon it."

It is clear that King K'inich Ahkal Mo' Nab' The Third wanted to assure his subjects that he had done all the things required of a king to prevent those comets from killing them. That's one of the big reasons for all of the inscriptions in the first place.

EVENTS IN THE VALLEY OF MEXICO:
THE FALL OF T̶̶̶̶̶̶̶̶ACA

Around the year 6̶̶̶̶ other people arrived in the Valley of Mexico, conquered the city of Teotihu̶̶̶̶lished their control there, and began their own raids into the Mayan lands.

The new rulers of̶̶̶̶y of Mexico were the Toltec, and once again their cultural traditions are quit̶̶̶̶ this time both from those of the Maya and from those of the Teotihuacans.̶̶̶̶n, these people's language is different (Nonoalca), and they appear without nea̶̶̶̶ural antecedent. My guess, and let me emphasize that this is merely a guess, is tha̶̶̶̶ese people may have also emigrated via large watercraft from the west coast of South America, and that their appearance in Mexico may be related to the disappearance of the Moche people from the coastal region of South America around 650 CE.

This time, we at least have materials relating to that movement, specifically *The Annals of the Cakquichiquels*, and what must be a very late pictographic version of the same, *The Codex Borgia.* The close parallels between these peoples and the Vikings in Europe appear quite striking to me, and so I note a few of them here. Watercraft played a role in these peoples' attacks, as may be seen by the boat depicted on the 10th page of *The*

Codex Borgia. In much the same way that the Vikings used dogs in their attacks, these people heaved containers of bees at their opponents, and this may be seen on the 8th page of the Codex. While I have not spotted a clear scene of this in the late *Codex Borgia* version, *The Annals of the Cakquichels* also relate these peoples' use of the bow and arrow, and his may be indicative of South American roots. The appearance of this new weapon would bear parallel with the Viking's introduction of the battle-axe in Europe.

THE COLLAPSE OF THE CLASSIC MAYA

Those looking for catastrophic ecological reasons for the collapse of the "Classic" Maya would do well to examine Linda Schele's work *The Code of Kings*, where she outlined the effects of this Toltec population movement.[25] The conquest of Teotihuacan by the Toltecs touched off a final devastating round of wars between those Mayan city-states which had been under Teotihaucan influence and those Mayan city-states which had not.

On the other hand, perhaps those looking for a catastrophic reason should not abandon hope. If the Toltec were in fact Moche immigrants, then it appears likely that the original Moche immigration from South America had been touched off by an earthquake which destroyed their irrigation systems.

THE ITZA ENTER THE YUCATAN

"4 Ahau [731 CE] was the name of the katun when occurred the birth of Pauahs [Puhs - reeds?], when the rulers descended. Thirteen katuns they reigned; thus they were named while they ruled.

"4 Ahau was the name of the katun when the rulers descended; the Great Descent and the Little Descent they were called. Thirteen katuns they reigned; so they were called. While they were settled, thirteen [katuns] were their settlements.

"4 Ahau was the katun when the rulers sought and discovered Chichen Itzá. It was there that miraculous things were performed for them by their lords. Four divisions they were, when the four divisions of the nation, as they were called, went forth. From Kincolah-Peten in the east, one division went forth. From Nacocob in the north, one division came forth. One division came forth from Holtun Zuyua in the west. One division came forth from Four-Peaked Mountain [to the south], Nine Mountains is the name of that land.

"4 Ahau was the katun when the four divisions were called. The four divisions of the nation, they were called, when the rulers descended. The rulers became lords when they descended upon Chichen Itzá. Then they were called the Itzá."[26]

(Footnotes)

[1] *Catastrophe: An Investigation into the Origin of the Modern World*, David Keys, Ballentine Books, New York, 1999

[2] Keys, op cit, p. 249-261

[3] Keys, op cit, p. 258

[4] Gregory of Tours' *History of the Franks*, IV.31, O.M. Dalton translation, Oxford, 1927, pages 140-141

[5] Gregory of Tours, History of the Franks, O.M. Dalton translation, Oxford, 1927

[6] H.F. V.33, annal entry for 580 CE

[7] H.F. VI.21, annal entry purportedly for 582 CE. For a discussion of this dating/text discrepancy see the Cambridge Conference archives

[8] Life of Saint Columba, Alan Orr Anderson and Marjorie Olgivie Anderson, Thomas Nelson & Sons, London & Edinburgh, 1961, p. 262-263

[9] Elias Johnson, Legends, Traditions, And Laws Of The Iroquois, Or Six Nations, and History Of The Tuscarora Indian, Union Printing and Publishing Company, Lockport, New York, 1881

[10] David Cusick's Ancient History of the Six Nations, Appendix A here

[11] Located and preserved by Kinietz and Voegelin, Shawanese Traditions, University of Michigan Press, Ann Arbor, 1939. See the Ancient History of the Shawnee, Appendix C here.

[12] Spy: *Maume-Esemauklilitar*, *mishinewaa* Howard

[13] Spy: *Maume-Esemaukeiitar*

[14] While the Piqua Nation inhabited the Maumee River Valley during the late European contact period, during the period being discussed here "Monongahela Culture" is found in a continuous band along the Ohio River up to the Monongahela River. Indeed, the Thawikila Nation were located on the Ohio River in the area of Sewickley Creek, just to the west of modern day Pittsburgh. For further discussion, see the introduction to the Ancient History of the Shawnee, Appendix C here.

[15] Again, located and preserved by Kinietz and Voegelin, *Shawanese Traditions*, University of Michigan Press, Ann Arbor, 1939 See the Ancient History of the Shawnee, Appendix C here.

[16] Discussed in Chapter 10 here.

[17] Some of these sites are listed in Chapter 17, Travel Tips

[18] Cusick, Appendix A

[19] Harold Osborne, *South American Mythology*, Peter Bedrick Books, New York, 1968, 1983, p. 56

[20] David Stuart's preliminary readings of the Temple XIX bench, available at mesoweb at changing locations

[21] Bede, Historia Ecclesiastica Genis Anglorum, V, passage recognized by A.A. Marden and E.G. Marden, "The Venerable Bede's Observation of the Comet of 729 AD", 65th Annual Meeting of the Meteoritical Society, 2002; citing also reports in the Parker manuscript of the Anglo-Saxon Chronicle, Matthew of Paris's Flores and Chronica Maior, and Bartholomew of Cotton's Chronicle

[22] For other inscriptions from Palenque mentioning G1, G2, and G3 see Chapter 6 here.

[23] Related to the "nine gods" or "nine steps" of the books of the chilam balam? Or "many"? See Chapter 8 here.

[24] Absolute Mayan dates have a range of about 3 years, depending on which starting

date for the count of days is used. Given the difficulty of the correlating Mayan calendar systems with western calendars, this cometary observation may help with the problem, providing Bede's calendar system is known, and that his observation was recorded and transmitted properly: Apparently these comets shows up in 730 CE in Chinese records.

[25] *The Code of Kings*, Linda Schele with Peter Mathews, Scribner, New York, 1998, p. 199-201

[26] Adapted from Ralph L. Roy's translation of *The Book of the Chilam Balam of Chumayel*, Carnegie Institution, Washington, D.C., 1933

Teotihuacan - Capital city of the Ancients of the Country

CHAPTER 12

THE MISSISSIPPIANS EMERGE:
THE HAUSTECA AND TOTONAC TRADING NETWORKS
IN NORTH AMERICA

THE LACK OF ARCHAEOLOGICAL DATA

Before beginning this chapter, I suppose that I need to take a few moments to describe the particularly tragic loss of a site, as it does much to explain our lack of knowledge about the peoples who are usually thought of by most people as the Moundbuilders, or the Mississippians, or the peoples of the Southern Ceremonial Cult.

In 1934 a number of archaeological sites along the Tennessee Valley were going to be inundated by the dams which were going to be built by newly elected President Franklin Roosevelt's Tennessee Valley Authority. These dams were being built both to provide the area with electricity, and as a way of employing people.

Since many significant archaeological sites were going to be flooded by the new dams, archaeologists began a letter writing campaign, and as a result of this, President Roosevelt put in place a rescue archaeology effort. In 1936, as the depression wore on, Roosevelt, sensing a good thing, decided to develop key archaeological sites. One of these sites is Ocmulgee in Macon, and another of them is Moundville in Alabama, and both are beautiful.[1] The third site Roosevelt wanted to develop was going to be Poverty Point and the nearby Coles Creek complex, but upon learning of Roosevelt's plan, the farmer who owned the land on which the Coles Creek site was situated hired a bulldozer and had the Coles Creek complex leveled flat.[2]

Aside from the loss of key archaeological information of the Coles Creek site, this destruction resulted in the loss of employment for thousands of local residents for generations, and condemned the area to continuing poverty. On the other hand, the farmer did keep his land.

ACCOUNTS OF THE HISTORIES OF
THE SOUTHERN CEREMONIAL PEOPLES:
THE SPREAD OF CORN (MAIZE) AGRICULTURE

With the reading of the Mayan glyphs, a new effort has begun to try to ascribe nearly all Native American cultural developments to diffusion from Central America. One big problem proponents of this theory have is the nearly complete lack in North America in later times of trade goods from Central America.

Amazingly enough, these peoples themselves have left us a detailed explanation for this lack of trade goods. We have actually had available for centuries two detailed descriptions of contact period Southern Ceremonial peoples. One of these was assembled at the time of the first Spanish contact with them by Peter Martyr, from

232

materials and interviews provided to him both by the participants, as well as by a Native American captive. The other description was written much later by the French colonist Simon Antoine Le Page du Pratz.

While du Pratz's account is much later, it is also far more detailed, as he was perfectly fluent in Natchez and enjoyed the friendship of their King, War Chief, and their High Priest. Le Page du Pratz preserved for us a part of the Natchez's Ancient Word, their oral account of their ancient history. du Pratz received the Ancient Word directly from his friend the Chief of the Guardians of the Temple, their high priest. What remainsof the Ancient Word of the Natchez can be found as one of the appendices at the end of this book.

Peter Martyr mentions the existence of a similar ancient history among the Duharhe: "None of them have any writing, but they preserve traditions of great antiquity in rhymes and chants...", but unfortunately this Duharhe history has been lost in its entirety.

The Ancient Word of the Natchez goes a long way towards explaining why there are so few Central American trade goods found in later Mississippian sites: they did not want them. And the Ancient Word is quite specific about this.

THE BEAUTIFUL COUNTRY:
THE NATCHEZ ARRIVE ON THE NORTHERN GULF COAST OF MEXICO[3]

> "Before we came into this land, Natchez, we lived to the southwest under the Great Sun. We lived in a beautiful country where the earth is always good.

> "The Ancient Word says nothing of what land we came from before this. All that it teaches is that our fathers who went there followed the sun [went to the west], and came with the sun from where it rises [from the east].

> "They were a long time on their journey, and they saw themselves at the point of dying utterly, when they found themselves brought into that beautiful country, without them searching for it at all."

While it is uncertain which of the coastal peoples of Central America the Natchez were related to, the Hausteca are very good candidates, based on matching the Chief of the Guardians of the Temple's account of events with the geography of the area.[4]

THE NATCHEZ ENCOUNTER THE TEOTIHAUCANS [OTOMIES?]:
A DETAILED DESCRIPTION OF TOLLA, THEIR CAPITOL CITY

> "On our arrival in that land we knew nothing of the Ancients of the Country. It was only a long time afterwards, when we were multiplied [i.l. the Natchez people had grown in number], that we both heard of each other, and we encountered each other with equal surprise on both sides.

> "The Ancient Word teaches us that when we arrived in that country, we found

them there in great numbers, and they appeared to have been there a long time: for they inhabited the entire coast toward the setting sun of the Great Water [Gulf of Mexico], as far as the cold country on this side of the sun [the mountains of central Mexico], and very far along the coast beyond the sun [the Pacific Coast].

"They had a very large number of large and small villages, all of which were built of stones, and in which there were individual houses large enough to lodge an entire village. Their temples were built with much skill and labor. They made very beautiful things with all kinds of materials, such as gold, silver, stones, wood, fabrics, feathers, and they made many other things in which they made their skills appear, as well as in manufacturing arms and in making war."

Ca 200 CE: THE TOLLAN FEDERATION FALLS, AND THE TOLLAN EMPIRE FORMED

"The two nations did not war together at all then, and they lived in peace for a great number of years. But then one of their chiefs, who was very powerful and a great warrior, undertook to make them his slaves, and he finally succeeded. And then he wished to subject us also.

Ca 348 CE: THE TOLLAN [TEOTIHAUCANS] ATTACK OUT OF THE VALLEY OF MEXICO

"All those who dwelt in the plains could not avoid submitting, and those who had retired into the mountains remained alone under obedience to the Great Sun. The Ancients of the Country wished, indeed, to force those of our people whom they had already subjugated to join them in making war on us, but they preferred to die rather than attack their brothers, especially the Suns [the nobility].

THE TOLLAN HELD BY THE NATCHEZ [HAUSTECA] AT THE MOUNTAIN PASSES

"After having reduced under their power those villages of our people who were in the plains, the Ancients of the Country came, indeed, as far as the mountains. But our warriors always repulsed them at the entrance to the mountains, and they were never able to penetrate there.

"And it was there that our Suns [nobility] remained, because the Ancients of the Country were unable to force us out with all of their warriors.

THE NATCHEZ [HAUSTECA] EVACUATION TO THE MISSISSIPPI RIVER

"Our entire nation then extended along the Great Water [the Gulf of Mexico] to where this Great River [the Mississippi River] loses itself [empties]. Some of our [lesser] Suns [princes were] sent up this river to find a place where they might conceal themselves, far from the Ancients of the Country, because after having been a long time good friends with them, they had become ill disposed and so numerous that we were no longer able to defend ourselves against them.

"But those who had ascended along the west side of the Great River [Mississippi River], having discovered this land which we inhabit, now crossed the river on a raft of dry canes. They found a country such as they desired, suitable for concealing themselves from the Ancients of the Country, and even easy to defend against them if they ever undertook to attack us here.

"On their return they reported this to the Great Sun and the other [lesser] Suns who governed the villages. The Great Sun immediately informed those who remained in the plains and were still defending themselves against the Ancients of the Country, and he ordered them to go into this new land and build there a temple and to carry there the eternal fire in order to preserve it.

"There came here a great number of men with their wives and their children. The oldest people and the [lesser] Suns, the relatives of the Great Sun, remained there with those who kept with the Great Sun in the mountains. They, as well as those who lived on the shores of the Great Water [Gulf of Mexico], remained there for a still longer time.

"A large part of our nation having then been established here, we lived a long time in peace and in abundance for many generations.

THE COLLAPSE OF THE TOLLAN EMPIRE, AND RISE OF THE TOLTECS

"On the other hand, those who had remained under the sun [in the south], or very near, for it was very warm there, did not hasten to come and join us, because the Ancients of the Country made themselves hated by all men- as much by their own nation as by ours.

"Here is how the Ancient Word says that that happened. The Ancients of the Country were all brothers - that is to say, they all came out of the same country - but each large village, on which many other smaller villages depended, had its head master, and each head master commanded those whom he had brought with him into that land. There was then nothing done among them that all had not consented to; but then one of these head masters raised himself above the others and treated them as slaves.

"Thus the Ancients of the Country no longer agreed among themselves. They even warred against one another. Some of them united with those of our nation who had remained, and by all of them working together, they sustained themselves there well enough.

THE EXTENT OF THE "MOBILIAN" OR "MISSISSIPPIAN" TRADE
FEDERATION

"This was not the only reason which retained our Suns in that country. It was
hard for them to leave such a good land; besides, their assistance was necessary
to our other brothers who were established here like ourselves, and who lived
along the shore of the Great Water [the Gulf of Mexico] on the side toward
the east.

"These brothers extended so far that they went very far beyond the Great Sun,
since there were some of them from whom the Great Sun heard sometimes
only at the end of five or six years, and there were yet others so far away from
us, whether along the coast or in the islands, that for many years they had not
been heard of at all."

So there you have it: these peoples were fleeing (in sequence) the Tollans, the Toltecs,
and the Aztecs, and they wanted to have nothing to do with any trade with them.

KOLOMOKI

The entire "Southern Ceremonial Complex" spread to other people with incredible
rapidity, for reasons which are currently unknown. It may have been the introduction
of corn; it may have been the general distribution of foodstuffs at monthly feasts; or
it may have been the use of new hallucinogens in their religion.[5] How they survived,
why they were accepted and not attacked - no one knows with any certainty what
happened.

Whether this spread occurred through the settlement of other refuges on the other
major rivers of the southeast which emptied into the Gulf of Mexico, which I suspect,
or whether it spread overland through trade, is also unknown. But spread it did:
by about 690 CE the complex appeared as far away from the Mississippi River as
Kolomoki, which lays in southern Georgia off of the Chattahootchie River.[6]

COLES CREEK CULTURES

The Natchez (Huasteca) technologies, corn (maize), shell tempered pottery, and the
bow were quickly adopted by the other peoples already living in the area. As these
peoples had already been cultivating squash, pumpkin, and seed bearing plants, it is not
surprising that they were able to quickly adopt cultivating corn (maize). I don't know
whether it was that the variety of corn (maize) used was particularly weak, or whether
cultivation techniques had not been perfected yet, but for the next millennium or so
Native Americans could only cultivate this corn (maize) in the wettest river bottom
lands. In this regard it is important to note that there were no honeybees in North
America before European contact, and this must have had a great effect on pollination
rates.

The nearby peoples on the Mississippi River began to experiment with shell tempering and higher firing temperatures, and at last perfected a fine black pottery, and would continue using this production method for the next thousand years.

The final technology that was introduced was the bow and arrow, whose adoption may be traced by the manufacture of smaller stone points. Despite what you might have seen on television, there were no bows and arrows in North America before about 400 CE. The bow and arrow was ideal for hunting, as it was more accurate than the atlatl and had better range than the blowgun.

TROYVILLE CULTURE

There was another separate contact between the peoples of North America and those of Central America, and it started ca. 400 CE and ran up the Atchafalaya River, which was the West Branch of the Mississippi River at that time. The culture that resulted from this contact is known as Troyville, and its key identifying marker is the appearance with absolutely no antecedents of well made pottery, pottery which is shell tempered, fired at high temperature, and features red and black markings on a fine white body. If one is looking for parallels for this pottery in Central America, the polychrome pottery of the Totonac people would be a good place to start.

THE 536 CE CLIMATE COLLAPSE AND THE MISSISSIPIANS

As was mentioned in Chapter 10, when the 536 CE climate collapse came it wiped out the Hopewell nut groves nearly entirely, to the point of freezing to death both the pecan and fruit trees. Most "Hopewell" societies came to an abrupt end. In contrast, Troyville and Coles Creek cultures, with their maize base, seem to have passed through the catastrophe with not too much effect. In addition, it may simply be that they were far enough south so that their nut tree groves and fruit tree groves did not freeze to death.

EVENTS CA 750 CE:
THE FORMATION OF THE GREAT RED RIVER RAFT
AND THE END OF TROYVILLE CULTURE AND TOTONAC
INFLUENCE IN THE NORTH

Prior to 700 CE there were two cultural centers in North America which reflected Central American influence. One of these was the Natchez culture, which extended along the East Branch of the Mississippi River, and the other was the Troyville Culture along the Atchafalaya River, which was the West Branch of the Mississippi River at that time. .

This situation underwent a dramatic change as a result of the formation of the Great Raft. What was the Great Raft? It was a massive blockage of downed trees along the Red River which stretched some 130 miles from Loggy Bottom near Nachitoches to Hurricane Bluff some 50 miles upriver from the modern city of Shreveport.

The sudden destruction of trees in this area also had consequences downstream. The Red River ran into the Mississippi River very near where the Mississippi met what was then its West Branch. Dead trees floated downstream to this junction and dammed that intake, turning the West Branch of the Mississippi in today's Achafalaya River. In the early 1800's this dam was some 30 miles long.

When did this event occur? Judging by simultaneous population movements, there is no doubt that it must have been around 750 AD. Troyville culture simply came to an end. While it looks like a few survivors staggered out of the zone and settled at the Caddo Mounds site, events in Arkansas are more interesting. Here, at Toltec Mounds, near Little Rock, survivors of the event built what can only be described as a Central American complex constructed of earth. The complex was the only one of its kind that I saw on my survey, where a main temple fronts a plaza which is framed on both sides by long platforms, all set out to astronomical alignments. It's a gem.

Bob Kobres, among other impact specialists, has brought up before the possibility that the Great Raft on the Red River was created by a Tunguska class impact event. While I can't prove that the Great Raft was caused by an impact, as near as I can determine there is no Native American tradition of a massive impact occurring there at this time.

The red and black on white Troyville pottery also shows up in coastal debris around Port Arthur, Texas. This debris undoubtedly comes from a "Kisselpoo" trading center, whose destruction by hurricane the local Atakapa people remembered in legend.[7] Was this hurricane the cause the Great Raft? Right now no one knows, but fortunately there is a good chance the work necessary to answer this question will be done in the near future.[8]

(Footnotes)

[1] *A New Deal for Southeastern Archaeology*, Edwin A, Lyon, University of Alabama Press, Tuscaloosa, Alabama, 1996

[2] Personal Communication

[3] The Ancient Word of the Natchez, Appendix B here

[4] According to an American Museum of Natural History internet site on the Huastec, the actual origin of the Huastec people is currently unknown. They report that both Fray Bernardino de Sahagun and Fray Juan de Torquemada relate that the first settlers arrived by sea, and settled at Tamoanchan, a place yet to be located, but pursuing this further is outside of the scope of the work at hand.

[5] Covered in Chapter 14 here.

[6] Thomas J. Pluckhahn, *Kolomoki*, University of Alabama Press, Tuscaloosa, 2003

[7] All presented at Museum of the Gulf Coast, Port Arthur, Texas

[8] There are no less than three federal agencies whose responsibilities require them to determine the weather history of the area. First among them is the Army Corps of Engineers, who are responsible for controlling flooding in the area. Second and third are the national weather service, the National Oceanic and Atmospheric Agency (NOAA), and the Federal Emergency Management Agency (FEMA), who are responsible for hurricane evacuation. Finally, a fourth Federal agency, the National Geological Survey, may be involved, as this would seem to fall under their responsibilities.

CHAPTER 13

THE KEY MARCO AND GENESEE IMPACTS

KEY MARCO:
A SMALL IMPACT EVENT?

As was mentioned earlier, some shell peoples appear to have survived on the West coast of Florida, and these people would re-emerge to dominate a large part of Florida by the time of Spanish contact. One of the most interesting sites which has been found so far in Florida is that at Key Marco, which is unusual because of the recovery there of a large number of wooden and organic artifacts. These artifacts have been dated to around 800 CE, though I understand this date is subject to debate.

What is quite interesting is the manner in which these perishable artifacts were preserved. The artifacts were found buried in the muck around a major urban complex, a complex which included ceremonial mounds, and the artifacts were accompanied by signs of fire. The hypothesis currently put forward is that a hurricane occurred, which started a fire, and then blew the burning artifacts into the muck. I don't know what you think of a raging fire burning in a hurricane, but it seems entirely more likely to me that what occurred was a detonation at an altitude of 5 kilometers or so of an impactor, with the thermal wave igniting the objects, only to have the blast wave arrive a few seconds later and blow the artifacts into the muck. This phenomena was seen at Tunguska, where trees were set on fire by the thermal wave from the detonation, only to have those fires extinguished a few seconds later by the arrival of the blast wave.

Given the cultural continuity of the shell peoples of Florida, and the prolonged interaction of both the Timucua and the Calusa with Spanish, French, and English colonists, it seems likely that their myths may have been at least partially recorded, but I do not believe that any materials relating to what occurred at Key Marco have been recovered yet.

EVENTS OF THE REIGN OF KING ATOTARHO IV:
AN IMPACT EVENT, AND WAR WITH THE MISSASSAUGA

The following passage is adapted from David Cusick's Ancient History of the Six Nations.[1] Using a rough date of 1600 CE for the Dutch appearing in the lands of the Five Nations, by Cusick's calculation we end up with a date of 800 CE for the following events.

> "Perhaps about 800 years before the Dutch arrived in the land of the Five Nations.

> "About this time the Mississaugers, who had their capitol at Twakanhah" [As will be shown in Chapter 14, Twakanhah was the city known today as Cahokia, and the Mississauga were their allies.], ceded their colonies lying between the

Keanauhausent (Oak Orchard Creek) and the River O-Nyakara, (Niagara River) to the Five Nations.

"About this time lived King Atotorho IV. There was a woman and son who resided near the fort, which was situated near a knoll, which was named Jenneatowaka, the original seat of the council fire of the Te-hoo-nea-nyo-hent, the Senecas. One day the boy, while amusing himself in the brush, caught a small serpent called Kaistowanea, in other words "With Two Heads', and he brought it to his apartment.

"The serpent was first placed in a small bark box to tame it, where it was fed with bird's flesh and other similar things. After 10 winters the serpent became considerable larger, and he rested on the beams within the hut, and the warrior was obliged to hunt deers and bears to feed the monster.

"But after awhile the serpent was able to maintain itself on various game; it left the hut and resided on the top of a knoll. The serpent frequently visited the lake, and after 30 years it had grown to a prodigious size, which in a short time inspired it with an evil mind against the people. In the night the warrior felt that the serpent was brooding some mischief and was about to destroy the people of the fort. When the warrior was acquainted of the danger, he was dismayed and soon moved to another fort.

"At daylight the serpent descended from the heights with the most tremendous noise. The trees were trampled down with such force that they were uprooted.
"

Clearly this is an asteroid or comet impact event, and clearly the tale of an impacting 'serpent' has been elided with a tale of the 'Serpent' (Mississauga) people who had been attacking earlier, and who now took advantage of the disaster which had befallen their enemy.

"And the serpent immediately surrounded the fort's gate. The people were taken improvidentially and brought to confusion; finding themselves circled by the monsterous serpent, some of them endeavored to pass out at the gate, and others, attempted to climb over the serpent, but were unable.

"The people remained in this situation for several days; the warriors made oppositions to dispel the monster, but they were fruitless. And the people, distressed of their confinement, found no other method open to them than to rush to pass out at the gate. But the people were devoured, all except a young warrior and his sister, who stayed back detained, and were the only people left exposed to the monster, and were left restrained, without hopes of getting release.

"At length the warrior received advice from a dream, and he adorned his arms with the hairs of his sister, by which he succeeded in shooting the serpent in the heart. And the serpent was mortally wounded, and it hastily retired from the fort and retreated to the lake in order to gain relief from its wound. The serpent furiously dashed on the surface of the water in the time of its agony; at last it vomited up the substance which it had eaten, and then it sank into the deep and died.

"As the serpent had been too powerful to be resisted, the people of the fort had not received any assistance from their neighboring forts. After the fort was demolished, the Council fire was removed to another fort called Thaugwetook, which was situated west of what is now known as Lake Geneva; and bulwarks were erected on Mountain Ridge, west of the Genesee River.

EVENTS OF THE REIGN OF KING ATOTARHO V:
THE OTTAWA APPEAR ON THE SOUTH SHORE OF LAKE ERIE

Following the Five Nations war against the Hopewell Hopewell, the Ottawas came to occupy the valley of the Shenango River tributary of the Allegheny River and the area between it and Lake Erie. As this area was held at the time of European contact by the Erie people, clearly the war which Cusick describes here was continued and finally led to an Iroquois victory.

"About this time reigned King Atotorho V.

"At Fort Kedauyerkowau, now known as the Tonawanda Plains, a party went to hunt and were attacked by the Ottawas, which created differences between the two nations, as the Ottawa entered the country on no terms but to commence hostilities.

"The Tohonyohent [War Chief] sent a band of warriors to attack some of the hunters, so as to retaliate the vengeance upon their enemies. The warriors advanced above the lake then named Geattahgweah, which is now known as Lake Chautauqua, and made encampment. They agreed to hunt for two days, after which they were to proceed towards the enemies' country.

"The warriors went in various directions to hunt. Now one of the warriors passed a small brook, where he discovered a strange animal resembling a dog, but he could not discover animal's head; the creature was a greyish color, and was laying asleep exposed to the rays of the Sun; and he also discovered a den, which he supposed the place of the animal's residence:

"The warrior returned to the camp that evening and told the others about the animal, and he informed them, as he imagined it was a very poisonous animal, that he was afraid to approach it again. But one of the warriors, a joker, laughed at him and called him a cowardly fellow; the joker determined to go himself and kill the creature without trouble, but he wished some of the warriors to be witnesses to the engagement;

"Accordingly the warrior went out, accompanied by a number of warriors; he was directed to the spot and he discovered the animal. After beating it short time with his club, he seized the animal and tied it with a tumline. But while he was lifting it, the creature immediately moved to its den. With all his might he held on to the tumline, but he could not stop it, and he was compelled to let go of the tumline when the creature went beyond his reach;

"The warrior was confused at not being able to kill the animal, and he hastened to retire from the spot. But when he was but a few paces from it he was taken with the pestilence which was influenced by the creature and he suddenly died;

"Another warrior was within sight and directly fled to carry the intelligence back, but he also died a short distance away. The others returned to their camp, but the pestilence soon prevailed among the warriors, and many of them died in the same manner; a few of them escaped by leaving the camp before the pestilence appeared, and thus ended the expedition.

"The Ottawas continued their hostilities and attacked the hunters; the Senecas sent out a small party, and fought them. They drove the enemy off, but their engagements were small, and they continued for many winters.

(Footnotes)
[1] Appendix A here

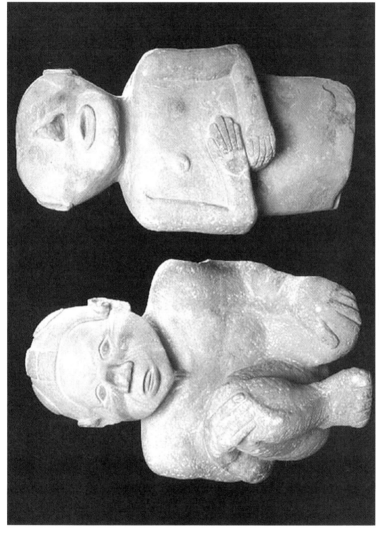

The Prophetic Couple

CHAPTER 14

THE LIFE OF THE MISSISSIPIANS:
THE PEOPLES OF THE SOUTHERN CEREMONIAL COMPLEX
AND THEIR TRADE FEDERATION

THE DIFFUSION OF THE SOUTHERN CEREMONIAL COMPLEX

My impression, based on the different body types, house types, and pottery types seen at Mississippian sites, is that this entire cultural complex spread more by diffusion than by conquest. It would appear that the Southern Ceremonial Culture was inclusive enough to quickly absorb other existing cultures.

All of these differing tribes appear to have been united by a common trade language, which is called today the "Mobilian Trade Language". My guess, based on the account given by the Natchez people in their Ancient Word (Chapter 12), is that this language is related to Huasteca.

SACRED ARCHITECTURE:
THE MOUNDS OF THE SOUTHERN CEREMONIAL PEOPLES,
AND THEIR FEDERATION STRUCTURE

An identifying characteristic of the Southern Ceremonial Cult peoples was that they operated in a federated manner, and were thus able to control large areas of land. Sometimes the federation centers were built at the river ends of trading paths; other times they were built at the headwaters of the river systems. Some of these federation centers, like Moundsville, had one very large mound surrounded by other large mounds, one for each of the villages in the federation, with other mounds nearby for the center's elite's use. Other federation centers, like Emerald Mound at Natchez and Ocmulgee Mound at Macon, were large leveled mounds, on which subordinate villages' ceremonial houses sat before the one large mound upon which the center's ceremonial temple was built, with other mounds present nearby for other uses.

A rough list of some of the major federation centers along the Mississippi River may be found in Chapter 17, Travel Tips; there are detailed area available studies for each of them which can be located by those so interested. The remains at Cahokia (Twakanhah) are unique among the federation centers, for it is well known that Cahokia (Twakanhah) was a federation of nearby federation centers, all of which have been lost to development.

What is more interesting, for me at least, and for many others, is to try and trace the federation centers of the states south of the Tennessee River, and to try to link them to the peoples who the very first European colonists despoiled. From Natchez, one key route was the Natchez Trace, which ran to Nashville and the federation center at Mound Bottom where the Harpeth River joins the Tennessee River.[1]

Alabama presents very interesting challenges[2]: the key site of Mauvila, which apparently controlled the Mobile River and access to the Gulf of Mexico, has yet to be located, even though many experts have spent decades searching for it. One key Alabama route ran up the Black Warrior River to the federation center at Moundsville, which I suspect was probably the original home of the Alabama. This route continued north along the Mulbery Fork of the Black Warrior River to the area around Bangor, where it crossed a mountain ridge to connect with the Locust Fork branch of the Black Warrior River, and then proceeded north down Big Spring Creek to the Tennessee River. Birmingham had a major federation center, which must have controlled the Cahaba River valley[3]. A series of federation centers laid just to the east of Montgomery along the Tallapoosa River, but whether they controlled the Coosa River as well as the Tallapoosa River is not known; I suspect that the Tuskigee controlled part of the Coosa River.

At the head of the Coosa River laid Etowah, and this certainly was the later point of trade with the Cherokee and their mica and copper. Etowah also must have traded Cherokee goods down the Chattahootchie River to federation centers at Columbus, Kolomoki, and to the Appalachi people at Tallahasse. Etowah also traded goods down the Ocmulgee River to the federation center at Macon, but the route through Atlanta is unclear.

In Florida, the federation center at Mount Royal controlled the St. John's River. The Mississippian sites along the rivers of South Carolina and North Carolina will be briefly mentioned in Chapter 15.

THE NATCHEZ ACCOUNT OF
HOW THEY ACQUIRED THEIR RELIGION:
THE PROPHETIC COUPLE[4]

Two items are uniformly found at in the temples at Southern Ceremonial sites: two small statues about three feet high, one female and one male, sometimes made of marble. While it has long been thought by many anthropologists that these figurines represented divinities, in point of fact they were representations of the prophetic couple of the Mississippians.

Though the Natchez placed the following passage in their Ancient Word before their arrival on the Gulf Coast of Mexico, given its similarity to events described in the religions of Central Mexico, most likely the Natchez acquired this religion after their move there, which was related in an earlier chapter of this book. Other indicators of a Mesoamerican source for Natchez religion are their use of ritual mats, thrones, and litters, resembling similar usage in Central America; yet another piece of evidence indicative of a possible Mesoamerican origin is that the key Natchez religious term "chill" ("Great") may be cognate with the key Mayan religious term "chillam". Proceeding to the account -

"A great number of years ago there appeared among us a man and his wife, who came down from the sun. It is not that we believe that the sun [in the heavens] had a wife who bore him children, or that this man and his wife were the descendants of the sun [which warms]; but when they first appeared among

245

us they were so bright and luminous that we had no difficulty in believing that they came down from the sun.

"This man told us that having seen from on high that we did not govern ourselves well, and that we had no master, each of us having presumption enough to think himself capable of governing others, while he could not even conduct himself, he had thought it fit to come down among us to teach us how to live better.

"Moreover, he then told us that in order to be in a condition to govern others it was necessary to know how to guide oneself, and that in order to live in peace among ourselves, and to please the Great Spirit, we must observe the following rules:
Never kill any one,
except in the defense of your own life;
Never know any other woman besides your own,
[when married];
Never take any thing which belongs to another;
Never lie, nor get drunk;
Do not be greedy,
but give freely and with joy,
that which you have;
Share your food generously,
with those who are in need of it."

"This man impressed us with these words, because he said them with authority; and he obtained the respect of the Old Men [the council] themselves, although he did not spare them more than others. The Old Men [the council] assembled, and resolved among themselves that since this man had so much intelligence to teach them what it was good to do, he must be recognized as their Ruler; so much the more as in governing them, himself he could make them remember better than any other what he had taught them.

"So the Old Men went in the early morning to the cabin where they had had him sleep, along with his wife, and they proposed to him that he be our ruler. He refused at first, saying that he would not be obeyed, and the disobedient would not fail to die.

"But finally he accepted the offer which was made to him on the following conditions:
That we would go to inhabit another country, which was better than that one which we were then in, and which he would show to us; that we would live in the future as he had taught us the evening before; that we would promise to recognize no other Ruler besides himself, and those who should descend from him and his wife; and that nobility should be perpetuated through the women, which he explained to us in this way:

246

"'If I have', he said to us, 'male and female children, they will not be able to marry each other, as they will be brothers and sisters.' To which he added, 'The boy shall take from among the people a girl who pleases him; this man shall be the Ruler [Great Sun]; but this man's sons shall not be even Princes [Suns], but only Nobles.'

"'The children of my daughter, [on the other hand], shall be Princes and Princesses [Suns]. The eldest of her male children shall be the Ruler [Great Sun], and her eldest girl shall be the Princess [Sun] who will give birth to the Ruler {Great Sun].

"'The descendants of the Ruler and the Princes shall descend in rank, but not those of the girl, even though this daughter or another Princess has married a man of the people.

"'The Princes and Princesses [Suns] shall not ally [marry] themselves together, nor yet with their own cousins, nor with the children of their own cousins."

"[And finally he said that,] 'In the absence of a sister of the Ruler, his nearest female relative shall be the mother of his successor.'

"Pursuing his speech, he then said to us that in order not to forget the good words which he had brought to us, a temple should be built, into which only the Princes and Princesses [male and female Suns] should have a right to enter to speak to the Great Spirit. In this temple should be eternally preserved a fire, which he would make descend from the sun [in the heavens], from where he had come. The wood with which this fire should be fed should be a pure wood without bark.

"Eight wise men should be chosen from the nation to guard this fire and tend it day and night; these eight Wise Men should have a Chief who would watch over the manner in which they performed their duty; any one of them who failed in it should be put to death.

"He then wished that at the other extremity of the country which we should inhabit (and our nation was then much more extensive than it is now) a second temple should be built, where in like manner fire should be kept which had been taken from the first, so that if the fire came to be extinguished in the one temple they could seek the other, in order to relight it. And he informed us that if this misfortune ever happened death would extend itself over our nation until the fire was relighted.

"They promised him to observe and perform all these things, and then he consented to be our Ruler, but he did not wish to be called by any other name than 'The', which means 'thee' [You]. "

The remains of the Hausteca city at Las Flores on Mexico's Northern Gulf Coast are quite unique in the Central American regions. If the Natchez account is to be believed, it may be highly possible that what is seen at Las Flores is a Mediterranean influence. Among the peoples of the Mediterranean Sea, "T'e" [Theous] meant "God", and this title was given by them to their rulers. While nothing is known of the rules of succession of the peoples of the Mediterranean Sea, it is well proven by their remains that every one of them had a group of powerful female leaders, and while these have been considered to be solely Priestesses, they were more likely matriarchs who bore the hereditary line, as the Suns did among the Southern Ceremonial Cult peoples .

"However, after his death, his descendants were called "Suns", because the man and woman came out originally from the sun [from the east?], and because the "The" was so brilliant that one could scarcely look at him.

"Then he had the temples built, established the Guardians of the Temple, eight for each temple, and for each temple he established a Chief of the Guardians."

THE MASTER OF THE CEREMONIES,
THE MASTER OF MYSTERIES

Continuing with Le Page du Pratz's account[5]:

"Besides the eight Guardians of the Temple, two of whom were always on watch, and the Chief of the Guardians of the Temple, there also belonged to the service of the temple a Master of the Ceremonies, who was also the Master of the Mysteries, since he conversed very familiarly with the Spirit(s). Above all these persons was the Great Sun, who was at the same time the Chief Priest and the Ruler of the nation."

THE CEIBA TREE

"In this temple two men tend the perpetual fire during each quarter of the moon. There are eight guardians for the four quarters, and a superior who is called the Chief of the Guardians of the Fire [Temple] to command them and to see that they do their duty, and to have the wood brought for this fire.

"This wood must be clear wood, and they employ for the fire only clear white walnut (or hickory) without bark. The logs are 7 to 8 inches in diameter by 8 feet long. They are placed near the temple about the trunk of a tree with a rather short stem.

"This tree is covered with thorns from the ground to its top. This passion-thorn [honey locust] tree does not rise above the height of a shrub, but its trunk is rather thick for its height. Its leaf resembles that of the black thorn, and its wood while it is green is not very hard. Its thorns are at least two inches long, and are very hard and piercing; within half an inch of their root two other small thorns grow out from them so as to form a cross. The whole trunk is covered with these thorns, so that you must be very wary how you approach it, or cut it.

"This shrub is held in great esteem among the Natchez; but I (Le Page du Pratz) never could learn for what reason. I have never been able to find out why the Natchez have respect for this tree wherever they find it, unless it be on account of the employment to which it is destined. "

The Mayan kingdoms raised a ceiba tree in the center of their city states, and it is a source of inhibitors for MAO-DMT hallucinogens. There is little mystery why Le Page du Pratz's good friend the Head of the Guardians of the Temple concealed this information from him.

THE FIRST ETERNAL FIRE

"And in presence of the entire nation, he made descend the fire of the Sun on walnut (hickory) wood which he had prepared, and when it was lighted, some of it was carried with much attention and respect into the other temple, which was at the farther extremity of our country. "

"Minoan" [Lycian] quartz lenses have been recovered on Thera, and these would have been perfectly capable of focusing the rays of the sun to start a fire. Le Page du Pratz sold his magnifying glass to the Natchez for an incredible price.

THE PROPHET'S END,
AND HIS FOUNDATION OF THE FEASTS

"He lived a very long time, and saw the children of his children.

"Finally, he instituted the feasts which you see."

THE PROPHET COUPLE AT
THE HARVEST FESTIVAL OF DUHARE

This religion was adapted with a remarkable consistency among all the peoples of the Southern Ceremonial Complex, who lived across the entire southeast of North America. Peter Martyr gives us an account of the Prophetic Couple among the Duharhe of today's South Carolina[6] :

"The natives have no temples, but use the dwellings of their sovereigns as such. As proof of this we have said that a gigantic sovereign called Dacha ruled in the province of Duhare: [His] palace was built of stone, while all the other houses were built of lumber covered with thatch or grasses. In the courtyard of this palace the Spaniards found two idols as large as a three-year old child, one male and one female. These idols are both called Inamahari, and had their residence in the palace.

"Twice each year they are exhibited. The first time (is) at the sowing season, when they are invoked to obtain the successful results for their labors. We will later speak of the harvest, {when} thanksgivings are offered to them if the crops are good; in the contrary case, they are implored to show themselves more favorable the following year."

[Skipping forward here, Martyr seems to be referring to the corn (maize) ceremony held at the henge, of which more later]

"The idols are carried in procession amidst pomp, accompanied by the entire people. It will not be useless to describe this ceremony. On the eve of the festival the King has his bed made in the room where the idols stand", [Which is separate from his normal sleeping quarters, which were located in another room in the structure or structures built on top of the mound], "and sleeps in their presence.

"At daybreak the people assemble, and the King himself carries these idols, hugging them to his breast, to the top of his palace, where he exhibits them to the people. He and they are saluted with respect and fear by the people, who fall upon their knees, or throw themselves to the ground, with loud shouts.

"The King then descends [the palace and/or the mound?] and hangs the idols, draped in artistically worked cotton stuffs, upon the breasts of two venerable men of authority. They are, moreover, adorned with feather mantles of various colors, and are thus escorted with hymns and songs into the country, while girls and young men dance and leap... The men escort the idols during the day, while during the night the women watch over them, lavishing upon them demonstrations of joy and respect.

"The next day they were carried back to the palace with the same ceremonies with which they were taken out.

"If the sacrifice is accomplished with devotion and in conformity with the ritual, the Indians believe they will be(come) rich in crops, bodily health, peace, or if they are at war, victory, from these idols. Thick cakes, similar to those the ancients made from flour, are offered to them. The natives are convinced that their prayers for harvests will be heard, especially if the cakes are mixed with tears."

THE GREAT SUNS IN
THE LANDS OF THE THUNDERBIRD PRIEST-KINGS

Despite the constancy in many aspects, this Natchez Central American culture did undergo some adaptation as it was adopted by the peoples of North America. Most prominent among the changes they made was the merging of the office of the Great Sun with that of their existing Thunderbird Priest-Kings.

These Thunderbird Priest-Kings are one of the key identifying characteristics of the Southern Ceremonial Culture. From images recovered through excavation, it is clear that these priest-kings wore large bird feathered cloaks shaped like wings. They had large pouches to contain their requisites of office hanging from their waists, wore "claws" on their feet, and either had their noses deformed into beaks through the

Thunderbird King

removal of their sides and septums, or wore bird beak masks. Their feet are always shown not touching the ground, and they are often shown with a hatchet and severed human head in their hands.

THE LITTERS OF THE THUNDERBIRDS
THE HARVEST FERSTVAL LITTER OF THE NATCHEZ GREAT SUN

The French colonists attested that the Natchez's King's feet never touched the ground, at least during ceremonial occasions, and they described the litters on which these kings were carried:

> "The old warriors prepare the litter on which the Great Sun is going to be brought to the open space. This litter is composed of four red bars which cross each other at the four corners of the seat, which has a depth of about one and half feet. The entire seat is garnished inside with undecorated deerskins, because it is not seen. Those deerskins which hang outside are painted with designs of different colors according to their taste. These deerskins conceal the seat so well that the substance of which it is composed can not be seen.

> "The back part of this seat is covered like the equipages we call chaises (souffets). It is covered outside and in with leaves of the tulip laurel. The outside border is garnished with three strings of flowers: the string of flowers which extends the farthest outside is red, and it is accompanied on each side by a string of white flowers.

> "Those who prepare this litter are the first and the oldest warriors of the nation. They place it on the shoulders of the eight warriors who are the only ones to take it out of the village. In this way there remain only 16 of the warriors there at the cabin of the Great Sun, because all of the other warriors have gone, a little after sunrise, with their Great Chief [of War] and those who command the warriors under his orders. The Great War Chief disperses these a hundred paces apart, and places eight warriors in each relay. For this purpose he chooses those of his warriors who are the strongest and the most vigorous. The other warriors wait with him at the open space to receive the Great Sun."

THE ROYAL LITTER OF THE DUHARHE

Peter Martyr's informants described the similar use of litters among the Duharhe:

> "Leaving the coast of Chicorana on the one hand [the left?], the Spaniards landed in another country called "Duharhe"... They are governed by a King of gigantic size, called Datha, whose wife is as large as himself; they have five children. In place of horses the King is carried on the shoulders of strong young men, who run with him to the different places he wishes to visit."

THE CLASS STRUCTURE OF THE NATCHEZ

Based on their architecture, symbols of decoration, and the family structures of related peoples, it appears that the peoples who adopted the Southern Ceremonial Complex earlier used the technology of the clan to organize their societies. On the same grounds, it appears that after they adopted the Southern Ceremonial Complex, they dropped the use of clans entirely.

As was seen above, the Natchez divided their society into the Great Sun, his immediate relatives the "Suns", the "Nobles", the "Honored Men", and the "Stinkards". The means of preventing inbreeding and ensuring representation is quite interesting, as rank was passed through the mother, and all of the upper classes, including the "Great Sun" himself, were required to marry "Stinkards". While men "ruled", the "Great Sun" himself inherited his office due to his relationship with his mother.

Among the Natchez, the public offices held by ability were the 8 Guardians of the Temple, the Chief of the Guardians of the Temple, who had the responsibility to preserve the Ancient Word, the Master of Ceremonies, who was their shaman and physician, and the Great Chief of the Warriors, who led the nation in war.

THE CLASS STRUCURE OF DUHARHE

As was seen above, the Durharhe had a king who was equivalent to if not actually a Great Sun. Possibly men from either the "Nobles" or "Honored Men" formed the judges who Martyr wrote about:

> "Justice is administered by magistrates, [the] criminals and the guilty being severely punished, especially thieves."

That the Duharhe had a Chief of the Guardians of the Temple may be seen in Martyr's statement that,

> "None of them have any writing, but they preserve traditions of great antiquity in rhymes and chants...",

as this history was maintained by the Chief of the Guardians of the Temple. Peter Martyr also provides us with a detailed description of the funeral of a King, which will be given below, and as the funeral orator recited the thunderbird priest-kings achievements in his eulogy, it is likely that this orator was the Duharhe Chief of the Guardians of the Temple, their head priest. These Chiefs of the Guardians of the Temple appear to have been the equivalent in some ways to the bards of the ancient Europeans, charged with preserving their tribes' lore.

Another commonly found image in Southern Ceremonial contexts is of dancing men in deer costumes, and I suspect that these are shaman-priests, as deer are often associated with herbs and plants in myths, and the use of plants for medical purposes and for ritual hallucination are related.

253

Among the Natchez this man was the Master of Ceremonies, who appears to have been responsible for these activities. Martyr attests also to these shaman/physicians among the Duharhe: "...This is the only medicament they use, and they never consult doctors, except experienced old women, or priests acquainted with the secret virtues of herbs."

THE "WITNESSES" TO WAR:
DUHARE BARDS AND SHAMAN/PHYSICIANS IN WAR

It may be possible that these as well as the shaman/physicians and astronomers were all included by the Natchez among the group they called "Honorable Men", but again this term may have simply referred to warriors. From Peter Martyr:

> "In the last named [the Tihe region of Duharhe] the inhabitants wear a distinctive priestly costume, and they are regarded as priests and venerated as such by their neighbors. They cut their hair, leaving only two locks growing on their temples, which are bound under their chin. When the natives make war against their neighbors, according to the regrettable custom of mankind, these priests are invited by both sides to be present, not as actors [participants], but as witnesses of the conflict.

> "When the battle is about to open, they circulate among the warriors who are seated or lying on the ground, and sprinkle them with the juice of certain herbs they have chewed with their teeth, just as our priests at the beginning of the Mass sprinkle the worshippers with a branch dipped in holy water.

> "When this ceremony is finished, the opposing sides fall upon one another. While the battle rages the priests are left in charge of the camp; [and] when it is finished they look after the wounded, making no distinction between friends and enemies; and [then they] busy themselves in burying the dead. The inhabitants of this country do not eat human flesh - prisoners of war are enslaved by the victors."

Clearly this was ritual warfare, and it left these people un-prepared when true enemies appeared later.

THE FEDERATION OF NATCHEZ

Why Emerald Mound near Natchez was abandoned by them remains a mystery, but it is probably related to the later Kushita, Choctaw, and Chickasaw migrations through the area, which will be related in the next chapter. When the French colonists first arrived, the Natchez ceremonial center was located in what had earlier been a minor outlying village, and their domain extended solely to a few more minor outlying villages.

THE FEDERATION OF THE DUHARHE

Peter Martyr told of the Federation of Duhare:

> "The Spaniards speak of still other regions - Hitha, Xamunambe, and Tihe [Anica/Tihe] - all of which are believed to be governed by the same king [Datha of Duharhe]. In the last named the inhabitants wear a distinctly priestly costume, and they are regarded as priests and venerated as such by their neighbors. They cut their hair leaving only two locks growing on their temples, which are bound under the chin."

And in another passage:

> "Their kings are of gigantic size, as we have already mentioned. All the provinces we have named pay them [their kings] tributes, and these tributes are paid in kind: for they are free from the pest of money, and trade is carried on by exchanging goods."

THE FOODS OF DUHARHE:

Semi-Domesticated Deer:

> "In all these regions they visited the Spaniards noticed herds of deer similar to our herds of cattle. These deer bring forth and nourish their young in the houses of the natives. During the daytime they wander freely through the woods in search of their food, and in the evening they come back to their little ones, who have been cared for, allowing themselves to be shut up in the courtyards, and even milked, (after) they have suckled their fawns. The only milk the natives know of is that of does, from which they make cheese."

Domesticated Fowl:

> "They also keep a great variety of chickens, ducks, geese, and other similar fowls."

Corn (Maize):

> "They eat maize bread, similar to that of the islanders [the base of Spanish operations at this time]; but they do not know the yucca root, from which cassabi, the food of the nobles [of the islands] is made. The maize grains are very much like our Genoese millet, and in size are as large as our peas.

Grain:

> "The natives cultivate another cereal called "xanthi"; this is believed to be millet but it is not certain, for very few Castillians know millet, as it is grown nowhere in Castille."

255

Roots:

"This country produces potatoes, but of small varieties."

Nut Trees, Fruit Trees, Alcohol, And Vegetables:

"There are in this country virgin forest of oak, pine, cypress, nut, and almond trees, amongst the branches of which grow riot wild (grape) vines, whose white and black grapes are not used for wine making, for the people manufacture their drinks from other fruits. There are like-wise fig trees and other kinds of spice plants. The trees are improved by grafting, just as with us, though without cultivation they would continue (to grow) in a wild state.

"The natives cultivate gardens in which grows an abundance of vegetables, and they take an interest in growing their orchards: they even have trees in their gardens. One of their trees is called "corito", the fruit of which resembles a small melon is size and flavor. Another called "guacomine" bears a fruit a little larger than a quince, of a delicate and remarkable odor, and which is very wholesome. They plant and cultivate many trees and plants, of which I shall not speak further, lest by telling everything at one breath I become monotonous."

THE MISSISSIPPIAN TRADE IN FOOD STUFFS

It is commonly assumed by North American archaeologists that the non-local pots which they find at their sites arrived there empty, as though the ancient Native American peoples were pot collectors struck by the beauty of the pieces they saw. The extraction of oil from nuts and its use as a very nutritious foodstuff is well attested in European contact accounts, and the trade in it must have started as soon as suitable pots were available. While the Native Americans lacked honey bees, they did have syrup from the sap of maple trees to use as a sweetener. Martyr's informants described alcohol made from fruits, and it is known that the peoples in the southeast brewed persimmon wine in contact times. The use of fermented beverages by the Maya and Aztec is well documented, though the exact date of their discovery of fermentation is unknown. I have seen it mentioned that the Aztec had 40 or so alcoholic beverages, and that the knowledge of fermentation did not spread seems unlikely. All of these would also have been traded, but without analysis of organic oils it can not be said when.

DEATH OF A DUHARE GREAT SUN, A THUNDERBIRD PRIEST-KING

As the Spanish were carrying European diseases, it is not surprising that we have received an account via Martyr of the death and burial of a thunderbird priest-king. Martyr himself makes the astronomical associations clear:

"Another of their frauds is as follows: When the chief is at death's door and about to give up his soul, they send away all witnesses, and then surrounding his bed they perform some secret jugglery which makes him appear to vomit sparks and ashes. It looks like sparks jumping from a bright fire, or those sulphured papers which people [Europeans] throw in the air to amuse themselves [fireworks]. These sparks, rushing through the air and quickly disappearing, look like those shooting stars which people [Europeans] call leaping wild goats. The moment the dying man expires, a cloud of those sparks shoots up 3 cubits high with a noise, and [then] quickly vanishes. They hail this flame as the dead man's [the dead king's] soul, bidding it a last farewell, and accompanying its flight with their wailings, tears, and funereal cries, absolutely convinced that it has taken its flight to heaven. Lamenting and weeping they escort the body to the tomb."

BURIAL AND THE AFTERLIFE AMONG THE DUHARHE

The thunderbird priest-kings body was then stripped of flesh, whether by internment, as Martyr thought, or by exposure is not clear.

"...after exhuming [digging up] a long buried skeleton, they erect a black tent out in the country, leaving one end open so that the sky is visible; upon a blanket placed in the center of the tent they then spread out the bones. Only women surround the tent, all of them weeping, and each of them offer[ing] such gifts as they can afford.

"The following day[?] the bones are carried to the tomb and are henceforth considered sacred. As soon as they are buried, or everything is ready for the burial, the chief priest addresses the surrounding people from the summit of a MOUND, upon which he fulfills the functions of orator. Ordinarily he pronounces an eulogy on the deceased, or [and?] on the immortality of the soul, or [and?] the future of life.

"He says that souls originally came from icy regions of the north, where perpetual snow prevails. They therefore expiate their sins under the master of that region, who is called Mateczunga; but they return to the southern regions, where another great sovereign, Quexuga, governs.

"Quezuga is lame, and is of sweet and generous disposition. He surrounds the newly arrived souls with numberless attentions, and with him they enjoy a thousand delights; young girls sing and dance, parents are reunited to children, and everything one formerly loved is enjoyed. The old grow young (there) and everybody is of the same age, occupied only in giving himself up to joy and pleasure."

Perhaps Martyr was lost by the next part of his informant's report, thrown off by the concept of asteroids as horned snakes and space as a cold dark lake:

"...These native also believe that we live under the vault of heaven; they do not suspect the existence of the antipodes. They think the sea has its gods, and believe quite as many foolish things about them as Greece, the friend of lies, talked about (the) Nereids and other marine gods - Glaucus, Phoreus, and the rest of them.

"When the priest has finished his speech he inhales the smoke of certain herbs, puffing it in and out, pretending to thus purge and absolve the people from their sins. After this ceremony the natives return home, convinced that the interventions of this imposter not only soothe the spirits, but contribute to the health of bodies."

BURIAL AND AFTERLIFE AMONG THE NATCHEZ

The Natchez also practiced the stripping of the flesh from the bones of a corpse before its burial, and they also believed in a Country of the Spirits. Simon Antoine Le Page du Pratz was a great friend of the Natchez people, and they allowed him nearly full access to their rites. Gordon Sayre has graciously allowed the following extracts to be adapted from his and his assistant Nicole Degli Esposti's new complete translation of Le Page du Pratz's History of Louisiana.[7]

"Besides, near these little temples some distinctive marks are always to be seen; either small elevations of earth or some little dishes which announce that in this place there are bodies interred. Or [else] one sees some raised tombs, if the nation has that custom.

"These tombs are raised about three feet above the earth. They rest on four feet, which are forked sticks planted deep enough in the earth and well secured to support the tomb, which, supported and thus borne on these forks, is eight feet long by a foot and a half wide. They place the body with the head at one end, in order that a space remain at the end where the feet are. Above the body they make an arbor of branches curved into a vault. They place straight pieces of wood at the head and at the feet, then they plaster these pieces of wood in order to enclose the body during a space of time sufficient to consume the flesh and dry up the bones.

"After this time they withdraw them to put them in a basket or coffer of cane covered with the same material and carry them into the temple with the others. As the body is not as long as the tomb, there remains a space of about a foot which is covered by the end of the vault but is not closed. It is there that they put the provisions that they bring to the dead for some time after death.

"In spite of their zeal to render the last duties to the dead, they are unable to satisfy themselves regarding those who are killed in war. They supply the deficiency after their manner, with sighs, tears, and cries, as soon as they learn the news, and often for longer than if they had died in the nation, where the custom is to weep for three days.

"There is no nation of Louisiana which knows the custom of burning bodies, used among the Greeks and Romans; nor the custom of the Egyptians, who preserved them perpetually. But they solemnize them, as I have just said, sometimes with pomp, sometimes with smaller ceremonies, which they take great care to conceal from strangers. One only sees them if he is a friend of the sovereign and can be alerted to be present...

Le Page du Pratz was just such a friend, and as he was an eyewitness of the burial of his close friend the Chief Warrior Tattooed Serpent, we know in detail the Natchez method of burying their nobles:

> "He [Tattooed Serpent] was on his bed of state, dressed in his finest clothing, his face painted with vermilion [red ochre], moccasined as if to go on a journey, and wearing his crown of white [peace] feathers mingled with red [war]. His weapons had been tied to his bed; these consisted of a double-barreled gun, a pistol, a bow, a quiver full of arrows, and a war club. Around the bed were all the calumets of peace which he had received during his life, and nearby had been planted a large pole, peeled and painted red [in this case the color of war], from which hung a chain of reddened cane splints, composed of forty-six links or rings, to indicate the number of enemies he had killed. I do not at all pretend in reporting this fact to guarantee the number of the exploits of this man.

> "All his people were around him. Food was served to him at his accustomed hours, as if he had been living, and his retainer [head servant], seeing that he did not touch it, said to him: 'You no longer wish, then, to take what we present you? Are these things no more to your taste? Why is it, then, that you rebuff us and our services do not please you any more? Ah! you do not [36] speak as usual. Without doubt you are dead. Yes, it is done. You are going to the country of the spirits, and you are leaving us forever.' Then [the head servant] uttered the death cry, which was repeated by all those in the cabin. They replied in the village, and from voice to voice the same cry passed in an instant into the other villages of the Nation, who all together made the air reverberate with their doleful cries.

> "The company in the cabin was composed of the favorite wife of the deceased, of a second wife, whom he kept in another village, to visit when his favorite wife was pregnant, his chancellor, his doctor, his head servant, his pipe bearer, and some old women, all of whom were going to be strangled at his burial. A noble woman joined herself to the number of the victims there; the friendship that she had for the Tattooed Serpent led her to join him in the country of the spirits. The French called her La Glorieuse, because of her majestic bearing and her proud air and because she was intimate only with distinguished Frenchmen. I regretted her [decision] so much the more [for] that, possessing a deep knowledge of simples [herbal remedies], she had saved the lives of many of our sick, and I myself had drawn good lessons from her." [This woman was a physician.]

This custom of the self sacrifice of a noble's retinue was a custom reflective of earlier times, when the Natchez were a much more numerous people. It appears to have been adopted by them to reduce intrigues and struggles for kingship within the nation, and a similar custom was held by the highest nobles for exactly this reason:

"When any of the Suns, either male or female, die, their law ordains that the husband or wife of the Sun shall be put to death on the day of the interment of the deceased: now as another law prohibits the issue of the Suns from being put to death, it is therefore impossible for the descendants of the Suns to match with each other."

Since the Natchez held a strong belief in a Country of the Spirits where one lived after death, the end of life by self sacrifice was held with less fear. In justifying her decision to kill herself to Le Page du Pratz, Tattooed Serpent's wife provided him with a brief description of this Natchez heaven:

"We will be friends for a much longer time in the Country of the Spirits than in this [one], because one can not die there again. It is always fine weather [there], one is never hungry, [and] because nothing is wanting, [one] lives better than in this country. Men do not make war there any more, because they are only one nation."

Given this strong belief in the Country of the Spirits, those who were killing themselves believed that they would continue to enjoy Tattooed Serpent's company there after their own deaths. The elderly also appear to have sacrificed themselves to reduce their burden on the rest of the trive, and to have ensured their offspring's favor and well being. But these were also strong social obligations, which is seen in the following:

"The same day at sunrise, while we were engaged in restraining the Great Sun [from killing himself in grief], a man named Ette-actal had been brought [in], escorted by thirty warriors... He had married a female Sun who had died, and according to the laws of his nation he ought to have died with her. But this law not being to his taste, as soon as he had seen her in agony [of death] he fled secretly toward the landing, took some provisions, descended the river non-stop in a little dugout, and went to place himself under the protection of Monsieur [de Bienville], the Commandant of the capital, offering himself to him as a hunter and one of his slaves. His service was accepted...

"The Natchez then even promised his master that he had nothing to fear because, the ceremony being completed and he not having been found [during] that time, he was no longer a lawful prize. This native, thus reassured, went from time to time to see his relatives and friends, and nothing had ever been said to him. But this last time, the Great Sun having learned from the French that Monsieur de Bienville had been recalled to France, considered that the letters of reprieve of Ette-actal were abrogated by the absence of his protector. Thus [the Great Sun] judged it suitable to make him pay his debt to the Tattooed Serpent in the capacity of a relation of his wife, and it was for this reason that they brought him.

"When this man saw himself in the cabin of the Great Chief of War, among the number of the victims who were going to be sacrificed to his manes, he was seized with the liveliest grief, to see himself taken this time without hope of safety, and [he] began to weep very bitterly. [Tattooed Serpent's] favorite wife perceiving this, said to him, 'Are you not a warrior?'

"'Yes,' said he, ' I am one.'

"'Nevertheless you weep,' she replied, 'Your life is then dear to you? If this is so, then it is not good that you come with us. Go away with the women.'

"He replied, 'Certainly life is dear to me. I have no children. It is well that I travel some time longer on the Earth, until the death of the Great Sun, and die with him.'

"'Go away, I tell you,' she said, 'it is not good that you come with us and that your heart remain behind you on the Earth. Once more, take yourself away from here, and let me see you no more.''

"Ette-actal had brought a little sack in which were the small utensils necessary for the [self sacrifice] ceremony, but without disturbing himself about them he left all; and satisfied still to have time to himself before the death of the Great Sun, at the last word of [Tattooed Serpent's] favorite wife he took flight, and disappeared like a flash. But in the afternoon three old women were brought, two of whom were his relations, who, being extremely aged and wearied of life, offered themselves to pay his debt. Although these two women were so old that for many years they had totally lost the use of their limbs, their hair was no grayer than is commonly that of women of fifty in France. They appeared in all respects to bear themselves well.

"The generosity of these two women purchased the life of the warrior Ette-actal, and acquired for him the rank of Honored man."

Finally, there was prisoner and infant sacrifice:

"A few moments afterwards the young Sun came to tell me that orders had been given (for he had promised, although feignedly, to have only those die who were in the cabin of the deceased, because they were his "food" [in other words, they were Tattooed Serpent's dependents]), that besides these, there would be put to death a bad woman, if she had not already been killed, and an infant which had already been strangled by its father and mother, a forfeit which purchased their lives at the death of the Great Sun, [and] ennobled them, and raised them from the rank of Stinkards."

Continuing with Le Page du Pratz's description of the burial of Tattooed Serpent –

"A few moments later the Great [Chil] Master of Ceremonies appeared at the door of the dead man's house with the ornaments which were proper to his rank, and which I have described. He uttered two words and the people in the cabin came out. These persons were the Tattooed Serpent's favorite wife and another wife, his chancellor, his doctor, his head servant, his pipe bearer, and some old women. Each of these victims was accompanied by eight male relations, who were charged with putting him or her to death. One [of them] bore the war club, raised as if to strike, and frequently imitating this motion. Another carried the mat on which to seat him, a third carried the cord for strangling him, another the [deer] skin, the fifth a dish in which were five or six balls of pounded tobacco to make him swallow in order to stupefy him. Another bore a little earthen bottle holding about a pint, in order to make him drink some mouthfuls of water in order to swallow the pellets more easily. Two others followed to aid in drawing the cord [for strangulation] from each side.

"A very small number of men suffices to strangle a person, but since this action withdraws them from the rank of Stinkards, [and] puts them in the class of Honored men, and thus exempts them from dying with the Suns, many more would present themselves [for this duty] if the number were not fixed at eight only. All these persons whom I have just described walk in this order, two by two, after their relation. The victims have their hair daubed with red [red ochre again] and carry in the hand the shell of a river mussel, which is about seven inches long by three or four broad. By that they are distinguished from their followers, who on these days wear red feathers in their hair; [on] the day of the death they [the followers] have their hands reddened, as being prepared to give death..."

"[After they] Arrived in the square, the mats of the foremost [of the companions] are placed nearest the temple, the favorite [wife] to the right and the other wife to the left of the road, the others afterward according to their rank, six or seven feet apart on the two sides of the road, the breadth of which between them is at least thirty feet. The persons who are going to die are made to sit down on their mats, then all the assembled make the death cry behind them. The relatives dance the Death Dance and the victims on their mats dance in time also, without leaving their places. After this dance the entire group returns to the cabin in the same order. This is a rehearsal of the tragedy that is going to be played out on the day of the funeral procession. It is done twice a day..."

The day of the funeral finally arrived –

"I have said elsewhere that the temple, the house of the Great Sun, and that of the Tattooed Serpent, were on the square; [and] that that of the great Sun was built on a mound of earth carried to a height of about eight feet. It was on this mound that we placed ourselves by the side of the dwelling of the Great Sun, who had shut himself in in order to see nothing. His wife [who actually held the royal bloodline], who was also there, was able to hear us, but we had no fear that she would reveal what we might say against such a cruel custom. This law did not please her enough for her to find fault with those who spoke ill of it. As for the Great Sun, he was on the other side [the inside] and was not able to hear our remarks. From this place, without disturbing the ceremony, we were able to see everything, even into the interior of the temple, the door of which faced us.

"At the appointed hour the Master of Ceremonies arrived, adorned with red feathers in a half crown on his head. He had his red baton, in the shape of a cross, at the end of which hung a cluster of black feathers. He had all the upper portion of his body reddened [red ochre again], with the exception of his arms, in order to let it be seen that he did not dip his hands in the blood. His belt, which girded him above his hips, was ornamented with feathers, of which one row was black and the following was red, and afterward alternately as far as the knees. His legs were of their natural color. He entered the house of the Great Sun in this dress to ask him, without doubt, for permission to start the funeral procession....

"As soon as the Master of Ceremonies went to the door of the deceased he saluted him, without entering, with a great "Hou!" ["Good!"]. Then he made the death cry, to which the people on the square replied in the same manner. The entire nation [then] did the same thing, and the echoes repeated it from afar.

"The body of the strangled infant was near the door by which the body of the dead man was to be brought out. Its father and its mother were behind it, leaning against the wall, their feet on some Spanish moss, esteeming themselves unworthy to walk on the earth until the body of the deceased had passed over it. As soon as the body appeared they laid their infant down, then raised it when [the body] was outside, in order to expose it at each circle which [the body] made until it had reached the temple.

"Tattooed Serpent, having come out of his cabin on his state bed, as I have pictured it [in the illustration], was placed on a litter with two poles, which four men carried. Another pole was placed underneath [the litter] toward the middle and crosswise, which two other men held, in order to sustain the body. These six men who carried it were Guardians of the Temple.

"The Great [Chil] Master of Ceremonies walked first, and after him the oldest of the war chiefs, who bore the pole from which hung the cane links. He held this pole in one hand, and in the other a war calumet, a mark of the dignity of the deceased. [This individual was probably Tattooed Serpent's successor as War Chief.] Then came the body, after which marched the procession of those who were going to die at his burial.

"Together they circled the house from which they had come out three times. At the third turn they took the road to the temple, and then the relatives of the victims placed themselves in the order which I have described for the rehearsal [of the funeral]. But they walked very slowly, because they were going straight to the temple, while the body circled about as it advanced in a manner of which I am not able to give a better idea than by the mark indicated on the plate [the illustration]. At each circuit made by the body, the man of whom I have spoken threw [the corpse of] his child in front of it, in order that the body should pass over. He took it up again by one foot to do the same at the other circuits.

"Finally the body reached the temple, and the victims put themselves in their places as determined in the rehearsals. The mats were stretched out. They seated themselves there. The death cry was uttered. The pellets of tobacco were given to them and a little water to drink after each one. After they had all been taken, [each victim's] head was covered with a skin on which the cord was placed around the neck, two men held it in order that it should not be dragged away [to one side] by the stronger party, and the cord, which had a running knot, was held at each end by three men, who drew with all their strength from the two opposite sides. They are so skillful in this operation that it is impossible to describe it as quickly as it is done.

"The body of the Tattooed Serpent was placed in a great trench in the interior of the temple on the right. His two wives were buried in the same trench. La Glorieuse [the female herbalist] was buried in front of the temple to the right and [Tattooed Serpent's] chancellor on the left. The others were carried into the temples of their own villages in order to be interred there. After this ceremony the cabin of the deceased was burned, according to custom."

The continuance of these customs during times of greatly reduced population undoubtedly helped along the Mississippian people's demise.

ASTRONOMERS AND HENGES, AND THE HARVEST FEAST OF THE DUHARHE

Another motif commonly found represented on artifacts from Southern Ceremonial sites is that of dancers dressed in snake costumes. I have little doubt that the people shown in these images were their "astronomers".

It is also well established that the Southern Ceremonial Cult Priest-Kings harnessed lightening in their rites: the post holes from trees used as lightening rods have been located on the tops of their temple mounds[8], and as I mentioned earlier there was no differentiation between lightening and bolides or impacts.

As Martyr reports that "Their year is divided into 12 moons.", there can be little doubt that their astronomy was based on modified lunar cycles. Martyr also provides us with a description of what appears to be a festival at a henge, which is probably the thanksgiving harvest festival alluded to earlier, and thus took place in the fall:

"Another feast is celebrated every year, when a roughly carved wooden statue is carried into the country and fixed upon a high pole planted in the ground. This first pole is surrounded by similar ones, upon which [the] people hang gifts for the gods, each one according to his means.

"At NIGHTFALL the principle citizens", [this would be the Suns, the lesser Suns, who were the queen and king's family, and the Nobles, and the Honored Men], "divide these offerings among themselves, just as the priests do the cakes and other offerings given them [the gods] by the women."

"Whoever offers the divinity the most valuable presents is the most honored. Witnesses [the Bards] are present when the gifts are offered, who announce after the ceremony what every one has given, just as notaries might do in Europe. Each one is thus stimulated by a spirit of rivalry to outdo his neighbor.

"From sunrise until evening", [Here begins the second day of the feast.], "the people dance around this statue, clapping their hands. And when NIGHTFALL has barely set in, the image and the pole on which it was fixed are carried away and thrown into the sea, if the country is on the coast, or into the river, if it is along a river's bank." [It should be remembered in this context that the horned snake asteroids and comets had a water "aspect", and that space was seen as a cold dark lake.]

"Nothing more is seen of it, and each year a new statue is made." [Although apparently the henge remained intact.]

THE HARVEST FEASTS OF THE NATCHEZ

Le Page du Partz provided us with detailed descriptions of the feasts of the Natchez, which are included in full in the Ancient Word of the Natchez (Appendix B), as according to the claim of the Ancient Word they were instituted by the Prophet. Le Page du Pratz was keenly aware that these festivals were used to distribute food to all of the united people:

"The Natchez begin their year in the month of March, [as was the practice in ancient Europe], and divide it into thirteen moons. At every new moon they celebrate a feast, which takes its name either from the principal fruits reaped in the preceding moon, or from animals that are then usually hunted. [I shall give an account of one or two of these feasts as concisely as I can.]

"These feasts are equally religious and political: religious in that they appear to be instituted to thank the Great Spirit for the benefits he has sent for men; political in that the subjects then pay their ruler the tribute which they owe him.

"But however absolute the authority of the Great Sun may be, and although many people give themselves to him to serve him, and a number of warriors attach themselves to his person, in order to follow him wherever he goes, and to hunt for him, yet he raises no stated impositions. And what he receives from those people appears to be given not so much as a right due to him, but as a voluntary homage and a testimony of their love for and gratitude to him.

"The ornaments [head dress and attachments] suitable to the supreme rank are the marks of sovereignty, and in the ceremonies their princes always wear them, if not all of them, then at least a part of them."

THE NATCHEZ HENGE

Le Page du Pratz describes the creation and use of a parallel but different area by the Natchez for their annual Feast of the Corn (Maize):

> "When the corn approaches maturity the warriors go to the place where the corn is eaten every year. At the edge of this open space they make a kind of granary, which they call "Momo-ataop", which means "valuable granary" or "venerable granary".

> "This open space is fairly large. It is, however, almost entirely shaded by the extreme height of the trees which surround it. It is covered with a beautiful lawn, the grass of which is cut from time to time, so that it may not get too high before the time of the feast. The trees which enclose this place create a large grove without any underbrush: beneath them, and around the open space, the grass is only as high as the knee, while farther off the grass has the same height as elsewhere, four to five feet...

> "These dispositions having been made, and the warriors' post having been reddened and planted by themselves in the middle of the open space, with a ceremony, for the Great War Chief has to hold the post while the warriors make it firm."

In the ensuing feast this warrior's post is used by the warriors to proclaim their feats; in other words, the post serves to establish the Natchez's lands.

THE NATCHEZ BALLGAME

The Natchez also played a ritual ballgame during their Feast of the Corn, and given its parallels with the ritual ballgames of the peoples of Central America, it is worth calling special attention to it here[9]:

> "Day having come, no one appears in the open space until the Great Sun comes out of his house toward 9 o'clock in the morning. He walks some moments alone with the Great War Chief, and has the drum, or the pot which serves in place of it, beaten against the post.

> "Immediately the warriors hasten to come out of their cabins, and form two troops which are distinguished by the color of the feathers with which their heads are adorned. The one has white feathers, and takes the side of the Great Sun; the other has red feathers, and is for the Great War Chief.

> "Then begins the game of the pelotte [ball], a little ball of deerskin of the size of a fist filled with Spanish beard. The Great Sun and the Great War Chief throw this ball back and forth for some time from one to the other. The two bands are extremely attentive to all their movements, for at the moment when one least thinks of it, the Great Sun throws the ball into the very thick of the warriors, who are then mingled and confounded together.

"This ball must never fall or be carried, as it would then be snatched forcibly
from the one who should seize it, and no one would help him: on this point
the interdiction is express. As this ball game has two goals, to reach the cabin
of the Great Sun or that of the Great War Chief, it is necessary that the ball
be pressed and urged by blows given with the palm of the hand toward one of
these two cabins.

"It is a real pleasure to see this ball spring sometimes to one side of the
open space, sometimes to the other, sometimes remaining in the middle,
then appearing decided to touch one of the goals, and at the last moment
be repelled by a hostile hand into its first uncertainty. The movement of the
warriors, and the innocent passion which they enter into for the honor of the
game, is not unaccompanied by noise. Fear, disquietude, and vexation have their
different cries. That of joy rises above all the others.

"Ordinarily the ball game lasts two hours, and the warriors sweat great drops.
Finally, the ball touches one of the two cabins, and the amusement is at an end.
The band which belonged to this cabin having won by this, receives from the
Chief of the opposite side a considerable pi'Esent (?) and the right to wear
distinguishing feathers as a mark of victory, until the following year or until the
next time they play ball."

A YUCHI HENGE TALE

The following fragment was recovered by Swanton from Tuggle's records of a person
who was among the last survivors of the Yuchi tribe, a tribe which had ended as a
separate group several hundred years earlier, and one that was on the very eastern
periphery of area of the Southern Ceremonial Cult. I repeat the tale here, for as near
as I know it's all that we have of it; perhaps a better version may be obtained from
Swanton or Tuggle's notes.[10]

"The people wished to find their medicine:
A Great monster Serpent destroyed the people.
They cut his [the Great Serpent's] head from his body.
The next day [age] the body and head were together again.
They again slew the monster. His head again grew to his body."
[This seems to be the growth of a comet's tail, recurring on a periodic basis.]

"Then they cut off his [the Great Serpent's] head and placed it on top of a
tree, so that the body could not reach it.
The next morning [age] the tree was dead, and the head united to the body.
They again severed it, and put it upon another tree.
In the morning the tree was dead, and the head and body were re-united.

"The people continued to try all the trees in the forest.
At last they placed the head over the tar tree, the cedar tree,
and in the morning the head was dead.
The cedar was alive, but covered with blood

267

which had trickled down from the head.

"Thus the Great Medicine was found."

THE FIVE NATIONS ACCOUNT OF
AN EXPEDITION TO THE WEST: A VISIT TO *TWAKANHAH* (CAHOKIA)

Adapted from David Cusick's Ancient History of the Six Nations.[11]

> "About this time reigned king Atotarho VII, who was authorized by the Senate
> to send an expedition to explore the countries towards the setting Sun in the
> west. " [Using Cusick's chronology, this expedition occurred ca 1000 CE.]

> "The King sent messengers to acquaint the Ottawas of his intention, and he
> asked them to make arrangements and to favor the expedition's passage, which
> they complied with, being agreeable to his request."

The Five Nations war with the Ottawa, who at this time occupied the region between
the valley of the upper Shenango River tributary of the Allegheny River and Lake Erie,
had just come to an end.

> "The King appointed two captains to command the expedition, and about
> fifteen men for the expedition were selected from the Five Nations.

> "After they were equipped and prepared, they commenced their journey and
> arrived at Sandusky."

The Missasaugers, the Snake-people, at this time occupied both the region around
Missasauga, Canada, on the north side of Lake Erie, which commanded the Niagara
River, and the area around today's Sandusky, Ohio, which commanded the rivers leading
from Lake Erie into the interior. An Algonquin people, the Missasauger had most likely
emigrated along with their fellow Algonquin Ottawa to the couth side of Lake Erie in
the vacuum following the climate collapse of 536 CE.

> "The King of the Ottawas sent along two warriors to accompany the
> expedition; on their way these warriors held several conferences with the
> nations, and all of them seemed to favor the expedition's passage.

> "They advanced to the Mississippi River, where a Duke of Twakanah had
> collected the people from several towns who came out to meet them. The
> people danced around them, singing, and beating their little drums. After these
> ceremonies had been performed, the band of warriors was invited into the
> national house. "

The account of the trip now begins to take mythical aspects, which is not surprising,
considering that it was over 800 years old by the time Cusick recorded it.[12]

> "The band crossed the Mississippi River and continued their course towards

the sunset in the west. They reached an extensive meadow; they discovered a curious animal - a winged fish, it flew about the tree; this little active creature moved like a humming bird.

"They continued their journey and came to the village of the Dog Tail Nation~ the expedition was accommodated, amused with dances, and was conducted to the chief 's house. They were astonished that the people had short tails like apes: a hole was made through their seats, through which they put their tails.

"The band continued in their direction west and came to another nation, and here too was kindly received, and their object was favorably accepted by the head men of that nation. During their stay, a certain warrior of the band courted a young woman, but the warrior died soon after the marriage. They observed that the people did not eat any meat, but drank the soup.

"The band continued their journey, but before they reached the Rocky Mountains, they were stopped by a Giant, and the band was compelled to return.

"After a long journey they came back to the Seat of the Council Fire and informed the King of all the particulars of their journey. "

(Footnotes)

[1] While it is usually thought that the Tennessee River received its name from the Cherokee town of Tenasi, perhaps it received its name from the Taensa people (Taensa-Sipu); which federation center the Taensa originally lived at is not known with any certainty.

[2] Essential sources are Thomas M. Owen, *Mounds and Prehistoric Works in Alabama*, Handbook of the Alabama Anthropological Society, Alabama Anthropological Society, 1910, Brown Printing, Montgomery, Alabama; and Amos J. Wright Jr.'s definitive work *Historic Indian Towns in Alabama*, 1540-1838, University of Alabama Press, 2003; early United States Geological Survey maps show Native American remains, which the USGS has deleted from their modern maps to discourage the plundering of sites; satellite images are now available online.

[3] Mary Gordon Duffee, "Sketches of Alabama", *The Alabama Review*, April, 1956, University of Alabama Press, 1970, p. 148

[4] The Ancient Word of the Natchez, Appendix B here

[5] The Ancient Word of the Natchez, Appendix B here

[6] Peter Martyr, Vatican diplomat and leading Spanish intellectual, was responsible for reporting the Spanish discoveries to the Vatican; he published this report in his *Seventh Decade* of 1525. His witnesses were Lucas Vasquez de Ayllon, the Captain of Ayllon's ship, and Franciso de Chicora. Francisco of the town of Chicora had been captured during a slave raid of 1521 and taken by Ayllon to Spain, as by his testimony Ayllon hoped to gain royal support for further ventures on the mainland. Ayllon succeeded in this and returned to North American, where Francisco would escape from him in 1526. The translation used here is that commissioned by John R. Swanton for his *Early History of the Creek Indians and their Neighbors*, Bureau of Ethnology Bulletin 72, 1922, p. 42-46. A new reprint of this work is now available from the University Press

of Florida. As a brief word of warning, we now know that Swanton's linguistic and toponomical analysis was faulty; for example, the Kushita were recent migrants into the southeast (see Chapter 15 and Appendices here). Chicora was a town on a river somewhere along the coasts of the Carolinas.

[7] available at http://darkwing.uoregon.edu/~gsayre/LPDP.html

[8] docent's report of excavation results at Cahokia

[9] The following passages have been adapted from the 1763 English translation of Simon Antoine's *History of Louisiana*, which is available as a Gutenburg e-text.

[10] John R. Swanton, *Myths and Legends of the Southeastern Indians*, Smithsonian Institution Bureau of American Ethnology, Bulletin 58, Government Printing Office, Washington, 1929, labeled by Swanton as Creek story n.90, acknowledging that it is Yuchi. Another variant was collected by Albert S. Gaschet, *Some Mythic Stories of the Yuchi*, American Anthropologist, original series, v.6, p 279-282, available via George E. Lankford, *Native American Legends*, August House, Little Rock, Arkansas, 1987, p. 57, with commentary. The henge story was part of the Yuchi creation story.

[11] Cusick, Appendix A here

[12] I leave it to others more familiar with the west and its peoples to try to recover any facts from the following remnants.

CHAPTER 15

THE END OF THE MISSISSIPPIANS

Ca 1000 CE: THE BALD MOUNTAINS IMPACT EVENT
AND THE CHEROKEE (TSULAGI, KITUAGI) MIGRATION INTO THE
VACANT LANDS

This version of the Legend of the Bald Mountains comes from Legends and Lore, University of Tennessee Newsletter, Knoxville, 1961 and was hopelessly romanticized by its compiler, David Harkness. It is thus important to remember a few very hard facts as you read through it. The area to the southwest of the Bald Mountains contains Copperhill, Tennessee, certainly a copper source for early Native American peoples. This was a very densely settled area: the owner of a property near Blairsville described giving to the local Boy Scouts a box some 1.5 x 1.5 x 2.5 feet long filled with stone implements, including archaic points, and this did not include buckets of stone tools which he had found. No people would have simply walked away from such valuable deposits. Second, the peoples who lived there at this time would have been under the rule of "thunderbirds", chiefs of the Southern Ceremonial Complex, who wore feathered costumes, "claws" on their hands and feet, and had their noses mutilated into "beaks" through removal of their sides and septum.[1]

THE LEGEND OF THE BALD MOUNTAINS

"A large and happy tribe of Indians once lived around the base of a range of the Appalachian Mountains, along the Tennessee-North Carolina boundary, northeast of the Great Smokies. Now known as the Bald Mountains, they were then covered from base to summit with gigantic trees, beneath which flourished a dense undergrowth of vines, bushes, and shrubbery.

"One day, to the terror of the tribe, an immense bird soared above them, overshadowing them with his outstretched wings. Finally, with terrific cries, he settled upon the very top of the mountains, shaking all the surrounding country as he came down. The bird sat there, ominously but quietly, and even the boldest hunter dared not pursue his game when it fled toward the summit of the mountains.

"One night, when the tribe was wrapped in sleep, they were suddenly awakened by the shriekings of the bird and the quaking of the earth at his movements. With one fell swoop he rushed down upon the valley like a storm, crying and roaring with ferocity, and causing the trees and rocks to shake. Men, women, and children fled in tumult and terror.

"Later they discovered that the monster had borne off in his cruel talons the beloved child of one of the chiefs.

"Every year thereafter, the feathered horror repeated his descent upon the tribe, with hideous sounds and awful commotions, always bearing off a young child as his prey. The terrified Indians invoked the help of the Great Spirit in their peril."

The Southern Ceremonial chiefs probably took a child from surrounding subordinate tribes as hostage or sacrifice as a way of expressing their power over them.

"Finally, a chief arose who would not endure the tyranny of the bird of the mountains. He called together all his warriors and urged them to join him in an all out attack on the winged creatures.

"When they finally reached the top of one of the mountains they froze in terror, for there they beheld not merely one monstrous bird, but as whole flock of the mammoth and savage fowls, with beaks and wings extended, ready to rush down and exterminate the invaders. The warriors cast their weapons away and fell upon their faces, to await the destruction so surely impending."

Southern Ceremonial Chiefdoms worked in a federated manner.

"At this moment the heart of the chief did not fail him. He was suddenly inspired with faith that the Great Spirit would not permit the whole tribe to perish before these evil birds. With a loud voice and hands raised to heaven, he earnestly besought the Great Spirit to interpose in behalf of the helpless and afflicted tribe.

"The Great Spirit heard, and before the birds could rush upon their victims, there flashed forth from every quarter of the sky great lightening which struck every bird, ripped the tress apart, and wrapped the entire mountain heights in a devouring fire. The tops of the mountains were burned off by the avenging fires of heaven, and the tribe raised loud and long its song of thanksgiving for this miraculous deliverance."

THE MATERIAL RECORD OF THE Ca. 1000 CE IMPACT EVENT

While no detailed search has yet been made of this area for remains from the impact, we do have some record of it in the form of the population movements which occurred after it. The people of the Pisgah culture[2] now moved into the area of the upper Pigeon River and upper French Broad River, spreading to the upper Tuckasegee River and upper Saluda River. The remainders of the Mississippian peoples who had survived the impact moved to the east, into the piedmont of North Carolina[3] and South Carolina.[4]

Ca 1000 CE:
THE KUSHITA (CREEK) AND LENNI LENAPE (DELAWARE)
MIGRATIONS BEGIN

News of the Bald Mountains impact must have quickly spread through the
Mississippian trade network. As the event would have thoroughly shown that the
Thunderbird Chiefs had no power with the sky gods, the power of the Priest-Kings
of the Southern Ceremonial peoples must have become severely impaired. Normally,
this impact event might have been blamed on some evil of the towns involved, and
the Southern Ceremonial peoples would have re-grouped, and then assimilated the
Cherokee. But for the Mississippians worse was to immediately follow, as the North
American equivalent of the Mongols now appeared in both the north and the south on
the west side of the Mississippian Trade Federation's lands.

THE TALE OF THE ANCESTORS:
THE KUSHITA (CREEK) MIGRATION STORY

The Muskogean peoples had detailed oral song cycles recounting their migrations,
similar to the Greek and Persian oral cycles, which they performed at annual harvest
festivals. All that we currently have left are fragments of them, and the badly
fragmented outline version of the Creek tale used here was recited in 1725 by Chekilli,
head chief of the Upper and Lower Creeks, in an obviously corrupted and shortened
form.[5] Another fragment of this migration legend which will be used here was gathered
by Benjamin Hawkins.in 1798.[6] The Chickasaw Creek also had their own migration
cycle, which they also recited at their annual busk, but all that remains of it are very
scattered fragments collected far apart.[7]

THE KUSHITA (CREEK) ARRIVE AT THE MISSISSIPPI RIVER:

> "Towards the Sun's setting the Ground opened, which is the mouth of the
> Ground. The Ground opened, and the Kashitas came out of its mouth and
> settled nearby. But the Ground was angry, and ate up their children.

> "They went further towards the setting of the Sun, but nevertheless our own
> part of the Kashitas turned back again and came to the same place, leaving the
> greater body behind, as they thought it might be best (to do so).

> "They settled there again, but the Earth still ate up their children. So in anger
> they went away towards the Sun's rising."

> "They came to a thick muddy river where they camped, rested, and slept one
> night."

The opening may refer to the Holocene Start impact event, with everything between
it and the Kushita arrival on the Mississippi River left out in this telling. That this
"muddy" river is with certainty the Mississippi River will be seen below. For "day" and
"night" here always read "age", as this was a customary usage.

ca 1000 CE: THE KUSHITA (CREEK) REACH THE RED RIVER:
THE END OF TOLTEC MOUNDS, ARKANSAS

"The next day [age] they began to travel again, and came in one day [age] to a
red, bloody river. They lived by that river and ate its fish for two years [ages],
but it was a low marshy place and they did not like living there."

ca. 1000 A.D. the Toltec Mounds culture came to an end, though it still survived in
the central and north parts of the Arkansas Plateau. Continuing the tale from another
fragment[8] :

"At the forks of Red River (We-cha-te-hat-che Au-fus-kee), west of the
Mississippi (We-o-coof-ke, muddy water), there are two mounds of earth. Here
the Kashita, Coweta, and Chickasaws found themselves. They were at a loss for
fire. Here they were visited by Hi-you-yul-gee, four men who came from the
four corners of the world. One of these people asked them, "Where will you
have your fire?' They pointed to a place, and it was made..."

THE KUSHITA (CREEK) MOVE TO SUNSET VOLCANO, ARIZONA,
WHOSE ERUPTION BEGAN 1064 CE.

Returning to the first fragment from the translator's notes:

"They went to the end of that bloody river and heard a thundering noise. They
went forward to hear where the noise came from, and they first saw a red
smoke, and soon after a mountain which thundered. Upon the mountain was
a singing noise, and they went up to see what it was. And it was a great fire
which burned upwards and made a singing noise. They called that mountain the
King of Mountains, and it thunders to this day."

At the end of the Red River, at its source, is Sunset Volcano, Arizona, the only active
volcano in the southwest of the United States, and it is known from the study of tree
rings that Sunset Volcano started to erupt in 1064 CE.

THE WALUM OLUM: THE ANCIENT HISTORY OF THE LENAPE

The ancient history of the Lenape survives today in a much abridged form which was
preserved by Constantin Rafinesque. The Lenape [Delaware] recounted their migration
cycle at their annual Big House Festival, and Rafinesque first acquired painted wooden
sticks which served as a mnemonic aid for this performance, only later acquiring a
phonetic record of the legend. As Rafinesque put it:

"These actual olum were at first obtained [by me] in 1820, as a reward for a medical
cure; [they were] deemed a curiousity, and were unexplicable. In 1822 were obtained
from another individual [not identified] the songs annexed thereto in the original
language, but no one could be found by me able to translate them.

" I had therefore to learn the language since [afterwards], by the help of Zeisburger [dictionary and grammar], Heckewelder [dictionary and grammar], and a manuscript dictionary [the source of which is unidentified, but perhaps the same source from which Rafinesque obtained the text of the Walum Olum itself], on purpose to translate them, which I only accomplished in 1833."[9]

While both the authenticity of the Walum Olum and Rafinesque's character have long been questioned, the Walum Olum's account of the Towakon, the Twakanhah people of the Five Nations, (below), proves beyond doubt that it is authentic, and that Rafinesque was an honest man. The text of the Walum Olum used here has been adapted to modern usage from the translation of Daniel Brinton, with major corrections made for his substantial errors in identification.[10]

Ca 1100 CE: THE LENAPE CONQUER AZTALAN, WISCONSIN

24. "After the Tally-Maker was chief,
the Man-Who-Shivered-with-Cold was chief,
who went south to the corn land.

25. "After the Man-Who-Shivered-with-Cold was chief,
the Corn-Breaker was chief, who brought about the planting of corn.[11]

26. "After the Corn-Breaker was Chief,
the Strong-Man was chief, who was useful to the chieftains.

27. "After the Strong-Man was chief, the Salt-Man was chief,[12]
and after him the Little-One was chief

THE LENAPE MOVE TO THE UPPER MISSISSIPPI RIVER VALLEY

28. "There was no rain, and no corn, so they moved further seaward
[south - the earlier direction of the lakes].

29. "At the place of caves, in the buffalo land,
they at last had food, on a pleasant plain.[13]

LENAPE METHODS OF WARFARE

It is likely that the Lenape used the same methods of warfare against the people who they encountered during their migration as they later used against the European colonists. This emphasized raids at ranges of up to several hundred miles against outlying settlements – in earlier times, foragers and hunters would have been their targets. While these raiding parties would kill some of their victims immediately, usually they captured prisoners, along with a witness, who would watch as they most brutally tortured their prisoners to death in stunningly creative ways. The witnesses would bring news of these tortures back home, and the news would quickly drive the residents into the shelter of palisaded forts.[14] Given the settled peoples methods of food gathering and hunting, this led to a failure of the food supply and weakness and disease.[15] Then the final blow would be made. These palisades appeared at Aztalan about 1100 CE.[16]

Several hundred years later, the Five Nations would be the first to discover that the most effective method of defense against this tactic, and as a matter of fact the only method of defense against this kind of attack, was to move in force at range against their villages, and genocidally eliminate the attacking warriors, absorbing some surviving women and children.[17]

Ca 1150 CE: THE FIVE NATIONS SEND AMBASSADORS TO THE LENTAHKEH AND OTTAWA, AND A GREAT FAMINE OCCURS

Adapted from David Cusick's Ancient History of the Six Nations.[18] Using Cusick's chronology, this event should have occurred ca 1150 CE.

"After a time the Five Nations desired to preserve the peace and friendship with the western nations. An ambassador was sent to the Lentahkeh nation, who inhabited the country east of Ohio River in what is now Kentucky.

"Another ambassador was sent, who went and lived among the Ottawas for several years. He married a woman and afterwards had two children by her.

"Now that Ambassador was invited to join a company going out a winter's hunt. They journeyed some distance and reached their hunting grounds, but the men were so unlucky hunting that they could kill but a few game.

"After a few days the people were destitute of provisions; the Leader of the company commanded the overseer to select two fat persons and to kill them without delay. This order was soon executed, and the flesh of these victims was distributed among the people.

"The leader commanded the people that if anyone killed any game the meat should be left with the overseer for distribution, and that whoever disobeyed, the offender would be punished in a severest manner. The Ambassador killed a bear, and the meat was disposed of according to the order."

[This did not help.] "The leader daily butchered two persons to feed the people, which only increased their distress. The people were so feeble that they were unable to hunt any more, and many of them began to famish. The Ambassador again killed another game animal, but he brought it secretly to his camp; but this was soon detected and rumored among the people.

"For this offence the Ambassador was ordered to appear before their tribunal. Some men were angry at him and sought to destroy him immediately; but the leader deemed it unjust, as this would violate the treaty they had entered with the Five Nations. However, to satisfy the people, the leader consented to use another method to destroy him: he commanded them to strip him and to seize his clothes and his instruments; after which they were to extinguish their fires, and then to remove their camps a half day's journey distance from his. The offender would then certainly freeze to death without any way out.

"But the Ambassador was ingenious: finding that he would be surprised, he instantly took a suit of dress and bow and arrows, and hid them under the hemlock boughs which were spread in the camp. In a short time his opponents entered the camp, and the ambassador was stripped without discrimination, as they had determined to: destroy him. His wife was compelled to leave him, or else she would share the same fate. The company then retired.

"The Ambassador dressed himself immediately and proceeded away, hoping to reach a fort situated near Lake Erie. But he was so fatigued that he could not travel very fast. About sunset he happened to approach the edge of a dark forest; he selected a spot where he encamped, but as he had no kind of food to eat was quite dejected. After making exertions to render himself comfortable but failed, the weather being unfavorable, as it was cold and cloudy, However, the Ambassador was seldom taken by surprise; and having a good understanding of astronomical. calculations, he ascertained that a storm was at hand. After kindling a fire he laid himself down to linger out the miserable existence which he was doomed to suffer.

"Early in the morning the Ambassador heard a noise, as though something was coming, which at once attracted his attention. He was afraid, as he presumed that some of his enemy had overtaken him. Fortunately, a young man came up and sat down. The visitor showed a friendly disposition, and after a short conversation the Ambassador related the story of his distressed condition. His visitor offered to relieve him as soon as possible; which promise the Ambassador received with sanguine expectations.

"The ambassador was advised that a snow would fall so deep that he would be in want of a pair of snow shoes, and the visitor offered the pattern and showed him how to make the shoes. The Ambassador was directed where to find game; and he did as he was bidden.

"At nightfall the young man made another visit, and he advised the ambassador where to catch bears; after the conversation the visitor disappeared. The Ambassador did as he was bidden, and he succeeded, and caught seven bears.

"After he had prepared some of the meat and the bears' oil he immediately went to the encampment in search of his wife and children. He found them almost perished, and first gave them each a spoonful of oil. They were soon relieved, and he directed them to his camp.

"The Ambassador was now relieved from his distress, while his enemy was lingering in despair. He examined their camp and was astonished to find that the people were utterly famished. They had become so weak and faint that they were not even able to make fire; those who had held out had had to eat human flesh as long as they could; they themselves were lying among the dead.

"The company was now exposed to destruction, as the people had put themselves in disgrace. The Ambassador refused to invite any of them to his camp except his wife's relatives; they were so worn out by the disasters that they did not reach his camp until next morning. By the Ambassador's exertions, after a few days the company's men's strength was revived to the point they were capable of hunting.

"After they returned to the town, the Ambassador was so shamefully abused by the people there that he was compelled to leave his wife and the country.

"About this time the Ottawas became a numerous and powerful nation, occupying an extensive country lying between Lake Erie and the Ohio River; it was thought that their national force amounted to about 4,000 warriors. "

Ca 1175 CE:
THE FAMINE CAUSES A PLAGUE

The following Lenape account of this plague[19] takes place after their move to the Buffalo Land, given above:

30. "After the Little-One came the Fatigued-One;
after him, the Stiff-One. [the Dead One – a corpse]

Ca 1175 CE:
DISEASE HITS THE MISSISSIPIAN TRADE FEDERATION

The following account of this plague was related to du Pratz by the Great Sun, their king.[20] The appearance of this plague may be placed at ca. 1175 CE, instead of at the time of European contact, for the following reasons. First, the Ancient History of the Lenape (Walum Olum) mentions an outbreak of disease at this time. Second, the extent of the "Mississippian" (Southern Ceremonial Cult) federation which the Great Sun describes is that which existed at this time. Third, there is no mention of the Kushita or Lenape incursions, which occurred after this plague hit. Finally, both the Ancient History of the Five Nations as well as in the Ancient History of the Lenape (Walum Olum) mention a climate collapse with starvation just prior to this outbreak, and it was most likely the cause of it.

"Our nation then extended for more than twelve days' journey from east to west, and more than fifteen days' jouney from south to north. It counted then 500 Suns, and you can judge by that what was then the number of the Nobles, the Honored men, and the common people.

"There are always two Guardians in the Temple to care for the sacred fire. But once in the past it happened that one of these two men went out for some purpose, and while he was away his companion fell asleep and let the fire go out.

278

"When he awoke, seeing the fire extinguished, fright seized him. But as his companion had not yet come back, he determined to conceal his fault, because he was easily able to do it, in order to escape the death which he had merited. He called then to the first passer and begged him to bring him fire with which to light his calumet (his pipe), a thing which this person did willingly, knowing well that it is not permitted to touch the eternal fire except to tend it, and that no other use could be made of it.

"Thus this fire was re-lighted with profane fire. Immediately sickness took hold of the Suns. In a few days they were seen to die in rapid succession, and it was necessary to send after them into the world of spirits many people to serve them. This mortality lasted four years, without anyone being able to guess what had occasioned it. Nine great Suns who succeeded each other died in this interval, and a multitude of people with them.

"Finally, at the end of this time the Guardian of the Temple himself fell ill. This bad man, feeling that he was not going to be able to live a long time, had word sent to the Great Sun at once that he had something to communicate to him of such great importance that if he died without revealing it all the Natchez would die.

"The Great Sun went to see him as quickly as possible. As soon as the sick man perceived him, his whole body trembled, and he appeared unable to speak. However, he spoke these words, although with difficulty:

"'" I am going to die, so it makes no difference to me whether the sickness or a man kills me. I know that I am a bad man for having for so long a time concealed, in order to preserve my life, what I am going to tell you. I am the cause of the death of my nation, therefore I merit death, but let me not be eaten by the dogs.'

"The Great Sun understood by these words that this man was guilty of some great crime, and that it was necessary to reassure him in order to draw from him his secret, which appeared to be of the last importance. He therefore told him that whatever he had done he might be assured that. he would not be put to death, and that he would be buried; that what he had promised him was as true as it was true that the Sun, their father, lighted them every day, and that he should hasten to speak before death prevented him.

"On this promise the bad guardian confessed all that he had done. Immediately the Great Sun assembled the old men, and by their advice it was resolved to go that very day to wrest fire from the other temple. That was executed and the Suns ceased dying."

Ca 1200 CE:
THE MISSISSAUGA NATION ATTACKS THE FIVE NATIONS

"In the reign of Kink Atotarho VIII, perhaps 400 years before the Dutch arrived in the lands of the Five Nations.[21]

Using a rough date of 1600 CE for the Dutch appearing in the lands of the Five Nations, by Cusick's calculation we end up with a date of roughly 1200 CE for the following events.

"About this time the Messissaugers who had their capitol in Twakanhah [Cahokia] began to wage a war against the Five Nations. The Senecas on the frontier were most engaged in the warfare.

"After various skirmishes the enemy was so excited that they determined to destroy Fort Kauhanauka. (Today this is in the Tuscarora Reservation near the town of Lewiston, New York.) But the Commander of the fort was aware of the danger, and he sent messengers to the forts in the vicinity, and about eight hundred warriors were collected together at Fort Kauhanauka.

"The Commander sent runners to observe the movements of the enemy. The army marched towards the river, and hid themselves among the bushes under the mountain; the enemy came up, and a bloody battle ensued. The enemy was repulsed and flew from their foe. The army retired to the fort, and soon after the Commander dispatched two runners to the forts on the Genesee River to procure assistance as soon as possible.

"The army received reinforcements, and they made bark canoes and carried them to the mouth of the Niagara River. Once the canoes were ready the Commander sent a chieftain and offered the enemy an intermission or parley, but the proposal was not accepted. The army immediately crossed the river and made a vigorous attack: the enemy was routed and fled from the bank without making resistance, retreating towards the head of the lake. After burning their huts, the army returned to the fort.

"But the disturbances were not quelled; small parties of the Senecas often took canoes and went by water towards the head of Lake Ontario, in search of the enemy. While they avoided attacking superior forces, several engagements were made on the lake with small parties of the enemy;

"After a while the Commander of Fort Kauhanauka was ardent to attack the main body of the enemy; he sent runners beyond the Genesee River, and obtained two thousand warriors. The army again crossed the Niagara River and proceeded towards the head of the lake, but before it reached the beach it met a strong force of the enemy.

"After a desperate contest, the army retreated; the Commander soon perceived that it was impossible to gain conquest, and sued for peace, offering to restore the prisoners which he had taken from them. This agreement was concluded."

SHORTLE BEFORE 1259 CE: SUNSET VOLCANO'S FINAL ERUPTION
LEADS THE MUSKOGEE TO LEAVE FOR THE EAST[22]

"On the mountain there was a pole which was very restless and made a noise,
and no one could say how it could be quieted. They took a motherless child
and stuck it on the pole, which killed the child. [They impaled the child on the
pole.] Therefore they took the pole and carried it with them as they went to
war..."

"A dispute arose as to which was oldest and who should rule. They agreed that
as they were four sorts of people, they would set up four poles and make them
red with (a) clay , which was at first yellow, but by burning became red. And all
would go to war following whichever of them could first cover their pole from
the root up to the top with the scalps of enemies - whoever did so would be
the eldest.

"They all tried to do it, but the Kushitas covered their pole to the top first, so
that it could not be seen. Therefore they were declared by the whole nation to
be the eldest. The Chickasaws covered their pole next, and then the Alilamus
[Choctaw] next. But the Abhikas could not raise their heap of scalps higher
than a knee."

THE MUSKOGEE ATTACK ACROSS THE MISSISSIPPI RIVER

In the Kushita migration legend, this passage is followed by one in which the Kushita
(Creek) are aided by a "red mouse", an obvious translation error, in attacking the King
of the "Birds", who is armed with bow and arrows. The next passage appears to have
them returning west to Hot Springs, Arkansas.[23]

The line of the Muskogee advance must have at first been back through Arkansas.
Nodena Ware, a sandy pottery from Arkansas with red markings on a white
background, is found at every destroyed Southern Ceremonial site just before or after
the time of its "abandonment".[24]

A fragment of the Chickasaw migration tale preserved by Haywood specifically
mentions their crossing of the Mississippi River, and the fight between their chief,
supposedly named No-hoo-to-ta-pa, with a king who calls himself the "Brother of the
Sun".[25] Buttrick stated that the Chickasaw crossing place was at Memphis, which had a
major Southern Ceremonial Cult center located at DeSoto Park.[26]   It appears that some
refugees from earlier Kushita conquests to the west who had found temporary refuge at
Chucalissa, just to the south of Memphis, found that refuge ended around 1230 CE.[27]
In any case, the towns of Towosaghy and Wickliffe near the junction of the Ohio River
with the Mississippi River were both abandoned around 1250 CE.[28]

THE NORTHERN MIGRATION:
THE LENAPE NATION SPLITS IN TWO, WITH ONE PART MOVING SOUTH[29]

31. "After the Stiff-One was chief, the Man-Who-Reproved was chief;
some disliked him, and [became] unwilling [to remain];
32. "becoming angry, they went off secretly, moving east.

33. "The wise ones who remained made the Loving-One chief.

34. "They settled again on the Yellow River,
and had much corn on stoneless soil.

35. "All being friendly, the Affable-Man was chief, the first of that name.
36. "He was very good, this Affable-Man,
and he came as a friend to all the Lenape.

37. "After this good one, Strong-Buffalo was chief and pipe-bearer."

THE LENAPE ENTER INTO PEACE WITH THE SIOUXIAN PEOPLES

While the people who Strong-Buffalo bore the peace pipe with is not identified in the
Walum Olum, we know from another source that about this time the Lenape formed an
alliance with Siouxian peoples.

"After a very long journey, and many night's [ages] encampments along the
way, they at length arrived on the Nae-Moesi Sipu, where they fell in with the
Mengwe, who had likewise emigrated from a distant country, and had struck up
on this river higher up. Their object was the same with that of the [Lenape], they
were proceeding on to the eastward, until they should find a country that pleased
them."[30]

Although the missionary John Heckwelder or his source used the term "Mengwe" here
to describe the Lenape's allies, a term which the Lenape later would use to describe the
Iroquoian peoples of the Five Nations, in this case the "Mengwe" were the Monacans
and Manahoacs, as Siouxian peoples would accompany the Lenape to the east, ultimately
settling in the piedmont regions of Virginia and the Carolinas.

AND THEN WAR WITH MISSASAUGA, NORTHERNERS,
AND TOWOKON [TWAKANHAH, CAHOKIA]

38. "Then Big-Owl was chief; then White-Bird was chief.

39. "The Willing-One was [both] chief and priest, and he made festivals.

40. "Rich-Again was chief; the Painted-One was chief.

41. "White-Fowl was chief;
and again there was war, in both the north and the south.

The central mound at Twakanhah, Towakon [Cahokia]

42. "The Wolf [Minsi clan] Wise-in Counsel was chief.

43. "He knew how to make war on all; he slew Strong-Stone.

44. "The Always-Ready-Man was chief;
he fought against the Snakes [Missasauga]."

These "Snakes" were the Missasauga who were located in the area of what is today Sandusky, Ohio. From David Cusick's Ancient History of the Six Nations, we know that the Missasauga were in alliance with the Twakanha [Cahokians].[31]

45. "The Strong-Good-Man was chief,
he fought against the northerners.

46. "The Lean-Man was chief;
he fought against the Towakon [Twakanhah- Cahokia] people."

This "leanness" here may indicate starvation.

THE LENAPE HELD BY THE TOWAKON [TWAKANHAH, CAHOKIA],
AND ATTEMPT FLANKING MANUEVER TO THE SOUTHEAST
BY ATTACKING TALEGEWI [THILIGOTHE, CHILICOTHE, SHAWNEE]

47. "The Opossum-Like-Man was chief; he fought in sadness.

The pictograph here seems to indicate that the Lenape divided, rather than opossum.

48. "And he said, "They are many:
let us go together to the east, to the sunrise."

49. "They separated at the Fish River [Mississippi River];
the lazy ones remained there.

THE TALLIGEWI [THILIGOTHE, CHILICOTHE, SHAWNEE]
ALLOW THE LENAPE TO PASS, AND THEN ATTACK

50. "The Cabin-Man was chief [of the Talligewi]:
the Talligewi [Thiligothe, Chilicothe] possessed the east.

51. "The Man-Who-Was-a- Strong-Friend was chief,
and he desired the eastern land.

52. "Some passed on east;
the Talegewi [Thiligothe, Chilicothe] ruler killed some of them.

53. "All said in unison, 'War, war.'

THE SIOUXIAN PEOPLES ALLY WITH THE LENAPE FOR WAR

"Fired at the treachery of these people, and the great loss of men they had
sustained, and besides, not being prepared for a conflict, the Lenape consulted
on what was to be done: whether to retreat in the best manner they could, or try
their strength, and let the enemy see that they were not cowards, but men, and
too high minded to suffer themselves to be driven off before they had made
a trial of their strength, and were convinced that the enemy were too strong
for them. The Mengwe [Siouxians], who had hitherto been satisfied with being
spectators from a distance, offered to join them, on the condition that after
conquering the country, they should be entitled to share it with them. Their
proposal was accepted, and the resolution was taken by the two nations, to
conquer or die."[32]

THE TALAMATAN [NEUTRALS] ARRIVE

54. "The Talamatan [Neutrals], friends from the north, came,
and they all went together.
55. "The Sharp-One was chief, he was the pipe-bearer beyond the river.
[Bearing the pipe indicates a diplomatic role, in this case the formation of the
alliance.]
56. "They [The Neutrals and the Lenape] rejoiced greatly that they should fight
and slay the Talegewi [Thiligothe, Chilicothe, Shawnee] towns.

THE POLITICAL SITUATION IN THE NORTH EAST

Brinton identified the Talamatan as the Huron nation, and he appears to have been close
to right. Most likely the Talmatan were the "Neutrals", as later below the Lenape speak
of their driving the Talamatan to the north of Lake Erie. At this time the "Neutrals"
occupied the area around today's Toledo, Ohio, and the Shawnee lived to their south.[33]

Ca 1250 CE, the Missasauga people held both the area of the junction of the Saint
Lawrence with Lake Erie, and the area around Sandusky, Ohio, which controlled the
rivers going inland. The Missasauga were in alliance with the people of Twakanhah, (i.l
"Cahokia") and they are referred to as being their allies by the Five Nations. The Ottawa
held the areas between the Eries and the Missasauga along the south shore of Lake Erie.

Between 1200-1300 CE the "Neutrals" were driven from the Toledo area by the
Missasauga of the Sandusky area. The Five Nations warred with the Missasauga ca 1200
CE. Cusick claims that the Eries emerged from the Seneca about this time, and this
increase may be another part of the Iroquoian retreat from the Toledo area. The Erie had
their home near Buffalo, New York, and the Erie Confederation appears to have included
those Iroquoian nations which were not in the confederation of the Five Nations. ca.
1250 CE the Five Nations attacked the Eries.

FIRE USED AS A WEAPON AGAINST STOCKADES:
THE TALEGAWE [THILIGOTHE, CHILICOTHE, SHAWNEE] SURRENDER

Angel Mounds - Reconstruction of a segment of the pallisade constructed for defense. The bridge on the right crosses a defensvie moat dug around the entire site.

57. "The Stirrer was chief;
the Talegawe [Thiligothe, Chilicothe, Shawnee] towns were too strong.

58. "The Man-Who-Built-Fires was chief:
they all gave to him many towns.

59. "The Man-Who-Broke-in-Pieces was chief:
all the Talegewi [Thiligothe, Chilicothe, Shawnee] went south.

60. "He-Who-Had-Pleasure was chief: all the people rejoiced."

THE TALAMATAN [NEUTRALS] DRIVEN
TO THE NORTH SHORE OF LAKE ERIE

61. "They [the Lenape] stayed south of the lakes;
while their Talamatan friends stayed north of the lakes.

62. "When the Long-and-Mild-Man was chief,
those who were not his friends [the Talmantan] conspired.

63. "The Truthful-Man was chief: the Talamatans made war.

64. "The Just-and-True-Man was chief: the Talamatans trembled.

THE KUSHITA CONTINUE TO MOVE EAST

Returning to the Kushita and their migration through the south, the next roughly identifiable location along their path is Coosa, which the invaders also attacked and conquered. Following this the next absolutely identifiable location is in the Bald Mountains.

"The next day they crossed over [the Aphoosapheesaw River] and came to a high mountain. They found some people there and hoped that they were the people who had made the White Path. Therefore they made white arrows and shot [them] to see if they were good people. But the people carried their white arrows off, made them red, and shot them back again.

"Then they took up the red arrows and carried them to their chief. Their chief told them that it was not good; if the arrows had returned white, they would have gone and got food for their children, but as they were red they should not go.

"However, some of them went to see what people they were and found that they had all left their houses. They saw tracks which went into the river, and saw that the tracks went into the river but did not get out, for they went to the other side of the river and could find no tracks.

"There is a mountain we call Motero, which makes a sound like the beating of a drum. Those people live there now; whenever we go to war, this sound is heard."

This can only refer to the Bald Mountains, were seismic activity does indeed produce a rhythmic sound, which was heard in the 1870's.[34]

THE LENAPE VICTORY OVER THE CHILICOTHE DIVISION OF THE SHAWNEE

Returning to the north...

1. "All were peaceful, long ago,
there in the Talega [Thiligothe, Chilicothe] lands:

2. "The Man-Who-Bore-the-Pipe was chief at the White River."

Again, the "pipe" referred to here is the calumet, and these lines probably indicate the complete surrender of the Lenape's enemies .The absolute location of "White River" is unknown.

3. "White-Lynx was chief, and much corn was planted.

4. "The Good-and-Strong-Man was chief: the people were many.

5. "The Recorder was chief: he painted the records.

6. "Pretty-Blue-Bird was chief, there was much fruit.

7. "Always-There-Man was chief: the towns were many.

THE LENAPE ATTACK UP THE OHIO RIVER:
THE NANTICOKES AND SHAWNEE FORCED TO LEAVE

8. "The Man-Who Paddled-up-Stream was chief:
he was much on the rivers.

9. "Little-Cloud was chief; many departed,
10. the Nanticokes and the Shawnees going to the south."

"MIDDLE" FORT ANCIENT CULTURE

The survivors of their attacks on the peoples of the Ohio Valley moved into the hill forts of the "Early" Fort Ancient peoples. Due to their re-occupation of some sites that had earlier been used by Adena and Hopewell refugees, some archaeologists refer to this as the "Middle" Fort Ancient Culture", even though culturally these people bear no relation to the "Early" Fort Ancient Culture. The differences are so immense that they can not all be catalogued here; suffice it to say that the "Early" Fort Ancient

Culture was nut-tree based, used organically tempered "pottery", and shared cultural traits with the Ohio Hopewell, while the "Middle" Fort Ancient Culture was corn based, used shell tempered pottery, and shared other cultural traits with the Southern Ceremonial Cult peoples.

THE KUSHITA MEET THE CHEROKEE, KUSHITA VERSION

[handwritten: CATAWBA / SAPONI]

Returning to the south...

> "They went along that river until they came to another water fall, where they saw great rocks and bows laid on the rocks. They believed that the people who had made the White Path had been there.

> "In all their travels they had two runners who went before the body of the people, and when they saw a mountain, the runners went up it and looked around and saw a town. They shot two white arrows into the town, but the people of that town again shot red arrows back. The Kushitas were angry with those people, and agreed to attack the town. If they took it everyone was to have a house.

> "They threw stones into the river until it was so shallow that they could walk across it, which they did. The people there were flat headed, and they took the town.

> "When they had done so they killed everyone there but two, whose tracks they followed and overtook a white dog [Chilluki, dog, an old Creek name for Cherokee], which they killed.

[handwritten: CATAWBA / SAPONI]

THE KUSHITA MEET THE CHEROKEE, CHEROKEE VERSION

The following is adapted from the version preserved by James Mooney in his Myths of the Cherokee, N 80. The Spirit Defenders of Nikwasi, with some of the "magical" elements, similar to magical elements found in the Song of Roland, removed.[35]

> "Long ago a powerful unknown tribe invaded the country from the southeast, killing people and destroying settlements wherever they went. No leader could stand against them, and in a little while they had destroyed all the lower settlements and advanced into the mountains. The warriors of the old town of Nikwasi, on the head of the Little Tennessee River, gathered their wives and children into the townhouse and kept scouts constantly on the lookout for the presence of danger.

> "One morning, just before daybreak,, the scouts saw the enemy approaching, and at once gave the alarm. The Nikwasi men seized their arms and rushed out to meet the attack. But after a long hard fight they found themselves overpowered and began to retreat.

> "Then suddenly a stranger stood among them and shouted to the chief to call

off his men and he himself would drive back the enemy... They fell back along the trail, and as they came near the townhouse they saw a great company of warriors...The Nunnehi poured out by the hundreds, armed and painted for the fight...

CATAUBA / Sa Poni

THE ~~KUSHITA~~ SURRENDER, CHEROKEE VERSION

"The invaders soon had to retreat, going first along the ridge which separates the French Broad [River] from the Tuckagee {River}, and then turning with it to the northeast...All along the ridge they fell, until when they reached the Tuckagee [River] not more than half a dozen were left alive, and in despair they sat down and cried out for mercy...

"Then the Nunnehi chief told them that they had deserved their punishment for attacking a peaceful tribe, and he spared their lives and told them to go home... They went home toward the north...

THE KUSHITA VICTORY, KUSHITA VERSION

"[They] pursued the two people until they came to the White Path again, and they saw smoke from where there was a town. They believed that they had found the people who they had traveled so long to see. It is the place where the Apalachicola [Pallachacula] people now live...

"The Kushitas were always bloody minded, but the Apalachicola people made them the Black Drink as a token of friendship, and told them that their hearts were white (peaceful), that they too must have white hearts, and lay down their bodies to show that they were white as well. They strove for the tomahawk, but the Apalichicola people by fair persuasion gained it from them and buried it under their house.

"The Apalichicola people then told them the chief should be one with their people, and gave them white feathers. Ever since we have lived together, and we shall always live together, and this should be remembered."

THE LENAPE REACH YOUNGSTOWN, OHIO

Returning to the north...

11. "Big-Beaver was chief,
at the White Salt Lick [Youngstown, Ohio].

The area of the Beaver River, which connects with the Ohio River west of today's Pittsburgh, was rich in beaver. The Beaver River connects with the Mahoning River, which flows through Youngstown, Ohio; Youngstown's salt licks were well known in colonial times, and led to the first European settlement there.

12. "The Seer, the praised one, went to the west:

13. "he went to the west, to the southwest, to the western villages.

THE LENAPE ATTACK TWAKANHAH [CAHOKIA] AGAIN:
TWAKANHAH [CAHOKIA] FALLS Ca 1300 CE

14. "The Man-Who-Was- Rich-Down-River was chief,
on the Talega [Thiligothe, Chilicothe] River [the Ohio River].

15. "The Man-who-Walked was chief, and there was much war:
16. "War again with the Towako [Twakanhah, Cahokia] people,
war again with the Stone [Sinako] people,
war again with the northern people [Lowako]."

Based on C14 dates, the Lenape and Mengwe defeated Twakanhah [Cahokia] around
1310 CE.

THE LENAPE CONTINUE THEIR ATTACKS EASTWARD:
THE LENAPE ATTACK NORTH ACROSS LAKE ERIE

17. "The Grandfather-of-the-Boats was chief: he went to lands in boats.

18. "The Man-Who-Hunted-In-The-Snow was chief:
he went to the north land.

THE LENAPE ATTACK THE CHEROKEE

19. "The one who Looked-About was chief,
he went to the Talega [Tsulagi-Cherokee] Mountains.

At a very distant time the Tsulagi [Cherokee] were related to the Thiligothe [Chilicothe],
who were conquered by the Algonquin Shawnee ca. 800 CE, and who subsequently used
their name.

THE LENAPE MOVE THEIR CAPITOL TO THE EAST

20. "The East-Villager was chief:
he was east of the Talega [Tsulagi-Cherokee].
21. "A great land and a wide land was the east land:
22. "a land without snakes [Missasauga?], a rich land, a pleasant land."

The missionary John Heckewelder preserved another Lenape account of this move.[36]

"For a long period of time - some say many hundred years - the two nations
[Lenape and the Siouxian Mengwe] resided peacefully in this country and
increased very fast. Some of their most enterprising huntsmen and warriors
crossed the great swamps, and falling on streams running to the eastward,
followed them down to the great Bay River (Susquehanna), and thence into the
bay itself, which we call Chesapeake.

291

Following reconnaissance,

"At last they [the Lenape and Mengwe] settled on the four great rivers (which we call Delaware, Hudson, Susquehanna, and Potomac)..."

(Footnotes)

[1] For Cherokee descriptions of the Nunnehi, see James Mooney, *Myths of the Cherokee*, Myth 78

[2] For dates for the introduction of Pisgah Culture, see Roy S. Dickens, *Cherokee Prehistory*, University of Tennessee Press, Knoxville, 1976. Dickens notes throughout the Connestee/Pisgah transition ca. 1000 CE; the Pisgah lack of elite burials (p. 211), and its significant differences from later southern influences (p. 212). I mention here that the sand tempering of Pisgah pottery is a northern trait, as are its ground stone tools, and its use of iron ochre (wodi) for decoration, all of which agree with a Pisgah origin to the northeast, as the Legend of the Bald Mountains states.

[3] For North Carolina population movements, see David G. Moore's *Catawba Valley Mississippian*, University of Alabama Press, Tuscaloosa, 2002, in particular for Pisgah dates, and Mississippian-style Burke incised pottery, defined p. 262, distribution map, p. 94. Includes a valuable 50 page discussion of the ethnographic work which has been done on the region, including the most recent work (p. 1-50). Specific note must be made of the citation here of Charles Hudson's notes on female cacique (Sun) in the area, p. 27, and distribution of Muskogee Micco and Ora titles (p 46) (Hudson, 1990, The Juan Pardo Expeditions).

[4] For South Carolina population movements, see David G. Anderson's *The Savannah River Chiefdoms, Political Change in the Late Prehistoric Southeast*, University of Alabama Press, Tuscaloosa, Alabama, 1994, in particular Mississippian complex distribution maps p. 236-244.

[5] The translation from which the version given here is adapted is that Albert S. Gatschet, *A Migration Legend of the Creek Indians*, D.G. Brinton, Philadelphia, v.1, v.2, 1884, 1889. For further discussion see Appendix D here.

[6] Benjamin Hawkins, A Sketch of the Creek Country in 1798 and -99, Georgia Historical Society Collections, 1848, cited by George E, Lankford, *Native American Legends*, August House, Little Rock, Arkansas, 1987, Tale 84, p. 144

[7] Discussed in Appendix D

[8] Hawkins, ibid.

[9] Constantin Rafinesque, *Ancient Nations*, p. 151.

[10] The Walum Olum, Appendix E here

[11] For a discussion of the appearance in eastern Wisconsin of Oneota culture, see Victoria Durst, *The People of the Dunes*, Whitefish Dunes State Park, 1993, p. 46-63

[12] For a discussion of the appearance of Oneota culture at Redwing, see Clark A. Dobbs, *Red Wing Archaeological Preserve*, Goodhue-Pierce Archaeological Society Planning Committee, Institute for Minnesota Archaeology, Minneapolis, 1990, p. 7

[13] For a discussion of the western Oneota culture appearance and distribution, see James L. Theler and Robert F. Boszhardt, *Twelve Millenia, Archaeology of the Upper Mississippi River Valley*, pages 152-155, particularly abandonment of effigy mounds, p. 155

[14] for examples see Thomas J.C. Williams, *A History of Washington County*, Maryland,

1906, p 37-45

[15] In their book on *The Gottschall Rockshelter*, Robert J. Salzer and Grace Rajnovich cite cannibalism at Aztalan, citing Fred A, Finney and James B. Stohlman, *The Fred Edwards Site, New Perspectives on Cahokia*, Prehistory Press, Madison. One problem assigning this here to a collapse is Oneota occupancy at Aztalan, following on the Stirling phase occupancy at the site.

[16] carbon dates at this site: Lynne Goldstine, Joan Freeman, *Aztalan State Park*, Wisconsin Department of Natural Resources, 1995 for group burials and stockade history.

[17] See for example, Robert Walter Smith, Esq., *History of Armstrong County*, Pennsylvania, Waterman Watkins & Co., Chicago, 1888, p. 313-315

[18] Cusick, Appendix A here

[19] The Walum Olum, Appendix E here

[20] The Ancient Word of the Natchez, Appendix B here

[21] Cusick, Appendix A here

[22] The translation from which the version given here is adapted is that Albert S. Gatschet, *A Migration Legend of the Creek Indians*, D.G. Brinton, Philadelphia, v.1, v.2, 1884, 1889. For further discussion see The Tale of the Ancestors, Appendix D here.

[23] The Tale of the Ancestors, Appendix D here

[24] site visits

[25] The Tale of the Ancestors, Appendix D here

[26] The Tale of the Ancestors, Appendix D here

[27] Gerald P. Smith, *Chucalissa Revisited*, Memphis State University, p. 6-7 for Mitchell phase

[28] site visits

[29] The Walum Olum, Appendix E here

[30] John Heckewelder, *History, Manners, and Customs of the Indian Nations*, ed William Cornelius Reichel, The Historical Society of Pennsylvania, 1876, p. 47

[31] Cusick, Appendix A here

[32] Heckewelder, ibid., p. 49-50

[33] For the archaeology of western Lake Erie, see David M. Stothers and James R. Graves, *Cultural Continuity and Change: The Western Basin, Ontario Iroquois, and Sandusky Traditions, A 1982 Perspective*, Archaeology of Eastern North America, Volume 11, 1983, p. 109-142.

[34] See The Tale of the Ancestors, Appendix E. I want to thank Ron Baalke for providing me with an article containing this information. on Motero. For another mention of this phenomenon, see Mooney, ibid., Myth 78

[35] Mooney, ibid, Myth 80, The Spirit Defenders of Nikwasi

[36] Heckewelder, ibid.., p. 50-51

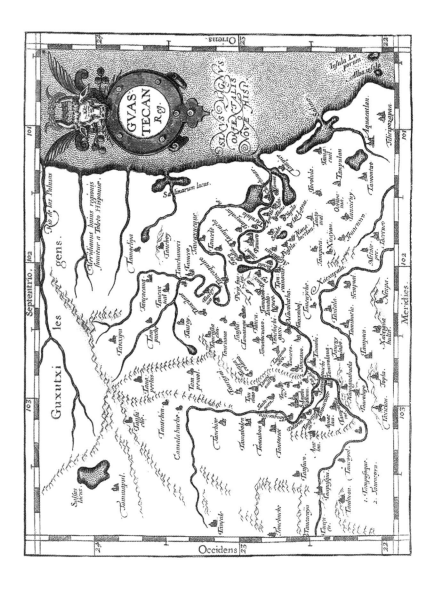

CHAPTER 16

THE EUROPEAN ARRIVAL

The Native American emigrations of the 1200's to1300's left enmities which European colonists were easily able to exploit, starting on the mainland with the Entrada of the Spanish Conquistador Cortez.

THE TRADE FEDERATION LEARNS OF THE SPANISH ARRIVAL

From the Ancient Word of the Natchez[1]:

"It was only after many generations that these Suns [nobles] came to join us in this country, where the fine air and the peace which we enjoyed had multiplied us into a number as great as the leaves on the trees.

"Then the Warriors of Fire came on floating villages [carvel class ships] from the side where the sun rises [the east]. The Warriors of Fire were bearded men, white but swarthy. They were called Warriors of Fire because their arms threw fire with a great noise, and killed at a great distance. They had other very heavy arms [cannons] besides these, which killed many people at a time, and which made the earth tremble like thunder.

THE TRADE FEDERATION LEARNS OF THE SPANISH BERTRAYAL
OF THEIR NATIVE AMERICAN ALLIES

"Our brothers [the Totonac and Otomie] were allied with them, although our Suns told them that these Warriors of Fire would subject them after they had subjected the Ancients of the Country.

"The Warriors of Fire conquered the Ancients of the Country, of whom they killed as many as there are spears of grass in the prairies. Though in the beginning they were good friends of our brothers [the Totonac and Otomie], ultimately they made them submit along with the Ancients of the Country, as our Suns had foreseen, and had foretold to them.

THE COASTAL LEADERS FLEE NORTH EAST MEXICO

"The Great Sun and the [lesser] Suns [princes] who were with him were unable to induce our brothers to follow them; and they took their farewells, therefore, in order to come alone to rejoin us here, for fear lest the Warriors of Fire should make them slaves, which they feared more than death. These Suns came alone with their slaves, because our other brothers did not wish to follow them.

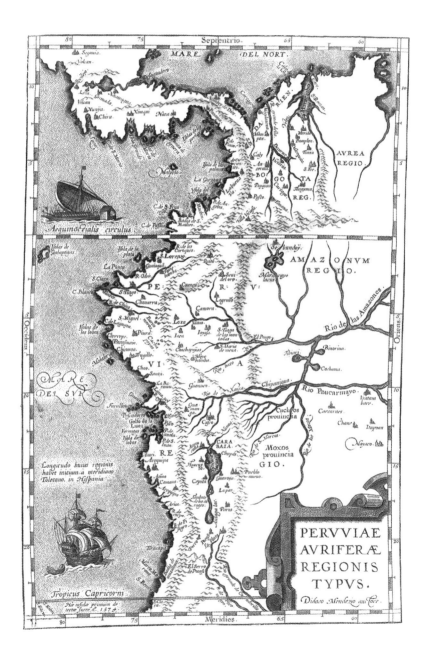

1540 CE: THE SITUATION AS DE SOTO FOUND IT

The peoples of south eastern North America were prepared for the arrival of the colonists, as news of the Spaniards had traveled to them from both the Caribbean Islands and central Mexico, and spread throughout the Trade Federation.

In 1540 CE de Soto found the southern peoples split into three groups. While some of the exact locations are in hot debate right now, the Kushita, Chickasaw, "Alabama" [Choctaw], and Abikas occupied a line stretching from east to west along the south side of the ridge of mountains which extends from the Appalachians out into the plain. The Southern Ceremonial peoples still held control along the river basins to the south of them, and despite the invaders' claims of having "white hearts", both the Kushita (Coosa) and the Chickasaw tried to secure de Soto as an ally so that they might attack these peoples.

Another pocket of Southern Ceremonial peoples had survived along the western Tennessee River, from the Cherokee lands west to where the Tennessee River joined with the Ohio River, [and even a short way up along the Wabash River from its junction with the Ohio River?]. These peoples had been north of the route of the Kushita (Creek) emigration, and southeast of the route of the Lenape emigration. These people were still powerful, but with the Muskogean peoples to their south, they did not attack the Cherokee, but instead held them under tribute.

Pockets of survivors from the emigrations were now starting to re-group as well. A small group had re-established itself at Kaskasia, south of Cahokia. Other groups were re-forming along the Arkansas and on the north of the Arkansas plateau.

But de Soto was not only able to kill Native Americans directly: he also brought along with his army European diseases which moved nearly as fast as his army did.

THE CHEROKEE (KITUAGI) ATTACK THE KWATANI

With the tribes to the west of the Cherokee decimated by de Soto and the European diseases and thoroughly disheartened and disorganized, and facing no threat from the south, the Cherokee began an attack on the Kwatani [Taensa?]:

> "The (Kwatani) were a mystical, religious body, of whom people stood in awe, and seem to have been somewhat like the Brahmins of India... The order was hereditary, in this respect peculiar, for among Indians seldom, and among the Cherokee never, does power pertain to any family as a matter of right...

> "Relying on their hereditary privilege and the strange awe which they inspired, they did not hesitate by fraud or violence to rend asunder the tender relations of husband and wife when a beautiful woman excited their passions...The people long brooded in silence over the oppressions and outrages of this high cast, whom they deeply hated but greatly feared...

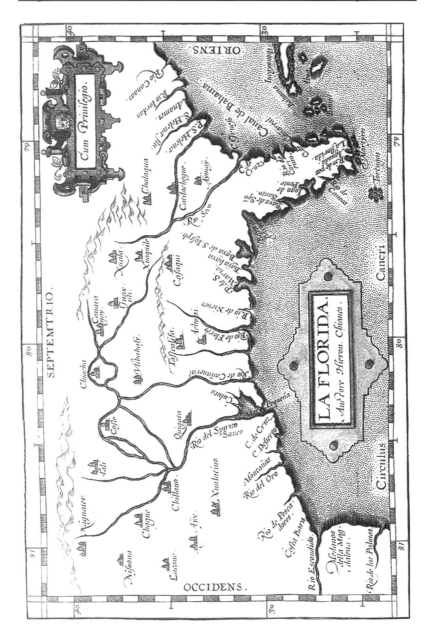

"Their extinction by massacre is nearly all that can be discovered about them...
The immediate provocation was the abduction of the wife of a young leader
...a member of an influential family... [identified by Haywood as the brother
of the leading chief of the nation])... His wife was remarkable for her beauty
and was forcibly abducted and violated by one of the (Kwatani) while he... was
absent on the chase.

"On his return he found no difficulty in exciting in others the resentment
which he himself experienced. So many had suffered in the same way, so many
feared that they might be made to suffer, that nothing was wanted but a leader.

"A leader appearing in the person of the young brave whom we have named,
the people rose under his direction and killed every (Kwatani) young and old.
...since time which no hereditary privileges have been tolerated among the
Cherokee." – adapted from information given by Chief John Ross[2]

THE KUSHITA (CREEK) COMPLETE THEIR CONQUEST

In a short while every Southern Ceremonial peoples that de Soto "visited" would be
nearly extinct. After de Soto's "visit", the Muskogean peoples, the Kushita, Choctaw,
Chicasaw, and Abekhas used the opportunity presented by the ravages of the epidemics
of the European diseases to sweep south and complete their conquest of most of the
earlier peoples of southeast of North America.

THE CLIMATE COLLAPSE ca 1576 CE

A period of extreme dry weather set in about 1545 CE in Central America. In the
highlands of Mexico this drought appears to have caused an outbreak of mouse bourn
plague, and roughly 80% of the population died.[3] It is currently held that this plague
was native to the Americas, but the only Native American accounts of earlier plague
outbreaks are those of ca 1175 CE given in Chapter 15. The drought intensified
in 1576 CE, and this led to the deaths of 50% of the remaining population in the
highlands of Mexico. I suspect that there was enough water in the lowlands that
rodents there did not have to forage far for foodstuffs.

We have Native American accounts of a drought extending through the plains to the
southeast of the United States, though exactly when these droughts occurred will not
be known until detailed tree ring studies are undertaken. There do not appear to have
been plague outbreaks in the north at this time, but instead large numbers of people
appear to have died directly of famine.

"The Creeks and Choctaws declared that about 300 years ago [which would
be about 1576 CE] when Alabama was full of buffaloes, a terrible draught
came upon the land and the rivers, so that there was no water except in small
pools miles apart. The large springs continued to run only in weak streams.
Thousands of trees perished, and deer, squirrels, rabbits and birds died.
Buffaloes in great numbers migrated to the Mississippi River.

"Finally the Great Spirit sent a rain from the big waters to the south that lasted a whole moon. Yet for a long time the game and fish were so scarce that the people almost perished. The Indians concluded that the fortunes of war had given their land to another race and that they were destined. to follow the buffaloes west." - anonymous, recorded by Mary Gordon Duffee[4]

"When we abandoned our former lands we set out without knowing whither we were going. Our motive for leaving the country we occupied was the scarcity of game....

"On arriving at the mouth of the Ny-Tonka (Ohio River), our Chiefs determined on separating the nations....

"After our separating, our party followed the course of the Ny-Tonka [Mississippi River]. The first [people with] red skins whom we met with were settled some way below the Ny-Whoutteh Junka [Arkansas River]; they were called Tonnika [Tunica]. We attacked and put them to flight.

"Some time afterwards we entered this river, which we call Ny-Jitteh. We soon discovered that there were other [people with] red skins in the country. Parties were sent out to look for them. They were found encamped in the Great Prairie [between Little Rock and the Post of Arkansas]. We attacked them; they made a valiant resistance, but we beat them and drove them away. This nation called itself Intouka; the whites at that period gave them the name of Illinois.[5] Then we were left entire masters of this country." - Paheka, Quapaw[6]

FRANCE, ENGLAND, DUTCH, SWEDEN

France, England, and the Dutch were all late comers in their settlement of the New World. Their primary goals at the time of their initial colonizations were the control of the long standing Spanish routes from the New World. These countries focused on the settlement of ports capable of hosting fleets capable of intercepting the Spanish Gold Fleets coming from Mexico and Peru.

Later these European countries would be drawn to the fur trade in North America, and would find that the recent migrations had caused no end of hatred among the peoples they found there, hatreds which they could turn to their advantage. At their first landing, the Europeans would support one people in their fight against another. After their allies had killed off their enemies, one people, entirely, the Europeans would then enlist new allies and turn on their old allies.

And so it went...

(Footnotes)

[1] The Ancient Word of the Natchez, Appendix B here

[2] This version of this tale is extracted from that gathered from Chief John Ross by Dr. J. B. Evans in 1866, and comes via Mooney via Dr. J. MacGowen, "Indian Secret Societies", *Historical Magazine*, Morrisiana, NewYork, 1896, p. 139

[3] Rudolfo Acuna-Soto, David W. Stahle, Malcolm K. Cleveland, Mathew D. Ferrell, "Megadrought and Megadeath in 16th Century Mexico", *Emerging Infectious Diseaseses*, v.8 n.4, April, 2002, Centers for Disease Control, Lexington, Kentucky

[4] Mary Gordon Duffee, Sketches of Alabama, The Alabama Review, April, 1956, University of Alabama Press, 1970, p. 278

[5] This identification by Paheka may refer to language or cultural affinities of the people who formerly resided at Toltec Mounds. Geographic identifications are by Izard.

[6] Paheka to George Izard, Notes Respecting the Arkansas Territory's Aboriginal Inhabitants, the Quapaw Indians, January 10, 1827, American Philosophical Society. This migration may be placed here instead of earlier on the basis of the Quapaw encounter with the Illinois.

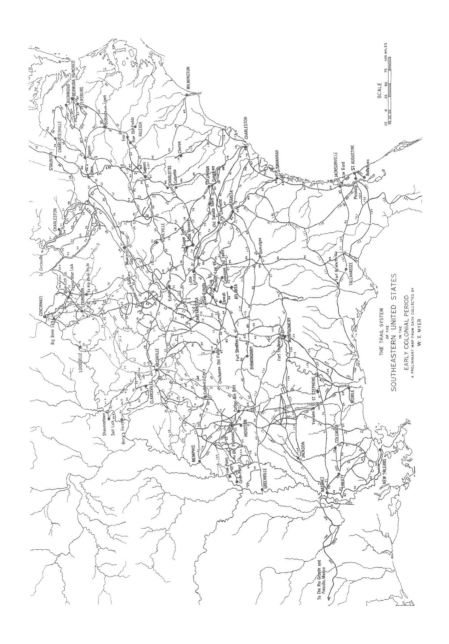

THE TRAIL SYSTEM
OF THE
SOUTHEASTERN UNITED STATES
IN THE
EARLY COLONIAL PERIOD
A PRELIMINARY MAP FROM DATA COLLECTED BY
W. E. MYER

SCALE

CHAPTER 17

TRAVEL TIPS

THE TERRAIN

Many believe that the plains in North America do not begin until one has crossed the Mississippi River, and that these plains are found only to the north and west of it. But the best way of thinking of the center of North America is as the bottom of a sea floor, which is what it was through most of the age of the dinosaurs. Two mountain chains border this plain, the Appalachian Mountains on its east side, and the Rocky Mountains on its west. The soil from this sea floor is rich in the north, and poor and sandy in the south.

On the plain's east side, a ridge of mountains projects out from the center of the Appalachian Mountains into the floor of this sea, with the Ohio River flowing along the north of this ridge and the Tennessee and Cumberland Rivers flowing through it. North of this ridge of mountains, the plains start after one crosses the Ohio River, with allowances for run off from the ancient rivers which ran out of the Appalachians.

South of this ridge of mountains, the rivers flow from the north to south through a rolling landscape and one into the Gulf of Mexico. The Big Black River and Pearl River run through the state of Mississippi, and the Tennesaw-Tombigbee-Black Warrior Rivers and the Tennesaw-Alabama-Coosa Rivers through the state of Alabama.

The Appalachian Mountains themselves continue south from where this ridge meets them well down towards the Gulf of Mexico. While the Chatahoochee River and Flint River flow through Georgia and then cut through the southern part of the Appalachian Mountains to flow into the Gulf, further east the rivers drain southeast towards the Atlantic Ocean: going from south to north, the Ocmulgee River, the Oconee River, the Savannah River, the Saluda-Broad-Catawba River fan draining through Charleston, and the PeeDee River flow into the Atlantic.

This ridge of mountains picks up again much to the west of the Mississippi River, where its mountains form the Ozark or Arkansas Plateau. Just as the Tennessee River flows through its middle on the east, the Arkansas River flows through it in the west. On the south side of this western ridge, the waters from the plateau feed the Red River, which flows east; south of the Red River, the rivers flow southeast to the Gulf of Mexico. To the north of this western ridge of mountains the rivers feed the Missouri River.

On the plain the land is so flat that water has a difficult time figuring out which way to flow: rivers change course within human lifetimes, often stranding older human settlements in land locked positions. One example of this is the Achafalaya River, which not only parallels the Mississippi River, but during "mound builder" times it actually was the "West Mississippi".

Another result of this flatness is that there were and are large areas of marsh, such as the Louisiana bayous. This marsh is not limited to the southern part of the plains, and parts of the plains of Illinois and Indiana were marshy before they were drained for agriculture.

But the plains are not all flat. Another process worth noting is that when prevailing westerly winds hit the eastern banks of rivers and rise up over them, they deposit higher and higher ridges of soil. When the
rivers shift course, these ridges remain behind as low hills.

STRIPPING OFF THE CULTURAL RESIDUE

One of the largest problems facing anyone working in strange territory is being able to strip off the current culture and other cultural residues so as to get to the landscape of the people at the time one wishes to study. In this case what we're trying to get to is the landscape at the time of the great Native American societies, and we will have to strip off later cultural layers to get to it. The most recent of these layers is that of the interstate highway system.

THE INTERSTATE HIGHWAY SYSTEM AND A FEW DRIVING TIPS

Most inter-city traffic in the United States travels on the interstate highway system, which needs to be stripped away first, as it is the most recent development. The interstate highway system was originally rationalized in the 1950's by President Eisenhower as a civil defense measure to ensure both quick evacuation of urban centers as well as the quick transport of military supplies. The rationale was that the major urban areas would be surrounded by ring roads, so that if nuclear explosions destroyed the city centers, the national lines of communications would survive. With low oil prices, and their ability to make point to point deliveries with no need for the loading and unloading of cargo, transport by lorry replaced transport by rail as the primary method of manufacturing transport in the United States.

Along these Interstate Highways you will usually see restaurants, petrol stations, motels (MOtoring hoTELS), and stores which are franchised throughout the United States. Inexpensive meals can be had at the fast food restaurants such as McDonald's, Burger King, Hardees, Wendy's, Taco Bell, Long John Silver, Popeye's, and sit down restaurants such as Denny's or Perkin's; mid-price ($45) lodging is nearly always available Motel 6 and Super 8 motels, provided you check in by 5 o'clock or so.

By using these, you'll be assured of receiving adequate services, but of a bland character. Since you'll be traveling on the local roads to visit the sites, why not take a chance to enjoy (or rue) local foods and local lodging? Good or bad, you'll be closer to actually having visited an area.

STATE TOURIST INFORMATION CENTERS

Free highway maps and brochures on historical attractions can be obtained at state tourist information centers. Often these are located on or near the Interstate Highways right at a state's borders. Guides at these information centers will gladly help you with any questions you may have; their information trustworthy and detailed, and their service is free.

DRIVING TIPS

This is as good a place as any to give some general tips for driving in the United States. And drive you will if you wish to see the remains, as with a few exceptions it is simply not possible to use public transit to visit Native American sites. The United States today is largely suburban, and the primary form of personal transport is by automobile. If you're visiting from abroad to visit Native American sites, renting a car is the best option.

Modern US transport lorries have very large blind spots and limited maneuverability and stopping power, and you must keep this in mind when driving around them, and you will always be around them anytime you are on the roads. These lorries actually do more damage to the interstate highways than their taxes pay for, and often the right lanes of highways are in very rough shape. One might think that size limits might be imposed, or that lorry taxes might be raised to pay for road damage, but the trucking associations are an extremely powerful political force. While it is now possible for rail companies to deliver entire lorry cargo trailers from one collection point to another collection point, with road travel on either end, at tremendous efficiencies in labor and fuel costs, political action has generally prevented them from doing this.

Since the right lanes of the interstate highways are in bad shape, use the left lanes to avoid fatigue during long distance drives. (Also, don't follow impact expert Gene Shoemaker's example, and when in the US remember to drive on the right side of the road!)

Road surfaces are not the only thing which one has to watch out for. In response to the danger presented by lorries, a good portion of the people here have started to drive for personal use what is euphemistically known as "sport utility vehicles", but might be better known as "suburban battle wagons". These are massive trucks, vans, and jeeps, which will pulverize any normally sized car which they happen to collide with. Because of their size you can not see the road around them, and this both gives them a certain amount of control over your movement, as well as blinding you to both to any dangers ahead and to signs giving directions to Native American sites. The best way of handling these large vehicles is simply to ignore the speed limits and drive around them if possible.

THE POST INDUSTRIAL LANDSCAPE

The primary roads to use when visiting Native American sites are the "US" system. These roads generally follow the oldest routes between cities, and thus follow the roads of the colonists, who themselves followed Native American trading paths.

Improvement of these roads, which started in the 1920's, was accelerated under the leadership of President Roosevelt in the 1930's. Until the construction of the interstate highway system, and before the advent of low priced jet travel, most Americans would spend their vacations driving along these roads, and it is often possible to find very low cost accommodation at older "motels" located along these roads, as well as excellent regional restaurants.

As you drive along these roads approaching the cores of the old urban centers, you will see mile after mile of suburban housing, followed by mile after mile of abandoned and derelict housing and manufacturing plants. Three factors came into play in producing this landscape: first, the automobile; second, race relations; and third, trade union policies.

To start with, by the 1920's to 1930's widespread ownership of the automobile allowed the expansion of cities beyond the areas served by the trolley cars then in use. The impulse to move to more open areas was given further stimulus in 1954 by the decision of the Supreme Court to stop the segregation of black and white schools. Whites fled the cities, and usually you will see a central city where development stopped in the late 1950's to early 1960's surrounded by prosperous counties.

A further complicating factor in the production of this landscape was the decision by many members of the Republican Party, under the leadership of Richard Nixon, to use this racism to break the trade unions, which had been strong supporters of the Democratic Party. In return for allowing segregated practices to continue, the Republicans were able to open US manufacturers to foreign competitors with far lower labor costs and supported national currencies, to encourage massive illegal immigration, and to stop the enforcement of laws respecting union formation and bargaining. Thus you will also see mile after mile of abandoned manufacturing plant along these roads.

"INDIAN" CASINOS

One way that some localities have attempted to compensate for this destruction of the manufacturing sector is through the promotion of gaming. All along the Mississippi you will "riverboat" casinos and "Indian" casinos. While Americans associate gaming with crime and have a certain religious guilt about it, the "riverboat" casinos are somehow justified on the historical basis that in the mid-1800's there were riverboats, and people did gamble on them.

The "Indian" casinos proceed on a different basis. A few years back it was discovered by several tribes that the treaties which had stripped them of their lands and put them on reservations also reserved certain legal rights to them. Included among these rights was the right to avoid taxes on cigarettes and gasoline, and it was later discovered that they also had the right to run gaming establishments.

As these casinos are located on the reservations to which the Native Americans were moved by the colonists, and often employ others, sadly they often offer little for those seeking to learn of a people's life. Thankfully this situation is changing today, with casinos in Wisconsin showing what can be done here. But be sure to check the tourist literature available at state tourist information centers before planning to visit them.

OBSERVATIONS ON GEORGIA, AN EXCEPTION TO THE RULE

Occasionally due to some peculiar combination of industry and political leadership, exceptions to this general pattern take place. The state of Georgia serves as an example. The core of Georgia's largest city of Atlanta is serviced by interstate highways some 16 lanes across, and it remains prosperous. The mid-sized town of Columbus, Georgia, is supported by the Army base of Fort Benning, has used its political power to secure federal funds, and hosts a college. The small Georgia town of Calhoun has used its political power to secure protection for its carpet manufacturing industry, and it has continued to prosper. It should be noted that people in Georgia drive in what I can best describe as a hurried manner.

OBSERVATIONS ON TEXAS, AN EXCEPTION TO THE RULE, ITS GOVERNOR, AND US PRESIDENT

Texas occupies an area so vast that many advertising firms design advertisements especially for it, separate from those seen in the rest of the nation. Texas's wealth is popularly believed to derive from its oil supplies and agricultural abundance; but as many other states have those resources, it is my belief that the source of its wealth lies elsewhere.

When one drives the roads in Texas, one is struck by their excellence. As an engineer from Louisiana put it, Texas's tertiary roads are better than Louisiana's primary roads. The source for this engineering expertise seems to be Texas's schools, specifically Texas A&M and the University of Texas. This excellence in engineering is also reflected in Texas's petrochemical industries and Texas's architecture. It is no accident that NASA has a major facility in Texas, and this can be seen as an effort by President Johnson to continue Texas's tradition of engineering excellence.

There is another side to this interest in space. At the outbreak of World War 2, as labor and electricity were widely available in the Barbeque Zone, many defense plants were built there. As normal manufacturing collapsed these plants played an increasingly important role in area economies. Texas has its share of these plants as well.

THE LOCATIONS OF FIRST COLONIAL SETTLEMENTS

Returning to the US highway system, often in the 1950's, before the interstate highway system came along, by-passes to divert traffic would be built around urban cores. Sometimes you will see signs marked"Business 40", etc., which bear a certain irony as these are the roads in the urban cores from which business has long since fled. Where these roads, and thus the colonial roads, and thus the Native American trading paths, cross the major rivers is usually the area that where you will find remains of Native American settlement sites.

While transport routes for the colonists and Native Americans were similar, their industries and living requirements differed greatly. Colonists had horses, used water power, had wells and privies, grew wheat, and used iron tools to build their defensive structures. Barbeque Zone Native Americans had no horses or water power, generally required a small stream to provide fresh water, required an alluvial soil to grow their maize, and had to depend on natural bluffs to some degree for their defense.

But even to get to the colonial layer one must strip away the layer of the trolleys and railroads. Trolley lines, usually built between 1875 and 1925, allowed the cities to expand. Oft times Native American sites would have been held out of development until this time period, but then used for some public function such as school or library construction. Parts of the remains may still survive, but other times all that is left of them is a "Mound Street" or "Mound Hill" road sign, if that.

Before the trolley lines had come the railroads, which made possible the transport of grains and live meat. The increased demand for grains and feeds for both local livestock as well as export (these were horse drawn societies, after all) led to the expansion of agricultural production. This led to the plowing under and leveling of many sites, and it is not unusual to find towns near these crossing points named "Mound", "Mounds", or "Moundville" with no mounds now present.

Generally, but with important exceptions, rail lines connected already existing riverboat towns, which in their turn had grown up where the colonial roads and thus the Native American trading paths had crossed rivers. Strip away the rail and riverboat industries, and you are at the level of the forts the colonists used for their wars against the Native Americans. The remains of the older occupation will be nearby.

TIPS ON VISITING "BAD AREAS"

The contemporary social factors described previously have left many Native American ruins located in what are euphemistically called "bad areas": areas with absolutely no industry, occupied by people descended from the African slaves the colonists brought over to work the land they took from the Native Americans. As a large portion of the leaders of these black communities were almost always employed in manufacturing, with the loss of industry they have lost their power. As if this was not bad enough, the highly addictive drug crack cocaine began to be used by some of these people; and then it got worse, as certain media executives, under the pretext of giving voice to the frustrations of these people, encouraged the use of this drug and the trade in it, and violence, and violence against women.

When visiting these areas my first suggestion is dress like a US native, and show no foreign clothing. Tennis shoes, blue jeans, and a standard cotton shirt will work well for men. Second, schedule your visits to these areas for early morning, as the criminal element is usually asleep at this time. Third, do not let your accent be overheard, which will identify you as a foreigner and thus an easy victim. Fourth, always remain aware of those in your surroundings. Fifth, always make sure that no valuables or anything which might be mistaken for a valuable are visible inside of your rental car.

NATIVE AMERICAN TRADE PATHS

Some contemporary authors belittle the trade paths of the Native Americans by describing them as "animal paths". While it is quite natural that migrating animals would take the easiest route through any landscape, Native American trade paths are far more complicated than that. First, a source of a trade good must be nearby. Second, Native Americans of the Barbeque Zone generally seem to have used dugout canoes to float down-river for trade, and then abandoned their craft and used land routes to walk home. Before the later migrations and the collapse of trade, which itself occurred just before European contact, these paths were in excellent shape, and travel at the rate of 50 miles a day over 500+ mile routes seems to have been common.

RECOMMENDED GUIDE BOOKS

Carrie Eldridge's excellent guides to southern Native American and early colonial trade paths, "An Atlas of Appalachian Trails" and "An Atlas of Southern Trails" are highly recommended, and I suggest if it is possible examining these two works in detail before visiting southern areas. An excellent introduction to the trails of the north east is Paul A.W. Wallace's Indian Paths of Pennsylvania, which is the definitive guide to the trade paths of Pennsylvania.

While no comprehensive guide to all Native American sites is currently available, there are several excellent regional guides. Susan L. Woodward and Jerry N. McDonald's "Indian Mounds of the Middle Ohio Valley" is an excellent introduction and guide to the Adena and Hopewell remains of that area. For those interested in Native American remains further to the east, Dr. McDonald and Woodward have also written "Indian Mounds of the Atlantic Coast: a Guide to Sites from Maine to Florida".

For the eastern ridge in Tennessee and Kentucky, Thomas M.N. Lewis and Madeline Kneberg's "Tribes That Slumber" provides an excellent introduction to the earlier peoples, while Barbar R. Duncan and Brett H. Riggs' "Cherokee Heritage Trails Guidebook" is the essential guide to Cherokee sites.

Roberta A. Birmingham and Leslie E. Eisenberg's "Indian Mounds of Wisconsin" provides a fine guide to Native American remains in Wisconsin, and Hugh Highsmith's "The Mounds of Koshkonong and Rock River" is a pleasant guide to the remains in the eastern part of that state. Deborah Morse-Kahn's "Archaeology Parks of the Upper Midwest" inventories and gives directions to sites in Minnesota, Iowa, and Northern Illinois.

For the more spiritual seeker, Brad Olsen's "Sacred Places of North America" is quite nice, and also lists many non-Native American sites along the road.

USING THE INTERNET TO PLAN YOUR TRIP

As both state park officials and the National Park Service have established internet web pages for the archaeological sites which they administer, you can use the internet to find out great deal about the different sites while planning your trip. That is, you can use the internet to find out about the sites if you know their names, so…

A LIST OF SITES

I've read an estimate that there were something like 10,000 major Native American sites in the United States at the time of European settlement. The following list is by no means complete, but just covers some sites in the Barbeque Zone and related trade areas which I've visited, as well as some that I have not gotten to yet. The list does not include Native American sites in the Southwest, California, the Pacific Northwest, or the Northeast of the United States. Aside from covering a limited geographic and cultural area, the list excludes most paleolithic and archaic period sites and caves, as they were outside the scope of an earlier survey which I performed. The names of sites and museums I have visited and can personally highly recommend are given in capital letters – this is not to say that all the sites listed smaller case are bad, as many of them I have not had the chance to visit yet.

PALEOLITHIC
o Thunderbird, Virginia (closed)
o Saltville, Virginia
o Mammoth Cave, Kentucky
o Russell Cave, Alabama
o Modoc Rock Shelter, Illinois – well, mesolithic, really - undeveloped

EARLY SOUTHERN
o POVERTY POINT, Louisiana, on tributary of Atchafalaya
o Watson Break, Louisiana, on the Ouchita River, a tributary of
   Achafalaya River, site in process of acquisition, 3400 BCE,
   includes ring mound and embankment
o Rock Eagle Effigy Mound, Etontown, Georgia
o PHARR MOUNDS, Mississippi
o Bear Creek Mound, Mississippi
o MARKSVILLE MOUNDS, Marksville, Louisiana – the Tunica Treasure House is
nearby

EARLY COASTAL
o Banana Bayou, Louisiana, 2,490 BCE
o Avery Island, Louisiana
o Pecan Island, Louisiana
o Two large mounds on the Louisiana State University Campus,
   Baton Rouge, Louisiana on the Mississippi River, dated to 3,000 BCE
o Kissimee Mound, Fort Bassinger, Florida
o Lower Suwanee National Wildlife Refuge, Florida,
   1 mound dated to 2,500 BCE

o Historic Spanish Fort, Florida, multiple mounds dating to
  2,000 BCE
o Museum of the Gulf Coast, Port Arthur, Texas – I liked it.

COPPER TRADER-ADENA
o Isle Royale National Park
o Adventure Copper Mine, Greenland, Michigan
o Saulte Ste. Marie, no remains, area only
o Toft Point, Door Peninsula, Wisconsin
o Copper Culture State Park, Oconto, Wisconsin
o NEVILLE PUBLIC MUSEUM, Green Bay
o Juneau Park, Milwaukee, Wisconsin
o Mound Cemetary, Racine, Wisconsin
o Sandusky, Ohio, Golf Course, area only, remains obscured
o NNN Cemetary, Cleveland
o Conneaut, Ohio
o McKee's Rock, Pittsburgh, site only, remains destroyed
o GRAVE CREEK MOUND, Moundsville, West Virginia, on Ohio River
o MARIETTA MOUND, Marietta, Ohio, on Ohio River
o Buffington Island Mound, Portland, Ohio
o Camden Park Mound, Huntington, West Virginia
o SOUTH CHARLESTON MOUND, Charleston, West Virginia
o Indian Mound Cemetery, Romney, West Virginia, late site, on path to Potomac

ADENA – HOPEWELL
Buy Woodward and McDonald's "Indian Mounds of the Middle Ohio Valley"
o Adena, Chillicothe, Ohio
o Portsmouth Mound Park, Portsmouth, Ohio
o Mount Horeb Earthworks, Lexington, Kentucky
o Shrum Mound, Columbus, Ohio
o Tarlton Cross Mound, Cross Mound Park, Tarlton, Ohio
o Miamisburg Mound, Miamisburg, Ohio, outside of Dayton, Ohio
o Neville, Ohio; Adena mound
o Enoch, Ohio; Adena mound
o Indian Park Mound, Cedarville, Ohio; Adena mound
o Mound Park, Portsmouth, Ohio
o River View Cemetery Mound, Aurora, Indiana
o Mounds State Park, Indiana
o PINSON MOUNDS, Tennessee, on the South Fork of the Deer River,
  tributary of Mississippi River – not yet landscaped, later adopted to Mississippian use
o Old Stone Fort, Manchester, Tennessee
o Alec Mountain, 7 miles northwest of Clarksville, Habersham County, Tennessee
  - important site - a circle 90 feet in diameter was enclosed by a wall 3 feet high

HOPEWELL
o Copperhill, Tennessee, near Hiwasee River, tributary of
  Tennessee River, source for pure copper sheets and nuggets
o Spruce Mountain Mineral District, Mitchell County, North Carolina,
  near the Holston and French Broad Rivers, tributaries of
  the Tennessee River, source for sheets of mica
o HOPEWELL CULTURE NATIONAL HISTORIC PARK, Chillicothe, Ohio,
  on Chillicothe River, on trade path
o NEWARK MOUNDS, Newark, Ohio, center for Flint Ridge flint trade
o Serpent Mound, Ohio – near Fort Hill complex, excellent visitor center
o Cincinnati, Ohio, area of mounds
o Vincennes Cemetery, Vincennes, Indiana, on Wabash River;
  Sugar Loaf Indian Mound, behind YMCA on Wabash Avenue
o Toolesboro Mounds, a Hopewell complex on the Mississippi River in eastern Iowa
o (?) across from Bonhomme Island, on Missouri River, Nebraska

STONE FORTS
("Early Fort Ancient" ("Hopewell" refuges) and
"Late Fort Ancient" (Shawnee and Mississippian refuges)
o Stonefort, Saline County, Illinois
o Giants City State Park, Carbondale, Illinois
o De Soto Falls, Alabama
o Charleston State Park, Fourteen Mile Creek, Indiana
(the next 8 sites come from a list assembled by Frank Coryell and Frank McPhillips)
o Devil's Back Bone at Rose Island
o Harrods Creek at the Ohio River
o Wiggins Point in Jefferson County, Kentucky
o Marble Hill in Clark County, Indiana
o Indian Fort Mountain, Bera, Kentucky
o the Falls of the Ohio River,
o Sand and Corn Islands in the Ohio River
o Big Graham Creek near Deputy, Indiana
o FORTHILL, Ohio, stone fort
o FORT ANCIENT, Ohio, stone fort
o Seip's Mound, Ohio
o LOOKOUT MOUNTAIN, Chattanooga, Tennessee, site of stone fort –
  an excellent way point for further travels in any direction
o McLemore's Cove, Kensington, Tennessee
o Fort Mountain State Park, Chatsworth, Georgia
o Rocky Face, Georgia
o Catoosa National Guard Rifle Range, Ringold
o Brown's Mount, near Macon, Georgia
o Ladd Mountain, near Cartersville, Georgia

MISSISSIPIAN - WEST
o Menard Hodges Mounds – acquired by NPS but undeveloped
o TOLTEC MOUNDS, Arkansas, near Arkansas River
o Troyville, Louisiana, on the Black River, a tributary of the Red River

313

o Coles Creek, Louisiana, a site on the Bayou Macon, a tributary running parallel and slightly to the
   west of the Mississippi River, 2 major mounds only, no flanking structures – remains no longer exist
o Spiro Mounds, Oklahoma, on the misleadingly named Canadian River,
   an extension of the Arkansas River

MISSISSIPIAN - CENTRAL
o Grand Village of the Natchez, Natchez, Mississippi
o EMERALD MOUND, huge mound, Natchez federation meeting site,
   Natchez, Mississippi
o Pocahantas Mound, Mississippi, off Natchez Parkway
o Owl Creek Mounds on Natchez Parkway, Mississippi
o Tunica
o Vicksburg, Mississippi, area only
o WINTERVILLE MOUNDS, Mississippi, near Mississippi River
o Jaketown, undeveloped major complex allied with Winterville
o Chucalissa, outlying small village near Memphis, Tennessee – very nicely done
o MEMPHIS, federation ceremonial complex, DeSoto Park,
   across from National Ornamental Metal Museum, undeveloped
o Parkins, Arkansas, European contact period site
o Obion site, Tennessee, on Obion River, tributary of Mississippi River
o Lilburn, southwest of New Madrid, undeveloped small federation center
o New Madrid, site to east across from Wolf Island - possible federation center?
o Towosahgy, minor village south of junction of Ohio and Mississippi Rivers
o Mound City, Illinois, at junction of Ohio and Mississippi Rivers,
   area only, only one mound remaining, on private land
o Wickliffe Mounds, Kentucky, at junction of Ohio and Mississippi Rivers
o CAHOKIA, Illinois, major religious center for tribes
   controlling the Mississippi, Missouri, Illinois, and Kaskasia
   Rivers
o DICKSON MOUNDS, Illinois, on Illinois River
o Toolesboro, Iowa, 2 large mounds between Lake Odessa and the
   Mississippi River
o Hanibal, Missouri; mounds in town, salt deposit to west
o The Galena district of Wisconsin, Native American source of lead
o AZTALAN and Rock Lake, Wisconsin. off a tributary of the
   Wisconsin River, on trade route to copper supplies in upper
   peninsula of Michigan. Numerous burials under stone piles, and
   mound complex which appears to be the northern most outpost of
   the Southern Ceremonial Cult peoples

MISSISSIPPIAN – EAST
o Kincaid Mounds, Metropolis, Illinois, across from junction of
   Tennessee and Cumberland Rivers with Ohio River, major center undeveloped,
   held by various private parties
o ANGEL MOUNDS, Kentucky, on Ohio River
o Albany Mounds, Albany, Illinois

o Savannah – site only, one base only remaining
o Shiloh Mounds on Shiloh Battlefield, south of Savanah,
  Tennessee, on Tennessee River
o Nanih Waiya, Mississippi
o Florence, Alabama, one mound on the Tennessee River
o Shell Mound Park, Dauphin Island, near Mobile, Alabama
o MOUNDSVILLE, south of Tuscaloosa, Alabama - a major federation center located
on the
Black Hawk River, a tributary of the Tombigbe River, which flows into the Gulf of
Mexico at Mobile
o University of Alabama campus, Tuscaloosa, Alabama – earlier site of 10 mounds
o Birmingham, Alabama, no remains -   a federation complex was situated on hill
overlooking airport, outlying settlement at Bessemer
o Fort Jackson-Fort Toulouse, minor village attached to major center
    up the Tallapoosa River from its junction with the Coosa River at Montgomery
o Bottle Creek, Mound Island, Mobile River, Alabama – inaccessible, annual tours held
by University of South Alabama, remains displayed in Museum of Mobile
o ? Mineral Mound State Park, Gilbertsville, Kentucky
o Harpeth State Park and Mound Bottom, on Harpeth River,
    tributary of Cumberland River,west of Natchez Trace
o Nashville, Noel Cemetery, area only
o Sellers Farm State Archaeological Area, Lebanon, Tennessee
o CHATANOOGA, Tennessee – no Mississippian remains left :p),
    but sacred area atop Lookout Mountain is one of my favorites;
    a very good place to stop on the road to other remains
o McMahan Indian Mound, Sevierville, Tennessee - near Pigeon Forge
    and its country music, near Gatlinburg,
    and on the route to Cherokee lands
o ETOWAH, Calhoun, Georgia – sadly, exhibited artifacts being re-interred
o sites on Chattahoochie River north of Atlanta
o OCMULGEE, Macon, Georgia, major federation center –
    local Air Force museum displays fantastic collection of US aircraft
o Rood Creek Mounds, Georgia – recently federally acquired, not developed in full
o Columbus, Georgia, no remains, area only
o Kolomoki Mounds, Georgia, on Chattahoochee River
o Knoxville, Tennessee, area only – World Exposition site

MISSISSIPPIAN - FLORIDA
o Crystal River Mounds, Florida, occupied 500 BCE - 1400 AD
o Weedon Island, Florida multiple mounds conquered sometime
  between 800 - 1000 AD
o Lake Jackson Mounds, Tallahasee, Florida, on Ochlockonee River,
  Southern Ceremonial federation site, 1200-1500 AD
o Mission San Luis de Apalachee, Talahasee, Florida
o Mount Royal, Florida, on St. John's River, Federation site
o Indian Temple Mound, Fort Walton Beach, Florida one large mound dated 1300's AD

CHEROKEE
Barbara R. Duncan and Brett H. Riggs' "Cherokee Heritage Trails Guidebook" is the essential guide to Cherokee sites, and you really need it if you're planning to visit the area.

CADDO
o Caddoan Mounds, Texas
o Nacadoches, Texas, area only
o (I am informed that the Indian Mounds at the Indian Mounds Recreation Area on the Sabine River in Texas are submerged.)
o Los Adaes, Louisiana
o Natchitoches, Louisiana
o Belcher Mound, Louisiana - small Caddoan site near Great Raft
ALGONQUIN
o Antietam, Maryland
o Pamunky Burial Mounds, Pamunky Indian Reservation, Virginia, on York River
o Sugarloaf, Kempton, Illinois, near Vermillion River on Illinois plains
o Numerous mounds along the Kankakee River, most known only to locals

EFFIGY
See Deborah Morse-Kahn's "Archaeology Parks of the Upper Midwest" for a much much fuller listing.
o Indian Mounds Park, Sheboygan, Wisconsin
o Lizard Mounds, North of Westbend, Wisconsin, 31 effigy mounds
o Fort Aitkinson, Wisconsin
o Madison, Wisconsin
o Wyalusing State Park, Prarie du Chien
o EFFIGY MOUNDS, 200 mounds including animal effigies, on the Mississippi River in Iowa

NORTH – Menominee and Dakota
o Perrot State Park, Trempealeau
o RED WING, Minnesota – beautiful scenery, nice museum, nice site
o Birkmose Park, Hudson, type site for this culture - fine
o MOUNDS PARK, St. Paul, Minnesota – tremendous view at this site, but unfortunately trees have been allowed to grow and obscure part of it.
o SCIENCE MUSEUM OF MINNESOTA, St Paul
o Indian Mounds Park, Rice Lake
o Sioux Falls, South Dakota – on eastern bank of Big Sioux River, 3 miles below falls, and 6 miles above falls

SEARCHING FOR THE CENTER: A TRIP ALONG THE MISSISSIPPI RIVER

What follows is a description of the sites along the Mississippi from Natchez to Cahokia. I suppose if you were flying in on a two week vacation you could come in at New Orleans, well know for its jazz, food, the sights of its French Quarter, and the mansions along its streetcar routes, (thought not as well known for its fine Mayan collections) and proceed to Natchez, perhaps visiting the early mounds on the campus of Louisiana State University at Baton Rouge along the way.

The trip starts at Natchez, Mississippi. While there most certainly were Southern Ceremonial sites further down the Mississippi river, sites which controlled traffic along the Gulf Coast, I don't believe that any of them survived. Natchez has two major sites available, the first of which is the Grand Village of the Natchez, which was one of the villages of the local tribe. The main federation complex was at Emerald Mound just north of town, and it is magnificent. As usual, the nature enthusiasts at the National Park Service have allowed large trees to grow on the periphery of this site, which completely block the view Emerald Mound commanded in Southern Ceremonial times. Natchez was the federation capitol for many of the tribes the Natchez Trace, a trading path which ran from Natchez to Nashville. Natchez has riverboat casino gambling, ante-bellum mansions, and it is a major tourist center. The town fathers are building a convention center, and I believe that that facility will definitely help to ensure their position as a major tourist destination, so watch out for room availability.

From Natchez, if one wanted to head for the Cherokee homeland, or to the Adena or Hopewell sites, and spend more time in these areas, instead of continuing to the center, one could head up the Natchez Trace to Nashville, visiting the sites along it on the way, particularly Harpeth State Park to the west of Nashville on the Tennessee River.

But at this point in our own trip we leave the Mississippi River, to visit the earlier "Hopewellian" site at Marksville. Louisiana has now set up a "Mound Trail", and information about the sites along it should be available in Marksville. From Marksville we head north to the Tunica Treasure House. There were Mississippian survivors of the arrival of the European colonists, and the Tunica Treasure House on the Tunica-Biloxi reservation near Marksville presents an excellent example of a Native people using casino revenues to regain their heritage. Perhaps someday the Tunica will be able to re-acquire their original tribal lands along the Mississippi River near Vicksburg. Heading further north we come to Poverty Point, a fine site from the first periods of the Native American development of high culture.

The route now returns to the Mississippi River at Vicksburg, a small town which is making an effort to duplicate Natchez's success. While Vicksburg's preserved remains are nowhere near those of Natchex, I prefer it to Natchez for its atmosphere: it's just funkier. Vicksburg has riverboat casinos, and a civil war battlefield which includes the wreck of the Union steam powered ironclad riverboat USS Cairo, which was sunk there by the first successful mine. The Cairo has been raised from the river bed and placed under one of the best pieces of architecture I have seen.

While early maps show that the Yazoo tribe, who controlled the Yazoo River, had a major town here on the east side of the river, there are no developed sites. I understand that the mounds across the Mississippi River from Vicksburg at Mound, Louisiana have recently been included in the Louisiana Mounds Trail. I personally enjoy staying at the very inexpensive Dixiana Motel, as it is right across the street from the Louisiana Battery's gun position. From the top of this mound (!) there is a commanding view of the junction of the Yazoo and Mississippi, but once again the naturalists at the National

Park Service have allowed trees to grow and partially obstruct the view.

The next Southern Ceremonial site heading north along the Mississippi River is Winterville Mounds, north of the town of Greenville. The Mississippi state legislature invested in Winterville Mounds and it features a museum whose architecture is some of the best I've seen. But they selected a contractor to run the facility, and whoever it was did not perform, and the facility was shut down when I visited several years ago. The guard graciously allowed me to walk the grounds, and here once again the naturalists have struck, as trees completely block the grounds of this magnificent complex. I don't know if all of the mound area was purchased by the state, or whether a part of it lies in the adjoining fields.

This is delta blues country ("Going down to Rosedale..."), and joints abound, but the racial tension is so thick now you can feel it as though it were fog. Ignore it and enjoy some barbeque and music. Speaking of Rosedale, I am almost certain that a major Southern Ceremonial site has (had?) to exist in this area on the Arkansas side of the river. It would be very interesting to look at high resolution radar images of the National Forest there.

If one were heading west to the pueblos, instead of heading for the center, this would be a good place to begin that journey. That route is covered below, but for the meantime let's stay on the Mississippi River.

Memphis comes next, and the political fate of the sites here is most interesting. Chucalissa, a small reconstructed village occupied from ca. 1200 to 1500 AD, was once Tennessee's biggest tourist attraction, until the opening to the public of Graceland, Elvis Presley's home. Remains of the main federation center survive near to the National Ornamental Metal Museum at DeSoto Park. State archaeologists tried to begin excavation there in 1984, but were completely stopped by Native American activist Gary Whitedeer. Since that time Chucalissa's budget has fallen from over $500,000 to just over $50,000. I find it somewhat ironic that "Chucalissa" means "Abandoned House" in the Choctaw language.

As for accommodation, there are many motels nearby on the road to Graceland. For lunchtime barbeque, I particularly recommend Kay's near to the DeSoto Park federation site: Elvis used to hang out here in the parking lot and flirt with the waitresses. I also must report that while unloading at my motel at 4 in the morning, after a 20 hour drive, I think I saw Elvis. Sorry to say, he was driving a black Jeep Wagoneer suburban battle wagon and weighed about 320 pounds (145.4 kilos for all you metric folk out there).

We now depart to the east of the Mississippi to Pinson Mounds. Pinson is a fine Adena-Hopewell site adopted to later Mississippian architecture. Unfortunately after some 40 years it still has not been landscaped, but it is a fine site to see the transition of cultures. I would be very surprised if a major federation site did not exist near where their rivers meet the Mississippi River at Hales Point, Tennessee.

Heading towards to the junction of the Ohio River and Mississippi River, a minor federation site can be found at Lilburn, west right off of the freeway at New Madrid.

Unfortunately the site is completely undeveloped, and doing so would require considerable effort and expense by the state of Missouri.

As I found out after my visit, there was a large mound in New Madrid at one point, and if it's there now it sure is a well kept secret. It was described as a major federation center to the east of New Madrid, across from Wolf Island, measuring 40 ft high, 200x200 ft at base with 11 small mounds on the 150x150 ft top.

The junction of the Ohio Rivers and Mississippi Rivers, the area which comes next, was one of the most densely settled areas in North America during Native American times. I think Cairo, Illinois serves as a good base when exploring the region. Cairo became a ghost town after rioting following Martin Luther King's assassination - its old riverboat era downtown is completely abandoned today, an this in itself is quite a sight. Cairo is "safe" now, and inexpensive food and lodgings can be found there.

Much of the remains are known to be destroyed, particularly those at Cairo and Mound City. The only way these will ever be "visited" is through computer re-creations, and someone needs to build VRML (Virtual Reality Markup Language) representations of these areas. As for physical remains, the experience is disappointing. Only one small mound remains on private land at Mound City. Towosaghy, while excellently preserved and displayed, is simply a small outlying village. Nearby Wickliffe Mounds is somewhat of a travesty. In the 1930's the height of scientific fashion was to macabrely display skeletons where found. In the 1950's ordinary houses were built to cover these displays, and as a result the site has lost all of its original landscape. In the 1980's a large number of artifacts were stolen from the site, whether by pot hunters or by activists is an open question. The skeletons were later replaced by reproductions. As a whole the experience is disappointing.

Welcome to the center.

A little up the Ohio River from its juncture with the Mississippi River are the Kincaid Mounds, which is the largest surviving complex in the area. It is undeveloped and part of it remains on a privately held parcels; the mounds there can be seen from the road, if one knows where to look. Nearby Fort Massic in Metropolis is a fine restored French-American fort, and if the state of Illinois spends money on Kincaid, they will have a fine tourist attraction.

As it is, Angel Mounds, a little up further still the Ohio River from its juncture with the Mississippi River, is closed much of the time, but is a well developed site. The early important colonial settlement of Vincennes is lies to its north, and besides its later importance in the colonial period, Vincennes has earlier Native American mounds – ask at the Visitor's Center about these. But this is a side trip to the east, with a return to the Mississippi.

If instead heading east to Angel Mounds, we head up the Mississippi River from its juncture with the Ohio River, or else drive over from Vincennes, we come to the American Bottoms, the site of Cahokia, a World Heritage Site. But before we get to Cahokia, there are the colonial French sites of Fort Kaskasia, the French town of Ste.

Genevieve, the Modoc Rock Shelter, and Fort des Chartres. While Fort Kaskasia is not developed, the site has a magnificent view. Ste. Genevieve, the location of Native American salt works, is restored as French colonial town, while Fort des Chartres is completely rebuilt. The Irwin Peithman Museum at Fort des Chartres is named after an excavator of the nearby Modoc Rock Shelter.

Continuing north, Cahokia itself is magnificent, and the state of Illinois is doing a first class job there. Cahokia was a federation center that had at least four other federation centers within its immediate control: one to the north controlling the Illinois River, one to the west controlling the Missouri River, the local center controlling the Cahokia River, and one to the south controlling the Kaskasia River. Illinois has spent $8.7 million on the project so far, and the site has what may be the best museum of its type in the US.
I do have to gripe that once again the "naturalists" are preventing the removal of trees to return the site to its original appearance. This isn't a nature area: it is a world heritage site. Another major problem is that Illinois will have to spend a whole lot more money to secure all of the site, on the order of millions of dollars. For example, one major mound now serves as the base for a warehouse lorry loading dock; another serves as the base for a semi-permanent caravan park. I am of the opinion this would be money well spent, as these cities are some of the most depressed in the US. At one recent point the biggest industry in East St. Louis was exporting the antique bricks produced when its abandoned buildings were torn down for safety reasons.

St. Louis still has some remnants of its golden age existant, particularly from its World's Fair in 1904; these can be found by checking a guidebook before you leave, and St Louis has a major airport offering connecting flights to international hubs.

I had thought that all of the mounds in the East St. Louis complex were destroyed long ago, but I may be in error, as I recently learned excavations are going on there now. There are probably Native American remains at Kaskasia, but if so their existence is kept quiet, and the same is true for any remains of the other complexes guarding the Illinois River. The mounds in St. Louis itself were torn down long ago, and its likely the only way they will ever be "visited" again is though VRML.

JOURNEYS NORTH FROM THE CENTER

From here, one could travel to the north, through Dickerson Mounds (perhaps Havana Mound will soon be developed) on to the Windy City, Chicago, well known for its museums and restaurants, and a very convenient place to fly out of.

Further north from Chicago an eastern route north could take you through Aztlan, and Madison, clean on up to Isle Royale, or one could go north through Effigy Mounds, Red Wing (a powerful site, with a nice museum and a cemetery complex on the casino lands across the river), Birkmose Park, Hudson, and to Mound Park in Sr. Paul/ Minneapolis, another city known for its good living, attractions, and airport.

JOURNEYS EAST FROM THE CENTER

Going to the east from the center at Cahokia, one could take routes in the north going through Hopewell sites and Adena sites, and onward by various routes through to either Washington, DC or New York and their points of interest and connecting flights.

Going to the south east, one could head through Nashville and its music, on to Chattanooga and Etowa and then on to Ocmulgee in Macon, flying out of hot Atlanta with its Underground; or one could continue on to Florida, with its mounds, Seminole refuges, beaches, and Disneyland. Another route from Chattanooga could take you into the Smokey Mountains, with the country music of Pigeon Forge, the spiritual power of Gatlinburg, and the beautiful drive over the mountains to the very nice Cherokee refuge hidden deep within them, continuing south to fly out of Atlanta

These routes can be run in either direction, but be sure to give yourself time to really relax and fully enjoy the experience of the remains and museums along the way. You can always return to the Interstate Highways if you get behind schedule...ughh!

THE TRIP WEST FROM WINTERVILLE TO THE PUEBLOS

The distance to the pueblos is immense, as the most easterly of them lie nearly a third of a continent away from the Mississippi River. If you hope to see any of them in the remainder of a two week vacation, it will be a hurried trip, and you will have to return to the Interstate Highways. You can see the sites, or drive, but you can not do both: remember that North America is a continent. To give you some idea of its size, it takes some 5 days of continuous driving to cross the United States from its Atlantic Ocean coast to its Pacific Ocean coast.

I would simply not advise trying to do it, and instead make a western trip to the pueblos a separate vacation. But since there are always people who want to see everything... There are two routes west, Interstate 20 and Interstate 40. Interstate 20 crosses Texas, and Texas is something of a country in itself. There are many fine airports in Texas from which you can catch flights out of if you decide to visit there.

To visit the pueblos I would take Interstate 40 west. From Greenville and the Winterville Mounds I would go on to Little Rock and the Toltec Mounds, connecting at Little Rock with Interstate 40. On Interstate 40, I would visit Spiro Mounds, and then I would drive like hell for New Mexico.

One first hits pueblo country in Albuquerque, New Mexico. Albuquerque has many ruins itself, and Santa Fe, and Taos, Chaco Canyon, and the infamous Los Alamos are all nearby. One could easily spend the remaining few days of a two week vacation right in this area, and then fly out of Albuquerque. This might be sensible, but then there are people with no sense...

Or one could see a site (but certainly not two) in Albuquerque, and press on to Flagstaff. This would take you past Barringer (Meteor) Crater, and on to Sunset National Monument and the superb Native American remains there, and the Grand Canyon. One could then turn south, visit perhaps one of the many remains along the way, and fly out of Phoenix. Of course there are people with even less sense than that...

Or one could head west for the Hoover Dam and Las Vegas and catch a flight out of there, or for Hollywood, and catch a flight out of Los Angeles. I am almost certain that you will be exhausted if you try to do this, and once again my frank advice is to make a western trip to the pueblos a separate vacation.

NATIVE AMERICAN SITES RIGHT OFF THE COAST TO COAST ROUTE

Few people are aware that major Native American sites lie right off of the freeway connecting Washington, D.C. with the west. These sites make excellent places to stretch your legs and grab a bite to eat. Heading east to west, the first site is the Adena site at Grave Creek Mound, in Moundsville, West Virginia, on the Ohio River. Next is the major Hopewell center at Newark, Ohio. And finally, the Mississippian world heritage site of Cahokia, Illinois is right off the freeway at the Mississippi River. On the way to Los Angeles, Albuquerque, New Mexico, has fine pueblo sites, and the unique remains at Sunset Volcano are one of my favorites.

CHAPTER 18

THE STATE OF NORTH AMERICAN ANTHROPOLOGY

Native American archaeology in the United States is in pretty hopeless shape, one far far worse than that of archaeology in Europe. With the US economy in a chronic state of stagnation, little federal funding is available for site acquisition or site development - in fact so little federal money is available that there are often not even adequate funds to maintain sites already developed.

The same is true on a state level, with some exceptions, in particular Illinois, Florida, and Arkansas. Since most archaeology that does manage to get done is funded on a state level, you get particularly restricted regional views that consider little beyond state boundaries, and often times there are no accepted terms for describing cultures. Furthermore, what terms are accepted are often named after type sites which bear no relation to the center of a culture, i.e."Adena" or "Hopewell".

The first "scientific" publication of Native American remains by Ephram Squier and Davis in 1848 focused on their own surveys in Ohio, and on the Mississippi, and guided developments in the field. As a result general knowledge of settlement patterns and exactly how wide spread cultures were is poor. An example of this is that due to accidents of funding and the non-publication of 18th century scholar C.S. Rafinesque's work, Kentucky is almost a blank slate for most of Native American settlement studies. Alabama nearly matches it.

While there is a lack of funds on the public level, such is not true on the private level. A sizable portion of the population feels that the best way of showing their admiration for the ancient inhabitants of North America is by buying artifacts plundered from ancient sites, and a large number of people have absolutely no qualm with either looting sites on public lands, or with opening graves on private property, and then stealing what they can.

While you might think that Native Americans might put some kind of stop to this trade, a large portion of them, in particular some "activists", are more of a hindrance than help. Native Americans generally hold as a religious belief that human remains should not be disturbed, and thus some are intentionally slandering the archaeologists by publicly calling them "pot hunters", and trying to tie them to this illegal trade.

The result of all of this is that North American archaeology is slowly coming to a standstill. Dating is rotten, and precise dating is usually non-existent. In contrast to Europe or the Middle East, Native American sites were generally not continuously and successively occupied, and many were meeting centers for larger outlying populations. Also, as the Native Americans of this region generally did not use full timber house construction, there are no burn layers to mark destruction. So in the cases where there was successive occupation, there is often no differentiation when different population groups are involved, and no dating, as most earlier excavations were undertaken before carbon 14 was available. There is little hope of improvement, since some Native

American activists are demanding not only the return of human remains, which pretty much precludes the study of population groups, but also the return and immediate re-internment of grave goods, which precludes carbon 14 dating.

Tree ring studies first had their start in the United States in the early 1800's, when colonists counted the rings of trees found on the tops of mounds to try to date the time of their abandonment. It was quickly pointed out that frosts would lead to what was perceived as the lack of a ring (microscopes being generally unavailable), and the technique was abandoned until it was revived in the 1920's working with timber preserved in pueblos in the south west. After a good re-start of tree ring dating, few series were developed for the eastern part of the country, and with tree ring series woefully underdeveloped, and samples rare, this exact dating technique was seldom used.

With Native American activists getting control of human remains, DNA tests to determine population movements has become nearly impossible, and that's if money were available to perform them, which it isn't. Also, it is not in some activists interests to conduct DNA tests, as oft times these DNA tests would show historical tribes to be relative late comers, and thus cast a shadow on tribal claims to lands. This does not only concern claims of Native Americans against European colonizers; for example, the Hopi and Navaho are currently engaged in a dispute over tribal lands which only DNA tests could satisfy.

Since the discovery of human remains leads to mountains of paperwork, the archaeological community as a whole simply does not want to find them. Thus they do not want to excavate any structures which could clear up questions of chronology and population movements. Instead there is an emphasis, which is becoming general in American archaeology, on rescue archaeology, which is funded by the gasoline taxes of the state highway departments, and on the "ecological" excavation of house sites, which it is hoped will not lead to the discovery of human remains. One major problem here is that Native Americans often buried children in or near their houses, and even this type of excavation may be stopped soon as well.

While I can sympathize with some Native Americans views, I can not agree with them. I'm not talking about digging up Mom and Dad here, or Grandma and Grandpa, and stealing their belongings, as indeed happened to some people. And I'm not talking about leaving human remains on display as some kind of freak show, which was considered the height of the scientific method during the 1930's at some sites. And having done it before, I can tell you that for me, at least, handling human remains is not something I enjoy. The thought of excavating an impact blast zone site in Harrapan region of India, where blasted and burned skeletons fill the streets by the thousands, makes me shudder.

But the living have rights as well as the dead. We, the living, have a need to know when the climate failed and the people starved to death; we need to know which diseases arose and spread and killed them; when it rained and flooded and they were washed away and drowned; when the earth quaked, or erupted, and buried them alive. And we have a need to know when the Unktena, the sky snakes, the asteroids and comets, hit their lands and killed them. I suppose that Native Americans stand as good a chance as anyone of dying in the next impact event, and I'm simply unwilling to enter into this kind of suicide pact with some of the activists. We need to know how man survived. Not excavating is the same as plucking out one's eyes.

THE DEVELOPMENT OF NORTH AMERICAN ARCHAEOLOGY

It is little wonder that the needs of the living and the scientific method used to satisfy those needs bear little weight with many Native American activists. European colonists in North America found it impossible to believe that ancestors of the peoples who they had recently either killed or run off their land had built the remains before them, and they spent decades trying to prove that someone else did it. In fact, a good number of the "scientists" in the early United States did their best to establish a bizarre Darwinian rationale to give moral justification for further genocide, in a manner very similar to that used in Nazi Germany. Little wonder then that some Native American activists lump archaeologists together with the pot hunters.

The source for most of this trouble lies in the sad fate of the brilliant 18th century scholar C.S. Rafinesque. Perfectly fluent in six languages, and with a complete command of the natural sciences such as they were at the time, Rafinesque applied himself to unraveling the mysteries of the ancient Americans. Having gained a thorough knowledge of European archaeology, again such as it was then, Rafinesque made the not unreasonable assumption that the North American earthworks had been built at the same times as similar works had been built in Europe and North Africa. Rafinesque assembled a catalogue of the Native American remains, and surveyed a number of them himself. He poured through the Native American myths and legends that were available at the time, and gathered similar materials from Central America, Siberia, and China. Well versed in Latin and Greek, Rafinesque poured through the classics looking for any relevant information, with the Atlantean myths and other such tales providing what they could.

Within this framework, Rafinesque fit all of the data he had acquired. However bizarre Rafinesque's work may seem to us today, the one thing that Rafinesque did not do was to belittle the role of the Native Americans. They may have been Atlanteans to him, but they were still Native Americans. Unfortunately Rafinesque died before he could publish his masterpiece.

Though his manuscript remained unpublished, even during his lifetime, Rafinesque made his work freely available, and it was used, particularly by those who were interested in dispossessing the Native Americans of their lands. First among these must be John Haywood of Tennessee, Rafinesque's contemporary, who in a bizarre twist used some of Rafinesque's material to deny Cherokee, Kushita (Creek), and Chikasaw land claims.

Those further interested in the development of North American archaeology may wish to check out "Mound Builders of Ancient America, the Archaeology of a Myth", by Robert Silverberg, which while it adequately catalogues the outrages, fails entirely in its assessment of Rafinesque's role in providing the fodder for them.

"MOUNDS"

Given this state of affairs, it is not surprising that in nearly all of the literature most early Native American peoples are popularly lumped together as "Mound Builders", as though they had nothing better to do for a couple of millennia than pile up dirt. This term obscures fundamental distinctions in the same way that referring to the British, French, German, Spanish, and Italians as "Brick Builders" would.

As mentioned elsewhere, earth was the construction material, and different Native American peoples used it at differing times to build simple graves, group graves, housing platforms, meeting place enclosures, observatories, defensive walls and moats, household defensive platforms, and temples. When these earth structures decayed they became mounds. Significantly, differing groups of early Native Americans in the Barbeque Zone, the south east of the continent, also used stone for some constructions at different times, but these constructions are poorly understood.

THE DEVELOPMENT OF NORTH AMERICAN MYTHOGRAPHY AND LINGUISTICS

As for mythography, while the first Europeans to contact the Native Americans made some efforts to record their cultures, the European diseases quickly took their toll, and then colonization proper began. During this period the main items of interest were the locations of rivers, paths, mountains, and towns, and how many warriors each town had, who they had recently fought, and who were their present enemies.

By the time the Europeans had stopped killing the Native Americans and started to record what they had to say, the tribes were in a thoroughly decimated and scattered state. Following Franz Boas, analysis was strictly forbidden, and a simple recording of the myths was the prime focus. The result was a mythography which focused on supposedly universal "themes" which were used to catalogue the myths, and the coherent world views of the different tribes were lost among these "themes". There was nearly no work done on migration myths, and as one might expect work done on myth development focused on post-contact myth development.

In the second generation the two best ethnographers were James Mooney and John Swanton, who both were thoroughly enamored with the people they were studying, Mooney the Cherokee, and Swanton the Creek. Neither had much mastery of the archaeology of their regions, and this for the most part was in a pretty undeveloped state during their time. This has had serious consequences beyond the study of population movements, in particular Swanton's ascription to the Creek of Peter Martyr's very complete description of Southern Ceremonial peoples, which Martyr gained via direct interview with Spanish explorers. While French descriptions of the Natchez Southern Ceremonial people are widely used today, thanks to Swanton's error Peter Martyr's incredibly detailed account of Southern Ceremonial peoples is for all purposes unknown; this is a blunder of the first magnitude. This extremely important account clears up a number of baffling problems, and moves a number of concepts from hypothesis to fact.

As for linguistics, often times the languages of tribes were "recorded" after they had been absorbed by other tribes, and thus the languages of those tribes were ascribed to them. This assignation was done even in cases where the absorbing tribe and absorbed tribe had earlier been fierce enemies. Since the lack of firm recordings did not discourage the linguists, it should come as no surprise that the lack of a firm archaeological record of migration did nothing to discourage them either. As always, linguistics proceeded apace. Nonetheless, one trudges on.

USE OF EUROPEAN CONTACT RECORDS

As for tribal locations, and thus tribal migrations, a hot debate is going on about the exact route of Spanish conquistador Hernando de Soto's through the Southeast. While some are trying to stop the debate by pointing to Swanton as an authority, field truth shows the currently accepted reconstruction of de Soto's route to be defective, at least in some particulars. The role in Native American commerce of the major copper and mica deposit in the Bald Mountains is ignored by all sides in this debate.

Another particular deficit is that the histories of Tennessee and Kentucky are widely represented as having started with the arrival of English colonists in the areas, and the French traders' records of their arrival there first and their contacts with tribes are generally ignored. Ignoring these French records of tribal locations naturally leads to a lack of understanding of tribal movements. Many Spanish contact records still lie undiscovered in the Spanish colonial archives, and are only now beginning to emerge. Swedish colonial archives for their Pennsylvania settlements remain undisturbed.

HOPE FOR THE FUTURE

The one encouraging item in all of this is that some Native Americans are now beginning to study archaeology, and some Native American peoples are beginning to take over responsibility for the care and study of their own people's archaeological remains. Respect for the dead does not have to be opposed to archaeology, and indeed, when remains are disturbed by modern construction, archaeology is the only way to fully recover those remains for re-internment. My own thinking is that the excavation of human remains should be conducted like an autopsy, and no one incapable of excavating them in this way should be allowed to do it. If enough money is made available, studies can be done, and the remains then re-interred to pass into time.

But that's just my opinion.

ACKNOWLEDGEMENTS

I apologize for what little is here. I have done as well as I could to determine the effects of asteroid and comet impacts upon the Native American peoples from what little has survived of their histories.

Thanks are in order to some of the many who helped me along the way, though certainly none of these kind people can be held responsible for the thoughts expressed in this book. While one may always hope for a civilized discussion based on evidence, as such things are unusual these days, and are more the exception than the rule, let me state again, given the controversial topics touched on here: None of these kind people can be held responsible for the views which I put forward in this book.[1] To those whose opinions I have offended, I offer my apologies. I have called it as I saw it, and written this book respecting the evidence instead of opinion.

First off, I need to thank Benny Peiser, the moderator of the Cambridge Conference, and Bob Kobres, the Cambridge Conference archivist until 2004. There were many others who worked through the historical materials on asteroid and comet impact well before my own efforts: Victor Clube, Bill Napier, Bob Kobres, Timo Niroma, Phil Burns, Duncan Steele, John Lewis, Mike Baillie, Don Yeomans and his team, including Kevin Yau Kevin and Paul Weissman for the Chinese materials, Bruce Masse, Dr Marie Agnes Courty, and many others. Hopefully I have mentioned everyone else in the footnotes and properly acknowledged their work. I also need to thank here Scott Manley and Raoul Lannoy for their help with astronomical materials.

Among the archaeologists, I certainly need to thank Jack Edlund, of the Fredericksburg area chapter of the Archaeological Society of Virginia, who introduced me to Payson Sheets, who first alerted me to Dr Peiser's work and the Cambridge Conference; Lee Vick, docent at Cahokia Mounds, the best docent I've ever come across; Dave Griffing, archaeologist at Poverty Point; Kathleen Bergeron of Marksville, and as a member of the Houma Tribe an eloquent spokesperson for a Native American view on anthropology; M. from Tennessee, whose anonymity will be protected; Bob Masse again, this time as an archaeologist instead of as an ethnographer, Harry Haynes of the Museum of the Middle Appalachians in Saltville, Virginia, Ned Jenkins at Fort Jackson, Linda Derry of the Cahawba Center for Archaeology; Doug Kullen for his help with southern Lake Michigan remains; David King for his help with the Kankakee River valley remains; Jim Woodring for his help with the Venango and Shenengo river valleys' remains; David S. Wiggins of the NPS and Nancy Woolworth for their help with the materials from the St Paul area; Merle Frommelt for his fine presentation of Effigy Mounds and skilful demonstration of the atlatl; Robert Boszhardt and the staff of the Mississippi Valley Archaeology Center at the University of Wisconsin, La Crosse campus for their help with the Trempealeau petroglyphs,; and Will Conway for his help with the Brownsville remains.

Acknowledgements

Among the librarians I need to especially thank Elizabeth Wills and David Crider of the Birmingham Public Library; Jim Reece, April Mitchell, and Suzette Raney of the staff of the Chattanooga Library; Debbie Zingaro and Elizabeth Seibert of the Conneaut library; Richard Anderson of the Danville Public Library; Tim Seman of the Public Library of Youngstown and Mahoning County; Eric Andserson of the Franklin Public Library, Barb Campbell of Wisconsin's Hurley Travel Information Center, Sharon Schroedeer of the library of The Goodhue County Historical Society, Red Wing, Minnesota; and the staff of the Newberry LIbrary for their help with materials from the Ayre collection, and Mr. Ayre himself for gathering these materials together in the first place.

Among the Native Americans who I have had the pleasure of talking with during the course of this work, besides Kathleen Bergeron of the Huoma, I need to mention Quiet Crow, of the Eastern Shawnee Remnant; Wayne Simmons, of the Cherokee, whose help with the western Cherokee was invaluable; and the late Walter Crouch, Choctaw astronomer and Cambridge Conference participant, whose controversial views on the Red Paint people inspired me to form my own. May his path be easy. I also greatly enjoyed the hospitality shown by the Ho Chunk of the Dells at their pow-wow.

For their moral support I need to thank Yarley Brohr and Christopher Ippolitto of Fredericksburg, Virginia. For help with my PC I need to thank Robert Gausman and Ann Brunnelle of Culpepper, Virginia, and for their aid and hospitality, Will and Danni Hemphill of Momensk, Illinois At Adventures Unlimited Press, special thanks go to David Hatcher Childress, his wife and colleague Jennifer, Mary (the Rock) Gash and Greg Gash, Pam and Clark (Mac guru) Childress (no relation to Dave), and Johann Wallette (all around help), and the staff of Sgt Pepper's Bar and Grill.

I would also like to thank mechanic John F. Marquess of Frei Chevrolet in Marquette, Michigan for his great work in keeping my car going.

Lastly, I need to thank Virginia Malone and Kathy Collins for their help in editing the manuscript.

Finally, I need to apologize to those many who helped me but whose names I have misplaced. Hopefully this book will see a second edition, and these particularly grievous errors may be corrected in it wherever they have occurred.

For Grandmother

E.P. Grondine
Kempton, Illinois
June, 2005

(Footnotes)

[1] I expect that some Native American activists will suddenly be surprised to find themselves in alliance with some of the more conservative archaeologists in their alarm at what has been written here. My experience has been that the more any people was traumatized in the European conquest, the more they lost their own history, and the more their need to create a new one to satisfy themselves. For every people, I have always used the earliest recorded history which can be verified by archaeological remains, where it survived.

I also expect to hear complaints from those who have argued from what may be a few scattered trade goods that the early appearance of metal working in North America was the result of a large European presence. While this notion satisfies a certain romantic impulse, to state that Native Americans were incapable of working metal themselves and trading it is racist in the extreme. Whenever these authors can point to the remains of a very early European colony in the Americas, I will be all ears, as will everyone else, but I doubt if any such colony will ever be found. This hypothetical early European presence is not to be confused with later possible European crossings to North America to obtain large trees for the manufacture of ocean going dugouts, a subject which was not commented on at all in this book.

Finally, I expect to hear from the remaining few astronomers who vociferously claim on the basis of absolutely no data at all that comet impacts with the Earth occur very, very, very rarely. While this may be true in the long run, it was not true for the recent past few millennia, as the evidence set out in this book indicates. While I can hope these astronomers are right about the odds in the long run, I doubt it. I suppose it is the skeptic in me.

Acknowledgements

DAVID CUSICK'S Sketches of

THE ANCIENT HISTORY OF THE SIX NATIONS

Brought into modern usage by E.P. Grondine
©copyright 2004 E.P. Grondine

THE AUTHOR'S PREFACE

I have long been waiting in hope that someone of my people, someone who has received an English education, would undertake the work of giving a sketch of the Ancient History of the Six Nations.

As I found no one who seemed to agree in this matter, after some hesitation I determined to commence that work myself. But I found that history itself involved with fables; and besides, examining myself, I found so small an education that it was impossible for me to compose the work without encountering much difficulty. After considering various reasons, I abandoned the idea.

Later, however, I took up a resolution to continue this work, for which I had taken great pains, first in procuring the materials, and then in translating the work into the English language.

I have endeavored to throw some light on the history of the original population of this country, a history which I believe has never been recorded. I hope this little work will be acceptable to the public.

DAVID CUSICK
Tuscarora Village, June 10th, 1825

THE EDITOR'S PREFACE

In the course of my research on other matters, I read David Cusick's Ancient History, and was delighted to find that it accurately recorded in fine style the Real People's memories of events more than 10,000 years old.

Though incredibly difficult to read, Cusick's work was accessible to me, as I had long been working with the writings of people who speak English as a second language, as well as with the writings of people who spoke and wrote the English of some 200 years ago.

As the thought struck me that a much larger audience would be able to enjoy our author's remarkable work, if only it were brought into modern usage, I proceeded to do so. Aside from correcting as little as possible the vocabulary and grammar of his work, the printed copy of Cusick's manuscript also reveals some of the editorial changes which he himself made, in particular as to his organization of the material he collected. Thus it also seemed proper to me to bring related materials together. I hope that those who work with the original will find that I have not taken too great a liberty here, but instead will keep in mind the general audience for which this edition is intended.

Finally, Cusick alluded to but omitted some materials, materials available in reliable form from other people. I have inserted those materials at the appropriate places in the History, carefully noting where they have been taken from.

My hope in doing all of this still remains that a larger public will be able to more fully enjoy the product of David's tremendous effort.

E.P. Grondine
Kempton, Illinois, September 1ˢᵗ, 2004

A NOTE ON CUSICK'S CHRONOLGY

From a passage of Cusick's concerning the Five Nation's final war with the Eries, it can be determined that his chronology was keyed to the Dutch appearing in the lands of the Five Nations, which was not the year Columbus discovered America, as Cusick thought.

The Five Nations kept wampum, belts of fine beadwork, which served as aids to memory in the recollection of events and myths. In the case of some wampum for historical events, every year a bead would be added to wampum, so that the exact year of their occurrence could be remembered. However, Cusick gave each of his Kings a reign of 50 years, and it thus appears that his informants used wampum which contained summaries of events for 50 year periods of time.

THE FOUNDATION OF THE GREAT ISLAND, NOW NORTH AMERICA; THE BIRTH OF THE TWO TWINS, AND THE CREATION OF THE UNIVERSE

Cusick preserves a very early Tuscarora version of the creation myths, one which contains no references to corn or other cultagens, as do the later northern versions. It is clear that these northern versions must have been modified into their present forms sometime after the introduction of corn ca. 100 CE.

Among the ancients there were two worlds in existence. The Lower World was in a great darkness, and it was the possession of a Great Monster, while the Upper World was inhabited by mankind.

And there in the Upper World a woman conceived, and would give birth to twin boys. When the time of her labor drew near, her situation seemed to produce a great distress in her mind, and she was induced by some of her relations to lay herself on a mattress which they prepared, so as to gain refreshment for her wearied body.

But while she was asleep, that very place sank down towards the dark Lower World. The monsters of the great water were alarmed at the appearance of her descending to the Lower World; in consequence of which all the species of the creatures were immediately collected into the place where it was expected she would land.

Outer space was often considered as dark water among many peoples, a type of ocean, and the monsters were the comets which they often observed. For a description of one of these monsters as a fiery dragon with a white tale see the Seneca version of the creation preserved by J. N. B. Hewitt.

When the monsters were assembled, they discussed the situation among themselves, and one of them was quickly appointed to search the great deep in order to procure some earth, if it could be obtained. Accordingly the monster descended; and he succeeded, and he returned to the gathering place.

Another requisition was presented, "Who can keep the woman secure from the terrors of the great water?" But none was able to comply, except a large Turtle, who came forward and offered them a proposal to endure her lasting weight, which they accepted.

The woman was as yet descending from a great distance. The Turtle executed upon the spot where she would land, and a small quantity of earth was varnished onto the back part of the Turtle. The woman alighted on the seat prepared, and she received a satisfaction. While holding her, the Turtle increased every moment and became a considerable island of earth, apparently one covered with small bushes.

Cusick was well aware of the phallic nature of this turtle (penis). The curvature of the shell of the Great Turtle explains the curvature of the Earth, which man can be viewed from high mountain tops.

The woman remained in that state of unlimited darkness until she was overtaken by the labor to which she was subject. While she was in the limits of distress, one of the infants in her womb was moved by an evil idea, and he was determined to pass out under the side of his mother's arm. Meanwhile the other infant endeavored in vain

335

to prevent him from accomplishing his plan. The woman was in a painful condition during the time of their struggle, and the infants entered the dark world by compulsion, and their mother died in a few moments.

Now the Twins had the power of sustenance without a nurse to feed them, and they remained in the dark regions. After a time the Turtle increased in size to that of a Great Island, and the infants grew up.

Now one of the Twins possessed an insolence of character, and he was named ENIGONHAHETGEA, which is to say, the Bad Mind. The other youth possessed a gentle disposition, and he was named ENIGORIO, which is to say, the Good Mind.

The Good Mind was not content to remain in the darkness, and he was anxious to create a great light in the dark world. But the Bad Mind was desirous that the world should remain in the state it was. The Good Mind determined to prosecute his designs, and therefore he commenced the work of creation.

At first he took his dead mother's head, of which he created an orb, and established it in the center of the firmament. And the orb became of a very superior nature to bestow light to the new world, and it became what is now the Sun.

And the Good Mind took the remnant his mother's body and formed another orb, which was inferior to the light of the Sun, and it became what is now the Moon. In this orb a cloud of legs appeared, to prove it was the body of the good mind of his mother. The former orb was to give light to the day, and the latter orb to give light to the night.

And the Good Mind also created numerous spots of light, the stars, and these were to regulate the days, nights, seasons, and the years, etc.

Now whenever the light from the Good Mind's new creations extended to the dark world, the monsters there were displeased and immediately concealed themselves further in the deep, lest they should be discovered by some human beings.

This passage describes the recession of comets from the inner solar system back out into deep space. During the period when these myths were being formed the Earth was being impacted by fragments of Comet Encke, with 'monsterous' effects.

The Good Mind continued with his work of creation, and he formed numerous creeks and rivers on the Great Island. And then he created numerous species of animals, from the smallest to the greatest, to inhabit the forests; and he created fishes of all kinds to inhabit the waters.

THE CREATION OF MANKIND

After the Good Mind had created the universe, he was in doubt respecting some being to possess the Great Island. And he formed in his own likeness two images from the dust of the ground, one male and one female, and by his breathing into their nostrils he gave them the living souls. And he named them EAGWEHOWE, which is to say, the Real People.

And for their maintenance the Good Mind gave the Great Island all the game animals; and he appointed thunder to water the earth by frequent rains, but only those rains agreeable to the nature of the system. After the Good Mind did this, the Great Island became fruitful, and the vegetation afforded the animals their subsistence.

Now while his brother the Good Mind was making the universe, the Bad Mind went throughout the Great Island, and he made numerous high mountains, and falls of water, and great cliffs. And the Bad Mind also created various reptiles which would be injurious to mankind. After the Bad Mind had done all of this, the Good Mind restored the Great Island to its former condition.

THE GOOD MIND APPOINTS THE THUNDERS TO PROTECT THE PEOPLE FROM THE BAD MIND'S SERPENTS (COMETS)

The following passage is adapted from the Mohawk version of the creation myth given by Seth Newhouse to J.N.B. Hewitt and preserved by him in his book on Iroquoian Cosmology.

Then, truly, during that time when the Good Mind was traveling again to inspect again the things which he had finished on this earth, then he saw another man.

And the Good Mind addressed the man, saying, "What are you doing as you go on your way?" The other said, "It seemed that it became necessary for me to see you." The Good Mind replied, "That is undoubtedly true."

The other person answered and said, "I desire that you should allow me to live. If you will consent to my request, I will give assistance to you: I will watch over the peoples' bodies, and I will also give them life and support, and moreover I will continue to defend the people who you created."

The Good Mind said: "Let me see what kind of power you have." Thereupon the man, whose name of old is Hi'non' [Thunder], started upon a run and went up into the clouds. Now, truly, rumblings were heard: it thundered in the clouds, and lightning was also sent out, and moreover so many flashes shot forth that they seemed as though only one from their rapidity.

So then the man descended to where the Good Mind was standing, and he said: "Now assuredly you saw what kind of power I have." The Good Mind said: "It is indeed true that you are able to do just as you told me. Are you also able to regularly throw water on this earth as the summers come?" The man answered, saying: "I am able to do so." Then the Good Mind said: "So then let me see how you will do this," and the man replied: "Yo'; so be it."

Now again he ascended on high to where the clouds are present. Now again it thundered and the lightning flashed, but besides this the clouds became thick and black, and then the rain came forward. From the sea the rain came over the dry land, and it was marvelous as it came along.

Then of course the rain passed, and the man again returned to the place where the Good Mind was. The Good Mind then spoke to him, saying: "What you are able to do is satisfactory. It will indeed come to pass, following closely the course pointed out by you in your request. Indeed, from now on it will be your duty to travel continually, for it was you yourself who requested this. Do not then ever fail to do your duty.

"You must, of course, be ever vigilant; if at whatever time there come dangers to the lives of men because of great serpents (comets) moving from place to place in the depths of this earth and the sea (space); if it comes to pass that at some time these great serpents desire to seize the people as they travel together from place to place, you must at once kill such serpents, and when you kill them, they will be that on which you will feed. Other animals also, equal in evil power to these, all such shall fare like the serpents. You will have to watch these forever, and have them as your adversaries.

"Now then, of course, I have finished this matter. Such is the office which you have assumed. People will name you "Our Grandfather whose voice is customarily uttered in diverse places.'"

Then, indeed, the two parted company.

THE BAD MIND TRAPS THE ANIMALS

Continuing with Cusick's account…

The Good Mind now accomplished the works of creation, not withstanding that the imagination of his brother the Bad Mind was continually evil. And the Bad Mind attempted to enclose all the animals of game in the earth, so as to deprive them from mankind. But the Good Mind released them from their confinement, and the animals were dispersed. But the traces they made remain on the rock near the cave where they were closed in by the Bad Mind.

Undoubtedly the preceding passage was offered as an explanation for the fossils which people had noticed. Given the Bad Mind's connotation as "Flint", to some degree this tale may also preserve a memory of hunting large game animals in their cave shelters.

THE BAD MIND CREATES THE PEOPLE TO THE SOUTH

The Bad Mind proceeded further in his desires and he made two images of clay in the form of mankind; but while he was giving them existence they became apes.

And when it became apparent to the Bad Mind that he did not have the power to

338

create mankind, he was envious against his brother; and again he made two beings of clay. The Good Mind discovered his brother's contrivances, and aided in giving them living souls.

It is said in an account which I believe to be fiction that these beings had the most knowledge of good and evil. It is also said that the beings became civilized people, and that they made their residence in the south part of the Great Island. It is said that afterwards they were destroyed by barbarous nations, and their fortifications remain ruined unto this day.

THE END OF THE ICE AGE Ca. 8,350 BCE

The following passage is adapted from the Mohawk version of the creation myth given by Seth Newhouse to J.N.B. Hewitt and preserved by Hewitt in his book on Iroquoian Cosmology. The "Bluebird" makes sense as a description of a comet.

It came to pass that the Good Mind, as he traveled from place to place, after a while went along the shore of the lake (Lake Ontario). There, not far away, he saw the Bad Mind making for himself a bridge of ice across the lake, a bridge which already extended far out on the water.

Thereupon the Good Mind went to the place where the Bad Mind was working, and when he arrived there, he said: "Tawi' skaron', what is this that you are doing for yourself?" The Bad Mind replied, saying: "I am making a pathway for myself." And then, pointing in the direction toward which he was building the bridge, he added: "In that direction there is a land where dwell great animals of fierce dispositions. As soon as I complete my pathway to that other land, thereafter they will habitually come over. Along this pathway they will be in the habit of coming across the lake to eat the flesh of human beings who are about to dwell on the earth."

So then the Good Mind said to the Bad Mind: "You should stop the work which you are doing. Surely the intention of your mind is not good." The Bad Mind replied, saying: "I will not cease from what I am doing, for, of course, it is good that these great animals shall be in the habit of coming here to eat the flesh of human beings who will dwell here."

So of course the Bad Mind did not obey and cease from building the bridge for himself, and thereupon the Good Mind turned back and reached dry land. Now along the shore of the sea grew shrubs, and he saw a bird sitting on a limb of one. The bird belonged to the class of birds which we call the bluebirds. And the Good Mind then said to this Bluebird: "You shall kill a cricket. You shall remove one hind leg from it, and you shall hold it in your mouth, and you shall go there to the very place where the Bad Mind is working. You shall land very near to the place where he is working, and you shall cry out." And the bluebird replied, saying: "Yo""

Thereupon the bluebird truly did seek for a cricket, and after a while it found one, and it killed it, too. Then it pulled out one of the cricket's hind legs and put it into its mouth to hold, and then it flew, winging its way to the place where the Bad Mind was at work making his ice bridge.

There it landed, near to him at his task. And of course it then shouted, "Kwe', kwe', kwe', kwe', kwe'."

At which the Bad Mind raised up his head and looked, and he saw the bluebird sitting there. He believed from what he saw that the bluebird held in its mouth the thigh of a man, and also that its mouth was wholly covered with blood.

It was then that the Bad Mind sprang up at once and fled. As fast as he ran the bridge of ice which he was making dissipated.

THE FINAL BATTLE BETWEEN THE GOOD MIND AND THE BAD MIND

Continuing with Cusick's account...

By now the Good Mind realized that his brother the Bad Mind was at variance with his works of creation, and that he did not feel disposed to favor any of his proceedings; and he gave his brother admonitions about his future state.

Afterwards the Good Mind proposed to his brother the Bad Mind to accompany him as he inspected the game, '&c.. But when they were a short distance from their nominal residence, the Bad Mind became so unmanly that he could not accompany his brother anymore.

The Bad Mind then offered a challenge to his brother, the Good Mind, and he proposed that whoever would gain the victory in it should govern the universe; and he appointed a day to meet for the contest. The Good Mind was willing to submit to his brother's offer, and he pretended to enter into a reconciliation with him; wherein he falsely mentioned that by whipping him with wild flag leafs it would destroy his temporal life; and the Good Mind also earnestly solicited his brother to notice the instrument of death, which he manifestly pointed out: if one used deer horns to beat his body, he would expire.

The 'Bad Mind' is also called 'Flint', and the battle here alludes to working flints with deer horns to make spear points. The Good Mind is also called 'Sapling', and the use of wild flag leaves and in other versions cattail plants must be some kind of allusion to either using flags to clear underbrush, or to using cattails to tie spear points to spears.

On the appointed day the engagement commenced, and it lasted for two days. After pulling up the trees and the mountains as does the track of a terrible tornado, at last the Good Mind succeeded in deceiving his brother with the flag leaves, and gained the victory by using the deer horns, as mentioned the instrument of death. And the Good Mind crushed the Bad Mind into the earth.

And the last words uttered by the Bad Mind were that he would have equal power over the souls of mankind after death; and he sank down to eternal doom, and became the Evil Spirit. After this tumult the Good Mind repaired to the battle ground, and then he visited the people and retired from the earth. .

THE COMING OF DEATH, AND THE CREATION OF THE CLANS

The following passage is adapted from Edward Cornplanter's telling of the Coming of Death, preserved by Arthur C. Parker in The Code of Handsome Lake

When the world was first made, man did not know that some time they must die. In those days everyone was happy and neither men, nor women, nor children were afraid of anything. They did not think of anything but doing what pleased them.

Then one day a prominent man was found on the grass. He was limp and he did not breathe. The people who saw him did not know what had happened. The man was not asleep, because he did not awaken. When they placed him on his feet, he fell like a tanned skin. They tried many days to make him stand up, but he would not. After a number of days he started to rot.

A woman said that the man must be wrapped up and put in the limbs of a tree. So the men did it, and after a while the flesh dropped from the bones, while some dried on. No one knew what had happened to cause such a thing.

Soon afterward a child was found in the same condition. It had no breath and it could not stand. It was not asleep, so they said. The people thought it was strange that a girl should act this way. So she was also laid in a tree.

Now many others did these things, and no one knew why. No one thought that he himself would do such a thing.

There was one wise man who thought much about these things, and he had a dream. While he slept the Good Mind came to him and spoke. He slept a long time but the other people noticed that he breathed slowly.

Now after a time this man rose up, and his face was very solemn. He called the people together in a council and addressed them.

The wise man spoke, and he said, "The Good Mind made every good thing and prepared the earth for people. Now it appears that strange events have happened. A good word has come to me from the Good Mind. He says that every person must do as you have seen the other persons do. They have died. They do not breathe. It will be the same with all of you. Your minds are strong, and the Good Mind made them that way so that you could endure everything that has happened. So then do not be downcast when I tell you that you all must die.

"Listen further to what I say. The name of the one who steals away your breath is S`hondowêk'owa. He has no face and does not see any one. You can not see him until he grasps you. Sometimes he just comes for a visit, and sometimes he stays with us until many are dead. Sometimes he takes away the best men and women and passes by the lesser ones. I was not told why he does this thing.

"S`hondowêk'owa wants to destroy every person, and he will continue to work forever. Every one who hears me, and every one not yet born, will die. There is more about you

341

than the living. Any moment you may be snatched by S`hondowêk'owa, he who works in the thick darkness.

"You must now divide yourselves into nine bands, five to sit on one side of the fire, and four on the other, and these bands shall care for their members. You must seek out all good things and instruct one another, and those who do good things will see when they die the place where the Maker of all things lives."

THE CREATION OF THE MASK PRIESTHOOD

The following passage is adapted from the Mohawk version of the creation myth given by Seth Newhouse to J.N.B. Hewitt and preserved by him in his book on Iroquoian Cosmology.

Now then, as it was the custom of the Good Mind to travel, he met a man.

The Good Mind asked the man: "What are you doing as you travel?" And the man replied, saying: "I have come inspecting the Earth, to see whether it remains just as I created it."

The Good Mind replied, saying: "Truly, indeed, this is a marvelous matter about which you are now on your way, because assuredly it was I, myself, who completed the Earth." The man answered, and said: "Not at all; for I myself have completed it."

Whereupon the Good Mind replied, saying: "Well then, if that is so, let it be made plain. At our two backs, at a distance, there is a range of high mountains of rock, whose rocks are so perpendicular that it appears like a wall. You must move them here close to your body. If, perhaps, you are able to do this, it will then be certain that you did indeed create the earth; if you will only speak, telling that mountain range to move itself here."

Thereupon the man said: "Thus it will come to pass." Then he called out, saying: "Come, mountain range, move yourself here. Stand beside my body." But the mountain range remained there unchanged; it did not move.

The Good Mind then spoke and said: "There, that is exactly what I have been saying, that you did not create the Earth." The man again replied, saying: "Well then, prove that you created the Earth. Come then, move that rock mountain here."

The Good Mind replied, and said: "Thus will I do." Thereupon he called out to the range of mountains. He said: "Come, move yourself here." Then, truly, it moved itself from there. And it came to a standstill close to his body, at his back: its cliff even lightly grazed his shoulder blades.

The Good Mind then said to the man: "Now turn yourself around and look where the range of mountains is." Whereupon the man turned about, and the rock struck his nose, and his nose became bent.

Then the man spoke, saying: "Truly, indeed, you created the Earth. It was not at all I who did it. If, then, you will consent that I may live, I will forever continue to aid you. At all times I will protect your people who are to dwell on this earth."

The Good Mind replied, saying: "Truly it shall thus come to pass. People shall forever call you "Mask", and also "Grandfather"."

THE SAINT LAWRENCE IMPACT

Continuing with Cusick's account…

About this time a great, horned serpent appeared on Lake Ontario. The serpent produced diseases and many people died, but by the aid of thunderbolts the monster was compelled to retire.

Then a blazing star fell into a fort situated on the Saint Lawrence and destroyed the people. This event was considered as a warning of their destruction.

After a time a war broke out among the northern families, a war which continued until they had utterly destroyed each other. The Great Island once again became the possession of fierce animals.

ANOTHER ACCOUNT OF THE SAINT LAWRENCE IMPACT

The following passages are taken from Tuscaroran Chief Elias Johnson's LEGENDS, TRADITIONS, AND LAWS OF THE IROQUOIS, OR SIX NATIONS, AND HISTORY OF THE TUSCARORA INDIANS.

A Great Horned Serpent also next appeared on Lake Ontario who, by means of his poisonous breath, caused disease, and caused the death of many.

At length the old women congregated, with one accord, and prayed to the Great Spirit that he would send their grandfather, the Thunder, who would get to their relief in this, their sore time of trouble, while at the same time burning tobacco as burned offerings. And so finally the monster was compelled to retire in the deeps of the lake by thunderbolts.

Before this calamity was forgotten another happened. A blazing star fell into their fort, situated on the banks of the St. Lawrence, and destroyed the people. Such a phenomenon caused a great panic and consternation and dread, which they regarded as ominous of their entire destruction. Not long after this prediction of the blazing star it was verified.

These tribes, who were held together by feeble ties, fell into dispute and wars among themselves, which were pursued through a long period, until they had utterly destroyed each other, and so reduced their numbers that the lands were again overrun with wild beasts.

At this period there were six families who took refuge in a large cave in a mountain, where they dwelled for a long time. The men would come out occasionally to hunt for food. This great cave was situated at or near the falls of the Oswego River.

The Holder of the Heavens then came and extricated these six families from the subterranean bowels and confines of the mountain. The people always looked to this divine messenger, who had power to assume various shapes as emergency demanded, as the friend and patron of their nation.

This company were a particular body, which called themselves of One Household. Of these there were six families, and they entered into an agreement to preserve the chain of alliance which should not be extinguished under any circumstance.

THE MIGRATIONS OF THE 6 FAMILIES

From the list of families given in the accounts of the first battles with the Giants, which from archaeological evidence can be shown to have occurred in fact ca. 4,500 BCE, I have placed Cusick's migration account this point.

By some inducement a body of people was concealed in the mountain at the falls named Kusk-Ehsawkich, which are now called the falls at 'Oswego'. When the people were released from the mountain, they were visited by the TARENYAWAGON, which is to say the Holder of the Heavens, who had the power of being able to change himself into various shapes.

The Holder of the Heavens ordered the people to proceed towards the Sun's rise in the east as he guided them. And they came to a river which was then named Yenonanatche, which is to say, 'Going round the Mountain', but is now known as the Mohawk River. And they went down along the bank of that river and came to where it discharged into a great river running towards the midday Sun in the south, then called the Shawnaytawty, which is to say 'Beyond the Pines', but now known as the Hudson River. They then went down the bank of that river and touched the bank of the Great Water (The Atlantic Ocean).

e people camped at that place and remained there for a few days. The people still e only one language together, but then some of the people went on the banks of at water towards the noonday Sun in the south, while the main group, under the of the Holder of the Heavens, returned as they had come, along the bank of aytawty (Hudson River).

Of le there was one particular part which called themselves One Household; of th there were six families, and they entered into an agreement to preserve their cl iance, which would never be extinguished in any manner.

The people advanced some distance up the river of Shawnatawty, 'Beyond the Pines", the Hudson, and the Holder Of the Heavens then directed the first family to make their residence near the bank of that river. That family was named Te-haw-re-ho-geh, which is to say 'A Speech Divided', now know as the Mohawk, and their language was soon altered.

The rest of the group then turned and went towards the Sun's setting in the west, and they traveled about two and a half days, until they came to a creek which was named Kawnatawteruh, which is to say 'the Pineries'. The second family was then directed by the Holder of the Heavens to make their residence near this creek, and the family was named Nehawretahgo, which is to say 'Big Tree', now called the Oneidas. And likewise their language was altered.

The company continued to proceed toward the Sunset under the direction of the Holder of the Heavens. The third family was directed by the Holder of the Heavens to make their residence on a mountain then named Onondaga, and which is still known as Onondaga. And that family was named Seuh-now-kah-tah, which is to say. 'Carrying the Name', and their language was altered.

The company continued their journey towards the Sun's setting in the west. The fourth family was directed by the Holder of the Heavens to make their residence near a long lake named Goyogou, which is to say 'A Mountain Rising from Water', now called Cayuga. And that family was named Shoneanawetowah, which is to say 'A Great Pipe', and their language was altered.

The company continued to proceed towards the sunset. The fifth family was directed by the Holder of the Heavens to make their residence near a high mountain, or rather knoll, located south of Canandaiga Lake, which was then named Jenneatowake. And the family was named Tehowneanyohent, which is to say 'Possessing a Door' now known as the Seneca, and their language was altered.

The sixth family went with the company that journeyed towards the Sun's setting in the west, and touched the bank of a great lake, which was named Kauhadgwarahka, which is to say 'A Cap', now known as Lake Erie. And they then went towards the southwest, the direction between the midday and setting Sun. They traveled a considerable distance, until they came to a river which was named Ouau-we-you-ka, which is to say, 'The Principle Stream', (now known as the Ohio River).

Now the people discovered grape vine lying across that river, by which a part of the people crossed over it. But while they were engaged in crossing over the river, the vine broke, and the people were divided. Those remaining on the one bank of the river became enemies to those who had crossed over it, and as a consequence of this they were obliged to end their journey.

The Holder of the Heavens instructed the people in the art of using bows and arrows, both in the time of game as well as in the time of danger. Associates were dispensed, and each family went to search for residences according to the conveniences of game.

The sixth family went toward the Sun's rise in the east, and touched the bank of the Great Water, the Atlantic Ocean. This family was directed by the Holder of the Heavens to make their residence near Cautanoh, which is to say 'Pine in Water', situated near the mouth of the Neuse River, now in the state of North Carolina. And this family was named Kautanoh, now called Tuscarora, and their language was also altered.

But the six families did not go so far as to loose the understanding of each other's languages. Mohawk was considered the oldest language of the confederacy:

Mohawk Tuscarora

1.	WUS-KOT,	1.	UNTCHEE
2.	TACK-NY,	2.	NAKETEE
3.	AU-SUH,	3.	AU-SH.
4.	KAU-VALY	4.	HUN-TOCK
5.	WISK	5.	WHISK
6.	YUA-YAK	6.	O-YAK
7.	GIA-TOCK	7.	GIA-NOCK
8.	SOT-TAI-GON	8.	NAKE-RUH
9.	TEW-DO	9.	NI-RUH
10.	OYA-L Y	10.	WOTS~HUH.

THE GIANTS APPEAR CA 4,500 BCE

In the ancient days, after the Great Island had appeared upon the big waters, and after the earth had brought forth trees, herbs, vegetables, and all else, and after the creation of the land animals, then the Eagwehoewe people, the Real People, were created too, and they resided in the north regions. And after a time some of those people became giants, and they committed outrages upon the inhabitants.

Now after many years a body of the Eagwehoewe people, the Real People, encamped on the bank of a majestic stream, and was named the Kanawage, now called the St Lawrence River.

It is interesting to note that the Kanawa River of West Virginia, which led to Tuscarora lands, also preserves this early Iroquoian word.

THE SHIP WRECKED PEOPLE: STALLINGS ISLAND CULTURE

After a long time a number of foreign people sailed from a port unknown; but unfortunately, before they reached their destination, the winds drove them on a contrary course. At length their ship wrecked somewhere on the southern part of the Great Island, and many of the crews perished. But a few active persons were saved, and they obtained some implements, and each of them was covered with a leather bag.

The Big Hawks carried them onto the summit of a mountain, but they remained there but a short time. The Big Hawks seemed to threaten them, and they were compelled to leave the mountain.

They immediately selected a new place for residence, and they built a small fortification in order to provide against the attacks of furious beasts, if there should be any made.

After many years the foreign people became numerous, and they extended their settlements. But afterward they were destroyed by the monsters which overran their country.

DESCRIPTION OF THE GIANTS

That these "Giants" actually existed has been proven beyond doubt by the recovery of their remains, particularly in bound scientific excavationa conducted in US in the early 1960's.

About the time this occurred the Eagwehoewe people lived on the Kanawagae River, or the St. Lawrence River. But they could not enjoy tranquility, as they were invaded by Giants who they called Ronnongwetowanea, who came from the north and inhabited it to a considerable degree.

Now the Giants' mode of attack was silly, as they never dared to fall upon an enemy without the prospect of success. They especially took advantage of the times when warriors were absent from a town. After plundering the people's houses and making captives of those who they found, they would then hastily retreat to their residence in the north.

THE SECOND BATTLE WITH THE GIANTS

One instance: A family of princes lived near the river St. Lawrence, a family which contained six brothers and a sister; and their father was a noble chieftain who had fallen in an earlier contest with the enemy Giants.

The "family" referred to here must have been composed of at least 7 Iroquoian peoples, with one of them ruled by a Queen and not by a King, as were the Five Families. Note also that their "father", a male ruler of the Families, had been killed in an earlier battle with the Giants.

One time these brothers went out on a day's hunt, and left their sister alone in the camp. Unfortunately, while they were gone, a Giant made a vigorous attack and the woman soon became prey to the invader.

In the evening the brothers returned to camp, and they were much grieved to discover that their sister was missing. They immediately made a search of the surrounding area, but the night became too late, and the darkness prevented them from carrying their search out further.

In the morning the eldest brother determined to pursue the enemy until he could discover something about their sister, and he promised to return in seven days if nothing should happen to him. Accordingly the Prince set out and pursued the traces of the enemy.

After he had journeyed three days he reached the Giant's residence about sundown. At first sight he discovered his sister was gathering some sticks for fuel near the Giant's house, but as he approached his sister she retired.

The Princess soon proved by her conduct that she had fallen in love with the Giant, and that it was impossible to gain her confidence. The Prince was now brought to the point of view of dreading the enemy; however, he was still willing to risk the dangers he knew he was about to meet.

If the monarchy of this earlier confederation corresponded to the later one, the Princess may perhaps be identified with a Queen of the Erie, formerly in control of the Shenango River watershed and adjacent areas on Lake Erie.

The Prince remained outside until about dusk, and then he entered the Giant's house. He was received happily by the Giant with the most favorable words, and his fears were soon dissipated as the Giant offered him his pipe as a tribute of his respect, which the Prince accepted.

After enjoying the evening meal, they talked together for a good while, without the least appearance of hostility. As the night was getting late, the Prince was invited to bed. But the Giant now began to act to deceive the Prince, as he commenced to amuse him for part of the night in singing songs. The Giant had determined to assassinate his visitor at his first opportunity.

Now the Prince was so fatigued by his journey that he was soon fast asleep, and the Giant killed him there in bed. He then deposited the Prince's body in a cave near his house where he stored the carcasses. The Giant was much pleased with his conquest over the Prince, and he advised his wife to watch daily in order that he might impose on another enemy.

The seven days during which the Prince had avowed to return elapsed. As his brother had not returned, the youngest of the brothers, (the) Donhtonha, was greatly alarmed at his disappearance, and he resolved to pursue him.

Now Donhtonha was a most stout and ferocious looking fellow, and after he armed himself, he commenced the journey to the Giant. Now Donhtonha also arrived at the place after the time mentioned, and he also found his sister, just as his brother had earlier. And before he had time to reconcile with her, she returned to the house, exactly as she had done before, and informed the Giant that some person was coming.

Donhtonha entered the Giant's house appearing very angry and ready to strike, and he enquired for his brother. This alarmed the Giant, and he was prompt to pacify Prince Donhtonha. The Giant replied that he had made peace with Donhtonha's brother, who had then gone on to visit some people in the neighborhood, and that he expected that he would return at any moment.

Upon this assurance Donhtonha's anger became somewhat abated; his sister provided some food, and he was soon enjoying their domestic felicity. But alas, the Giant was far from being friendly, and he was only taking the time to form a plan to deceive his visitor.

The evening was growing late, and Dohhtonha was out of patience waiting for his brother to return, and he renewed his enquiries. So the Giant invited his visitor to bed, where he hoped to kill him.

Now the Giant rose from his seat and commenced his usual custom in singing. But Prince Donhtonha perceived that some evil plan was being carried out against him, and he resolved to abandon the bed for a while. He begged leave for a few moments, and went out after various considerations from being imposed.

There Donhtonha procured some pieces of wood which produced a faint light in the night, and he put them above his eyelids and again went back to the bed. The giant was now deceived, for while his visitor was asleep, his eyes appeared as though he was continually awake.

As soon as daylight came, Donhtonha hurried from the bed. He was about to make a search for his deceased brother, but the Giant protested this to him, which soon excited his suspicions of the act. After a long debate Donhtonha attacked the Giant, and a severe fight ensued.

At last Donhtonha killed the Giant, and he burnt him in the ruins of his house. But the Giant's spirit fled to the heavens and changed into one of the eastern stars.

Now during the engagement Donhtonha's sister had become aggrieved, and she fled to the wilderness, and lamented there for her deceased husband. And she died in despair, but her spirit also became one of the stars, one of the northern stars.

After his conquest Donhtonha took up his search for his brother again. He discovered the remains of his brother, wept over them, and burnt them to ashes.

A THIRD BATTLE WITH THE GIANTS

At another time another group of Ronnongwetowanea Giants attacked a small town located on the bank of the Kanawage River (St. Lawrence.) This occurred during the season when the people went out to hunt, and there was nobody left in the town except an old chief and his attendant, who was named Yatatonwatea.

While these two were enjoying their repose in the house, they were suddenly attacked by a Ronnongwetowanea Giant. But Yatatonwatea went out the back door and escaped, deserting the aged chief to his fate.

The enemy, however, spared no time, and the chase was soon on; this caused Yatatonwatea to retreat as fast as possible. Yatatonwatea attempted to make resistance in various places, but he was compelled to retire at the very appearance of the enemy.

He endeavored to gain his retreat by traversing various creeks and hills, but it was in vain.

Yatatonwatea then undertook a new method of making a small effect upon the progress of his enemy. After running some distance, he discovered an imposition which his enemy would promptly cherish, and he drove a flock of pigeons in their way to amuse them until he could hide himself under the bank of the river.

Unfortunately the flattering hope was seen to fail: Yatatonwatea remained there but a short time before he saw the enemy was coming at full speed, and he was soon obliged to abandon the position and continue his flight.

Again, Yatatonwatea tried to conceal himself among the rocks of the mountain, but in the meantime the enemy advanced every moment. At this he became dismayed, finding that nothing could resist the impetuosity of his pursuer.

But determined not to surrender as long as he was capable of keeping out of their reach, Yatatonwatea immediately took the path which led to the hunting grounds, in search of some of his people. Fortunately at a short distance he met two warriors, and he was instantly supported, and made a vigorous resistance. During the battle the warriors conducted themselves as heroes, which ultimately gained them the triumph, notwithstanding that one of them received a severe wound by club. After terrible combat the Ronnongwetowanea were exterminated.

Yatatonwatea hastened to the hunting encampment with an alarm whoop and advised the people of the substance of what had happened, and the dangers which the enemy presented to their now vacant towns. As soon as the people received this intelligence, they immediately returned to their settlements.

900 BCE:
THE FINAL BATTLE AGAINST THE GIANTS

A convention was then held by the chieftains in order to take some measures to defend their country. As the Ronnongwetowanea tribe were not numerous, the chieftains deemed it expedient to raise a large force, and therefore sent a few hundred warriors to subdue them.

After decisive contests the warriors gained the victory, and it was supposed that the Ronnongwetowanea tribe has ever since ceased to exist.

This fate probably befell them about 2,500 winters before the Dutch came to the lands of the Five Nations.

Using a rough date of 1600 CE for the appearance of the Dutch in the lands of the Five Nations, we end up with a date of 900 BCE for this event, a date which agrees well with the date of the appearance of Adena culture. As is demonstrated here, a fragment of Comet Encke struck the Atlantic Ocean ca 1059 BCE and produced an impact mega-tsunami. The destruction of their trading network by this impact undoubtedly hastened the Giants demise.

THE EVIL SHOTYERRONAGWEA

This account of the Evil Shotyerronagwea appears to be an account of the emergence of the Schahentoar-ernons, the Caranotouan or Skendowanna, i.l. the Wyoming people.

The depredations of their enemy, which the Giants had so often exercised upon the inhabitants, were now terminated, and the country enjoyed many winters without disturbance.

About this time a mischievous person named Shotyerronagwea at first distinguished himself as being of a good character while visiting the people, and meanwhile he gained their confidence. By doing this he fairly concealed himself from being discovered in his real designs, and in a short time he began to injure the people. He assassinated two warriors secretly, and then he violated six virgins, and more…

These lines probably summarize the defeat of the Iroquoian peoples living to the north of the St. Lawrence River. The "two warriors" were most likely the military commanders of two tribes, while the "six virgins" were most likely six Queens of these matriarchal people.

Next Shotyerronagwea ventured to break the harmony of the nation, and he created dissensions among the people. At this the chiefs were so offended that they banished him from the villages.

When he received this treatment, Shotyerronagwea deemed it proper to desist from going back to any of the towns. Instead he immediately crossed the Saint Lawrence River and moved towards the midday Sun in the south. And he came to a town situated south of the Great Lake (Lake Erie?), and he was received there with kindness.

But his entertainment could not appease his evil designs. Though he appeared reconciled, one night while at the dancing house he killed several warriors. Shotyeronagwea then discovered that this offence should prove fatal to his person, and he was compelled to leave the town and go some other place to do mischief.

Shotyeronagwea was the greatest mischievous person who ever existed on the continent. He was considered an agent sent from the Bad Spirit itself.

THE QUISQUISS AND BIG ELK

About this time the big Quisquiss (perhaps the Mammoth) invaded the settlements south of the lake (Ontario). The furious animal pushed down the houses and made a great disturbance.

The people were compelled to flee from the terrible monster, as the warriors made opposition to it but failed. At length a certain chief warrior collected the men from several towns together and a severe engagement took place.

At last the monster retired, but the people did not remain long without being disturbed: a Big Elk invaded the towns next. The animal was furious and destroyed many persons, but the men were soon collected, a severe contest ensued, and the monster was killed.

HOPEWELLIAN FEDERATION CA 100 CE:
THE REFORMATION OF THE LONG HOUSE OF THE FIVE FAMILIES

Again, the first confederacy of the Families is mentioned in the accounts of their battles with the Giants, which can be dated on archaeological grounds from ca. 4,500 to 900 BCE, as well as from Cusick's own accounts. But there was also a later confederacy; it is also clear that Cusick confused the two, and placed the initial migration at 100 CE, when it is clear from Cusick's use of the Annals materials that the new confederation of the Five Families was formed about this time. The new confederation appears to have been based on a "Hopewellian" model, and of particular note is the introduction of corn, beans, squashes, potatoes, and tobacco agriculture.

The Holder of the Heavens returned to the Five Families and formed their mode of confederacy, which was named Ggo-nea-seab-neh, which is to say 'The Long House', which included first, the Teakawrehhogeh people; second, the Newhawthetahgo people; third, the Seuhnaukata people; fourth, the Shoneanaweto people; and fifth, the Tehooneanyohent people.

About this time it is supposed the Holder of the Heavens, an agent from the Superior Power, solemnly visited the families, and he instructed them in various things respecting the Infinity, matrimony, moral rules, worship, and other things. And he warned them that an Evil Spirit was in the world, and would induce the people to commit trespasses against the rules he had given them. And he offered them a favorable promise: if they remained in obedience to the rules he had given them, their souls would enter the place of happiness; but to those who were disobedient, their souls would be sent to a state of misery.

And he gave them seeds for corn, beans, squashes, potatoes, and tobacco, along with directions on how to cultivate them. And he gave them dogs to aid them in pursuing the game, and he repeated his instruction on the game, and promised them that the great country was given to them for their maintenance.

When he ended the interview of consolation he left.

THE KNOWLEDGE GIVEN BY THE HOLDER OF THE HEAVENS:

THE CLAN SYSTEM ADMINISTERS THE LAW

Each nation contains a set of generations or tribes [clans], viz.: Otter, Bear, Wolf, Beaver, Turtle. Each tribe [clan] has two chiefs to settle the disputes, &c.

If a man commits murder, the nearest relation of the slain dispatches the murderer with a war club; the slain and the murderer are put into one grave. Sometimes the relations of the offender present a belt of white wampum to make atonement.

Adulterous women are punished by shaving their heads, and they are banished from the town. Thieves are punished by whipping them severely. To recover debts, creditors generally apply to the [clan] chiefs; the payment is made up for by the re1atives of the debtor.

RELIGIOUS RITES

The tribes [clans] have a certain time of worship. The False Faces (Masks) first commence the dances; they also visit the houses to drive away sickness, and do other similar things.

Each town or district is allowed to sacrifice a couple of white dogs. The dogs are painted and ornamented with strings of wampum; they then throw the dogs into the fire, and some tobacco, and addresses the Maker. By doing this they pretend to furnish the Maker with a coat of dog skin and a pipe full of tobacco. After this they have dances for several days.

Private feats are guided by dreams.

THE DEER

The 'Skunatoh' or deer was the most useful game of the Five Nations.

These animals can run a considerable distance in a day, and the people have a small dog in aid them in overtaking deer. But the deer very seldom stop when pursued by dogs, for these creatures generally go in a river or lake, and in this situation the dogs are compelled to leave them. By this method wolves are also prevented from chasing these anima1s.

The hunters have never seen a deer lying dead, except in rare instances. Instead, when deer get old they throw themselves into a river and die there.

If a person found a dead deer it was considered a bad sign: that person or some of his relatives would die in the course of a few moons. The person would find another way. If a deer ran off and barked at a hunter it was a bad sign: his wife has committed adultery, in consequence of which he cannot kill any deer.

When a person intends to hunt deer, he procures a medicine and vomits once daily for twelve days. After this he procures some pine or cedar boughs and boils them in a clay kettle, and after he removes this from the fire, he takes a blanket and covers himself over with it to sweat. A person who uses this medicine does not a11ow a woman with child or uncleanness to eat any of the venison.

The people sometimes go out to hunt as the corn begins to grow on the ears. They make long brush fence and remove the leaves on both sides of the fence. The deer will follow the path, and the hunter can easily kill the game.

In the hot days of summer hunters go and watch in the night at the salt licks. Another mode of killing deer then is that they take slivers of basswood bark and proceed to the place of the hunt, and obtain a canoe and go into a river or lake in the night, provided with light by torches of the basswood slivers.

Bear, elk, and buffalo, were found in the territory of the Five Nations. The moose inhabit the spruce country and the heads of the Mohawk River; this country was never inhabited by any kind of people in the winter season: the snow fell so deep it was thought that country would always remain a wilderness.

In the river and lakes are found various kinds or fishes.

The people had implements which they used to make bows and arrows. Their kettles were made of baked clay; in these they boiled their meat. Their awls and needles were made of hard bone; a pipe for smoking was made of baked clay, or soft stone; a small turtle's shell was used to peel bark; a small dry stick was used to make a fire by boring it against seasoned wood.

THE ASTRONOMY OF THE FIVE NATIONS

The people had particular times of the moon [months] to make maple sugar, to plant corn, and to hunt deer and other animals.

The seasons of the year, they are directed by the seven stars of the heavens.

When warriors traveled in a great forest, they were guided by a northern star.

If the Sun or the Moon was eclipsed they believed that the Evil Spirit darkened it. The people assembled and made a loud noise to scare the Evil Spirit from the orb.

They believed that the clouds in the Moon were made of earth and inhabited by people.

THE FLYING HEADS [WHIRLWINDS]

Perhaps about 1400 years before the Dutch came to the lands of the Five Nations, about one hundred winters after the people [had] left the mountain.

Using a rough date of 1600 CE for the appearance of the Dutch, and Cusick's later note on the date of the migration, we end up with a date of 200 CE for this event. In legends, the word "head" was used by this people to describe whirlwinds. For another example of this see the legend of Man-Eater and His Brother Whirlwind, in Seneca Indian Myths, collected by Jeremiah Curtin.

The five families grew, and made some villages in the country. The Holder of the Heavens was absent from the land, which was destitute of the visits of the Governor of the Universe. This caused the time when they were invaded by the monsters called Konearaunehneh, which is to say, the 'Flying Heads', which devoured several people of the country. The Flying Heads made their invasions during the night; but the people were attentive to escape by leaving their huts and concealing themselves in other huts prepared to that purpose.

For instance, there was an old woman who resided at Onondaga. She was left alone in the hut at evening, while the others deserted. She was sitting near the fire parching some acorns, when a monsterous Head made its appearance at the door. While watching the woman, the monsterous Head was amazed to see her eat the parched acorns, which he thought were the coals of the fire. The old woman convinced the Flying Heads to eat the fire's coals, and by this put the monsters to flight.

And ever since that time the Flying Heads have disappeared, and it was supposed that they were concealed in the earth.

There is no real explanation as to why these particular whirlwinds, tornadoes, were so remarkable as to be remembered for many years. It may be that they were related to impacts - the mention of coals may be significant here. Another possible explanation may be that a period of extreme drought led to extreme fire conditions, and what was remembered here were simply the fire-storms which occurred due to these conditions.

THE MISSISSAUGA ALGONQUINS; AND DESCRIPTIONS OF THEIR LATER SETTLEMENT AT CONNEAUT, Ca 1800 CE

The 'Lake Serpent' referred to in following passages are a reference to the Massasauga (Rattle Snake) people. As the Five Nations wars with these people are described in depth by Cusick throughout his History, the Editor includes the following little known information here.

The Mississauga people are of Algonquin stock, related to the Ojibwa (Chippewa), Ottawa, and Saulteux peoples. As regards the Mississauga's name and their original location, the following information from Historical Sketches of Darlington County by J. T. Coleman is self explanatory:

'As regards the reptiles, a very popular, but erroneous, impression exists, that some of the snakes and lizards in our immediate vicinity are poisonous. With but one exception, there is not a poisonous reptile known in Canada, and even this one is limited to a very small extent of territory. It is known as Crotalis Massasauga, a small Rattlenake, found in the vicinity of Niagara, Hamilton, and some of the most southern portions of Lake Erie. They have, however, of late years, become very scarce. The average length of this snake is from two feet six inches to three feet'

From the description of the location derived from Cusick's passages which are immediately below, at this earlier period the Mississauga also controlled the area further down-river.

As will be seen in later passages of Cusick's History, and as is known from the archaeological record, the Mississauga occupied both the Mississauga area as well as the area around Sandusky, Ohio from about 900 CE onward. They were in an alliance with the people of the empire of the city of Twakanhah, now known by the name 'Cahokia', in other words the people now known as the 'Mississipians' of the American Bottoms area.

ATER MISSASSAUGA SETTLEMENT AT CONNEAUT Ca 1800 CE

ve Nations had vanquished the Wendat (Wyandot, Huron) and Atiquandaronk (.   ak) (Neutral) Iroquoian peoples, the Mississauga moved into their lands of the around Mi.   .., Ontario.

But also during this period, a part of the Mississauga people moved into lands around the Shenango River watershed and its junction with Lake Erie, lands which Cusick describes in this work as being held around 900 CE by the Ottawa people.

From History of Ashtabula County, Sketch of the Early Settlement of Conneaut Township, Harvey Nettleton, Geneva Times:

[Conneaut] itself seemed to combine many of the advantages which are deemed desirable by uncivilized man. The forest afforded plenty of game, the stream that flowed at their feet, as its name signifies, produced an abundant supply of fish [the author thought that the name 'Coneaut' meant "River of Many Fish', where it may mean 'the Oak' or 'the Boundary Marker'], while the alluvial lands along the bottoms furnished a soil well adapted to their rude method of cultivation.

"But their numbers were diminished by the encroachments of the whites, they were despoiled of their hunting grounds, which had been wrested from them by the Treaty of Greenville, and were ultimately compelled to evacuate the country.

'The last of these people who have resided permanently at Conneaut was a remnant of the Massasauga Tribe, under a chief of the name of Macqua Medah, or Bear's Oil. His village was situated about the head of the spring immediately in the rear of the spot where the Conneaut House now stands, and consisted of some thirty or forty families. This fountain affords a supply of pure water, and produces a little rill, which empties into the main stream at the foot of the hill near the bridge.

'On the arrival of the first settlers, their cabins to the number of thirty or forty were still standing, and it is said presented an appearance of neatness and comfort seldom seen among the Indians. They were of rude structure from twelve to fifteen feet square, built of logs and covered with bark. Their door casings and partitions were likewise of bark, displaying a good degree of skill and ingenuity in their construction.

'The settlers, not being very deeply impressed with the dignity of their public edifices, converted their council house into a barn, and their king's palace into an aviary, or hen roost.

'They found a square post eight or ten feet high and painted red, which was planted in the ground on the margin of the creek, near where the bridge now stands, that was supposed to indicate that the lands between it and the creek, where their cornfields were situated, were not to be intruded upon by the whites...

'The mounds that were situated in the eastern part of what is now the village of Conneaut and the extensive burying ground near the Presbyterian Church, appear to have had no connection with the burying places of the Indians. They doubtless refer to a more remote period and are the relics of an extinct race, of whom the Indians had no knowledge"

From History of Ashtabula County, William W. Williams, Williams Brothers, Philadelphia, 1878:

'The tribe, however, which was the most numerous was that of Massasaugas, a people who belonged to the Delawares, but who had been permitted by the Iroquois to leave their haunts on the Ohio and occupy this region.

[Though both peoples are Algonquin, the author is mistaken here in his assertion that the Massasaugers "belonged to" the Delaware (Lenape), people of the Eastern Algonquin stock. The Missassauga were and are of Northern Algonquin stock.]

"They were a harmless people, evidently intimidated by the conquests which had been gained over them. Years ago the Iroquois had subdued the whole Delaware race, or, to use their own expressive language, had "eaten them up" and "made women of them;" that is to say, they were obliged to give up all warlike expeditions and to live at peace.

Thus they lost their warlike propensities, and now dwelt wherever they were permitted to stay. This was the people with which the white settlers first came in contact. They had their village or encampments at Conneaut and in the township of Wayne. The remains of their camps are still found in various localities. One is on the bank of the Pymatuning and the southeast corner of Wayne, situated on the east side of the river.

'Other traces of Indian encampments are found in the south part of the county. One in the town of Andover, not far from the Pymatuning, covered nearly an acre of ground, and the land is still very rich where the Indian village stood. Near this encampment many stone implements have been found. A nest of leaf-shaped flint implements, consisting of two hundred and fifty pieces, has been found buried in a swamp, and partly covered with sand to mark the spot. It is stated that traces of former occupation were found in the township of Wayne, on the very spot where the first log church built by the whites formerly stood. In tilling the soil, after the destruction of the house, there was discovered an immense quantity of the bones of deer, bears, and other wild animals.

INDIAN DANCES.

The Massasauga tribe was very religious, and punctually observed their ancient feasts. They are described by the first settlers as occasionally holding dances and pow-wows for heathen worship on the site of the old fort. Some of these were performed with great solemnity. One has been described by Joshua Fobes as follows: "They arrange themselves in circular form around a large fire, one of them with a sort of drum, beating on it to mark the time, while the rest, stooping forward, kept up a sort of jumping dance, with much prolonged activity, all the time singing the words 'He-up-a-he-oh-a, He-up-a-he-oh-a' in a monotonous manner."

THE DANCE OF THE MOON.

'One of their modes of worshipping the Great Spirit was described to Mr. Joel Blakeslee by a lady, one of the first settlers in Williamsfield, who often visited the Indian camp, and in the night season witnessed the solemn ceremony. She describes it as follows: "When the hour arrived the worshipers arranged themselves in two lines, one of males, the other of females. Three or four Indians, drummers, sitting on the ground with their single-headed drums and single drum-stick, struck up the solemn tones, accompanied with the voice. At that, all parties in both lines commenced an active and regular motion

to and fro towards one another and back again, all keeping exact time with their feet to the drum, while their voices, united in solemn tones, chanted aloud the following notes:

Weter-weter we-hah,
Weter weter, we hah.
Weter weter, we hah wah.
How-we-ah,
How we ah hah.
How we ah,
How we ah hah wah.
High-tonne-ah,
High tonne ah hah wah;
High tonne ah, we ah hah wah.

"This tune, expressed in a plaintive voice and accompanied by the melancholy sounds of the drums and the measured tread of the dancers, gave an air of solemnity to the whole. To witness one of these exhibitions of a savage worship at midnight, by moonlight or torch-light, in the otherwise silent hours of night when all nature was hushed in soft and deep repose, was indeed impressive."

This company of Massasaga Indians consisted of twenty or twenty-five families; they lived by hunting till about the time of the arrival of the whites. Friendly intercourse was kept up between them and the settlers, and through the efforts made in their behalf they soon became more civil, turned their attention to cultivating lands and raising corn and cattle.

INDIAN TRADING.

'It is told of them that, notwithstanding the efforts made in their behalf, the Indians played a trick with some of their benefactors, which showed their inherent treachery. Good old Father Wakeman engaged to let them have an excellent piece of ground for corn-land, consisting of about five acres. He prepared the ground in good season and style, expecting that the Indians would work upon the halves.

' The Indians came and were punctual to their contract, and about the time the corn was to be gathered, Mr. Wakeman was so well pleased that he told his wife to prepare a good dinner for the whole gang, as he would give them a good feast for their faithfulness.

Just at this time one of Mr. Wakeman's friends came and asked him "what had become of his corn." Mr. Wakeman started over the ridge which lay between his house and corn-field; but when he arrived at the top, behold, not, a stalk remained! It had been cut up close to the ground, nothing remaining but the roots.

Wakeman then directed his course to the Indian camp, where he found the Indians, old and young, feasting on roasted corn. They had carried the whole crop on their backs, going a considerable distance around through the woods to prevent discovery, and had taken it to the camp. Mr. Wakeman concluded the next time to till his own land.

These Indians afterwards joined the British in the war with the Americans in 1812, and did not again appear in this vicinity.

OTHER NATIVE AMERICAN PEOPLES AT CONNEAUT

'Other Indians who were found in the county at the time of its first settlement were members of the different tribes from the east and the west. It appears that the township of Windsor was the chief resort of these wild hunters. It is stated that at one time there were over four hundred gathered there, engaged in hunting and fishing. Among them the Ottawas, Chippewas, Cayugas, and Tonawandas, and others.

From Introduction to the Study of Mortuary Customs Among the North American Indians by Dr. H. C. Yarrow:

'As a somewhat curious, if not exceptional, interment, the following account, relating to the Indians of New York is furnished, by Mr.Franklin B. Hough, who has extracted it from an unpublished journal of the agents of a French company kept in 1794:

"Saw Indian graves on the plateau of Independence Rock. The Indians plant a stake on the right side of the head of the deceased and bury them in a bark canoe. Their children come every year to bring provisions to the place where their fathers are buried. One of the graves had fallen in and we observed in the soil some sticks for stretching skins, the remains of a canoe, &c., and the two straps for carrying it, and near the place where the head lay were the traces of a fire which they had kindled for the soul of the deceased to come and warm itself by and to partake of the food deposited near it.

'These were probably the Massasauga Indians, then inhabiting the north shore of Lake Ontario, but who were rather intruders here, the country being claimed by the Oneidas."

THE LAKE SERPENT: THE MISSISSAUGA ATTACK

After a. short time, the people were invaded by the monster of the deep: the Lake Serpents [Mississauga – rattlesnakes] traversed the land, which interrupted their intercourse. The five families were compelled to make fortifications throughout their respective towns, in order to secure themselves from the devouring monsters.

Their manner of making a fort was this. A first they set fire against as many trees as would be required to make the fort. They then used stone axes to rub off the coals, so as to make the fires burn quicker. When a tree burnt down, they put fires to it about three steps apart and burnt it for half a day. These logs were then collected to a place where they were set up in a circle according to the size of the fort, and then earth was heaped on both sides of the circle. A fort generally had two gates: one for passage in and out, and the other to obtain water.

THE STONISH GIANTS:
ARMORED EUROPEANS APPEAR CA. 350 CE

Perhaps about 1250 years before the Dutch came to the lands of the Five Nations, about two hundred and fifty winters since the people left the mountain…

Using a rough date of 1600 CE for the Dutch appearing in the lands of the Five Nations, by Cusick's calculation we end up with a date of 350 CE for the appearance of the Stonish Giants, in other words Armored Europeans. In other tales, it is stated that the Stonish Giants skins were so hard that they could deflect arrows, a description of European armor. One later appearance of the Stonish Giants in Cusick's History will coincide exactly with the Norse presence in North America, and will include a description of a Norse compass.

To date, no archaeological evidence has been found of a European contact in the area around 350 CE, but this will most likely change.

The Five Families became numerous and extended their settlements. As their country had been exposed to the invasions of the monsters, the people had not been able to enjoy but a short space of time without being molested by them.

About this time a powerful tribe of the wilderness, called Otne-yar-heh, which is to say Stonish Giants, overran the country.

It is held in the traditions of the Shawnees that the Stonish Giants descended from a certain family which had journeyed on the east side of the [Ohio] river, but went toward the northwest after they were separated due the vine breaking.

Here Cusick, working with Shawnee materials, conflates the Stonish Giants with the Giants proper.

This family was left alone by the Holder of the Heavens to seek its habitation, and the rules of humanity were forgotten, and afterwards they ate the raw flesh of the animals. At length they practiced rolling themselves on the sand, and by means of this covered their bodies with hard skin, (Elias Johnson adds to this, ' so that the arrows of the Tuscaroras only rattled against their rough bodies and fell at their feet.') These people became Stonish Giants, and were dreadful invaders of the country.

It is said that Sir William Johnson, the Superintendent of the Six Nations, had a picture of a giant. Probably the English have recorded this in their Histories concerning North America.

The warriors were immediately collected from several towns and a severe combat took place, but the warriors were overpowered and the people fell at the mercy of the invaders. The people were now threatened with destruction, and the country was brought to subjection for many winters.

As the people had been reduced so often they could not increase their number, while the Stonish Giants were so ravenous that they devoured people of almost every town in the country.

But happily the Holder of the Heavens again visited the people, and he observed that they were in a distressed condition because of the enemy. He proceeded to banish their invaders by using a strategy. He changed himself into a Stonish Giant and combined with the Stonish Giants, and he induced them to let him lead them to destroy the people of the country.

But after a days march they did not reach the fort at Onondaga, where they intended to attack, and he ordered them to lay in a deep hollow for the night; they would make their attack the following morning. As the day dawned, the Holder of the Heavens ascended upon the heights, and he overwhelmed them with a mass of rocks.

And only one of the Stonish Giants escaped to announce their dreadful fate, and after that event the Stonish Giants left the country and sought asylum in the regions of the north.

This hollow is said to be not far from Onondaga. Some say the Stonish Giants retreated by way of Mountain Ridge and crossed to the north below Niagara Falls.

The families were now preserved from extinction.

THE MISSISSAUGA DRIVEN FROM THE LANDS OF THE FIVE FAMILIES:
THE HOLDER OF THE HEAVENS BANISHES THE LAKE SERPENT

The Lake Serpent discovered the powerful operations of the Holder of the Heavens, and instantly it retreated into the deep places of the lake.

After this banishment, the monster of the deep made its appearance in the country: a snake with the shape of a human head opposed the passage between the Onondaga family and Goyogouh (Cayuga) family, which prevented their intercourse, as the Snake had seated itself near the principle path which led through the settlements of the Five Families.

The people were troubled by their condition, and finally they decided to resist. They selected the best warriors at Onondaga, and after they were organized and prepared, they proceeded to that place. After a severe conflict the Snake was killed.

The lake serpent was often seen by the people, but the thunder bolt either destroyed the Serpent or compelled them to retire into the deep.

By Cusick's placement of it, this victory should have occurred between 350-400 CE.

THE FIVE NATIONS' ACCOUNT OF
THE FIVE FAMILIES WAR WITH THE HOPEWELL

About this time there were various nations who inhabited the southern country. These nations had descended from the families which were dispersed after the vine broke on the Ohauweyoka River (Ohio River).

The Holder of the Heavens visited the Five Families and instructed them in the art of war, and favored them to gain the country beyond their limits; after which he disappeared.

THE TUSCARORA ACCOUNT OF
THE FIVE FAMILIES' WAR WITH THE HOPEWELL

Perhaps about 1,200 years before the Dutch appeared in the lands of the Five Nations

Cusick or his printer appear to have misplaced the following two Tuscaroran passages, setting them "Perhaps about 2,200 years before Columbus discovered America", for which read "before the Dutch appeared in the land of the Five Nations", as explained elsewhere. Clearly these passages belong here, agreeing as they do with the Five Nations' account of their southern war given immediately above. If either Cusick's wampum count, manuscript, or the printed version is changed to read "Perhaps about 1,200 years before the Dutch appeared in the lands of the Five Nations.", it yields a date of about 400 CE, bringing these passages into closer agreement with the archaeological record.

About this time the northern families formed a confederacy, and seated a great council fire on the Saint Lawrence River. The northern families possessed the bank of the Great Lakes; while in the countries in the north there were plenty of beavers, the hunters were often opposed there by the Big Snakes.

As was explained earlier, the "Big Snakes" are the Mississauga (Rattlesnake) people.

The people living on the south side of the Big Lake (Lake Erie) made bread of roots, and obtained a kind of potatoes and beans found in the rich soil there.

The northern nations appointed a Prince, and they immediately journeyed to the south and visited the great Emperor who resided at the Golden City, the capital of their vast empire.

The reference here to the "Golden City" certainly relates to the Hopewell practice of covering their earth structures with a layer of yellow clay. As for the Golden City's location, my guess is that it refers to the Hopewell remains which were located at the junction of the Ohio River with the Mississippi River, but it may perhaps refer to the remains at Newark, Chillicothe, or Portsmouth.

After a time the Emperor built many forts throughout his dominions, and almost penetrated to Lake Erie. This produced great excitement, as the people of the north felt that they would soon be deprived of the country on the south side of the Great Lakes. They determined to defend their country against any infringement by this foreign people.

A long bloody war ensued which perhaps lasted about one hundred years. The people of the north were too skillful in the use of bows and arrows, and could endure hardships which proved fatal to the foreign people. At last the northern nations gained the conquest, and destroyed all the foreigners' towns and forts, and left them in a heap of ruins..

THE FIVE FAMILIES DISSOLVE;
THE FIVE NATIONS UNITED UNDER KING ATOTARHO I OF ONONDAGA

Perhaps 1000 years before the Dutch came to the country of the Five Nations.

Using a rough date of 1600 CE for the Dutch appearing in the lands of the Five Nations, by Cusick's calculation we end up with a date of 600 CE for the reformation of the Long House at Onondaga.

About this time the Five Families became independent nations, and they formed a council fire in each nation, &c; Unfortunately, a war broke out among them.

During these unhappy differences, Atotarho was the most hostile chief. Atotarho resided at the fort of the Onondaga; his head and body were ornamented with black snakes, and his dishes and spoons were made from the skulls of his enemies.

After a while Atotarho requested the people to change his dress. The people immediately drove away the black snakes, a mass of wampum was collected, and the chief was soon dressed in a large belt of wampum . He became a law giver, and he renewed the chain of the alliance of the Five Nations, and framed their internal government, which took five years to accomplish.

At Onondaga a Tree of Peace was planted, which reached the clouds of Heaven. Under the shade of this tree the Senators were invited to set and deliberate, and smoke the pipe of peace as ratification of their proceedings. A great council fire was kindled under this majestic tree, which has four branches, one each pointing to the south, west, east, and north.

The neighboring nations were amazed at the powerful confederates. The Onondaga people were considered the heart of the country: numerous belts and strings of wampum were left with the famous chief as records of alliance and other things.

After he had accomplished the noble work he was immediately named Atotarho, King of the Five Nations.
And it was governed by the Senate, which was chosen by the people annually.

The succession of the kings followed the woman's line.

EXTRACTS FROM TUSCARORA CHIEF ELIAS JOHNSON'S
ACCOUNT OF THE FOUNDING OF THE LONG HOUSE

The following passages are taken from Tuscaroran Chief Elias Johnson's LEGENDS, TRADITIONS, AND LAWS OF THE IROQUOIS, OR SIX NATIONS, AND HISTORY OF THE TUSCARORA INDIANS.Elsewhere in his work Johnson identifies the location of Hiawatha's village as being at what is now Cross Lake, New York. From the mention of "simple government" in the following passage, it would appear that Hiawatha led the prior federation of the Families.

While Hiawatha was thus living in domestic life quietly among the people of the hills, and administering their simple government with wisdom, they became alarmed by the sudden news of the approach of a furious and powerful enemy from north of the great lakes.

As the enemy advanced, they made an indiscriminate slaughter of men, women and children. The people fled from their villages a short time before them, and there was no heart in the people to make a stand against such powerful and ruthless invaders.

 In this emergency, they fled to Hiawatha for his advice. He counseled them to call a general council of all the tribes from the east and west. "For," said he, "our strength is not in the war club and arrows alone, but in wise counsels." He appointed a place on the banks of Onondaga Lake for the meeting. It was a clear eminence from which there was a wide prospect. Runners were dispatched in every direction, and the chiefs, warriors, and headmen forthwith assembled in great numbers, bringing with them, in the general alarm, their women and children. Fleets of canoes were seen on the bosom of the lake, and every interior warpath was kept open by the foot-prints of the different tribes hurrying to obey the summons of Hiawatha.

AN IMPACT EVENT ENDS
THE EARLIER FEDERATION

The following passages in Johnson's account may describe an impact event which occurred, one which destroyed Hiawatha's ability to lead the federation of the Five Families. It is known that the impact of a fragment of Comet Encke destroyed the city of Bazas, in what is now France, ca. 580 CE, for which see Chapter 11 here.

All but the wise man himself had been there for three days, anxiously awaiting the arrival of Hiawatha, when a messenger was dispatched after him. They found him gloomy and depressed…

The day was calm and serene. No wind ruffled the lake, and scarcely a cloud floated in the sky above. But while the wise man was measuring his steps towards the place designated for the council, and while ascending from the water's edge, a rumbling and low sound was heard, as if it were caused by the approach of a violent, rushing wind. Instantly all the eyes were turned upwards, where a small and compact mass of cloudy darkness appeared. It gathered in size and velocity as it approached, and appeared to be directed inevitably to fall in the midst of the assembly…

…But the force of the descending body was that of a sudden storm. They had hardly taken the resolution to halt when an immense bird, with long, extended wings, came down with a swoop. This gigantic agent of the sky came with such force that the assembly felt the shock…

…But Hiawatha was inconsolable for his loss. He grieved sorely, day and night, and wore a desponding and dejected countenance. But these were only faint indications of the feelings of his heart. He threw himself upon the ground, and refused to be comforted. He seemed dumb with melancholy, and the people were concerned of his life. He spoke nothing; he made no answers to questions put to him, and laid still as if dead.

THE COUNCIL MEETS

Continuing with Johnson's account:

After several days the council appointed a certain merry-hearted Chief to make him a visit, and to whisper a word of consolation in his ears to arouse him from his stupor. The result was successful. He approached with ceremonies and induced him to arise, and named the time when the council would convene. Yet haggard with grief, he called for refreshments and ate. He then adjusted his wardrobe and headdress and went to the council. He drew his robe of wolf-skin gracefully around him, and walked to his seat at the head of the assembled chiefs with a majestic step.

Stillness and the most profound attention reigned in the council while he presided, and the discussion opened and proceeded. The subject of the invasion was handled by several of the ablest counselors and the bravest warriors. Various plans were proposed to defeat the enemy.

Hiawatha listened with silence until all had finished speaking. His opinion was then asked. After a brief allusion of the calamity which had befallen him through the descent of the great bird by the Great Spirit, he spoke to the following effect:

"I have listened to the words of the wise men and brave chiefs, but it is not fitting that we should do a thing of so much importance in haste; it is a subject demanding calm reflection and mature deliberation.

Let us postpone the decision for one day. During this time we will weigh well the words of the speakers who have already spoken. If they are good, I will then approve of them. If they are not, I will then open to you my plan. It is one which I have reflected on, and feel confident that it will insure safety."

When another day had expired, the council again met. Hiawatha entered the assembly with even more than ordinary attention, and every eye was fixed upon him, when he began to address the council in the following words:

"Friends and Brothers: You being members of many tribes, you have come from a great distance; the voice of war has aroused you up; you are afraid for your homes, your wives, and your children; you tremble for your safety.

"Believe me, I am with you. My heart beats with your hearts. We are one. We have one common object. We come to promote our common interest, and to determine how this can be best done.

"To oppose those hordes of northern tribes, singly and alone, would prove certain destruction. We can make no progress in that way. We must unite ourselves into one common band of brothers. We must have but one voice. Many voices makes confusion.

We must have one fire, one pipe and one war club. This will give us strength.

"If our warriors are united they can defeat the enemy and drive them from our land; if we do this, we are safe.

"Onondaga, you are the people sitting under the shadow of the Great Tree, whose branches spread far and wide, and whose roots sink deep into the earth. You shall be the first nation, because you are warlike and mighty.

"Oneida, and you, the people who recline your bodies against the Everlasting Stone, that cannot be moved, shall be the second nation, because you always give good counsel.

"Seneca, and you, the people who have your habitation at the foot of the Great Mountain, and are overshadowed by its crags, shall be the third nation, because you are all greatly gifted in speech.

"Cayuga, you, whose dwelling is in the Dark Forest, and whose home is everywhere, shall be the fourth nation, because of your superior cunning in hunting.

"Mohawk, and you, the people who live in the open country, and possess much wisdom, shall be the fifth nation, because you understand better the art of raising corn and beans and making cabins.

"You five great and powerful nations, with your tribes, must unite and have one common interest, and no foes shall disturb or subdue you.

"And you of the different nations of the south, and you of the west, may place yourselves under our protection, and we will protect you. We earnestly desire the alliance and friendship of you all.

QUEEN COMES FROM SQUAWKIHAWS PEOPLE

"And from you, Squaw-ki-haws (being a remote branch of the Seneca Nation), being the people who are as the Feeble Bushes, shall be chosen, a Virgin, who shall be the peacemaker for all the nations of the earth, and more particularly the favored Long House, by which name this confederacy shall ever sustain.

 If we unite in one band, the Great Spirit will smile upon us, and we shall be free, prosperous and happy; but if we shall remain as we are we shall incur his displeasure. We shall be enslaved, and perhaps annihilated forever.

"Brothers, these are the words of Hiawatha. Let them sink deep into your hearts. I have done."

A deep and impressive silence followed the delivery of this speech. On the following day the council again assembled to act on it. High wisdom recommended this deliberation.

The union of the tribes into one confederacy was discussed and unanimously adopted. To denote the character and intimacy of the union they employed the figure of a single council-house, or lodge, whose boundaries be co-extensive with their territories. Hence the name of Long House.

WAR WITH THE SQUAWKIHOWS PEOPLE:
THE FIVE NATIONS REVOLT

Continuing with Cusick's account:

About this time, the Tehooneanyohent, or Senecas, were at war with the Squawkihows, a powerful tribe which passed on the banks of the Genesee River. After various engagements, the Senecas sent an army to scourge this enemy, but they were repulsed with severe losses.

The melancholy intelligence of this was soon conveyed to Onondaga, and the King informed of their defeat. A powerful army of the allies was soon directed against the Squawkihows. After a long siege their principal fort was surrendered without condition, and their chief was taken prisoner and put to death. The war was terminated, but after their conquest a remnant of the Squawkihows were allowed to remain in the country and become vassals to the Five Nations. The government ordered the Senecas to settle the country and to build forts on the Genesee River so as to keep Squawkihows in subjection, fearing that in time they might create a rebellion.

The Senecas now possessed the land along the bank of the Great Lake, now called Lake Ontario, to the creek called Kenaukarent, now called Oak Orchard. The bank of the river O-Nyakarra, now called the Niagara River, was possessed by the Mississaugers, who had their capitol in Twakanhah.

Cusick identifies the Mississauga throughout his work as being of Twakanhah. As will be seen later in his History, Twakanhah was the city we know today as "Cahokia". As has been pointed out previously, the Mississaugers occupied from ca. 900 CE on both the Niagara River and Sandusky, Ohio regions, and were in friendly contact with the Cahokians.

EVENTS DURING THE REIGN OF KING ATOTARHO II
THE BIG BEAR: THE ANDASTE ATTACK

Following the Five Nations war against the Hopewell, (the Tallegewi, Thilicothe, Tsulagi, Cherokee et al.), Algonquin peoples, the Shaswnee, came into their lands from the north. The Andaste, whose national totem was the bear, moved to the east and settled on the Susquehannah River.

About this time, the Oyalkquoher, or 'Big Bear', invaded the territory of the Five Nations. The hunters were often attacked by these monsters.

At the village of Ohiokea, situated west of Oneida Creek, a small party went out to hunt and encamped near Lake Skonyatales. One morning while they were in the camp a noise broke out near the lake. A man was sent immediately to see the tumult, and he saw a great bear on the bank rolling down stones and logs: the monster appeared to be

The Wray Figurine - an Adena Bear Warrior

in a great rage.

A lion then came out of the lake and suddenly fell upon the bear; and a severe contest ensued. After a time the bear was beaten and was compelled to leave the shore.

The next day the men went in search of the bear, and they found the bear's remains: one of its fore legs was so heavy that two men could not lift it but one hand high. They procured some of its meat, useful for purposes in time of war.

THE GREAT MOSQUITO

About this time a great mosquito invaded Fort Onondaga. The mosquito was mischievous to the people: it flew about the fort, and with a long stinger sucked the blood out of a number of lives. The warriors made several attempts to expel the monster, but failed.

The country was invaded until the Holder of the Heavens was pleased to visit the people; while he was visiting the King at Fort Onondaga, the mosquito made its appearance as usual and flew about the fort. The Holder of the Heavens attacked the monster, but it flew so rapidly that he could hardly keep in sight of it.

But after a few days chase, the monster began to fail. He chased it on the borders of the great lakes towards the sun setting in the west, and around the great country. At last he overtook the monster and killed it near the salt Lake Onondaga, and its blood became the small mosquitoes.

EVENTS OF THE REIGN OF KING ATOTARHO III
SOHNOUREWAH THE SHAWNEE

Following the Five Nations war against the Hopewell, (Talegi, Thillicothe, Tsulagi, Chilicothe et al.), the Shawnee came to occupy the Ohio River valley and those parts of Pennsylvania to the east. Their archaeological remains are today identified as those of the Monongahela Culture.

About this time the Oneidas had extended their forts down the Kaunsehwatauyea River, now known as the Susquehana River.

At a fort situated on that river, there was a certain woman who delivered a male child of uncommon size. When he was twelve years of age, he was nearly as large as a grown person, and he would beat his playmates, which created disputes. But his mother would correct him, and afterwards she prevailed, and he promised never to injure his people.

When grown up he became a giant and was a great hunter. His mother was provided with venison continuously, and he was so strong that when he returned from hunting he would have five or six deers and bears strung around on his belt.

The giant was named Sohnourewah, which is to say 'Big Neck', now known as the Shawnee; he inhabited the bank of the river, and now he brought home the suits of dress and the scalps from those whom he had killed.

The Sahwaunoo Nation [on the Hudson] sent messages to Fort Kaunasenwatayea [the Fort on the Susquehanna] to report the conduct of Soh-nou-re-wah, [the Shawnee], but the business was left to the relatives of Soh-nou-re-wah, [Shawnees], who persuaded him to reform his behavior for the future.

But Soh-nou-re-wah, [the Shawnee] remained only two winters without making disturbances; he went down the river and whenever he came to a town, he committed the same outrages upon the inhabitants, and plundered the people of their clothes, and skins, and other things.

Again the Sahwaunoo [on the Hudson] sent a deputy to Fort Kaunasenwatayea [on the Susquehanna River], who reported not only their resentment, but their determination to make hostile aggressions if no satisfaction was made on their part.

The Chief Nenauretahgo [of Fort Kaunasenwatayea] sent a belt of wampum and offered terms of peace, which were accepted. But Sohnourewah the Shawnee was not disposed to favor the treaty: he left the fort and went down and settled on the bank of the Kaunasenwatayea (Susquehanna) River, and commenced to build a fort.

Cusick notes here: This fort was situated on the south bank of the Susquehanna River. In 1800 I went over the ground myself and viewed the mound there.

This may account for Cusick's mention of Shawnee traditions, as Shawnee had occupied the area just previously, and by 1800 some few remaining Shawnee people may have been still living in the Pecqua area.

Sohnourewah the Shawnee was frequently visited by his relatives there; and after the fortification was completed he resolved to continue to war against his enemies. As he had done before, Sohnourewah the Shawnee went from time to time and attacked the people who lived on the river: he would lay in ambush near their path, and whenever the people passed he shot them. He used a plump arrow, which was so violent that it would break a body into two parts. Sohnourewah the Shawnee became so mischievous to the people that his relatives were obliged to form a plan to destroy him. But Sohnourewah would not be easy to quell, as it was supposed that ten warriors were not sufficient to equal his strength.

Now three warriors of his native people went to his fort on the Kaunasenwatayea (Susquehanna) River, bringing him his favorite dish, a mess of huckle berries and other things. Sohnourewah was pleased with their visit and the food which they gave him; but while he was eating it one of the warriors, instantly stepped on the bench where he was sitting and gave a fatal blow to the giant's head with a. club which he had concealed under his cloak.

Sohnourewah was so distracted by this that he ran out the fort, intending to cross the river, but he sank in the mire which was near the river's bank. The three warriors prevailed and killed him on the spot. The warriors then spoiled his house and obtained a large quantity of skins, and other things, and the fort has been ruined ever since.

EVENTS OF THE REIGN OF KING ATOTARHO IV:
AN IMPACT EVENT, AND WAR WITH THE MISSASSAUGA

Perhaps about 800 years before the Dutch arrived in the land of the Five Nations.

Using a rough date of 1600 CE for the Dutch appearing in the lands of the Five Nations, by Cusick's calculation we end up with a date of 800 CE for the following events.

About this time the Mississaugers, who had their capitol at Twakanah, ceded their colonies lying between the Keanauhausent (Oak Orchard Creek) and the River O-Nyakara, (Niagara River) to the Five Nations.

About this time lived King Atotorho IV. There was a woman and son who resided near the fort, which was situated near a knoll, which was named Jenneatowaka, the original seat of the council fire of the Te-hoo-nea-nyo-hent, the Senecas. One day the boy, while amusing himself in the brush, caught a small serpent called Kaistowanea, in other words "With Two Heads', and he brought it to his apartment.

The serpent was first placed in a small bark box to tame it, where it was fed with bird's flesh and other similar things. After 10 winters the serpent became considerable larger, and he rested on the beams within the hut, and the warrior was obliged to hunt deers and bears to feed the monster.

But after awhile the serpent was able to maintain itself on various game; it left the hut and resided on the top of a knoll. The serpent frequently visited the lake, and after 30 years it had grown to a prodigious size, which in a short time inspired it with an evil mind against the people. In the night the warrior felt that the serpent was brooding some mischief and was about to destroy the people of the fort. When the warrior was acquainted of the danger, he was dismayed and soon moved to another fort.

At daylight the serpent descended from the heights with the most tremendous noise. The trees were trampled down with such force that they were uprooted.

Clearly this is an asteroid or comet impact event, and clearly the tale of an impacting 'serpent' has been allided with a tale of the 'Serpent' (Mississauga) people who had been attacking earlier, and who now took advantage of the disaster which had befallen their enemy.

And the serpent immediately surrounded the fort's gate. The people were taken improvidentially and brought to confusion; finding themselves circled by the monsterous serpent, some of them endeavored to pass out at the gate, and others, attempted to climb over the serpent, but were unable.

The people remained in this situation for several days; the warriors made oppositions to dispel the monster, but they were fruitless. And the people, distressed of their confinement, found no other method open to them than to rush to pass out at the gate. But the people were devoured, all except a young warrior and his sister, who stayed back detained, and were the only people left exposed to the monster, and were left restrained, without hopes of getting release.

At length the warrior received advice from a dream, and he adorned his arms with the hairs of his sister, by which he succeeded in shooting the serpent in the heart. And the serpent was mortally wounded, and it hastily retired from the fort and retreated to the lake in order to gain relief from its wound. The serpent furiously dashed on the surface of the water in the time of its agony; at last it vomited up the substance which it had eaten, and then it sank into the deep and died.

As the serpent had been too powerful to be resisted, the people of the fort had not received any assistance from their neighboring forts. After the fort was demolished, the Council fire was removed to another fort called Thaugwetook, which was situated west of what is now known as Lake Geneva; and bulwarks were erected on Mountain Ridge, west of the Genesee River.

EVENTS OF THE REIGN OF KING ATOTARHO V:
THE OTTAWA APPEAR

Following the Five Nations war against the Hopewell, (Tsulagi, i.l. Chilicothe et al.), the Ottawas came to occupy the valley of the Shenango River tributary of the Allegheny River and the area between it and Lake Erie.

About this time reigned King Atotorho V.

At Fort Kedauyerkowau, now known as the Tonawanda Plains, a party went to hunt and they were attacked by the Ottawas, which created differences between the two nations, as the Ottawa entered the country on no terms but to commence hostilities.

The Tohonyohent [War Chief] sent a band of warriors to attack some of the hunters, so as to retaliate the vengeance upon their enemies. The warriors advanced above the lake then named Geattahgweah, which is now known as Lake Chautauqua, and made encampment. They agreed to hunt for two days, after which they were to proceed towards the enemy's country.

The warriors went in various directions to hunt. Now one of the warriors passed a small brook, where he discovered a strange animal resembling a dog, but he could not discover animal's head; the creature was a greyish color, and was laying asleep exposed to the rays of the Sun; and he also discovered a den, which he supposed the place of the animal's residence:

The warrior returned to the camp that evening and told the others about the animal, and he informed them, as he imagined it was a very poisonous animal, that he was afraid to approach it again. But one of the warriors, a joker, laughed at him and called him a cowardly fellow; the joker determined to go himself and kill the creature without trouble, but he wished some of the warriors to be witnesses to the engagement;

Accordingly the warrior went out, accompanied by a number of warriors; he was directed to the spot and he discovered the animal. After beating it short time with his club, he seized the animal and tied it with a tumline. But while he was lifting it, the creature immediately moved to its den. With all his might he held on to the tumline, but he could not stop it, and he was compelled to let go of the tumline when the creature went beyond his reach;

The warrior was confused at not being able to kill the animal, and he hastened to retire from the spot. But when he was but a few paces from it he was taken with the pestilence which was influenced by the creature and he suddenly died;

Another warrior was within sight and directly fled to carry the intelligence back, but he also died a short distance away. The others returned to their camp, but the pestilence soon prevailed among the warriors, and many of them died in the same manner; a few of them escaped by leaving the camp before the pestilence appeared, and thus ended the expedition.

The Ottawas continued their hostilities and attacked the hunters; the Senecas sent out a small party, and fought them. They drove the enemy off, but their engagements were small, and they continued for many winters.

EVENTS OF THE REIGN OF KING ATOTARHO V:
THE WAR WITH THE OTTAWA CONTINUES, FINALLY BROUGHT TO AN END

In the days of King Ototarho VI, perhaps 650 Years before the Dutch arrived in the lands of the Five Nations.

Using a rough date of 1600 CE for the Dutch appearing in the lands of the Five Nations, by Cusick's calculation we end up with a date of roughly 950 CE for the following events.

At Fort Keadanyeekowa, now known as Tonawanda Plains, a small party went out to make an incursion upon any enemy who may be found within the boundaries of the kingdom.

This 'enemy' would have been the Andaste, the Bear. It is possible that the "Lizard" are Ottawa, thought to be Missassauga.

The party penetrated the Ohio River and encamped on its bank; as they were out of provisions, the warriors were anxious to kill some game. A certain warrior discovered a hollow tree, and supposing a bear in the tree, he immediately reported it to the party; the warriors hoped to obtain the bear, and they went to the tree.

One of them climbed the hollow tree and put a fire into it, in order to drive out the creature; the other warriors made ready to shoot. But they were mistaken, and there instantly came out of the tree a furious Lizard, which quickly grasped one warrior and leaped into the hollow of the tree, where its young ones devoured his corpse.

A grumbling noise ensued, the warriors were terrified at the monstrous creature and were soon compelled to retire, except one of them who stayed at the tree while the others fled. He remained there until the victim was eaten, and the last warrior had been chased away.

The warrior then immediately left the tree, and ran on the way back. Fortunately, he met the Holder of the Heavens who advised him to stop, and offered him aid in making resistance, which the warrior accepted. The Holder of the Heavens instructed the warrior to make a fire without delay, and to get some sticks to use to prevent the Lizard's flesh from re-uniting the body, which would be effective.

The warrior's Protector then changed into a lion and laid in wait. In a short while the monster came up, and a severe engagement took place between the lizard and the lion. The warrior hastened with the stick and began to hook the parts of the Lizard's flesh which had been bit off by his Defender, and he threw them into the fire.

By this means the monster was quelled. The warrior thanked the Holder of the Heavens for his personal preservation. The Protector vanished out of his sight, and the warrior returned to the Fort Keadanyeekowa and related the occurrence.

The war raged: the Senecas had sent out parties against the Ottawas and obtained various successes, and at last the Ottawas sued for peace. After a few winters the Senecas gained their mutual intercourse with the Ottawas and other neighboring nations. .

EVENTS OF THE REIGN OF KING ATOTARHO VII:
THE EXPEDITION TO THE WEST: A VISIT TO TWAKANHAH, i.l. CAHOKIA

About this time reigned king Atotarho VII, who was authorized by the Senate to send an expedition to explore the countries towards the setting Sun in the west.

The King sent messengers to acquaint the Ottawas of his intention, and he asked them to make arrangements and to favor the expedition's passage, which they complied with, being agreeable to his request.

The King appointed two captains to command the expedition, and about fifteen men for the expedition were selected from the Five Nations.

After they were equipped and prepared, they commenced their journey and arrived at Sandusky. The King of the Ottawas sent along two warriors to accompany the expedition; on their way these warriors held several conferences with the nations, and all of them seemed to favor the expedition's passage.

They advanced to the Mississippi River, where a Duke of Twakanah had collected the people from several towns who came out to meet them. The people danced around them, singing, and beating their little drums. After these ceremonies had been performed, the band of warriors was invited into the national house.

The band crossed the Mississippi River and continued their course towards the sunset in the west. They reached an extensive meadow; they discovered a curious animal - a winged fish, it flew about the tree; this little active creature moved like a humming bird.

They continued their journey and came to the village of the Dog Tail Nation~ the expedition was accommodated, amused with dances, and was conducted to the chief 's house. They were astonished that the people had short tails like apes: a hole was made through their seats, through which they put their tails.

The band continued in their direction west and came to another nation, and here too was kindly received, and their object was favorably accepted by the head men of that nation. During their stay, a certain warrior of the band courted a young woman, but the warrior died soon after the marriage. 'They observed that the people did not eat any meat, but drank the soup.

The band continued their journey, but before they reached the Rocky Mountains, they were stopped by a giant, and the band was compelled to return.

After a long journey they came back to the seat of the council fire and informed the King of all the particulars of their journey.

AMBASSADORS SENT TO THE LENTAHKEH AND OTTAWA,
AND A GREAT FAMINE OCCURS

After a time the Five Nations desired to preserve the peace and friendship with the western nations. An ambassador was sent to the Lentahkeh nation, who inhabited the country east of Ohio River in what is now Kentucky.

Another ambassador was sent, who went and lived among the Ottawas for several years. He married a woman and afterwards had two children by her.

Now that Ambassador was invited to join a company going out a winter's hunt. They journeyed some distance and reached their hunting grounds, but the men were so unlucky hunting that they could kill but a few game.

After a few days the people were destitute of provisions; the Leader of the company commanded the overseer to select two fat persons and to kill them without delay. This order was soon executed, and the flesh of these victims was distributed among the people.

The leader commanded the people that if anyone killed any game the meat should be left with the overseer for distribution, and that whoever disobeyed, the offender would be punished in a severest manner. The Ambassador killed a bear, and the meat was disposed of according to the order.

[This did not help.] The leader daily butchered two persons to feed the people, which only increased their distress. The people were so feeble that they were unable to hunt any more, and many of them began to famish. The Ambassador again killed another game animal, but he brought it secretly to his camp; but this was soon detected and rumored among the people.

For this offence the Ambassador was ordered to appear before their tribunal. Some men were angry at him and sought to destroy him immediately; but the leader deemed it unjust, as this would violate the treaty they had entered with the Five Nations. However, to satisfy the people, the leader consented to use another method to destroy him: he commanded them to strip him and to seize his clothes and his instruments; after which they were to extinguish their fires, and then to remove their camps a half day's journey distance from his. The offender would then certainly freeze to death without any way out.

But the Ambassador was ingenious: finding that he would be surprised, he instantly took a suit of dress and bow and arrows, and hid them under the hemlock boughs which were spread in the camp. In a short time his opponents entered the camp, and the ambassador was stripped without discrimination, as they had determined to: destroy him. His wife was compelled to leave him, or else she would share the same fate. The company then retired.

The Ambassador dressed himself immediately and proceeded away, hoping to reach a fort situated near Lake Erie. But he was so fatigued that he could not travel very fast. About sunset he happened to approach the edge of a dark forest; he selected a spot where he encamped, but as he had no kind of food to eat was quite dejected. After making exertions to render himself comfortable but failed, the weather being unfavorable, as it was cold and cloudy, However, the Ambassador was seldom taken by surprise; and having a good understanding of astronomical calculations, he ascertained that a storm was at hand. After kindling a fire he laid himself down to linger out the miserable existence which he was doomed to suffer.

Early in the morning the Ambassador heard a noise, as though something was coming, which at once attracted his attention. He was afraid, as he presumed that some of his enemy had overtaken him.

Fortunately, a young man came up and sat down. The visitor showed a friendly disposition, and after a short conversation the Ambassador related the story of his distressed condition. His visitor offered to relieve him as soon as possible; which promise the Ambassador received with sanguine expectations.

The ambassador was advised that a snow would fall so deep that he would be in want of a pair of snow shoes, and the visitor offered the pattern and showed him how to make the shoes. The Ambassador was directed where to find game; and he did as he was bidden.

At nightfall the young man made another visit, and he advised the ambassador where to catch bears; after the conversation the visitor disappeared. The Ambassador did as he was bidden, and he succeeded, and caught seven bears.

After he had prepared some of the meat and the bears' oil he immediately went to the encampment in search of his wife and children. He found them almost perished, and first gave them each a spoonful of oil. They were soon relieved, and he directed them to his camp.

The Ambassador was now relieved from his distress, while his enemy was lingering in despair. He examined their camp and was astonished to find that the people were utterly famished. They had become so weak and faint that they were not even able to make fire; those who had held out had had to eat human flesh as long as they could; they themselves were lying among the dead.

The company was now exposed to destruction, as the people had put themselves in disgrace. The Ambassador refused to invite any of them to his camp except his wife's relatives; they were so worn out by the disasters that they did not reach his camp until next morning. By the Ambassador's exertions, after a few days the company's men's strength was revived to the point they were capable of hunting.

After they returned to the town, the Ambassador was so shamefully abused by the people there that he was compelled to leave his wife and the country.

About this time the Ottawas became a numerous and powerful nation, occupying an extensive country lying between Lake Erie and the Ohio River; it was thought that their national force amounted to about 4,000 warriors.

EVENTS OF THE REIGN OF KING ATOTARHO VIII:
THE MISSISSAUGA ATTACK

In the reign of King Atotarho VIII, perhaps 400 years before the Dutch arrived in the lands of the Five Nations.

Using a rough date of 1600 CE for the Dutch appearing in the lands of the Five Nations, by Cusick's calculation we end up with a date of roughly 1200 CE for the following events.

About this time the Messissaugers who had their capitol in Twakanhah began to wage a war against the Five Nations. The Senecas on the frontier were most engaged in the warfare.

After various skirmishes the enemy was so excited that they determined to destroy Fort Kauhanauka. (Today this is in the Tuscarora Reservation near the town of Lewiston New York.) But the Commander of the fort was aware of the danger, and he sent messengers to the forts in the vicinity, and about eight hundred warriors were collected together at Fort Kauhanauka.

The Commander sent runners to observe the movements of the enemy. The army marched towards the river, and hid themselves among the bushes under the mountain; the enemy came up, and a bloody battle ensued. The enemy was repulsed and flew from their foe. The army retired to the fort, and soon after the Commander dispatched two runners to the forts on the Genesee River to procure assistance as soon as possible.

The army received reinforcements, and they made bark canoes and carried them to the mouth of the Niagara River. Once the canoes were ready the Commander sent a chieftain and offered the enemy an intermission or parley, but the proposal was not accepted. The army immediately crossed the river and made a vigorous attack: the enemy was routed and fled from the bank without making resistance, retreating towards the head of the lake. After burning their huts, the army returned to the fort.

But the disturbances were not quelled; small parties of the Senecas often took canoes and went by water towards the head of Lake Ontario, in search of the enemy. While they avoided attacking superior forces, several engagements were made on the lake with small parties of the enemy;

After a while the Commander of Fort Kauhanauka was ardent to attack the main body of the enemy; he sent runners beyond the Genesee River, and obtained two thousand warriors. The army again crossed the Niagara River and proceeded towards the head of the lake, but before it reached the beach it met a strong force of the enemy.

After a desperate contest, the army retreated; the Commander soon perceived that it was impossible to gain conquest, and sued for peace, offering to restore the prisoners which he had taken from them. This agreement was concluded.

THE STONISH GIANTS APPEAR AGAIN:
THE VIKING'S COMPASS

About this time the Stonish Giants were diminished, with but very few found in the north regions. The Stonish Giants understood the language of the Five Nations, but they were a most savage tribe, and often attacked the hunters, but that set of hordes were extirpated

At Onondaga two men went out to hunt beaver. The men crossed the St. Lawrence River, and went far into the north, where they discovered a number of beaver dams and killed many beavers.

One day one of the men went alone in. search of beaver, but unfortunately he was taken prisoner by the Stonish Giant. The man was compelled to run a race with the [Stonish] Giant for a considerable distance. After midday the man gained and almost went out of sight, but the [Stonish] Giant whooped, by which the man was so affected that he fainted and fell down. The [Stonish] Giant took advantage of him and soon passed him.

The man was dismayed, and he turned his course and sought to escape. He endeavored to hide himself : he climbed a small tree and bent it to another tree, and leaped from tree to tree, until he reached a large basswood stump which had sprouted several branches.

There he seated himself in the midst of it and watched his pursuer: In a few moments the [Stonish] Giant came up and examined the stump for some time; at length the Giant exhibited a curious instrument, which he called a pointer. This pointer possessed a power of the nature: it directed the [Stonish] Giant where to find game, and the giant could not live without it. The man observed the motion of the pointer's hand, and as it was about to point to him, he jumped from the stump and seized it by the fingers, and instantly possessed the valuable instrument.

The [Stonish] Giant was defeated and immediately entreated him for the pointer, and offered to show the man the medical roots as a mark of friendship, which offer was accepted.

The pointer was restored to its owner, after which the [Stonish] Giant retired. The man came home and began to doctor, and cured many diseases: he was skilled in the business and drew from people the hair and worms which the witches had blown into their bodies.

A HISTORY OF WITCHCRAFT, AND A PURGE OF WITCHERS

It was supposed that the Skau-Nvatohatihawk, now the Nanticoke, a people in the south, first founded witchcraft. Great pains were taken to procure the snakes and roots from which the stuff was made to poison people.

The witches formed into a secret society; they met in the night and consulted on various subject respecting their engagements. When a person became a member of their society, he was forbidden to reveal any of their proceedings.

In the night, the witches could turn into foxes and wolves, and run very swiftly, attended by flashes of light. The witches sometimes turned into a turkey or big owl and could fly very fast, and go from town to town, and blow hairs and worms into people.

If the witches were discovered by some person they turn themselves into a stone or rotten log, and in this state they were entirely concealed

About fifty persons were indicted for being witches and were burned to death near Fort Onondaga by order of the National Committee [Senate] of the Five Nations.

A CHANGE IN BURIAL CUSTOMS

About this time a strange thing happened near the village of Kaunehsuntahkeh, which was situated east of Oneida creek. A man and his wife and another person returned from hunting, but before they reached the village the night became too late: they went into a house to stay over the night, the house where the dead bodies were deposited.

379

They kindled a fire and went to sleep, but when the: fire went out the room became dark, and the man heard something gnawing. The man kindled the fire, and he discovered that the other person was dead, eaten by a ghost. He was so frightened that he trembled, and he immediately told his wife to quit the room as soon as possible. He himself remained a few moments and then he also left the house and followed his wife and overtook her, as she had become faint and could not run fast. They saw a light coming and supposed that the ghost was chasing them. Fortunately they gained the village~

The next day the people went to the house where the dead bodies were deposited and burned the dead bodies. This important event was soon made known among the Five Nations, and afterwards they changed their mode of burial, now setting the dead person's posture facing to the east; but again they were troubled by the dead bodies and were compelled to make some alterations in burial.

THE VISIT OF A CHRISTIAN HOLY MAN TO THE TUSCARORA AROUND THE YEAR 1225 CE

The sixth family, the Esaurora, or Tuscarora, was visited by a person, who went to see their amusements. But he was abused by some of the ball-players: he punished the offender: by throwing him into a tree. He then suddenly disappeared, but the person came again and released the fellow from the tree.

The visitor appeared to be a very old man. He appeared among the people for a. while, and he taught them many things: how to respect their deceased friends, and to love their relations, &c.,

He informed the people that the whites beyond the Great Water had killed their Maker, but he had risen again; and he warned them that the whites would in some future day take possession of the Big Island, and it was impossible to prevent it: the red children would melt away like snow before the heat.

The aged became sick, and he told them to get different kinds of roots, to cure the diseases; and he also showed them the manner of mourning, &etc.

The aged man died among them and they buried him, but soon after some person went to the grave and found that he had risen.

And they have never heard of him since.

EVENTS OF THE REIGN OF KING ATOTARHO IX: THE ERIE AND THE MISSISSAUGERS DEFEAT THE FIVE NATIONS

In the reign the King Atotaro IX, perhaps 350 years before the Dutch arrived in the land of the Five Nations.

Using a rough date of 1600 CE for the Dutch appearing in the lands of the Five Nations, by Cusick's calculation we end up with a date of roughly 1250 CE for the following events..

About this time the Kanneasto-karoneah or Erians sprang from the Senecas, and became a numerous and powerful nation, occupying the country lying between the Genesee River and the Niagara River. It is thought that their national sovereignity was confirmed by the Senate of the Five Nations.

Cusick may be mistaken here, as perhaps the Eries had long been in existence – most likely they were mentioned in the tale of the Giants from ca 3,000 BCE (above). While of Iroquoian stock, in contrast to the Five Families, the Eries, like the Wendat (Huron), were ruled by women, Queens, instead of by men. Elsewhere Cusick calls the Erie by other names; perhaps the word "Kanneasto" is related to the word "Conestoga", later applied to the Andaste people.

Their Queen, named Yagowanea, resided at Fort Kauhanauka, which as mentioned before is now in the Tuscarora Reservation near Lewistown, New York. She had influence among the people, and extended her authority over twelve forts of the country.

'Yagowanea' is related to the Wendat (Huron) word 'Yegowaneh', 'Great Woman', which appears to be the title of the Queen of the female ruled Iroquois peoples.

A treaty of peace was concluded between her and the Messissaugers, who had their capitol at Twakanhah. After a time dissensions broke out between the Five Nations and the Messissaugers, and hostilities soon commenced; nonetheless, the war was regulated under her control.

The Queen lived outside Fort Kauhanauka in a long house which was called a 'Peace House'. She entertained the two parties who were at war with each other: indeed, she was called the 'Mother of the Nations'. Each nation sent her a belt of wampum as a mark of respect.

But while the Five Nations were engaged in the war, she admitted two Canandaiga warriors into her house; and just as they began to smoke the pipe of peace, a small party of the Messissaguers also came into the house. The Queen was informed that the two warriors of Canandaigua had been over the (Niagara) River and killed a young prince of the Messissaugers. This offence was too great to let pass by without condemning the murderers, and for this reason she gave them up. But she betrayed her visitors: she advised the Messissaugers to kill the warriors, which was soon executed, and the Messissaugers soon retired.

The Queen immediately went and consulted the chieftain of the Canandaigua band, stationed at Fort Kanhait-aunekay, east of Onondaga Village, now the Buffalo Reservation; and from there she went to Fort Kauquatkay, situated on Lake Erie, the residence of the Kaunaquavouhar, a chief in command of the Erian forces. She then dispatched two runners to assemble the people at Fort Kanquatkay; the Queen also sent an embassy to form an alliance with the Naywaunau-kauraunah, a savage tribe who were encamped on Lake Erie, to unite against the Five Nations.

These Naywaunau people are not further identified by Cusick, but perhaps were an Algonquin people related to the Lenape.

During the absence of the Queen from Fort Kauhanauka, a woman went privately and took a canoe and proceeded as fast as possible on Lake Ontario toward Canandaigua. She left the canoe at some place and then went through the woods, and came late in the evening to Canandaigua, a fortified town. She immediately informed the governor, Shorihowane, that the Erians were making preparations to destroy the people living on the east side of Genesee River. The woman gave directions on how to send spies.

The Governor rose in the morning and sent out two fast runners to Fort Kauhanauka to ascertain the facts of the matter. The two spies came to an old cornfield south of the fort, where they met some boys who were out hunting squirrels. The spies made inquiries and received all the necessary information concerning the Erian's council at Kauquatka, and returned home as fast as possible.

Governor Sorihowane received the news. The business was so pressed that it was impossible for him to procure any aid from the allies. He collected the warriors from the neighboring forts, amounting to fifteen hundred men, besides the women and the old men. The governor separated the people into three divisions: first, the men between thirty and fifty years of age; second, the men from twenty to thirty years of age; and third, the women and old men. The Governor commanded the leaders to be in good courage and to use all the means in their power to defeat the enemy.

After he paraded the divisions, they marched towards the Genesee River. The army halted at Fort Kawnesats, situated on a small lake east of Genesee. The women and old men were instructed to remain at the fort to cook and provide provisions for the people.

The governor had sent runners to observe the motions or the enemy. The runners now came in and announced that the Erians had crossed the Genesee River. The divisions immediately proceeded forward and laid an ambush on both side the enemy's path; the first division was in placed in front, to commence the action at the advance of the enemy. As a stratagem a certain warrior was dressed with a bear skin and was seated on the path a little distance from the front of the division; meanwhile the enemy came up and saw the bear sitting at ease. They chased it, which brought them in the midst of the first division; at once it burst forth in a most hideous yell, followed by the rattling of their war clubs.

After a severe contest the first division was compelled to retreat, but the second division up to assist and the battle was renewed. At last the Erians fled from the field, leaving behind six hundred warriors slain. The enemy hurried to cross the Genesee River, but the Governor declined to chase them, and returned to Canandaigua instead.

About this time the King of the Five Nations ordered the Great War Chief Shoribowane, a Mohawk, to march directly with an army of five thousand warriors to aid the Governor of Canandaigua against the Erians. He was to attack Fort Kauquatkay and endeavor to extinguish the council fire of the enemy, who were becoming dangerous to the neighboring nations;

But unfortunately, during the siege a shower of arrows flew from the fort and the Great War Chief Shorihowane was killed. His body was conveyed back to Genesee and was buried in a solemn manner, but however the siege continued on afterwards for several days.

The Queen sued for peace, the army immediately ceased from hostilities and left the Erians in entire possession of the country.

THE INTRODUCTION OF POISONED ARROWS INTO WARFARE

About this time the Oneidas killed a very poisonous blue otter; the meat was very carefully preserved, with some used to hunt, and some to poison arrows when going out to war. Some of the witches obtained this meat to poison people.

THE TUSCARORA WAR WITH THE NANTICOKE

The sixth family made its residence near the mouth of the Neuse River in what later became North Carolina, and became three tribes: the Kautanohakau, the Kauwetseka, and the Tuscarora. And they united into a league and were at war with the Nanticokes, totally on the sea shores.

EVENTS OF THE REIGN OF KING ATOTARHO X

In the reign Atotorho X, perhaps about 250 years before the Dutch arrived in the lands of the Five Nations. The Oyalquarkeror, Big Bear, continued to invade the country at Onondaga.

Using a rough date of 1600 CE for the Dutch appearing in the lands of the Five Nations, by Cusick's calculation we end up with a date of 1350 CE for the following events. The "Big Bear" appear to be the Andaste.

A party went and encamped a day's journey distance from the village, where they hunted and killed a few deer. One morning a woman left the camp and was going home to pound corn and to supply the men with provisions. But before she reached half way she was attacked by the monstrous Bear, and was soon devoured.

As she did not return, the men were anxiously waiting, and they were suspicious about her whereabouts, and a man was sent to see if she was coming. He advanced to where she had been assaulted, and discovered the place of her remains, and he soon perceived her fate.

He immediately reported this and the men immediately proceeded to the place, and while they were examining her remains the bear made a vigorous attack. The men met a severe engagement, but in a short time the monster was killed. They procured some of its meat for useful purposes.

EVENTS OF THE REIGN OF KING ATOTARHO XI

In the reign of Atortarho XI, perhaps about 150 years before the Dutch appeared in the lands of the Five Nations. About this time, the Tuscaroras sent messengers and renewed their intercourse with: the Five Nations.

Using a rough date of 1600 CE for the Dutch appearing in the lands of the Five Nations, by Cusick's calculation we end up with a date of 1450 CE for the following events.

TUSCARORA CENSUS OF THE FIVE NATIONS

By this time the Long House became numerous and powerful. Each nation could muster as follows: the Mowhawks, 5,000 warriors; the Oneidas, 3,500 warriors; the Seneca 6,000 warriors; the Onondagas, 4,000 warriors; the Cayugas, 4, 500 warriors; for a total of 23;000 warriors.

The Mowhawk were considered the oldest brother and appointed to keep a watch towards the sunrise in the east; the Senceas were appointed to keep a watch towards the sunsetting in the west.

The Bear tribes (clans) nominate the Chief Warrior of the nation. The laws of the confederation provide that the Onondagas furnish the King, and the Mohawks the Great War Chief of the Five Nations.

The Senators met annually, at Fort Onondaga to promote their national prosperity.

The Long House was composed of free and independent nations, and these have been acknowledged as such in the treaties made with them by neighboring nations. Every independent nation has a government of their own. They each have a national committee which meets occasionally. They each have a Chief Ruler, called the 'Aukoyaner', a peace-maker who is invested with authority to administer the government. No one can hold the office of the 'Aukoyaner', or 'Lord', except for members of the Turtle tribe [clan]. While he governs the nation, he is not allowed to go out to war: his duty is to stay home and preserve peace among his people.

Each nation has a right to punish individuals of their own' nation for offences committed within their jurisdiction. Each nation is bound to oppose any hostile invasions of an enemy.

THE CENSUS OF THE TUSCARORA

The Tuscaroras were yet numerous and had twenty four large towns, and probably could muster 6,000 warriors. They possessed the country lying between the sea shores and the mountains which divide the Atlantic states. But afterwards a contest arose between them and the southern nations: the Oyatoh, Kwntariroraunuh, and Caweda.

THE ALLIANCE FORMS, AND THE TUSCARORA DEFEAT THEIR ENEMIES

The war lasted for many years, and unfortunately the Tuscaroras became so distressed that their frontier settlements were considerably reduced. But the Tuscaroras then sent messages and received assistance from their brethren the Five Nations, and war was carried on for sometime.

At last the enemy was compelled to suspend their hostilities.

A COMET IMPACTS, AND THE SPANISH ARRIVE

About this time an earthquake was felt throughout the Kingdom, and it was thought that a large comet fell into some of the lakes; other signs were seen in the heavens.

The Defender ceased from visiting the people in bodily form, but appeared to the prophet. In a dream he foretold that the whites would cross the Big Waters and bring some liquors and buy up red people's lands. He advised them not to comply with the wishes of the whites, lest they should ruin themselves and displease their Maker: They would destroy the Tree of Peace and extinguish the Great Council Fire at Onondaga, which was so long preserved to promote the national sovereignty.

This passage probably reflects the arrival in the lands of the Five Nations of news of the Spanish settlement in the Caribbean.

EVENTS OF THE REIGN OF KING ATOTARHO XII: DEFEAT OF THE MOHEGANS

In the reign of Atotarho XII, perhaps about 50 years before the Dutch arrived in the lands of the Five Nations.

Using a rough date of 1600 CE for the Dutch appearing in the lands of the Five Nations, by Cusick's calculation we end up with a date of 1550 CE for the following events.

The Tehatirihokea, or Mohawks, were at war with the Ranatshaganhna, supposed Mohegans, who occupied the opposite bank of the Skaunataty or Hudson River. The war was maintained by small expeditions: the Mowhawks would cross the river and attack the enemy, their canoes continuously kept in the river to cover their retreat.

But after a while the Mohegans expaliated the war: The Chief of the Mohawks received orders from the King, and invited the two confederate nations, the Oneidas and the Onondagas, to unite against the common enemy. The band of the combined forces immediately crossed the river and took their revenge upon a part of the country, and the enemy were compelled to sue for peace.

EVENTS OF THE REIGN OF KING ATOTARHO XIII

In the reign Atotarho XIII, *[in the year 1608, the Dutch arrived in the lands of the Five Nations.]*

When the Dutch began to trade with the Five Nations, they immediately supplied them with firearms. The Five Nations used these weapons to attack all nations trading with any other nation than the Dutch, attacking the peoples who traded with the French colonists, the English colonists, and later with the Swedish colonists along the Delaware River. The attempt by Sweden to found a colony at the mouth of the Delaware River for trade in beaver fur and tobacco cultivation greatly intensified these wars.

From European records, both the Lenape and the Erie are known to have been defeated during this time, and these defeats are described in the following passages of Cusick's Ancient History. Thus it is clear that Cusick's chronology needs to be set against the Dutch arrival in the lands of the Five Nations, rather than against Columbus' discovery of America.

The Keatahki-chroneah (Lenape) were fighting with the neighboring tribes, and were injurious to the frontier settlements. The Five Nations sent Thoyenogea with an army of 5,000 warriors and defeated the Keatahki-chroneah, and drove them west of the Ohio River; and they laid waste the enemies country, and attacked other tribes, &c.

About this time the Erians declared a war against the Five Nations. A long bloody war ensued, and at last the Erians were driven from the country, and are thought to have been incorporated with some of the southern nations, after which the kingdom enjoyed itself without disturbance for many years.

THE ANCIENT HISTORY OF THE NATCHEZ: THE ANCIENT WORD

Given by the Chief of the Guardians of the Temple to Simon Antoine Le Page du Pratz, and preserved by him

Adapted to Modern Usage By E.P. Grondine ©copyright 2004-2005

INTRODUCTION

Little is known about the life of Simon Antoine Le Page du Pratz, the man who preserved for us the Ancient Word of the Natchez. While the period of Le Page du Pratz's life while he was in Louisiana is well documented by his own account of it, his life before and after this remains a mystery to this day.

For example, Le Page du Pratz's earlier military service is known from his writing, but nothing of its dates, his rank, or where he saw service. Le Page du Pratz is known to have had some training in the classics, architecture, engineering, and mathematics, but where and when is unknown. Of his relationship with the Scotsman John Law, who fathered the Mississippi Scheme, the French colonial effort in Louisiana, the collapse of which bankrupted France, and who earlier smuggled English craftsmen to France, nothing is known. Of Le Page du Pratz's relation as an agent in Louisiana for Hubert, little is known, and there is even uncertainty as to his title. Of Le Page du Pratz's life and family after his service in Louisiana, nothing is known.

What is known is that Simon Antoine was a great friend of the Natchez people, and he was nearly perfectly fluent in their language.

"Having arrived [in 1718] at Choupic Creek, the Sieur Lavigne, a Canadian, lodged me in a cabin of the Aquelou-Pissas [people], whose village he had bought. He gave other [cabins] to my workmen for their lodging; and we were all happy to find, upon our arrival, that we were under shelter, in a place that was uninhabited.

"A few days after my arrival I bought an Indian female slave from one of the inhabitants, in order to have a person who could dress our victuals, as I perceived the inhabitants did all they could to entice away our labourers, and to gain them by fair promises.

"As for my slave and me, we did not understand one another's language; but I made myself to be understood by signs, which these natives comprehend very easily: she was of the nation of the Chitimachas, with whom the French had been at war for some years."

It turned out that the language of the Chitimacha was near to the language of the Natchez. By 1720 du Pratz desired to go to Natchez, and his slave decided she would go with him, as she had relatives there. Hearing of her plan, her old father offered to buy her back from du Pratz. The Chitimacha girl, however, refused to leave her master, whereupon, her father performed a rite of his tribe, which made her the ward of the white man--a simple ceremony of joining hands.

LE PAGE DU PRATZ MASTERS NATCHEZ

[I wish to thank Gordon Sayre of the University of Oregon and his assistant Nicole Degli Esposi for permission to reproduce the following from their new translation of Le Page du Pratz, currently available at http://darkwing.uoregon.edu/~gsayre/LPDP.html.]

"Most of the Natchez speak the common language [Mobilian jargon] fairly well, and I understood that in such a way to be able to comprehend that which had to do with the needs of life and that which concerned trade.

"However, I also wanted to learn the language of this nation [the Natchez], so that I could talk to the women who simply don't speak the common language and who often bring us many of the necessary things in life. I would then be quite at ease in questioning them and in answering them back.

"What further increased my desire to know their language was a desire to educate myself about the history of this nation, which seemed to me distinct amongst the others, and which I had heard celebrated for its spirit and its good qualities.

"So, I told my slave to ask some of her relatives among the Natchez to come to my place. Through the good relations that I had with him whom she brought to see me [this man was quite possibly du Pratz's slave's father], I convinced him to arrange for me to interview those who were most respected".

"The first person who I met was the Chief of the Guardians of the Temple. I devoted myself to getting to know him, without relying on the superiority that we naturally have over them through our enlightenment, our sciences, and our arts. I was charmed to behold a man who, better than any other, could give me the instruction which I wished for about their religion, their temple, which I saw from the first days of my arrival, and the eternal fire that was maintained there. What also gave me great pleasure was that he knew the common language; I had through this means much greater capacity.

"I offered him much friendship and I behaved with him in a way that was so well mannered, so frank, and so liberal, conforming altogether into their manners of civility, that I was fully assured of his trust. I made myself a true friend, and as I found in him all of the candor, spirit, and prudence that I could [323] have wanted, I sincerely accorded him my friendship.

"It was through his [The Chief of the Guardians of the Temple's] own enterprise that I came to know the Great Sun, or Sovereign of the Nation, and his brother Tattooed with a Serpent who was the Chief Warrior.

"In this way, in a little time, I attracted great attention among the Natchez. I easily learned the language of the people, and I did not delay to learn a little of that of the Nobles, which I learned through the frequency with which I encountered certain ones and through putting what I already knew into use."

THE ANCIENT WORD

What was the Ancient Word of the Natchez, and how was it preserved by them? Le Page du Pratz gives us this account:

"These people have no assistance from writing, and are able to preserve their own history only through tradition. Thus it is impossible for them to learn it except by frequent conversations. The old men are the depositaries of this, and as it has been very faithfully transmitted from generation to generation, they call it "The Ancient Word."

"What contributes much to preserve this in all its purity is that they do not teach it to all the young people indifferently. This tradition is all their science and the only authority in which they are able to base their reasonings. This is why reason makes them vividly conscious of the fact that they ought not to waste this treasure, and that the surest means of preserving it unaltered is not to entrust such a precious deposit to people who do not have the prudence necessary to make good use of it, or who in a little while would entirely deform it by additions or by omissions equally unfortunate to the truth.

"They therefore choose for this purpose those among their youths of whom they have the best opinion, in order to teach them the things of the past. Moreover, this choice is very easy for them, because their children are always under their eyes, and the old men are in a very good position to know them, one cabin ordinarily embracing an entire family."

Despite Le Page du Pratz's assertion that the Natchez had no alphabet, they did have pictoglyphic records to aid in the recall of the Ancient Word. Simon Antonine had seen these himself, although he was unaware of it:

"The eternal fire is in the first part of the temple. In the other and more secluded part are two planks worked by hand on which are may minute carvings which [I was] unable to make out, owing to insufficient light."

These writings were known to the Natchez priesthood, the Guardians of the Temple as "speaking cloths" ["speaking stuff", Swanton translation], the term they applied to European books.

THE END OF THE NATCHEZ

In the northern regions of North America the English had long been using the Five Nations as mercenaries to attack the peoples with whom the French traded in the north. In the southern regions of the continent, the English employed the Cherokee, Kushita, Chikasaw, and Chotaw peoples for the same purpose, to attack those peoples who traded with the French. As part of their coordinated strategy to remove the French from North America, the English had continued to try to enlist the Natchez to their side.

Le Page du Pratz stayed with the Natchez for eight years, until 1728, when he took up an appointment as manager of the Company of the West's plantation. The French governor managed to appoint Sieur Chepart as the new commandant to the Natchez, a man whose greed in demanding their lands under cultivation threatened them with starvation, and who thereby drove the Natchez straight into the arms of the English.

By this time Le Page du Pratz's Natchez friends the Great Sun and the Great Chief of the Warriors Tattooed with a Serpent were both dead. One year after he left the Natchez, they rose up and slaughtered the entire French colony, while Le Page du Pratz was busy putting down a slave revolt around New Orleans.

The resulting French reprisals finished with the end of the Natchez as a separate people. Those who surrendered were at first enslaved on what was now the King's plantation, which du Pratz is strangely silent about, given that he was that plantation's manager. Then their women and children, including all of the noble line, were then sold into slavery in Santo Domingo.

Further details of Simon Antoine's role in the end of the Natchez are unknown.

THE FRAGMENTS OF THE ANCIENT WORD

One final mystery about Simon Antoine is why he did not publish his memoirs until some 18 years after his return to France.

After the Natchez revolt, Le Page du Pratz continued on in Louisiana for another 6 years, until 1734. After his return to France, the record then goes silent, perhaps due to the pubic anger which had followed on the collapse of John Law's schemes for the development of colonies in Louisiana.

Sometime before 1753, Le Page du Pratz began to help Dumont de Montigny with his book, Memoires Historiques sur La Louisiane. Perhaps this work led Simon Antoine to author a series of magazine articles for the Journal Oeconomique, a Paris periodical devoted to scientific and commercial topics. These articles which were published in twelve installments between September 1751 and February 1753 as "Memoire sur la Louisiane" by Monsieur Le Page du Pratz

One result of Le Page du Pratz's efforts was undoubtedly renewed French interest in their North American colonies. Another result was renewed English interest in the French colonies, and it is possible that his writings set the stage for the English military operation to take control of the Ohio River, and their resulting war with France, which is known in the United States as the "French and Indian Wars".

In his final book of 1758, which collected together these articles, Simon Antoine, Le Page du Pratz, stated that he did not write a dictionary of the Natchez language, because it would be useless: the few Natchez who were left alive after the French reprisals had been absorbed into the Chickasaw nation.

THE SWANTON TRANSLATION

What follows has been assembled and adapted to modern usage from those fragments of the Ancient Word which du Pratz preserved for us, and more specifically those fragments of his writings which the anthropologist John Swanton had translated into English for his book "Indian Tribes of the Lower Mississippi Valley". It is unfortunate that Swanton never understood that the Natchez were originally not a Mushkogean people.

THE INTRODUCTION OF
THE CHIEF OF THE GUARDIANS OF THE TEMPLE

The duty which I have obliges me to know all that you ask of me. I am going then to relate it to you. Listen to me.

THE CREATION

It was necessary for Le Page du Pratx to undertake some discussion with the Chief of the Guardians of the Temple to learn that they called their creator "Coyocop-Chill". "Coyocop" is usually translated as "spirit", though it also has the sense of "force" and "mind". The word "Chill" is without doubt cognate with the Mayan word "chillam", which they applied as the title of their chief priest, the "Chillam Balam". These Mayan chief priests were responsible for preserving their sciences and performing astrological forecasts, and the title "Chilam Balam" may be translated as 'The Kings's Celestial Interpreter, though this does not capture all of its nuances. While the Natchez word "chill" has many of the same connotations, it is usually simply translated as "supreme", "great", or "grand".

The Great Spirit is so powerful
that all things were nothing before him.
The Great Spirit has made all that we see,
and all that we are able to see.

The Great Spirit made all things by his will.
The Great Spirit created all things by his goodness alone;
He is so good that he is not able to do harm to anyone,
even if he wished it.

The Great Spirit created the Servant Spirits [Coyocop-Thecou],
so that they would to always be present before him.

THE CREATION OF MAN

The Servant Spirits made in the universe the beautiful works which we admire,
but the Great Spirit himself formed man with his own hands alone.

The Great Spirit kneaded a little earth and water together,
and he made of it a little man.
After He had made, formed, completed, and rounded him, and found him to be good,
He placed him on the Earth and breathed upon him.
Immediately this little figure thought, acted, walked,
and found himself a grown man very well shaped,
and he began to grow [reproduce].

[Simon Antoine noted that this resembled making pottery.]

The Great Spirit formed man first,
because as the stronger and the more courageous,

391

he was going to be the chief and the stay of the woman
who the Great Spirit made [next] to be his companion.

THE GOOD SPIRIT AND THE EVIL SPIRIT: TLALOC

*There was also an Evil Spirit in the Natchez creation myths, who Le Page du Pratz mentions
incidentally. However, the Evil Spirit's place in the grand scheme of things is obscure, either because
either the Chief of the Guardians of the Temple withheld that knowledge, or Le Page du Pratz did
not understand him, or what is most likely, Simon Antoine himself concealed that information from
his French Catholic audience.*

They [the Natchez] believe the existence of two Great Spirits, a Good [Spirit, the Great
Spirit] and a Bad [Spirit, the Evil Spirit]. They do not, as I have said, invoke the Good
Spirit; but they pray to the Bad [Spirit, the Evil Spirit], in order to avert from their
persons and possessions the evils which he might inflict upon them.

They pray to the Evil Spirit, not because they think him almighty, for it is the Good
Spirit whom they believe so; but [they pray to him] because, according to them, he
governs the air, the seasons, the rain, the fine weather, and all that may benefit or hurt
the productions of the Earth.

THE EVIL SPIRIT CAUSES A GREAT FLOOD

The air was filled with other spirits,
of which some were worse than others;
and they [the other spirits] had a chief [the Evil Spirit]
who was yet worse than themselves.

Then a great rain fell on the Earth so abundantly and for such a long time
that it was nearly completely covered with water.

Almost all men were destroyed by the water,
except for a very small number who saved themselves on a very high mountain.
After the flood, these few people repeopled the earth

All fire was extinguished on the Earth.
But a little bird named Caily-oily,
which is entirely red (the cardinal),
had hung on by his claws to the heavens during the whole time of the flood.
He now brought fire [back to the Earth] from the heavens.

This is most likely a reference to a comet.

The Great Spirit found the Chief of the Spirits of the Air so bad
that he had tied him forever.
Thus these Spirits of the Air no longer do as much harm,
especially when one prays to them to do no evil.

THE PROPHETIC COUPLE APPEAR

Mississippian [Southern Ceremonial cult] temples usually contained a male and female figurine. While it has long been thought that these figurines represented divinities, in point of fact they were representations of the prophetic couple described in the following passage.

While the Natchez placed this event here at this time in their Ancient Word, given its similarity to events described in the religions of Central Mexico, most likely the Natchez acquired this religion after their move to the Gulf Coast of Mexico, which will be related in the next part of their Ancient Word Other indicators of a Mesoamerican source for Natchez religion are their use of ritual mats, thrones, and litter, which resembles similar usage in Central America. Another piece of evidence indicative of a possible Mesoamerican origin is that the key Natchez religious term "chill" may be cognate with the key Mayan religious term "chillam".

A great number of years ago there appeared among us a man and his wife, who came down from the sun. It is not that we believe that the sun [in the heavens] had a wife who bore him children, or that this man and his wife were the descendants of the sun [which warms]; but when they first appeared among us they were so bright and luminous that we had no difficulty in believing that they came down from the sun.

This man told us that having seen from on high that we did not govern ourselves well, and that we had no master, each of us having presumption enough to think himself capable of governing others, while he could not even conduct himself, he had thought it fit to come down among us to teach us how to live better.

"Moreover, he then told us that in order to be in a condition to govern others it was necessary to know how to guide oneself, and that in order to live in peace among ourselves, and to please the Great Spirit, we must observe the following rules:

Never kill any one,
except in the defense of your own life;
Never know any other woman besides your own,
[when married];
Never take any thing which belongs to another;
Never lie, nor get drunk;
Do not be greedy,
but give freely and with joy,
that which you have;
Share your food generously,
with those who are in need of it."

This man impressed us with these words, because he said them with authority; and he obtained the respect of the Old Men [the council] themselves, although he did not spare them more than others. The Old Men [the council] assembled, and resolved among themselves that since this man had so much intelligence to teach them what it was good to do, he must be recognized as their Ruler; so much the more as in governing them, himself he could make them remember better than any other what he had taught them.

So the Old Men went in the early morning to the cabin where they had had him sleep, along with his wife, and they proposed to him that he be our ruler. He refused at first, saying that he would not be obeyed, and the disobedient would not fail to die.

But finally he accepted the offer which was made to him on the following conditions:

"That we would go to inhabit another country, which was better than that one which we were then in, and which he would show to us; that we would live in the future as he had taught us the evening before; that we would promise to recognize no other Ruler besides himself, and those who should descend from him and his wife; and that nobility should be perpetuated through the women, which he explained to us in this way:

"If I have", he said to us, "male and female children, they will not be able to marry each other, as they will be brothers and 1sisters". To which he added, "The boy shall take from among the people a girl who pleases him; this man shall be the Ruler [the Great Sun]; but this man's sons shall not be even Princes [the Suns], but only Nobles."

"The children of my daughter, [on the other hand], shall be Princes and Princesses [the Suns]. The eldest of her male children shall be the Ruler [the Great Sun], and her eldest girl shall be the Princess [the Sun] who will give birth to the Ruler [the Great Sun].

"The descendants of the Ruler and the Princes shall descend in rank, but not those of the girl, even though this daughter or another Princess has married a man of the people.

"The Princes and Princesses [the Suns] shall not ally [marry] themselves together, nor yet with their own cousins, nor with the children of their own cousins."

[And finally he said that,] "In the absence of a sister of the Ruler, his nearest female relative shall be the mother of his successor."

Pursuing his speech, he then said to us that in order not to forget the good words which he had brought to us, a temple should be built, into which only the Princes and Princesses [the male and female Suns] should have a right to enter to speak to the Great Spirit. In this temple should be eternally preserved a fire, which he would make descend from the sun [in the heavens], from where he had come. The wood with which this fire should be fed should be a pure wood without bark.

Eight wise men should be chosen from the nation to guard this fire and tend it day and night; these eight Wise Men should have a Chief who would watch over the manner in which they performed their duty; any one of them who failed in it should be put to death.

He then wished that at the other extremity of the country which we should inhabit (and our nation was then much more extensive than it is now) a second temple should be built, where in like manner fire should be kept which had been taken from the first, so that if the fire came to be extinguished in the one temple they could seek the other, in order to relight it. And he informed us that if this misfortune ever happened death would extend itself over our nation until the fire was relighted.

They promised him to observe and perform all these things, and then he consented to be our Ruler, but he did not wish to be called by any other name than "The", which means "thee" [You].

While one is clearly looking here at an indigenously developed culture, speculating on the question of a possible Mediterranean influence on the Early Formative peoples of the Huasteca region leads to tantalizing possibilities. Among the Bronze Age peoples of the Mediterranean Sea, "T'e" [Theous] meant "God", and this title was applied to their rulers, and while nothing is currently known of the rules of succession of the Mediterranean Bronze Age peoples, it is well proven by their remains that every one of them had a group of powerful "Priestesses" who may have paralleled to some degree "the Suns" of the Natchez. And though nothing of Mediterranean Bronze Age manufacture has ever been recovered to date in the limited excavations which have been undertaken in the Huasteca region, female religious figurines similar to those found in the Bronze Age Mediterranean have been found there in abundance. [a summary of the results of Gordon F. Ekholm's excavations in Huasteca is available online at http://anthro.amnh.org/anthropology/research/ekholm.html.] While to my knowledge there was no earlier development of such a female figurine tradition anywhere in the Americas, anyone wishing to speculate any further on these matters would be well advised to wait for the ground truth which will someday come from excavations in Huasteca.

However, after his death, his descendants were called "Suns", because the man and woman came out originally from the sun *[from the east?]*, and because the "The" was so brilliant that one could scarcely look at him.

Then he had the temples built, established the Guardians of the Temple, eight for each temple, and for each temple he established a Chief of the Guardians.

THE MASTER OF THE CEREMONIES, THE MASTER OF MYSTERIES

Besides the eight Guardians of the Temple, two of whom were always on watch, and the Chief of the Guardians of the Temple, there also belonged to the service of the temple a Master of the Ceremonies, who was also the Master of the Mysteries, since he conversed very familiarly with the Spirit(s). Above all these persons was the Great Sun, who was at the same time the Chief Priest and the Ruler of the nation.

THE CEIBA TREE

In this temple two men tend the perpetual fire during each quarter of the moon. There are eight guardians for the four quarters, and a superior who is called the Chief of the Guardians of the Fire [Temple] to command them and to see that they do their duty, and to have the wood brought for this fire.

This wood must be clear wood, and they employ for the fire only clear white walnut (or hickory) without bark. The logs are 7 to 8 inches in diameter by 8 feet long. They are placed near the temple about the trunk of a tree with a rather short stem.

This tree is covered with thorns from the ground to its top.

This passion-thorn [honey locust] tree does not rise above the height of a shrub, but its trunk is rather thick for its height. Its leaf resembles that of the black thorn, and its wood while it is green is not very hard. Its thorns are at least two inches long, and are very hard and piercing; within half an inch of their root two other small thorns grow out from them so as to form a cross. The whole trunk is covered with these thorns, so that you must be very wary how you approach it, or cut it.

This shrub is held in great esteem among the Natchez; but I never could learn for what reason. I have never been able to find out why the Natchez have respect for this tree wherever they find it, unless it be on account of the employment to which it is destined.

THE FIRST ETERNAL FIRE

And in presence of the entire nation, he made descend the fire of the Sun on walnut (hickory) wood which he had prepared, and when it was lighted, some of it was carried with much attention and respect into the other temple, which was at the farther extremity of our country.

[In his book "Unearthing Atlantis", Charles R. Pelligrino describes the late Spyridon Marinatos's recovery of a Bronze Age quartz convex lens on Thera (page 219, 1991 edition. The Natchez would offer Simon Antoine a small fortune for his "burning glass", but he declined and instead offered it to them as a gift.]

THE PROPHET'S END, AND HIS FOUNDATION OF THE FEASTS

He lived a very long time, and saw the children of his children.

Finally, he instituted the feasts which you see.

THE FEASTS OF THE NATCHEZ

Le Page du Pratz provided us with these descriptions of the feasts of the Natchez, which according to the claim of the previous line of the Ancient Word were instituted by the Prophet.

The Natchez begin their year in the month of March, [as was the practice in ancient Europe], and divide it into thirteen moons. At every new moon they celebrate a feast, which takes its name either from the principal fruits reaped in the preceding moon, or from animals that are then usually hunted. [I shall give an account of one or two of these feasts as concisely as I can.]

These feasts are equally religious and political: religious in that they appear to be instituted to thank the Great Spirit for the benefits he has sent for men; political in that the subjects then pay their ruler the tribute which they owe him.

But however absolute the authority of the Great Sun may be, and although many people give themselves to him to serve him, and a number of warriors attach themselves to his person, in order to follow him wherever he goes, and to hunt for him, yet he raises no stated impositions. And what he receives from those people appears to be given not so much as a right due to him, but as a voluntary homage and a testimony of their love for and gratitude to him.

The ornaments [head dress and attachments] suitable to the supreme rank are the marks of sovereignty, and in the ceremonies their princes always wear them, if not all of them, then at least a part of them.

THE FEAST OF THE WINTER SOLSTICE:
THE BATTLE TO SAVE THE SUN

The first moon, [which corresponds roughly with our month of March], is called the Deer Moon, and it begins their new year. It is celebrated by them with universal joy, and is at the same time an anniversary memorial of one of the most interesting events in their history.

[This entire spectacle is very interesting, and not being entirely satisfied with what the Chief of the Guardians of the Temple told me about them, I wished to see these feasts with my own eyes, and I have seen them more than once.]

In ancient times a Great Sun suddenly heard a great tumult in his village, and he left his cabin quickly to quiet it. As a result he fell into the hands of a hostile nation which had come to surprise them, but the warriors immediately ran to the Great Sun's assistance and took him back, and put their enemies to flight.

This feast probably celebrates the return of warm weather after winter, the liberation of the sun from the depths of winter.

In order to remember this honorable deed of their history, all the warriors separate themselves into two bodies which are distinguished by the color of their feathers: the one party has white feathers, while the other, which represents the enemy, has red ones.

These two bands place themselves in hiding near the cabin of the Great Sun. Then the band of the enemy, at the head of which is the Great War Chief, comes out first. It advances a short distance, making many movements and contortions and uttering great cries. The Great Sun then comes out of his cabin in all his apparel, rubbing his eyes as if he had just been awakened. The enemies then throw themselves upon him and endeavor to carry him away, when the other warriors rush up and take him out of their hands.

This action takes place without any accident on either side and without quarrels, but not without noise. The cries of the enemies' while they attack are the cries of death; those of the nation attacked are the cries of fear and terror. There are some cries heard which seem to be intended to encourage the warriors of the nation, but the enemy continues the cries of death so long as the Great Sun is in their hands.

The nation running against the enemies approaches them. Both sides make many movements which denote the strategies of war, and these go on for about a half an hour. During this time the Great Sun defends himself alone with a war club of the ancient pattern, one made entirely of wood. He knocks down a great number of the enemy without touching them - the mere motion of the blow throws them down, and in fact the blow approaches so near the enemies' heads that one would say that he really struck them.

[*Simon Antoine notes here:* I was surprised to see this venerable old man, the Great Sun, playing such a magnificent role with so much activity and address; one whose glances shot terror into the hearts of his enemies, to which they bore witness by their different cries.]

Then the nation attacked came and engaged the enemies, who trembled upon seeing the fury painted in their eyes, and the gestures of those arriving, and then changed their cries. Those warriors representing the Natchez knocked down a great number of the enemy, who rose again after the Natchez had passed beyond them.

Finally the enemy flees, and are pursued as far as a wood, which is represented by a bower of canes. This is always left after the feast for the young people.

The Natchez then bring back the Great Sun. Satisfied with such a complete victory, and at having rescued the Great Sun from such great danger, they utter cries of joy, with which the air reverberates, and which echoes from the neighboring woods repeat in their turn.

The entire nation, which sees the Great Sun's return testifies to its satisfaction by redoubled cries of joy mingled with love. The old men, the women, and the children, who are merely spectators along the edge of the open space, endeavor to imitate the warriors by their cries of joy.

THE FEAST OF THE WINTER SOLSTICE:
THE SEPARATION OF HEAVEN AND EARTH

The Great Sun, having been led back to his cabin, rested there and recovered from the violent movements he had gone through with. [These movements were such that an actor of 30 would have had difficulty in sustaining them for such a long time; nevertheless, the Great Sun was more than 90 years old.]

While the Great Sun rests, the warriors who had represented the enemies reenter among the people in groups, pretending to be ignorant whether their ruler is wounded or not. Because they do not see him appear, they utter sighs so plaintive that they draw pity from strangers.

Scarcely has the Great Sun rested for half an hour when he comes out of his cabin without his crown. Cries of joy and respectful salutation are then heard from all sides, but these cease as soon as they see him take the road to the temple.

The Great Sun stops in the middle of the open space in front of the temple, before which he makes a kind of obeisance, bending very low without bending his knees, and he takes up a little earth which he throws on his head, and then turns successively toward the four quarters of the earth, doing the same thing in each direction.

Then, without changing his position, the Great Sun stares at the temple, which he has to the south of him, and he extends his arms horizontally. He then remains in this attitude about half an hour, without any more movement than that of a statue.

Then the Great [Chill] Master of Ceremonies comes to relieve the Great Sun and he does the same thing. The Great Master of Ceremonies is himself relieved at the end of an identical period of time by the Great War Chief, who in his turn remains there for an equally long time.

A profound silence is preserved during the prayer which the Great Sun makes, and when he has reentered his cabin plaintive cries begin again, which they cease after the Great Master of Ceremonies and the Great War Chief have completed their ceremony. For then the Great Sun comes out of his cabin, dressed with the ornaments which proclaim his dignity: these are the feather crown, and a necklace of large pearls and feathers which hangs down from it.

They bring his throne, which is a large stool with four feet made from one piece of wood. This throne is covered with a beautiful skin, well painted and ornamented with different designs. The Great Sun seats himself on his throne, and the warriors cover his shoulders with a beautiful bison robe and his feet with many furs.

As soon as the ruler appears on his throne cries of happiness are heard, and these last until the end of the feast. The women make him presents of different kinds, while uttering loud cries of joy, and the last who brings the presents ends the feast.

All these outside ceremonies being finished, the Suns [Princes and Princesses] conduct the sovereign back into his cabin. If there are strangers present, the Great Sun has them invited to eat.

[One can rest by taking a walk until evening if he wishes to see the dance, which takes place on every feast day in the cabin of the Great Sun.]

THE MID-SUMMER HARVEST FEASTS

The second moon, which corresponds to our month of April, is called the Strawberry Moon, as that fruit then abounds in great quantities.

The third moon, *[which corresponds to our month of May]*, is that of the Small Corn. This moon is often impatiently looked for, for their crop of large corn never suffices to nourish them from one harvest to another.

The fourth moon is that of the Watermelons, and it corresponds to our month of June.

The fifth moon, which corresponds to our month of July, is the month of the Fishes [or Peaches]. In this month they also gather grapes, if the birds have suffered (allowed) them to ripen.

The sixth moon, which corresponds with our month of August, is that of the Mulberries. At this feast they also carry fowls to the Great Sun.

THE FEAST OF THE SUMMER SOLSTICE:
THE FEAST OF THE TUN OF IMPORTANCE:
THE FEAST OF THE NEW CORN (MAIZE)

The seventh moon, which corresponds with our month of September, is the month of the Maize, or Great Corn. This feast is beyond dispute the most solemn of all of them.

This feast principally consists of eating in common, and in a religious manner, the new corn, which has been sown expressly for this purpose, with suitable ceremonies.

THE CLEARING OF NEW FIELDS

The Feast of the Corn required that new lands be cleared annually. Thus after many years a large area would be have been converted from forest to crop lands.

When the warriors wished to sow this new corn they choose a new plot of earth, on that within the memory of man has never been cultivated. First they cut the canes, the creepers, the vine stalks, and all that makes a thick forest. Then they peel the bark from the trees down to the wood from their bases to the height of two feet.

All that which has been cut and laid on the earth may cover it to a depth of two feet. It is left thus for fifteen days, after which the warriors set fire to it. The fire burns so hot and rises so high that it burns even the tops of the trees, and brings down the sap which may have gone up them, which burns the roots of the canes and the rest of the underbrush, at least in great part, so that the fire leaves only some green canes, the roots of which extend so deeply into the earth that it is unable to damage them; but these die during the year.

All that concerns the working of this field and the farming of this corn is done only by the warriors, from the time they have begun to cultivate it, to the moment of the feast, and the Great War Chief is always at their head. These warriors are not only the ones who clear the field and put it in a condition to receive seed: they are also the ones who sow the maize, and weed it as many times as are necessary. The smallest operations are not in the least unworthy of their hands.

It would be a profanation if any other person than the warriors should touch this field, and if it happened that a native other than a warrior put his hand on it, this grain is so much respected and so sacred, it is believed that he would never be able to go away from the field, but would perish there miserably.

THE CONSTRUCTION OF THE GRANARY

When the corn approaches maturity the warriors go to the place where the corn is eaten every year. At the edge of this open space they make a kind of granary, which they call "Momo-ataop", which means "valuable granary" or "venerable granary".

This open space is fairly large. It is, however, almost entirely shaded by the extreme height of the trees which surround it. It is covered with a beautiful lawn, the grass of which is cut from time to time, so that it may not get too high before the time of the feast. The trees which enclose this place create a large grove without any underbrush: beneath them, and around the open space, the grass is only as high as the knee, while farther off the grass has the same height as elsewhere, four to five feet.

The granary which the warriors make for storing this corn (maize) is of circular shape, and raised two feet above the earth. It is furnished inside with cane mats. The bottom is made of large whole canes, and the outside is also provided with these canes, because the teeth of the rats, however good, are unable to make an opening in them, on account of the natural varnish which covers them. This also prevents the rats from going up the sides of the granary in order to enter through the covering, which, owing to the manner in which it is made, protects this grain from the greatest storms.

Le Page du Pratz adds that the French call this granary "the tun" on account of its round shape, but DuMont states that the French adopted the word "tun" from the Natchez. In the next paragraph, Simon Antoine also notes that this "tun" has the shape of a tower, rather than that of a French "tun". This tower form may be reflected in the design of Mesoamerican observatories, and thus the Natchez word "tun" may be related to the Mesoamerican word "tun". The Natchez appear to have had a year of roughly 360 days, as 13 moons times 28 days per moon is 354 days.

All things being thus disposed and prepared for the harvest, and the corn (maize) becoming ripe, the warriors go to gather it. They put it in cane baskets and carry it to the granary, where other warriors take it, climb the ladder, and throw it into the granary, which has rather the shape of a tower than of a tun with regard to its diameter and height.

When this corn (maize) is entirely enclosed, it is well covered, and left without fear of thieves.

The Great Sun is informed that all is ready for the feast. He then sets whatever day pleases him for eating it in common and in his presence.

The feast day being fixed, the necessary arrangements for this ceremony are made some days before this time. The cabin of the Great Sun is built opposite to the granary, while the cabin of the Great War Chief is built at the side of the granary. The cabin of the ruler is built on an elevation of earth about 2 feet high, which has been brought hither, and is made by the warriors out of grass and leaves (?).

At the same time the warriors of each family come to make a cabin for the use of all of their relations.

The feast day having at last arrived, the entire nation begins to prepare itself at daybreak. The old men, the young people, the women, and the children leave the village at sunrise. Each one brings the utensils necessary for preparing the grain, and as soon as they arrive at the open space they collect wood to make a fire at the proper time.

THE HARVEST LITTER OF THE GREAT SUN

The old warriors prepare the litter on which the Great Sun is going to be brought to the open space. This litter is composed of four red bars which cross each other at the four corners of the seat, which has a depth of about one and half feet. The entire seat is garnished inside with undecorated deerskins, because it is not seen. Those deerskins which hang outside are painted with designs of different colors according to their taste. These deerskins conceal the seat so well that the substance of which it is composed can not be seen.

The back part of this seat is covered like the equipages we call chaises (souffets). It is covered outside and in with leaves of the tulip laurel. The outside border is garnished with three strings of flowers: the string of flowers which extends the farthest outside is red, and it is accompanied on each side by a string of white flowers.

THE DISPOSITION OF THE WARRIORS

Those who prepare this litter are the first and the oldest warriors of the nation. They place it on the shoulders of the eight warriors who are the only ones to take it out of the village. In this way there remain only 16 of the warriors there at the cabin of the Great Sun, because all of the other warriors have gone, a little after sunrise, with their Great Chief [of War] and those who command the warriors under his orders. The Great War Chief disperses these a hundred paces apart, and places eight warriors in each relay. For this purpose he chooses those of his warriors who are the strongest and the most vigorous. The other warriors wait with him at the open space to receive the Great Sun.

THE PLANTING OF THE WARRIORS' POST

These dispositions having been made, and the warriors' post having been reddened and planted by themselves in the middle of the open space, with a ceremony, for the Great War Chief has to hold the post while the warriors make it firm.

THE CARRYING OF THE LITTER

The Great Sun, when the sun is a quarter of the way up, [at 9 o'clock] goes forth from his cabin adorned with his head dress [crown] and the other ornaments which indicate his dignity.

On the instant, the warriors who have remained to carry him utter many redoubled cries in succession, and with so much strength that those who hear them may be assured that these men are not consumptives. As the warriors of the relays are not more than a hundred paces apart, they hear the first cries and repeat them on the spot, so that in a minute they are informed of the Great Sun's departure at the open space, although it is half a league [a mile or mile and a half] distant from his cabin.

The Great Sun seats himself in the litter, adorned with the ornaments suitable to the supreme rank. Then the eight oldest warriors place him in the litter, which is already on the shoulders of those who are going to carry him. The cries are continued from his departure from his cabin until he is beyond the village, which is at most a matter of two minutes.

Those who carry the Great Sun and those who receive him do it with so much speed and skill that a good horse would be able to follow them only at a canter, for those who await him at each relay lift him from the shoulders of those who arrive with so much agility that he does not stop at all, and does not stop going with the same speed; thus the entire journey lasts only six or seven minutes at most.

THE SANCTIFICATION OF THE FESTIVAL GRONDS,
AND THE BLESSING OF THE CORN

Scarcely have those in the open space perceived the Great Sun, than the whole nation which is awaiting him fills the air and the neighboring woods with cries of joy.

The Great Sun arrives in the open space at the side of the cabin which has been prepared for him. Before descending the Great Sun makes a circuit of the square sedately. When he is in front of the grain [in the tun] he salutes it with "hou ho'u hou" (Good good good), repeated three times, long drawn out, and made with respect. All of the nation replies to this salutation with nine other "hou's" (Good), which are not at all confused; so that at the ninth "hou" (Good) the Great Sun sets his foot to the earth and seats himself on his throne.

All the warriors who the Great Sun has left behind follow him at their leisure, but without stopping, and there remain in the cabins of the nation only the old men and the old women who are no longer able to walk, and the sick. [*Simon Antoine notes:* There are but too many of these old people to whom life has become insupportable; although the body is in very good health, their legs refuse service.]

THE CREATION OF A NEW FIRE

The Guardians of the Eternal Fire do not leave the temple; their wives carry them some of the dishes prepared of this grain to eat.

The Great Sun lets his warriors rest, and gives time for the making of a new fire, which comes from a violent rubbing of wood against wood. Any other fire would be profane.

During this interval the Great Sun remains with the other Suns (Princes only), each of whom is ornamented with a little head dress, the feathers surmount each being not more than four inches long and all equal in length. Only the Great War Chief [*who was at that time was the brother of the Great Sun*] was distinguished from the other Suns. He had a large white feather fastened to his hair, at the end of which was a red tuft which carried a tassel of the same color. This feather extended above the others in his head dress by about two inches.

PRAYER TO THE WEATHER SPIRITS

When the Great War Chief sees all of the warriors awaiting his orders at the doors of the cabins belonging to their families, he goes with four warriors previously chosen and named to distribute the corn (maize) to the women. The Great War Chief presents himself with these four warriors before the throne and says to the Great Sun: "Speak, I await your word." Then the ruler rises, comes out of his cabin, and bows toward the four quarters of the world, commencing with the south.

As soon as the Great War Chief and the warriors have gone to the granary, the Great Sun raises his arms and his hands toward heaven, where he also directs his gaze, and says: "Give the corn (maize)," and at once he seats himself.

The Great War Chief thanks the Great Sun with a single "ho'u" (Good), long drawn out, and goes on. The Suns *[Princes and Princesses]* whose cabins are nearby also thank the Great Sun with three hou's (Good's). Then all the men do the same thing, repeating "hou" (Good) nine times, but three at a time, with a little time between.

The women and all the young people of both sexes keep a profound silence and prepare their baskets to go after the corn (maize). They go to the granary as soon as the thanks of the people have been given.

During the time of the thanksgivings, the four warriors along with their Great War Chief arrive at the granary, and each ascends a ladder, and they quickly take the covering off of the granary, throw the pieces aside, and give grain to the female Suns, and afterward indifferently to all the women who present themselves.

As soon as these women have received this corn [maize], they run and flee as if they had stolen it. Those who have remained in the cabins place themselves in front of the others and seem to wish to snatch it from them.

They then empty it on skins and husk it quickly. Scarcely have they enough of the maize [corn] to make one crushing than they put it into their mortars to grind it. The pot is on the fire with boiling water, or water ready to boil. They throw this meal into it and hasten to cook it. As soon as it is cooked they await the word to eat it, and they never touch any of it before that.

This whole operation is gone through with so much eagerness that one would think that they had not eaten for four days. The servants of the Great Sun, although very numerous, do not have their food prepared as soon as the others, because they do not hasten, in order to give the other women time to prepare theirs.

In the midst of all these movements the warriors who are then at leisure amuse themselves by singing war songs to the sound of the pot which serves them as a drum *[a pottery drum covered with deer skin].*

THE RECEIVING OF THE FOOD

When they see that all is cooked, which they know by observing a woman at the door of each cabin, the Great Sun's Speaker or Chancellor (Attendant, Messenger) says to the Great (Chill) Master of Ceremonies, "Eillpaill" (See if the provisions are cooked!).

They bring it to the Great Sun in two plates, one of each kind (?). The Great Sun rises, and they give him one of these dishes. He goes out and presents it to the four quarters of the world, then sends it to the Great War Chief, saying in a loud voice "Pachcou" (Eat!), and it is then that everyone eats.

The repast lasts a rather long time, because the warriors eat first, and then the boys of all ages, except those who are nursing. Finally the women and the children eat, and it is necessary to allow intervals, so that the women may have time to crush more corn (maize) and cook it, because only this corn [maize] is eaten until all the corn [maize] in the granary is eaten.

THE WARRIORS DECLARATION OF FEATS

As fast as the warriors finish their repast, they go outside and remain standing in front of their cabins. As soon as there are enough of them, they form two responsive choirs along the two sides of the open space and sing songs of war. This concert lasts only about a half an hour and is ended the instant that the Great War Chief goes to strike a blow on the [warriors'] post. This signal, which stops the singers, opens the scene for speeches.

The Great War Chief begins immediately. He relates his exploits and the number of enemies he has killed, and he finishes his speech in a raised tone of voice, to which those who are acquainted with the deeds he has mentioned answer with a great "hou" (Good) in order to certify to its truth.

Then all the warriors in turn, according to the degree of estimation in which they are held, do the same thing as their Great War Chief did.

Finally the young men have permission to go and strike the *[warriors']* post and say, not what they have done, for they have never been to war, but what they propose to do. This is a kind of training for them for which their parents and their friends take care to prepare them, for as it is an honor to them to speak well in public, and it is a disgrace to acquit themselves poorly.

The warriors either applaud the young men with a "hou" (Good), which as has been seen is of common usage, or they give witness to their small satisfaction by lowering their heads and keeping silence. The desire of meriting public approval in the present, and of acquiring in the future the same glory which warriors enjoy, excites in the young men a lively emulation.

THE MAIZE DANCE

However, night comes. The open space is then surrounded with more than 200 torches made of dried canes, which they take care to renew *[as they burn]*. These torches are the size of a small child and bound in five places.

In the great light which these torches shed they ordinarily dance until day break. The dances are always the same, and he who has seen one has seen all.

Here is how they are disposed. In the middle of a vacant space, proportioned to the number of those who are going to dance, a man seats himself on the earth with a pot in which there is a little water, and which is covered with a deer skin stretched extremely tight. He holds this pot in one hand and beats time with the other.

Around him the women arrange themselves in a circle at some distance from each other, having in their hands very thin disks made of feathers which they turn while dancing from left to right. The men enclose the women with another circle, which they form at some distance from them. They never hold each other by the hand, but leave a space sometimes as wide as 6 feet between themselves.

Each one has his chichicois (rattle) with which he beats time. The chichicois is a gourd pierced at its two ends, through which a stick is passed, with the longest end of the stick serving as a handle, and in which some little stones or dry beans have been placed.

As the women turn from left to right, the men turn from right to left, and all keep time with an accuracy which must be considered surprising. The intervals which they leave between themselves make it convenient fro them to leave the dance when they are tired, and to reenter it without causing any trouble.

The circles contract and enlarge according to necessity, always keeping time. The dancers being able to rest and be replaced by others, [for in great families all do not dance at the same time], their dances ordinarily last all night. It may be understood without difficulty that in this manner they might be able to dance forever, the dancers being able to retire without interrupting the dance, and reenter it in the same way when they have recovered their strength.

I need to mention besides that, that during this feast there is never any disorder or quarrel, not only on account of the presence of the Great Sun and the good custom they have of living in peace, but also because during it they eat only the sacred grain and drink nothing but water.

THE SACRED BALL GAME

Day having come, no one appears in the open space until the Great Sun comes out of his house toward 9 o'clock in the morning. He walks some moments alone with the Great War Chief, and has the drum, or the pot which serves in place of it, beaten against the post.

Immediately the warriors hasten to come out of their cabins, and form two troops which are distinguished by the color of the feathers with which their heads are adorned. The one has white feathers, and takes the side of the Great Sun; the other has red feathers, and is for the Great War Chief.

Then begins the game of the pelotte (ball), a little ball of deerskin of the size of a fist filled with Spanish beard.
The Great Sun and the Great War Chief throw this ball back and forth for some time from one to the other. The two bands are extremely attentive to all their movements, for at the moment when one least thinks of it, the Great Sun throws the ball into the very thick of the warriors, who are then mingled and confounded together.

This ball must never fall or be carried, as it would then be snatched forcibly from the one who should seize it, and no one would help him: on this point the interdiction is express. As this ball game has two goals, to reach the cabin of the Great Sun or that of the Great War Chief, it is necessary that the ball be pressed and urged by blows given with the palm of the hand toward one of these two cabins.

It is a real pleasure to see this ball spring sometimes to one side of the open space, sometimes to the other, sometimes remaining in the middle, then appearing decided to touch one of the goals, and at the last moment be repelled by a hostile hand into its first uncertainty. The movement of the warriors, and the innocent passion which they enter into for the honor of the game, is not unaccompanied by noise. Fear, disquietude, and vexation have their different cries. That of joy rises above all the others.

Ordinarily the ball game lasts two hours, and the warriors sweat great drops. Finally, the ball touches one of the two cabins, and the amusement is at an end. The band which belonged to this cabin having won by this, receives from the Chief of the opposite side a considerable pi'Esent (?) and the right to wear distinguishing feathers as a mark of victory, until the following year or until the next time they play ball.

THE WARRIORS DANCE

Following this ball game the warriors dance the War Dance to the sound of the pot
[pottery drum]. After this dance they go to bathe, an exercise of which they are very fond, especially when they are a. little heated or fatigued.

THE END OF THE FEAST OF THE GREAT TUN

The rest of the day is passed like the preceding, and the feast lasts as long as there is corn (maize) to eat, for they do not bring any of it back to the village. And even when there is no more corn (maize) to distribute, all the cabins are visited to know how much remains to each family. Where a too large quantity is found, a corn (maize) tassel is suspended at the door, and those who do not have enough are informed by this of the place where they may find some. Thus all the corn (maize) is shared equally, and finished at the same time.

Report of this being made to the Great Sun, he has the pot beaten and gives orders to return to the village. The warriors are disposed in relays by the Great War Chief to bring their ruler back to his cabin in the same way that they brought him out, and when he arrives there he sends them out to hunt, as much for himself as for them.

Thus is terminated the great Feast of Corn (Maize).

THE FEASTS OF THE HUNTS

In the autumn, or in the beginning of Winter, all works in the fields are then at an end, or at least the hurry of them is over.

In the month of September, the meadows, the grass of which is then dry, are set on fire, and the ground becomes smooth and easy to walk on. Hence it is that at this time clouds of smoke are seen for several days together to extend over a long track of country, sometimes to the extent of between twenty and thirty leagues *[40 to 90 miles]* in length, by two or three leagues in breadth, more or less, according as to how the wind sets, and is higher or lower.

This season is also the most commodious for traveling over those countries, because by means of the rain, which ordinarily falls after the grass is burnt, the game spread themselves all over the meadows, and delight to feed on the new grass; this is the reason why travelers more easily find provisions at this time of year than at any other.

The eighth moon is that of Turkeys, *[which corresponds to   our month of October]*.

The ninth moon is that of the Buffalo, *[which corresponds to our month of November]*. It is then that they go to hunt that animal.

Having discovered whereabouts the herd feeds, they go out in a body to hunt them. Young and old, girls and married women, except those who are with child, are all of the party, for there is generally work for them all. Some nations are a little later in going out to this hunting, that they may find the cows fatter, and the herds more numerous.

The tenth moon is that of Bears, *[which corresponds to our month of December]*. At this time of hunting the feasts are not so grand and solemn, because a great part of the nations are accompanying the hunters in their expeditions.

THE FEASTS OF THE STORES

The eleventh moon is named the Cold-meal Moon, *[and corresponds to our month of January]*.

The twelfth moon is that of Chesnuts. While this nut has been gathered long before, nevertheless it gives its name to this moon.

Lastly, the thirteenth moon is that of Walnuts, and it is added to complete the year. It is then they break the nuts to make bread of them by mixing with them corn (maize) flour.

THE BEAUTIFUL COUNTRY:
THE NATCHEZ ARRIVE AT THE NORTHERN GULF COAST OF MEXICO

"Before we came into this land, Natchez, we lived to the southwest under the Great Sun. We lived in a beautiful country where the earth is always good.

"The Ancient Word says nothing of what land we came from before this. All that it teaches is that our fathers who went there followed the sun, *[went to the west]*, and came with the sun from where it rises *[from the east]*.

They were a long time on their journey, and they saw themselves at the point of dying utterly, when they found themselves brought into that beautiful country, without them searching for it at all.

THE NATCHEZ ENCOUNTER THE TEOTIHAUCANS (OTOMIES):
A DETAILED DESCRIPTION OF TOLLA, THEIR CAPITOL CITY

"On our arrival in that land we knew nothing of the Ancients of the Country. It was only a long time afterwards, when we were multiplied *[the Natchez people had grown in number]*, that we both heard of each other, and we encountered each other with equal surprise on both sides.

The Ancient Word teaches us that when we arrived in that country, we found them there in great numbers, and they appeared to have been there a long time: for they inhabited the entire coast toward the setting sun of the Great Water *[the Gulf of Mexico]*, as far as the cold country on this side of the sun *[the mountains of central Mexico]*, and very far along the coast beyond the sun *[the Pacific Coast]*.

They had a very large number of large and small villages, all of which were built of stones, and in which there were individual houses large enough to lodge an entire village. Their temples were built with much skill and labor. They made very beautiful things with all kinds of materials, such as gold, silver, stones, wood, fabrics, feathers, and they made many other things in which they made their skills appear, as well as in manufacturing arms and in making war.

While it is not known with certainty which of the coastal peoples the Natchez were related to, the Hausteca are good candidates, based solely on the geography of the area and the Chief of the Guardians of the Temple's account of events.

Ca 200 CE: THE TOLLA FEDERATION FALLS,
AND THE TEOTIHUACAN EMPIRE FORMED

The two nations did not war together at all then, and they lived in peace for a great number of years. But then one of their chiefs, who was very powerful and a great warrior, undertook to make them his slaves, and he finally succeeded. And then he wished to subject us also.

THE TEOTIHUACANS ATTACK OUT OF THE VALLEY OF MEXICO

All those who dwelt in the plains could not avoid submitting, and those who had retired into the mountains remained alone under obedience to the Great Sun. The Ancients of the Country wished, indeed, to force those of our people whom they had already subjugated to join them in making war on us, but they preferred to die rather than attack their brothers, especially the Suns (the nobility).

THE TEOTIHUACANS HELD BY THE NATCHEZ
AT THE MOUNTAIN PASSES

After having reduced under their power those villages of our people who were in the plains, the Ancients of the Country came, indeed, as far as the mountains. But our warriors always repulsed them at the entrance to the mountains, and they were never able to penetrate there.

And it was there that our Suns (nobility) remained, because the Ancients of the Country were unable to force us out with all of their warriors.

THE EVACUATION TO THE MISSISSIPPI RIVER

Our entire nation then extended along the Great Water *[the Gulf of Mexico]* to where this Great River *[the Mississippi River]* loses itself (empties). Some of our *[lesser]* Suns *[princes were]* sent up this river to find a place where they might conceal themselves, far from the Ancients of the Country, because after having been a long time good friends with them, they had become ill disposed and so numerous that we were no longer able to defend ourselves against them.

But those who had ascended along the west side of the Great River *[the Mississippi River]*, having discovered this land which we inhabit, now crossed the river on a raft of dry canes. They found a country such as they desired, suitable for concealing themselves from the Ancients of the Country, and even easy to defend against them if they ever undertook to attack us here.

On their return they reported this to the Great Sun and the other *[lesser]* Suns who governed the villages. The Great Sun immediately informed those who remained in the plains and were still defending themselves against the Ancients of the Country, and he ordered them to go into this new land and build there a temple and to carry there the eternal fire in order to preserve it.

There came here a great number of men with their wives and their children. The oldest people and the *[lesser]* Suns, the relatives of the Great Sun, remained there with those who kept with the Great Sun in the mountains. They, as well as those who lived on the shores of the Great Water *[the Gulf of Mexico]*, remained there for a still longer time.

A large part of our nation having then been established here, we lived a long time in peace and in abundance for many generations.

THE COLLAPSE OF THE TEOTIHUACAN EMPIRE,
AND RISE OF THE TOLTECS

On the other hand, those who had remained under the sun *[Great Sun or sun? in the south]*, or very near, for it was very warm there, did not hasten to come and join us, because the Ancients of the Country made themselves hated by all men- as much by their own nation as by ours.

Here is how the Ancient Word says that that happened. The Ancients of the Country were all brothers - that is to say, they all came out of the same country - but each large village, on which many other smaller villages depended, had its head master, and each head master commanded those whom he had brought with him into that land. There was then nothing done among them that all had not consented to; but then one of these head masters raised himself above the others and treated them as slaves.

Thus the Ancients of the Country no longer agreed among themselves. They even warred against one another. Some of them united with those of our nation who had remained, and by all of them working together, they sustained themselves there well enough.

THE EXTENT OF THE "MOBILIAN" OR "MISSISSIPPIAN" TRADE
FEDERATION

This was not the only reason which retained our Suns in that country. It was hard for them to leave such a good land; besides, their assistance was necessary to our other brothers who were established here like ourselves, and who lived along the shore of the Great Water [the Gulf of Mexico] on the side toward the east.

These brothers extended so far that they went very far beyond the Great Sun, since there were some of them from whom the Great Sun heard sometimes only at the end of five or six years, and there were yet others so far away from us, whether along the coast or in the islands, that for many years they had not been heard of at all.

Ca 1200 CE:
DISEASE HITS THE TRADE FEDERATION
Related to du Pratz by The Great Sun, their king.

The appearance of this plague or influenza may be placed at Ca 1200, instead of at the time of European contact, for the following reasons. First, the Ancient History of the Lenape (the Walum Olum) mentions an outbreak of disease at this time. Second, the extent of the "Mississippian" (Southern Ceremonial Cult) federation is that which existed at this time. Third, there is no mention of the Kushita or Lenape incursions, which appear to have occurred after the plague hit. Finally, both the Ancient History of the Five Nations as well as in the the Ancient History of the Lenape (Walum Olum) mention a climate collapse with starvation just prior to this, which most likely led to the outbreak.

Our nation then extended for more than twelve days' journey from east to west, and more than fifteen days' journey from south to north. It counted then 500 Suns, and you

411

can judge by that what was then the number of the Nobles, the Honored men, and the common people.

There are always two Guardians in the Temple to care for the sacred fire. But once in the past it happened that one of these two men went out for some purpose, and while he was away his companion fell asleep and let the fire go out.

When he awoke, seeing the fire extinguished, fright seized him. But as his companion had not yet come back, he determined to conceal his fault, because he was easily able to do it, in order to escape the death which he had merited. He called then to the first passer and begged him to bring him fire with which to light his calumet (pipe), a thing which this person did willingly, knowing well that it is not permitted to touch the eternal fire except to tend it, and that no other use could be made of it.

Thus this fire was re-lighted with profane fire. Immediately sickness took hold of the Suns. In a few days they were seen to die in rapid succession, and it was necessary to send after them into the world of spirits many people to serve them. This mortality lasted four years, without anyone being able to guess what had occasioned it. Nine great Suns who succeeded each other died in this interval, and a multitude of people with them.

Finally, at the end of this time the Guardian himself fell ill. This bad man, feeling that he was not going to be able to live a long time, had word sent to the Great Sun at once that he had something to communicate to him of such great importance that if he died without revealing it all the Natchez would die.

The Great Sun went to see him as quickly as possible. As soon as the sick man perceived him, his whole body trembled, and he appeared unable to speak. However, he spoke these words, although with difficulty:

" I am going to die, so it makes no difference to me whether the sickness or a man kills me. I know that I am a bad man for having for so long a time concealed, in order to preserve my life, what I am going to tell you. I am the cause of the death of my nation, therefore I merit death, but let me not be eaten by the dogs."

The Great Sun understood by these words that this man was guilty of some great crime, and that it was necessary to reassure him in order to draw from him his secret, which appeared to be of the last importance. He therefore told him that whatever he had done he might be assured that. he would not be put to death, and that he would be buried; that what he had promised him was as true as it was true that the Sun, their father, lighted them every day, and that he should hasten to speak before death prevented him.

On this promise the bad guardian confessed all that he had done. Immediately the Great Sun assembled the old men, and by their advice it was resolved to go that very day to wrest fire from the other temple. That was executed and the Suns ceased dying."

Du Pratz added the following: This expression, "to wrest fire," appearing extraordinarily to me, and I asked the Great Sun what it signified. He replied that it was necessary that the fire be carried away by violence and that blood be shed over it; unless on the way *[to do this]* lightning was seen to fall on a tree and set fire to it, then they might spare themselves the trouble of going farther and take this fire, but that of the Sun was always' preferable.

THE SPANISH ARRIVAL

It was only after many generations that these Suns *[nobles]* came to join us in this country, where the fine air and the peace which we enjoyed had multiplied us into a number as great as the leaves on the trees.

Then the Warriors of Fire came on floating villages (carvel class ships) from the side where the sun rises [the east]. The Warriors of Fire were bearded men, white but swarthy. They were called Warriors of Fire because their arms threw fire with a great noise, and killed at a great distance. They had other very heavy arms (cannons) besides these, which killed many people at a time, and which made the earth tremble like thunder.

THE SPANISH CONQUER THE AZTEC,
THEN TURN ON THEIR ALLIES

Our brothers *[the Totonac and the Otomie]* were allied with them, although our Suns told them that these Warriors of Fire would subject them after they had subjected the Ancients of the Country.

The Warriors of Fire conquered the Ancients of the Country, of whom they killed as many as there are spears of grass in the prairies. Though in the beginning they were good friends of our brothers *[the Totonac and Otomie]*, ultimately they made them submit along with the Ancients of the Country, as our Suns had foreseen, and had foretold to them.

THE COASTAL LEADERS FLEE NORTH EAST MEXICO

The Great Sun and the *[lesser]* Suns (princes) who were with him were unable to induce our brothers to follow them; and they took their farewells, therefore, in order to come alone to rejoin us here, for fear lest the Warriors of Fire should make them slaves, which they feared more than death. These Suns came alone with their slaves, because our other brothers did not wish to follow them.

THE CLOSING WORDS
OF THE CHIEF OF THE GUARDIANS OF THE TEMPLE

Do not ask me for more, for the Ancient Word says nothing besides this, and no Old Man will ever tell you what I do not tell you."

THE ANCIENT HISTORY OF THE SHAWNEE

Assembled from Their Legends by E.P. Grondine
©copyright 2004 E.P. Grondine

FORWARD

Having been greatly impressed by David Cusick's Ancient History of the Six Nations, I thought that the Shawnee legends might benefit from being assembled together in a similar manner. This task proved difficult, as the Shawnee were a federation of five distinct nations, each of whom had their own versions of their own events, their very own very distinct and different histories.

Before the time of European contact, those nations were spread in a large band along the Ohio River, occupying the areas where the remains of the Monongahela Culture are found today. Shawnee is an Algonquin language, and it is known that these people emigrated from north of the Lake Erie around 900 CE. David Cusick's account of them in his Ancient History of the Six Nations places the Shawnee along the Susquehanna River at this time, and his account there agrees well with the archaeological record of the Monongahela Culture.

In the south, along what are known today as the lower Ohio River and the Cumberland River, these migrating Algonquin people conquered the existing Chilicothe and Mekoche peoples. These peoples were Iroquoian peoples with their own legends of migration from the south; it appears that the Algonquin Shawnee adopted these legends as their own after their conquest of them. To make this clearer, it has been pointed out many times that the Shawnee accounts of creation and migration agree with those of the Cherokee; indeed, it can be asserted that the Chilicothe people, the Tshilikauthee in another English phonetic representation, are none other than the Tsulagi, one part of the Cherokee.

Another remainder of these Tshilikauthee people, who lived a little to the west on the Mississippi River in the American Bottoms area, were also most likely the same people the Lenape later knew as the Taligewi. The Mekoche legends appear to have been somewhat different than those of the Chilicothe [Tshilikauthee], and what remains of them are given below.

Based on the Shawnee accounts, it appears that after these first conquests they then migrated from this southern base, moving northward up the Ohio River to the areas where the Five Nations first encountered them ca 900 CE. Things then remained in this state for about 500 years.

At the time of European contact, the Dutch provided the Six Nations with firearms, hiring the Six Nations as mercenaries to preserve their trade monopoly, and the Sixe Nations used these firearms to attack those peoples who were trading with France, England, and Sweden. While the Native American peoples had long been fighting with simple weapons for the control of resources, the slaughter caused by the introduction of these firearms was immense.

The nations which composed the Shawnee confederacy were dispersed, and it is quite difficult to establish their earlier areas of occupation. After the Six Nations' attacks, one group of Shawnee migrated west to the area around Starved Rock, on the Illinois River, while another group migrated into Westo lands in the area which later became known as Savanah [Shawnee] Georgia.

Of the five Shawnee nations, the Chilicothe [Tshilikallthee] nation occupied the area around the town known today as Chilicothe, Ohio. They are reported by Open Door to have moved to Starved Rock, Illinois, but after the defeat of the Six Nations by the western peoples in the later half of the sixteenth century they would return to Chilicothe, Ohio.

According to the Shawnee migration legends, the Algonquin "Chilicothe" encountered the Mekoche in their original lands, and event which took place shortly before 900 CE based on the archaeological record. And at the time of European contact some 650 or so years later, the Algonquin Chilicothe nation still lay immediately adjacent to the Algonquin Mekoche areas. Thus there is little doubt as to the location of the Mekoche nation.

After the Six Nations attacks in the mid 1600's, the Mekoche [Meguatchkai] nation still occupied the area between the lower Ohio River, which the Shawnee knew as the Mos-Opelea-Cipi [Appalachian River] and the Cumberland River, which the Shawnee knew as the Skipa-Cipi [Big Turkey River]. In the late 1600's the Mekoche were in trade the Spanish in the southeast through the lands of the Cisca people, and their neighbors to the north were the Chaskepe, or Casquinampo. (Shawnee!, James H. Howard, p 6)

In the legends below, the Pikowitha are clearly described as being what are know today by the archaeologists as a Red Ochre or Red Paint people, who lay further up Ohio River from the Mekoche. These Pikowitha were driven by the Six Nations attacks to the area around Starved Rock, Illinois. Following the Six Nations defeat by the western peoples, the Pikowitha were visited at nearby Fort St Louis (Peoria, Illinois) in 1692 by representatives of the Muncy nation, who persuaded them to move to their lands on the Susquehanna River. During the early 1700's, some Pikowitha were located near Pequea on the southern Susquehanna River.

In the migration accounts given below, the Kishpoko nation is described as being further up the Ohio River from the Pikowitha. Given the Kishpoko nation's involvement in a war with the Catawba, also given below, their lands ca 900 CE should have been somewhere around the Kanawa River's junction with the Ohio River in West Virginia.

The Thawikila nation were located on the Ohio River in the area of Sewickley Creek, just to the west of modern day Pittsburgh. Most likely the Thawikila were driven to Georgia by the Six Nations, and returned to their original home following the Six Nations defeat by the western peoples.

After the Six Nations defeat by the western peoples, another large group of Shawnee also returned from the Savanah area to the area of the upper Potomac River near what is now Cumberland, Maryland. This area lies on the path to the north, and this path to the north connects at Bedford, Pennsylvania with the path to the west and the Ohio River. Another group of Shawnee returned to the Bedford area. The national affiliation of these groups is currently unknown, but it is possible that they represented other parts of the Thawikila nation, who were also returning to the lands which they had occupied before the Six Nations' attacks.

While after the war with the Six Nations, the Cumberland River in Tennessee was known as the Shawnee River, it appears that the Shawnee knew the Ohio River itself as the Shawnee River in earlier times, and before that the original Chilicothe and Mekoche peoples knew the Mississippi River as the Shawnee River.

As for the Shawnee nation of the Shawnee Confederacy, it may have been completely extinguished by the Six Nations during their attacks on the other European trading partners. The Shawnee currently view the Shawnee as being a mobile military group which regulated the interplay between the different nations, going where they were needed. As such the Shawnee would have been the first to have borne the brunt of the attacks of the Six Nations.

Another difficulty in assembling this history lay in the development of these legends over time, as many differing versions of them were preserved at various different times, and were influenced by the European and African migration to North America.

Finally, there are the problems of the translations, and particularly the skills of the earlier translators. It is often not so much the case that Native Americans spoke "pidgin", but that the translators did. The translators also often felt secure in inserting their own commentary into the tales, without identifying it as such.

In assembling this History, I have tried to fix some of these problems through the use of adaptations of the tales as recorded. My hope is that in trying to improve the translations of the legends, I have not changed their substance. To keep my own commentary separate from the legends themselves, it is always identified by the use of italics. It is my hope that my understanding has been accurate, and not confused.

With these restraints kept firmly in mind, my final hope is that the reader will nonetheless enjoy and find of some use the History assembled here. For this assemblage the Editor has made use of the best source available to him, which was the collection of Shawnee myths given by James H. Howard in his excellent book Shawnee! (Ohio University Press, Athens, Ohio, 1981).

The original sources are indicated throughout in the following manner:

Open Door - Tenskwatawa, 'Open Door', the Shawnee Prophet - Adapted from the accounts given by Tenskwatawa, 'Open Door', the Shawnee Prophet, to Governor Lewis Cass and recorded by C. C. Trowbridge, and located and preserved by Kinietz and Voegelin. (Shawanese Traditions, University of Michigan Press, Ann Arbor, 1939).

Black Hoof - Adapted from the accounts given by Black Hoof to Governor Lewis Cass and recorded by C. C. Trowbridge, and located and preserved by Kinietz and Voegelin. (Shawanese Traditions, University of Michigan Press, Ann Arbor, 1939).

James Clark – adapted from the accounts given by James Clark to C.F. Voegelin and E.W. Voegelin and preserved by them in their work The Shawnee Female Deity in Historical Perspective.

Charles Bluejacket – adapted from the version preserved by Joab Spencer in his work The Shawnee Indians.

Nancy Sky - adapted from the version given by Nancy Sky to Voegelin and Voegelin and preserved by them in "The Shawnee Female Deity in Historical Perspective".

THE GREAT SPIRIT AND THE FIRST CREATION - James Clark

In the beginning there was the Great Spirit,
formed of wind, invisible,
but with the will a man.
He lives above the sun.
There was just space,
and no earth, no water.

The Great Spirit said, "Let there be a woman"
and as soon as he spoke there was a being formed like a woman: Grandmother.
Then the Great Spirit gave to Grandmother
the work of creating this earth, the sun, water, people, animals.

GRANDMOTHER: THE MOON - Tenskwatawa, 'Open Door', the Shawnee Prophet

In another passage later in the creation story, Open Door identifies Grandmother as being the Moon.

The Great Spirit told them that he was going to leave them, and would not be seen by them again, and that they must think for themselves, and pray to their Grandmother, the Moon, who was present in the shape of an old woman.

In other versions, Grandmother is seen as living on the Moon, with the Moon's terrain viewed as an old woman bending over her pot.

DESCRIPTION OF THE FIRST CREATION - James Clark

Before the flood,
Grandmother and the Evil Spirit and her Grandson
and the great giants were all on this Earth which she had made,
and the people talked to them.
She is the one the people saw and knew.

In this first creation people lived a long time and died four times, but not so today. After Grandmother did her creating, she made the rules which are to be fulfilled.

This version of creation agrees well with the Iroquoian versions of creation as preserved by theTuscarora. It undoubtedly comes from either the Pikowitha, who were a Red Ochre people, or the Mekoche, immigrants from the south.

The "flood" mentioned is most likely a memory of the Great Atlantic Mega-Tsunami of 1050 BCE, caused when a fragment of Comet Encke impacted in the Atlantic Ocean, and the "giants" are most likely a memory of Homo Grigorii in North America.

THE FLOOD - Nancy Sky

Long ago there were people right here, the one [Great Spirit?] who created us, our Grandmother, and her grandson, the little boy Rounded-Side.

Grandmother told her grandson Rounded Side, "Don't go that way, you must always go this way."

But her grandson Rounded Side thought to himself, " I wonder why is that forbidden?" *(In his commentary Howard mentions an Absentee Shawnee variant, where the prohibition is specifically against going west.)*

Then her grandson Rounded Side ran off and he went that way.

Finally her grandson Rounded Side found a house, and he went into it. Inside there was a big man with a big stomach. Her grandson Rounded Side stayed there for a while, and finally late in the evening he went home.

Grandson Rounded Side then went back again to the house, and he mocked the hoot owl [along the way?]. He was moving very fast, running with a knife in his hand. Then he stuck the big man with the big stomach, he stuck him right in his stomach. *(In his commentary Howard mentions that in the Absentee Shawnee variant the boy cut a transparent fish monster.)*

Then water began spilling out from his stomach. Grandson Rounded Side ran outside, as he was being chased by the water.

Grandson ran home, moving very fast. He came running up there to his Grandmother.

Then Grandmother and her grandson Rounded Side ran away from the water together. They climbed on a tree. *(In his commentary Howard mentions that in an Absentee Shawnee variant Grandmother and her grandson Rounded Side escape the flood in a boat.)*

THE SECOND CREATION - Nancy Sky

All the people were drowned, and Grandmother became sad.

Finally Grandmother called to Crawfish, and he came. He brought earth in his hand.

Crawfish is most likely an allusion to the Milky Way. In his commentary on this tale Howard mentions that in an Absentee Shawnee variant, Turtle and Water Lizard [Serpent, i.l. Comet] dive unsuccessfully before Crawfish dives and brings up mud.

Grandmother took the earth from Crawfish, and he brought earth again, and a little bit more again.

Then Grandmother called the Buzzard, and he came. The Buzzard rubbed some of the earth on his wings. "You must dry the Earth," she told him.

Then the Buzzard went away, he went and dried the Earth He flew over the Earth until it was dry all over.

In a Cherokee account of creation preserved by Mooney, the existence of mountains is explained as the marks left by flapping of the Buzzard's wings.

When it got dry, then the water went below.

However, the old people were all dead.

In his commentary Howard mentions that in a Cherokee Shawnee variant, the Creator deliberately instigated the flood to destroy the people whom she made in the first creation because they were too large, too strong, too destructive. These undoubtedly are distant memories both of the "Giants" as well as of the Great Atlantic Mega-Tsunami.

THE SECOND CREATION - Charles Bluejacket

After the flood Grandmother lived in a valley. When the sense of her loneliness and destitution came over her she began to weep very bitterly.

Then there appeared a heavenly messenger who asked her why she was so sorrowful. She told him that she was just a poor old woman alone, and that there was to be an end of her people. Then said the visitor, 'Remember how the first man was made,' and then he left her.

From this she knew that a new Creation was meant, so she made small images of children from the earth as directed, just as the Great Spirit had made the first man.

But when she saw that they had no life she wept again.

And again the heavenly messenger appeared and inquired the cause of her grief. She said she had made children from clay, but that they were only dirt. Then said the visitor, "Remember how the Great Spirit did when the first man was made."

At once she understood, and she breathed into their nostrils and they became alive.

THE SECOND CREATION - Tenskwatawa, 'Open Door', the Shawnee Prophet

The Great Spirit told them that he would give them a piece of his heart, which was good, and would mix it with the hearts which they had, so that a part of their hearts at least should be good.

"Now", said the Great Spirit, "I can hear, and will give you ears that you may distinguish the least noise. I can speak, and I will give you tongues that you may talk with each other. I will also give you of my teeth to chew your food-which shall be corn, beans, cucumbers, squash melons, and elk, deer, bear, buffalo, turkey, and raccoon and small game. Of vegetables you shall have twelve kinds, and of meats twelve kinds.

The Laws of the Shawnees also had 12 sections. The reference to corn indicates the time of their adoption, roughly at the time of the emergence of "Hopewell culture", ca the year 0 CE.

"And now I have finished you and all things else. Remember who made you and these things and do not at any time attribute their formation to anyone but me. Your age shall be 200 years, and then your head shall become white like mine, and you will drop down. When you become thus advanced in years you must tell your children all that I have told you, so that it may be transmitted to the latest posterity

"You are now about to go the Island which I have made for you, and which rests upon the back of a Great Turtle who carries it as his load. You must call this Turtle your Grandfather: He will hear all your complaints and he will treat you as his grand children.

"If anyone of you should drop down before he reaches 200 years, you will put upon him some of this medicine which I give you, and he will get up again.

"As I shall not always be with you, you will require assistance from other sources. I therefore give you the Sun to take care of you and to give you light during the day, and the Moon for the same purpose at night. I will also put some of my grey hairs upon one of you, and he shall be an old man, and you shall call him your Grandfather."

THE SECOND CREATION - Black Hoof

When the waters of the deluge had entirely overspread the earth, all its inhabitants were destroyed but Grandmother, who ascended to the clouds, where she gave way to grief at the loss of her grand children, and lamented that there appeared no probability of her having any more connections to gladden her heart. The Great Spirit witnessed her affliction and bid her cease to mourn.

Sometime after this event the Great Spirit, in order to purify himself, and to resuscitate the powers of thought and invention, which had long been dormant, collected the different kinds of roots which he prepared for a medicine. With a decoction of these he washed his body, and soon he became very pure and white. The Great Spirit then commenced a series of meditations, which resulted in a determination to renew and re-people the earth.

Accordingly, the Great Spirit sent a Crawfish (Milky Way) below the surface of the waters (space), with directions to bring up a small quantity of the earth from there to the Great Island which we inhabit. The Crawfish obeyed his order, and from the earth

421

contained in the paws of this little animal the Great Spirit reformed the earth.

When the Great Spirit had accomplished the formation of this Island he made some very large animals and placed them upon it, at the four cardinal points of the compass, to keep it steady.

These "very large animals" of the Shawnee directly reflect the Mayan concept of Bacab, who keep the sky and the Earth separate. In the Mayan worldview, the impact of an asteroid, or more importantly comets, was thought to be due to a failure of a Bacab.

The Great Spirit formed the founders of each nation next. He would place them in the center of the Great Island, and distribute all the lesser animals promiscuously throughout the island.

The founder of each nation was made by the Great Spirit in the heavens, and when they were finished he brought them down and gave them a place upon the Earth. While he was descending he sang four songs, which were adopted by the people. This accounts for the great difference in the manner of singing among different nations, each set of songs being appropriated to the nation at whose descent they were sung.

THE CREATION OF WOMEN - Black Hoof

None but males were created above. After the men had descended, the Great Spirit formed a female and gave it to one of the males, with a view to their increase. Much difficulty was at first experienced in producing a union of the sexes, but the object was ƒsat length accomplished.

THE CREATION OF WOMEN - Tenskwatawa, 'Open Door', the Shawnee Prophet

After the Great Spirit made the Island, he thought it necessary to make also human beings to inhabit it, and with this view in mind he formed a man and a woman.

But the Great Mind discovered that one of their principal defects consisted in his misplacing their privates to the forehead instead of the middle of the body. Seeing this he immediately took apart their limbs and reformed them.

In this second formation he placed their privates under the arm of the man and the woman, but finding that this would not do either he became vexed and threw away the different members of the body.

After some time employed in thinking about the means necessary to accomplish his desired end, he set himself to work again to put man and woman together, and at last made them as they now are, and he was satisfied.

Then the Great Spirit's mind was a good deal troubled to know how this man and woman should commence to increase. He placed them together side by side, and retiring a few paces he seated himself to survey them. He thus changed their position to each other frequently, at each change seating himself to examine the effect, until they faced each other. And by dint of his changing and moving them, they became connected in the act of intercourse.

When the Great Spirit saw this he deemed it good, and having told them how to proceed, he left them to their will.

After some time the woman was discovered to be pregnant, and in about a year was delivered of a child. The Great Spirit then told the man and woman that they should live, increase, and multiply in that manner, that he had made them, and that thereafter they must make themselves.

THE MEKOCHE MIGRATION FROM THE SOUTH:
PEOPLE DESCEND TO THE GREAT ISLAND
Tenskwatawa, 'Open Door', the Shawnee Prophet

The Great Spirit then opened the door of the skies, and the people looking down saw
the Great Island. By this time there were 12 men at the residence of the Great Spirit;
they were all Shawnee, the roots of the 12 clans(?).

The Great Spirit told them they must go down to live upon island, and that the voyage
would take them 12 days.

These days are midsummer days, which occur only once a year, and so they are equal to
years. As with many things here, these years are numbered by 12.

The Great Spirit told them that in the mean time he would finish every thing to be
created upon the earth, that means must be provided for their subsistence on the earth
where they were to live, and that as he had taken his time to make them, he must also
proceed gradually in forming all things below.

THE GIVING OF THE COUNCIL FIRE, AND APPOINTMENT OF LEADERS

After he had done this, the Great Spirit thought to himself that he had given a heart to
every thing which he had made except to the Great Island, whereupon he made a heart
for it of the old man.

Then he told the men that the old man, being the first which he had formed, should
be called, Kwikule, and that he would make another who should be called Mekwikla.
He told them that Kwikule should be the head of the nation, and Mekwikla the next in
power.

*"Mekwikla" seems to be a reference to the founder of the Mekoche. The Cisca nation lived to the
south of the Mekoche, and the reference to Kwikule may refer to some very early alliance between the
two peoples.*

THE DESCENT FROM THE HEAVENS
- Tenskwatawa, 'Open Door', the Shawnee Prophet

After this the Great Spirit put the 12 men and the two old men he had created - he had
created two to supply their place in the original number - in a large thing like a basket
and told them he was going to put them on the Great Island. The old man first named
[Kwikule] carried with him in a pack on his shoulders all the good things entrusted to
his care for the benefit of the people.

THE MEKOCHE MIGRATION FROM THE SOUTH
- Tenskwatawa, 'Open Door', the Shawnee Prophet

The first earth they saw in their journey was on the other side of the great lake (the
Gulf of Mexico), and when they had arrived on the sea shore they stopped and rested.

The old man [Kwikule] told them that the place where his heart was, was in a northern direction from them and at a great distance. They could see nothing but water and knew not how they were to cross the great water to the Island.

The old man [Kwikule] then took from his pack a gourd and began to sing. They sang for a period of twelve days, during which time they ate nothing but a few roots. The old man then told the people that the Great Spirit had promised to grant them all they desired, and that they must pray to him to remove the water which impeded their journey to the Island. Soon afterward the water was dried up and they saw nothing but sand.

THE ORIGINAL CHILICOTHE

The old man then observed that as he was too old to lead the party he would give his pack to one of the others, and he appointed Chilicothe to be the leader and bearer of the pack, and told him that he [Kwikule] would remain behind.

So Kwikule seated himself on that which was the shore, and the young leader Chilicothe went forward with the band, which by this time had become quite numerous. When they had arrived on the opposite shore they encamped and remained for the period of twelve days employed in singing, during which time, as before, they abstained from eating. They then sent the waiting servant [messenger] to Kwikule, who had remained behind, to find out (tell him?) what course they had come, but the waiting servant returned, and told them that the waters had returned to their place and that he could see nothing else.

Then Mekwikla made a speech to the people and told them he was satisfied of the power and justness of the Great Spirit, and that they must remove farther to the north, but that he would remain on the shore to look back to his friend Kwikule who remained on the opposite side of the sea.

These two old men have since turned into rocks and sit in their respective positions at this day, where they will remain so long as this Great Island stands.

THE ORIGINAL CHILICOTHE MIGRATION NORTH: THE SHAWNEE

Chilicothe [the founder of the Chilicothe nation] then commenced his march to the north, followed by all the people. After traveling 12 days they thought they must have arrived at the place of their destination, and they stopped.

Soon after, the Great Spirit visited them and told them that they had reached the place where he had placed the heart of one of the old men. He told them that they should thenceforth be called Shawnee, and that the river upon whose banks they had camped would bear the same name, Shawnee.

The Great Spirit told them that he was going to leave them, and would not be seen by them again, and that they must think for themselves, and pray to their Grandmother, the Moon, who was present in the shape of an old woman.

THE SHAWNEE - Black Hoof

The Great Spirit was more favorable to the Shawnee than to any other nation. He gave them a piece of his own heart.

The Shawnees were placed down by the Great Spirit in the center of the Great Island, and they found none about them who spoke their own language. They were taught, in common with their neighbors, to avoid every thing evil, and to pursue the one Great Road which led to their father, the Great Spirit.

THE COUNCIL FIRE, A PIECE OF THE GREAT SPIRIT'S HEART
- Tenskwatawa, 'Open Door', the Shawnee Prophet

The [council] fire, which is there kept in a small hollow rock, was brought by Chilicothe through the sea, on his back, to the Shawnee River [the Ohio and/or the Mississippi River]. This stone - it is so called, but is not really stone - is about ten inches long and five inches broad, and is suspended by a string from the roof of the lodge. It requires no wood, but is everlasting.

This council fire was undoubtedly a piece of meteoritic iron, struck by flint to produce sparks with which to start fires. It was lost during the European attacks.

METHOD OF KEEPING THE COUNCIL FIRE
- Tenskwatawa, 'Open Door', the Shawnee Prophet

The care of this fire is now (1825-1828) committed to two men, one of the Chilicothe nations and the other of the Kishpoko nation. This charge however formerly belonged to the Mekoche nation family but after a battle between the Six Nations and the Shawnees it was taken from them.

Upon the death of either of these men another from the same nation appointed in his stead. The keepers of this fire are members of the Panther and Turtle clans of the Chliicothe and Kishpoko nations, and are chosen by their respective nations.

The office continues until death. The keepers are permitted to marry, but they never go to war, nor is the fire taken with the war party. One of these keepers lives in a lodge, one apartment of which is set apart for the council fire. The other keeper lives close at hand. The keepers visit the apartment containing the fire once or twice a week.

Visitors are not permitted to enter this lodge unless on important business, and women are not allowed to enter at all. The office is not confined to Chiefs, but common people are commonly appointed.

The stone containing the council fire is rolled in a dressed deerskin, which is itself wrapped in a dressed buffalo skin. My father told me when I was a boy that these skins had been worn out and renewed three times since the council fire was brought across the sea.

THE MARCH UP THE MISSISSIPPI - Unknown, via Trowbridge

When Chilicothe had arrived with his warriors on this side of the ocean [the Gulf of Mexico], they were one day traversing the borders of the sea, and they found a large animal (a crocodile) lying dead upon the shore.

They immediately cut him open and took out his heart, which, along with a piece of his flesh, they deposited carefully in a bag and carried it with them on their journey.

Upon their arrival at the Shawnee River [the Mississippi River] they began to encounter difficulties. Opposition was made to their progress by those who inhabited the adjacent country, and they were compelled to send out scouting parties and war parties in order to maintain their possessions.

FIGHT WITH THE TURTLE

One of these parties consisting of seven warriors and their waiting man or cook, and after traveling a long time they arrived at the banks of a small lake, where they found an immense turtle resting on the shore. The leader proposed that the party should get upon the turtle's back to see if he could bear their weight. Accordingly he sat the example and his warriors followed him.

The increasing weight made the Turtle move, and the servant objected to following his companions. They ordered, insisted, and entreated the servant, but all in vain.

In the mean time the Turtle moved to the water. The warriors, finding that they could not prevail upon the servant to follow them, concluded to abandon the Turtle. But they found themselves sticking fast to his back. Supposing that their moccasins caused this adhesion, they cut them loose from their feet, but all their exertions availed them nothing. The turtle waded into deep water, and at length sank, carrying his load along with him.

The servant remained upon the shore of the Lake a long time, expecting their return, but at length his patience became exhausted, and he shaped his course for the village. When he arrived there he related the circumstances of the excursion and the fate of his companions.

The old men assembled and listened with astonishment to the servant's narrative. They were much perplexed to know what course to take, but finally resolved to trust in their great medicine for relief, and to visit the spot where their friends had disappeared, for the purpose of rescuing them.

Accordingly eight of them, accompanied by the waiter, set out for the lake, carrying with them their medicine bag and the heart and flesh which they had taken from the animal on the borders of the sea.

The servant led them to the spot, and after having made an encampment at some distance from the shore, they erected a forked stick about 2 feet high at the edge of the water, and another forked stick at the spot where the warriors had got upon the back of the Turtle. Upon these forked sticks they laid a pole or beam, and in the middle of the space between the sticks they kindled a small fire (a council fire, described here as a fire for smoking meat).

Then they returned to their encampment where they commenced singing a song to their grandfather, the Turtle, imploring him to come and expose himself at the fire. They continued this song all night, and about midnight they heard a noise at the fire.

In the morning they sent the servant to see if anything was there. He returned, telling them that their grandfather lay by the side of the fire, dead, and that blood was running from his nose. The old men went down and found the Turtle as the man had described him. They took some of the blood from his nose and mixed it with a small quantity of their medicine, and by using this compound they restored him to life.

They then told the turtle to be gone, that they did not want him there, and that his proper place was the water. The turtle took their advice and left them.

FIGHT WITH A GREAT SERPENT (COMET):
AN IMPACT MEGA-TSUNAMI, AND THE OTHER MEDICINE

Trowbridge's unknown informant placed these passages here. If his memories of their placement in time were accurate, then the passages could remember Comet Encke and the Great Atlantic Mega-Tsunami of ca.1050 BCE. Alternatively, the "Turtle" referred to could be the "Great Turtle", and the passages may remember the impacts at the start of the Holocene ca. 8,4000 BCE.

The party immediately returned to their encampment and recommenced their song. In this song they did not solicit the visit of the Turtle, but of their other grandfather, the Serpent, who inhabited and had charge of the lake. They continued the song without cessation all the day and the succeeding night, and they heard at midnight a similar noise at the fire.

In the morning the servant was dispatched to the fire as usual to ascertain if anything was there. The servant found a large serpent, but not the one who had charge of the lake, also lying dead by the side of the fire.

Upon acquainting the old men with these facts, they went down to the fire and by the power of the compound of medicine and blood used before they resuscitated him as well. They told the Serpent that it was not himself, but his master whom they wanted, so that they might ascertain the cause of the evil treatment which had been given by one of his subjects (the turtle) to their companions.

The Serpent accordingly fled to the water, and the old men returned to their camp, where they recommenced their songs. They fasted and did not cease to sing for some days and nights. At length about midnight a terrible noise was heard in the water, and afterwards at the [council] fire.

In the morning the servant was sent as usual to see what was to be seen, and he found the King of the Serpents lying there dead, the blood streaming from his nose to the ground. The old men went down in great eagerness, but they did not restore him to life, fearing his power, and despairing of the recovery of their brothers. On the contrary, they proceeded to cut up his carcass.

The King of the Serpent's body was like that of a snake, and he had the head, horns, and neck of a large buck. His body was cut into small pieces and every thing connected with it, even the excrement, was carefully preserved. The head, horns, flesh and other parts were mixed with the heart and flesh of the animal found upon the sea shore, and forms the medicine which the witches use.

It is still preserved, and the flesh, though many thousand years old, is as fresh as if it had just been killed. By means of this medicine they can take a piece of stick, of dirt, a hair or any thing else, and transform it into a worm, which they depute and send to any distance to accomplish their designs against the victims of their power.

THE MEKOCHE AND PEKOWITHA - Black Hoof

The Mekoche were put upon the Great Island on the borders of Shawnee [Ohio/ Mississippi] River. They had not been there long when they discovered the Pekowitha, who told them that they came from Weskumuisa [the Red Man, Waaskoomisar,], a man in the south. These two nations soon became incorporated with each other.

THE PEKOWITHA NATION
- Tenskwatawa, 'Open Door', the Shawnee Prophet

Four days after the departure of the Great Spirit, the old men sent out some of the young men to hunt, telling them, that if they killed any game they must not leave a single thing behind, but bring it all home. Accordingly the young men hunted and killed an elk. But he was so large that they could not carry it all home, and so they left the Elk's backbone on the ground, as the most valueless part.

When they returned and the old men saw that the Elk's backbone was missing, they sent the hunters after it. But these arriving at the place where they had killed the Elk found the bone moving, and then they found to their surprise that the backbone turned into a man whose body was red.

At the command of the old men they led him into the camp where he was asked whence he came, but he could give no account of himself. From this man sprung the Pekowitha nation. As this man derived his existence neither from the Great Spirit nor from human beings, but from an animal, he was appointed head of the warriors of the Shawnee people, and they called him Weskumisa [Waaskoomislili] because he was red.

THE MEKOCHE
- Tenskwatawa, 'Open Door', the Shawnee Prophet

It became necessary now to appoint some person to take care of the great medicine [council fire] which had been given them by the Great Spirit, and accordingly they assembled in council to make the choice. But being divided in opinion, they spent seven days in fruitless efforts to elect someone to the distinguished office.

At last a man unknown to them all appeared suddenly in the council, entirely naked. As none knew him, he passed the first day unnoticed. On the following day, he came again, covered all over with white paint or clay.

During the contest this man arose and told the members of the Council that he was of the Mekoche nation of the Shawnee people, and that the title of Great Chief was to be held by his family. And he told them that the office of keeper of the medicine [council fire] was due to him, because his heart was as white and pure as the paint on his body.

He then left the Council and remained absent until the next day, when he came again to urge upon them his claims to the office. These were founded upon the facts of his being a great chief, and of his being without blood in his body, as his heart and flesh were white.

At length the Council concluded to trust to his professions, and to try him they gave him one part of the medicine, without informing him however that he had not the whole.

THE MIGRATION OF THE ALGONQUIN "CHILICOTHE"
FROM THE NORTH ca 900 CE,
AND THEIR CONQUEST OF THE MEKOCHE - Black Hoof

The Chilicothe, at present one of the nations of the confederacy, lived on the opposite side of the sea [Lake Erie]. They sent out a scout [*Maume-Esemauklilitar, mishinewaa* Howard] to explore the country. He reached the sea coast, and discovered the island, of which he informed his chiefs.

They resolved unanimously to go to the island in search of the people who might inhabit it, and accordingly marched down to the sea shore. Many leaders were appointed to conduct them across the sea, but every one refused, until at last one of the Turtle clan accepted the appointment and led on.

The whole party followed him and reached the shore of the island in safety, having marched all the way upon the bottom of the sea. When they arrived an encampment was immediately formed, and a fire was enkindled, the smoke of which ascended to the clouds.

The Mekoche, whose residence was not very distant, discovered this smoke and dispatched a scout [Maume-Esemaukeiitar] to ascertain its cause. He returned and reported that a great body of people were encamped at the fire. The Chiefs directed him to go back and salute them as cousins, in the name of the whole nation.

The Chilicothe rejected this offer, and many others which were made, but at length onsented to be called grandfathers.

THE CONQUEST OF THE PEKOWITHA AND THE KISHPOKI - Black Hoof

The Chilicothe soon after came to live with their new relatives. The Kishpoko were found near the Pekowitha, and were incorporated with the Mekoche in the same manner [as the Mekoche had been]. And the Shawnee, who had previously constituted a separate nation, also joined the confederacy.

THE MIGRATION OF THE ALGONQUIN THAWKILA - Black Hoof

The Confederacy's force was further augmented by the addition of the Thawikila [Thauweekeelau] who also came across the sea.

THE CONFEDERACY FORMS

They do not know why the confederated nations adopted the name of one of the nations, but they suppose that it was because the Shawnees were most numerous.

The tribes all spoke the same language, which greatly facilitated their union. When these tribes had confederated they formed twelve large villages.

WAR WITH THE KUSHITA (CREEK)
- Tenskwatawa, 'Open Door', the Shawnee Prophet

The date of the Kushita migration can be set at around 1400 CE, with their crossing of the Mississippi River at what is now Memphis, Tennessee, just to the south of the Mekoche lands. These peoples were in the process of completing that emigration and their conquest of the earlier peoples of the south east at the time of the Spanish conquistador de Soto's expedition in 1540, and both the Kushita and the Chicasaw would attempt to enlist him as their ally.

Soon after the Mekoche became Great Chief, the Shawnee heard that there were other people on the Island, and they set out to go and see them.

When they approached their camp, their new neighbors sent them a messenger to warn them not to come to their village. But the Shawnee fearlessly approached, disclosing to the Kushita [Creeks], for these were the new comers, their origin and other things.

When they came to the description of their medicine [council fire, nation], the Kushita [Creeks] pretended to doubt the truth of the story, whereupon the Shawnee, angered, destroyed all the Kushita [Creeks] by the power of the medicine [council fire. federation].

The next day however, the Shawnee brought some of them back to life by the same means, and compromised with them, thereafter calling them their brothers.

Their visit to the Kushita [Creeks] completed, the Shawnee returned to their own village, where they had left the Mekoche [Great Chief], and from there they proceeded to the north.

WAR WITH THE CATAWBAS - Tenskwatawa, 'Open Door', the Shawnee Prophet

[The Catawba were a Souian people, part of one of the late migration waves.]

After the old men [the ancient founders of the nations] had died, and after other nations had sprung up, the people began to wage war against each other. The Shawnee, Pekowitha, and Kishpoko nations of the Shawnee federation went to war against the Catawbas.

In their first expedition, they took 2 female prisoners near the camp of the Catawbas. One of the possessors of these female chiefs was a young warrior of the Mekoche nation. Afterwards, a man found him asleep, and being curious to know if he really had no blood *[since he was of the royal line]*, as he had pretended, he tomahawked and scalped him.

When the murderer returned with his prisoner, who was the same female which the young Mekoche had taken, he carried her to the father of the young man, [also a Mekoche], as he desired him to accept the scalp and the prisoner as a present. The old man, supposing it to be the scalp of a Catawba, accepted the gift, and called the female prisoner his granddaughter.

However, the old man continued to grieve for the loss of his son for two or three years, at which time his granddaughter, the female prisoner, having learned to speak Shawnee, told her grandfather all the circumstances of the young man's murder. The old man returned to examine the scalp for a scar which was on the head of his son before his death, and finding the scar there, was convinced of the truth of the facts alleged by his granddaughter.

WAR WITH THE OJIBWE;
WAR WITH THE SIX NATIONS
Tenskwatawa, 'Open Door', the Shawnee Prophet

The old man [of the Meckoche] then called a council of his old friends, and he explained to them these facts, which were proved by the production of his son's scalp.

To avenge themselves for his death they put his scalp into an earthen pot filled with blood, and sent it to the Ojibwe [Chippewa] and other surrounding nations as a challenge to war. The other nations accepted the challenge, and were severally beaten by the Shawnees.

This displeased the old men who had promoted the war so much that they sent the kettle with the scalp to the Six Nations, in hopes that their strength and prowess would overpower their own nation and give them cause to exult in their downfall.

The Six Nations prepared for battle, and came on, to the number of 7,000 men. They attacked the Shawnee village at the break of day, and had well nigh killed the whole of the Shawnee warriors, when the remaining few took the weapons and habiliments of those who had been killed and put them upon the women, the latter joining the warriors' party. By their numbers and appearance they so deceived the Six Nations that they supposed themselves attacked by a fresh force, and they fled.

MEKOCHE REMOVED AS LEADERS OF FEDERATION
- Tenskwatawa, 'Open Door', the Shawnee Prophet

By this time the warriors and chief men found out the cause of the war, and they determined to take the medicine [council fire] from the Mekoche nation.

They accordingly watched for their opportunity, and taking from him the 1/2 of the medicine [council fire] originally given, they returned to Chilicothe. The Chilicothe were on the Mississippi River, where the council fire was kept.

This event most likely occurred in the period after the move by the Chilicothe to Starved Rock on the Illinois River in 1683, and their subsequent move to Chilicothe, Illinois.

After the Six Nations defeat by the western peoples, the Chilicothe would return to their homeland, the area around today's Chilicothe, off the Ohio River. A partial solar eclipse was visible along the path of their return, at the junction of the Ohio River with the Mississippi River, the area of today's Shawnee Springs near Cairo, Illinois, on June 22 ,1694, and a full solar eclipse was visible there on October 4th, 1717. [I wish to thank Raoul Lannoy for his help in identifying this eclipse.]

But the Chief of the Mekoche nation protested against the taking of the medicine [council fire], and he claimed the right to keep it, on account of his family being very ancient. The Chief of the Chilicothe nation was obliged to convince him of his own power by shooting the Sun, which occasioned an eclipse, and darkened the earth until they restored its light by the medicine (council fire).

The Chief of the Mekoche nation then confessed the superior power of the Chilicothe, and consented to relinquish his claim to the medicine (council fire), but only on the condition that he was not entirely deprived of character and standing in the federation. Whereupon they appointed the Chief of the Mekoche nation to be the counsellor for the whole confederacy.

But this character they do not sustain at the present day (1825), as the federation is divided.

ANOTHER ACCOUNT OF THE TRANFER OF THE COUNCIL
FIRE FROM THE MEKOCHE
Tenskwatawa, 'Open Door', the Shawnee Prophet

The care of this [council] fire is now committed to two men, one of the Chilicothe nation, and the other of the Kishpoko nation. This charge however formerly belonged to the Mekoche nation, but after a battle between the Six Nations and the Shawnees, it was taken from them.

THE ANCIENT HISTORY OF THE KUSHITA:
THE TALE OF THE ANCESTORS:
THE KUSHITA (CREEK) MIGRATION LEGEND

Adapted to Modern Usage By E.P. Grondine
©Copyright 2004-2005   E.P. Grondine

INTRODUCTION

Many Native American peoples had detailed oral song cycles recounting their histories, comparable in many ways to the Greek and Persian oral historical cycles. These songs were dramatically performed in the present tense, often accompanied by set dances, with each passage having an emphasizing and distinctive percussion accompaniment. Many peoples performed their entire oral song cycle yearly at their annual fall harvest festivals; in this specific instance, the Kushita (Creek) recited their migration story at their annual busk festival.

All we currently have left of most of these oral historical cycles are scattered fragments. The badly fragmented outlin7e version of the Kushita (Creek) cycle given here was recited in 1725 by Chekilli, head Chief of the Upper and Lower Creeks, and we have the original translators notes of it in an obviously corrupted and shortened form. The translation from which the version given here is adapted is that Albert S. Gatschet, A Migration Legend of the Creek Indians, D.G. Brinton, Philadelphia, v1, v2, 1884, 1889. Another fragment of this cycle was preserved by Benjamin Hawkins. (A Sketch of the Creek Country in 1798 and -99, Georgia Historical Society Collections, 1848, cited by George E, Lankford, Native American Legends, August House, Little Rock, Arkansas, 1987, Tale 84, p. 144)

The Chickasaw also had their own migration cycle, which they also recited at their annual busk, but all that remains of it are very scattered fragments collected far apart. It was heard from them by James Adair, who makes a brief mention of it in Argument XIII of his History of the American Indians. In his 1930 edition of Adair's work, Samuel Cole Williams refers to other fragments of the Chickasaw migration cycle, which had been personally collected by Henry Rowe Schoolcraft (Information Indian Tribes, I, 309 et seq.), Horatio Bardwell Cushman (History of the Choctaw, Chickasaw, and Natchez Indians, 1899), and Tilly Buttrick (Voyages, Travels, Discoveries, 1812-1819, Boston, 1831), the last spurious. John Haywood also preserves fragments of the Chickasaw migration cycle in his Natural and Aboriginal History of Tennessee, and Simon Antoine Le Page du Pratz referred to key events in it in his Memoire sur la Louisiane.

THE TALE OF THE ANCESTORS

THE VERY BEGINNING OF THE KUSHITA (CREEK) MIGRATION STORY:
THE START OF THE HOLOCENE

"Towards the Sun's setting the Ground opened, which is the Mouth of the Earth.
The Earth opened, and the Kashitas came out of its mouth and settled nearby.
But the Earth was angry, and ate up their children.

"They went further towards the setting of the Sun,
but nevertheless our own part of the Kashitas turned back again and came to the same place,
leaving the greater body behind, as they thought it might be best to do so.

"They settled there again,
but the Earth still ate up their children.
So in anger they went away towards the Sun's rising.

THE KUSHITA (CREEK) REACH THE MISSISSIPPI RIVER

"They came to a thick muddy river where they camped, rested, and slept one night.

The muddy river here is the Mississippi River, as will be seen immediately below. The Kushita usage of the terms "day", "night", and "year" in the Tale of the Ancestors is not literal, but likely related to far longer astronomical periods of time.

ca 1000 CE: THE KUSHITA REACH THE RED RIVER

"The next day [age] they began to travel again,
and came in one day [age] to a red, bloody river.
They lived by that river and ate its fish for two years [ages].
But it was a low marshy place, and they did not like living there."

Continuing the Tale of the Ancestors from another fragment (Lankford's tale 84):

"At the forks of Red River (We-cha-te-hat-che Au-fus-kee),
west of the Mississippi River (We-o-coof-ke, muddy water),
There are two mounds of earth.
Here the Kashita, Coweta, and Chickasaws found themselves.

ca. 1000 A.D. the Toltec Mounds culture came to an end, though it still survived in the central and north parts of the Arkansas Plateau. Continuing with the Lankford fragment -

"They were at a loss for fire.
Here they were visited by Hi-you-yul-gee,
four men who came from the four corners of the world.
One of these people asked them,
"Where will you have your fire?"
They pointed to a place,
And it was made..."

Ca 1064 CE:
THE KUSHITA MOVE TO SUNSET VOLCANO

At the end of the Red River, at its source, is Sunset Volcano, Arizona, the only active volcano in the southwest of the United States, and it is known from the study of tree rings that Sunset Volcano started to erupt in 1064 CE. Returning to the fragment given by Chelikilli -

"They went to the end of that Red River, and heard a thundering noise.
They went forward to hear where the noise came from, and they first saw a red smoke, and soon after a mountain which thundered.
Upon the mountain was a singing noise,
and they went up to see what it was.
And it was a great fire which burned upwards
and made a singing noise.
They called that mountain the King of Mountains,
and it thunders to this day.
They took and saved some of the fire from this mountain.

EVENTS AT SUNSET VOLCANO

"Here they met the people of three different nations.

These three peoples were without doubt the Chickasaw, the Choctaw, and the Abhikas [Apaqua]. In the fragment preserved by Lankford, this meeting occurred on the Red River, instead of at Sunset Volcano; my guess is that the fragment preserved by Lankford is correct, as the united forces were able to triumph over the peoples they encountered on their migration west. The following tale of the fire may represent an interaction between these four peoples, as each people would have had its own fire, but perhaps it may represent interaction with the local peoples.

"From the East, a white fire came to them; which, however, they would not use. From the South (Wahalle), a fire came to them which was blue; neither did they use it. From the West, a fire came to them which was black; nor would they use it. At last, from the North, came a fire which was red and yellow. This fire they mingled with the fire they had taken from the mountain, and this is the fire they use today. This fire too sometimes sings, [as did the mountain from which it came.]"

According to the tale, besides their fire, the Creek also obtained a knowledge of some hallucinogens and pharmaceuticals at Sunset Volcano:

"Here they also found four herbs or roots, which sang and disclosed their virtues. The first of these was Pasaw, (the translator glossed this as rattlesnake root, a datura which is also a hallucinogen at larger doses). The second of these was Micoweanochaw (the translator glossed this as red-root). The third was Sowatchko, (which grows like wild fennel); and the fourth, Eschalapootche, (the translator glossed this as little tobacco, native tobacco, which is much stronger than the tobacco smoked today). "

Either the translator or Chelikilli discussed these drugs at some length:

"These herbs, especially the first and third, they use as the best medicine to purify themselves at their Busk. At this Busk, which is held yearly, they fast, and make offerings of the first fruits. Ever since they learned the virtues of these herbs, their women, at certain times [during menstruation], have had a separate fire and remain apart from the men five, six, or seven days for the sake of purification. If they neglected this the power of the herbs would depart, and the women would not be healthy."

It seems likely to me that the Kushita may also have acquired their culturally important ball game, which they called "the brother of war", by playing on the ball court found at Sunset Volcano.

SHROTLY BEFORE Ca 1259 CE:
SUNSET VOLCANO'S RENEWED ACTIVITY LEADS THE KUSHITA TO LEAVE

"On the mountain there was a pole
which was very restless and made a noise,
and no one could say how it could be quieted.
They took a motherless child and stuck it on the pole, which killed the child.
[They impaled the child on the pole.]
Therefore they took the pole
and carried it with them as they went to war...

THE KUSHITA GAIN LEADERSHIP THROUGH A WAR

"A dispute arose as to which was oldest and who should rule.
They agreed that as they were four sorts of people,
they would set up four poles and make them red with clay –
with that clay which was at first yellow, but by burning became red.

And all would go to war
following whichever of them could first cover their pole
from the root up to the top with the scalps of enemies –
whoever did so first would be the eldest.
"They all tried to do it,
but the Kushitas covered their pole to the top first,

so that it could not be seen.
Therefore they were declared by the whole nation to be the eldest.
The Chickasaws covered their pole next,
and then the Atilamus [Choctaw] next.
But the Abhikas could not raise their heap of scalps higher than a knee.

THE MUSKOGEE CONFEDERATION
DEFEAT THEIR NEXT ENEMY BY STRATEGEM

The following passage describes the abduction and impregnation of a Muskogee woman by a king of an enemy people. As to who these enemies were, there is little to go on, but the Thunderbird priest kings of the Mississippian peoples are well known. The woman's son is then used by the Muskogee to sabotage their enemy's defenses. Blue was the color of the south.

"At that time there was a bird, the King of Birds. This bird was of large size, blue in color, with a long tail, and swifter than an eagle, which came every day and killed and ate their people. They made an image in the shape of a woman and placed it in the way of this bird. The bird carried it off, kept it a long time, and then brought it back.

"They left the image of the woman alone, hoping it would bring something forth. After a long time a red mouse [war spy] came forth from it; the Bird was the father of the Mouse. They took council with the Mouse how to destroy its father.

"Now the Bird had a bow and arrows, and the Mouse [spy] gnawed the bowstring, so that the Bird could not defend itself, and the people killed it. They called this bird the King of Birds."

Either the translator or Chelikilli next discussed the Kushita bird symbolism at some length:

"They think the eagle is also a great King, and they carry its feathers when they go to war or make peace: the red feathers mean war; the white feathers, peace. If an enemy approaches with white feathers and a white mouth, and cries like an eagle, they dare not kill him.

1259 CE: SUNSET VOLCANO'S FINAL ERUPTION,
AND A RETURN TO HOT SPRINGS, ARKANSAS?

While trade paths may have been considered by the Kushita as white "peaceful" paths, and Mississippian foot paths were generally white, as the vegetation along them was knocked down by the footsteps of traders passing over them, in the following passage the grass and everything are described as being white. This is probably because "everything" was covered by ash from Sunset Volcano's final eruption in 1259 CE.

"After this they left that place, and came to a white foot-path. The grass and everything around were white; and they plainly perceived that people had been there. They crossed the path, and slept near there. Afterward they turned back to see what sort of path that was, and who the people were who had been there, in the belief that it might be better for them to follow that path. They went along it to a river called Coloose-hatche, that is, the Smoking River, because it was rocky there and smoked."

Hot Springs, Arkansas, may be the "Smoking River" referred to here. The line of the Kushita advance must have run through Arkansas, as Nodena Ware, a sandy pottery from Arkansas with red markings on a white background, is found at every destroyed Southern Ceremonial site in or just before or after the time of its "abandonment".

THE CHICASAW CROSS THE MISSISSIPPI RIVER

While it is difficult to trace the route of the Kushita at this point, a fragment of the Chickasaw migration tale preserved by Haywood in his Natural and Aboriginal History of Tennessee is quite specific in its details of the Chickasaw crossing of the Mississippi River. It also provides specific details about the war between the Chickasaw chief, supposedly named No-hoo-to-ta-pa, with a king who calls himself the "Brother of the Sun", which is a formal and correct Mississippian title, as the right to rule was matriarchal, and the Sun was the woman though whose line the kingship passed The version given here has been adapted from that preserved by John Haywood in his Natural and Aboriginal History of Tennessee.

"Our forefathers came from the west many years ago in the time of No-hoo-la-pah, Tuskah-Hamah, or the beloved red chief. A great nation made war upon our tribes who resided upon those great rivers which run from the western mountains (the Rocky Mountains) into the great waters of the south (the Gulf of Mexico).

With this nation we had long been connected in amity and friendship. We had associated with them in war, and in the chase, and often smoked together the pipe of peace. Their chiefs claimed kindred with the sun, and were more absolute than ours. We were permitted to eat with them, hunt with them, go to war with them, but not to intermarry with them. Their ruler was the Brother of the Sun."

No-hoo-to-ta-pah, the ruler of the Chickasaw, had a son who had distinguished himself as a great warrior in several battles against the nations of the west. He had eclipsed all the children of the Sun with whom he fought, in annoying the enemy. After a long and bloody war, carried on jointly with our ally against the enemy, we returned victorious. No-hoo-tota-pah had been the first in command, but the victory had been achieved by his son, who in imitation of our allies, had been styled the Morning Star.

On our return through the country of our allies, the Brother of the Sun entertained our warriors for several days, during which Morning Star was permitted to partake of the feast of the Sun, which was celebrated in honor of the conquerors. Mora, the daughter of the Brother of the Sun, officiated as priestess."

These were a Mississippian people, who had a matriarchal royal lineage, while the Kushita were patriarchal, which accounts for some of the confusion here. Mora, referred to her as the eldest daughter of the Great Sun, who himself is properly referred to here as the "Brother of the (female) Sun", was herself a woman, and most likely must have been the female Sun through whom the kingship would have passed. Instead of being the daughter of the Great Sun, Mora was more likely the daughter of the female Sun. Mora's brother would have been the next Great Sun, the next ruler.

"Morning Star was the first who was presented to receive consecration. The ceremony ended in the captivation of the hero and of the priestess. The moment was auspicious. Morning Star could withstand the honors which were administered to him, but he fell victim to the hand which had administered them. Mora felt what she had communicated, and sympathized with the heart which she subdued.

"Morning Star resolved to conquer for Mora; Mora wished no longer to be a holy virgin, and to live only for the hero. But Mora was the descendant of the Sun, and her lover was the son of a subordinate chief. A connection between them was impossible.

"Mora was sensible of her divine origin, and she knew that she could not be obtained with the consent of her father. She determined to elope with her lover to his own tribe, and she professed herself willing to be the wife of the Morning Star. He was to take her from the Temple of the Sun.

"The Brother of the Sun and No-hoo-to-ta-pah, Ruler of the Chickasaw, were taking leave of each other in the long smoke; but Mora and Morning Star were already on the wing. The Brother of Mora [who was the son of the female Sun, and thus due to be Ruler of this people] had been jealous of the Morning Star. Morning Star's courage and skill had entitled him to the first honors among the warriors, but the Brother of Mora could not bear the comparison. The Brother of Mora concealed himself in an ambush to destroy Morning Star as he returned home, and while Mora and Morning Star thought themselves safe, the Brother of Mora let fly an arrow, and Morning Star fell at her feet. Mora escaped while her brother scalped her lover Morning Star. Mora wandered off and was never heard of again.

"No-hoo-to-ta-pah, Ruler of the Chickasaw, immediately demanded the murderer. His demand was refused, and both sides resorted to war: by the Brother of the Sun for the loss of his daughter, and by No-hoo-to-ta-pah for the death of his son. And a bloody war ensued. "

While the point of the Kushita's crossing of the Mississippi River is unclear, in any case, the towns near to the junction of the Ohio with the Mississippi at Towosaghy and Wickliffe are both abandoned around 1250 AD. The fragment of the Chickasaw cycle preserved by Buttrick states that the Chickasaw crossing place was at Memphis, which has a major Southern Ceremonial Cult center located at DeSoto Park.

THE CHICKASAW CONTINUE EAST

Adapted from another fragment preserved by Haywood -

"Our first land was a long distance to the west of the Mississippi River. Some of our priests dreamt of white [lighter skinned] people living towards the sun's rising in a fine country, and our ancestors started east, and were traveling for many years.

"The leader of the priests brought a pole along which he set up every night. Whichever way the pole leaned in the morning, the people kept as their course all that day. The pole constantly leaned towards the east, until they came to the east of Old-Town. Then the pole leaned back towards the west, and they came back to Old-Town, and camped till the pole stood straight. And there they made the first settlement."

The Muskogean term for Old Town is so common as to be for all purposes useless in trying to identify a specific location for this "Old Town"

THE KUSHITA CONQUER THE COOSA

While the following geographical identifications are tenuous, to say the least, the cycle earlier had the Kushita near Sunset Volcano, Arizona, and it will shortly have them fighting the Cherokee. The Kushita had to move east from one place to the other in some manner.

It has been thought that the Coosa were an original Mississippian people who ruled the watershed of what is today known as the Coosa River in northeast Alabama, but there are several problems with this. Assuming that the Kushita people led the Muskogeean federation's migration to the east, and that this migration was not led by the Chickasaw people, they should now have been in the general area of the northwest of today's state of Alabama. As the Kushita state that the Coosa were the next people they encountered, thus the Coosa nation would probably having then have been living at that time in an area along what are known today as the Tombigbee River and Black Warrior River.

As a general practice, Muskogee peoples would establish red (war) town near a white (peace) town which they had conquered. These "red towns" would control the conquered area and rely for their existence on tribute exacted from the "white towns". In this way the Muskogeean peoples would absorb the peoples which they conquered, and as will be seen below, it seems entirely likely that they absorbed the Coosa in exactly this manner, and then took their name with them as they continued onward to the east.

"They crossed the river, going toward the sunrise, and came to a people and a town named Coosaw. Here they remained four years."

"The Coosaws complained that they were preyed upon by a wild beast, which they called man-eater, which lived in a rock. The Kushitas said they would try to kill the beast.

"They dug a pit and stretched over it a net made of hickory-bark. They then laid a number of branches, crosswise across the path, so that the man-eater could not follow them, and, going to the place where the man-eater lay, they threw a rattle into his den. The man-eater rushed forth in great anger, and pursued them through the branches. They then thought it better that one should die rather than all of them, so they took a motherless child and threw it before the man-eater as he came near the pit. The man-eater rushed at it and fell in the pit, over which they threw the net, and killed him with blazing pine-wood.

Either the translator or Chelikilli next discussed this man-eater at some length:

"His bones, however, they keep to this day; on one side, they are red; on the other, blue. The man-eater used to come every seventh day to kill the people; therefore, they

442

remained there seven days after they had killed him. In remembrance of him, when they prepare for war, they fast six days and start on the seventh. If they take the man-eater's bones with them, they have good fortune."

THE KUSHITA MOVE SOUTH

The lack of corn and the simple technologies which Chelikilli described in the next passage seem strangely out of place.

"After four years they left the Coosaws, and came to a river which they called Nowphawpe, now Callasi-hatche. There they tarried two years; and, as they had no corn, they lived on roots and fishes, and made bows, pointing the arrows with beaver teeth and flint-stones, and for knives they used split canes.

"They left this place, and came to a creek called Wattoolahawka-hatche, Whooping-creek, so called from the whooping of cranes, a great many being there; they slept there one night."

While today the southern winter home of the whooping crane is limited to Gulf Coast of Texas, in these times it extended further to the east along the Gulf Coast, into the coastal areas of today's state of Alabama.

THE KUSHITA MOVE NORTH

"They next came to a river in which there was a waterfall; this they named the Owatunka River. "

"The next day they reached another river, which they called the Aphoosa pheeskaw."

It seems likely to me that this "Aphoosa pheeskaw" may have been the Euphasee River, known today as the Little Tennessee River, as following this river would place the Kushita at the next firmly identified locations.

THE KUSHITA BATTLE TO CHEROKEE LANDS:

"The next day they crossed over [the Aphoosapheesaw River] and came to a high mountain.
They found some people there and hoped that they were the people who had made the White Path.
Therefore they made white arrows (peace arrows) and shot [them] to see if they were good people,
but the people there carried their white arrows off, made them red (war arrows), and shot them back again.

"Then they took up the red arrows and carried them to their chief.
Their chief told them that it was not good;
if the arrows had returned white,
they would have gone and got food for their children,

443

but as they were red, they should not go.

"However, some of them went to see what people they were,
and found that they had all left their houses.
They saw tracks which went into the river,
and saw that the tracks went into the river but did not get out,
for they went to the other side of the river and could find no tracks.

"There is a mountain we call Motero,
which makes a sound like the beating of a drum.
Those people live there now (1735);
whenever we go to war, this sound is heard."

*"Motero" most probably refers to a spot in the Bald Mountains, where seismic activity does indeed
produce a rhythmic sound, which was heard in the 1870's. See On A Series Of Earthquakes In
North Carolina, Commencing On The 10th Of February, 1874, Warren DuPre, Annual Report
Of The Board Of Regents Of The Smithsonian Institution, Showing The Operations, Expenditures,
And Condition Of The Institution For The Year 1874. I want to thank Ron Baalke for bringing
this report to my attention.*

The people who lived in the Bald Mountains in 1735 were the Cherokee.

THE KUSHITA MEET THE CHEROKEE, KUSHITA VERSION

"They went along that river until they came to another water fall,
where they saw great rocks,
and bows laid on the rocks.
They believed that the people who had made the White Path had been there.

"In all their travels they had two runners
who went before the body of the people,
and when they saw a mountain,
the runners went up it and looked around and saw a town.
They shot two white arrows (peace arrows) into the town,
but the people of that town again shot red arrows (war arrows) back.

The Kushitas were angry with those people,
and agreed to attack the town.
If they took it everyone was to have a house.

"They threw stones into the river
until it was so shallow that they could walk across it, which they did.
The people there were flat headed,
and they took the town.

"When they had done so
they killed everyone there but two,
whose tracks they followed

and overtook a white dog [Chilluki, an old Kushita (Creek) name for Cherokee], which they killed.

THE KUSHITA MEET THE CHEROKEE, CHEROKEE VERSION

The following is adapted from the version given by James Mooney, Myths of the Cherokee, with some "magical" elements, similar to magical elements found in the Song of Roland, removed.

"Long ago a powerful unknown tribe invaded the country from the southeast, killing people and destroying settlements wherever they went.

No leader could stand against them, and in a little while they had destroyed all the lower settlements and advanced into the mountains.

The warriors of the old town of Nikwasi, on the head of the Little Tennessee River, gathered their wives and children into the townhouse and kept scouts constantly on the lookout for the presence of danger.

"One morning, just before daybreak,
 the scouts saw the enemy approaching, and at once gave the alarm.
The Nikwasi men seized their arms and rushed out to meet the attack.
But after a long hard fight they found themselves overpowered,
and began to retreat.

"Then suddenly a stranger stood among them
and shouted to the chief to call off his men,
and he himself would drive back the enemy...
They fell back along the trail,
and as they came near the townhouse
they saw a great company of warriors...
The Nunnehi poured out by the hundreds,
armed and painted for the fight...

THE KUSHITA SURRENDER, CHEROKEE VERSION

"The invaders soon had to retreat,
going first along the ridge which separates the French Broad River from the Tuckagee River,
and then turning with it to the northeast...
All along the ridge they fell,
until when they reached the Tuckagee River
not more than half a dozen were left alive,
and in despair they sat down and cried out for mercy...
Then the Nunnehi chief told them
that they had deserved their punishment for attacking a
peaceful tribe, and he spared their lives and told them to go home...

They [who?] went home toward the north...

445

THE KUSHITA SURRENDER, KUSHITA VERSION

Having been blocked by the combined Cherokee-Nunnehi alliance, the Kushita now returned to their route to the south. The Apalachee people controlled the Chattahoochie River along its entire length during this period, and Appalachicola itself in later times was located at the junction of the Chattahoochie River with the Flint River.

"[They] pursued the two people until they came to the White Path again,
and they saw smoke from where there was a town.
They believed that they had found the people who they had traveled so long to see.
It is the place where the Apalachicola [Pallachacula] people now live...

"The Kushitas were always bloody minded,
but the Apalachicola people made them the Black Drink as a token of friendship,
and told them that as their own hearts were white (peaceful),
that they too must have white hearts,
and lay down their bodies, to show that they were white as well.

The Kushita strove for the tomahawk,
but the Apalichicola people by fair persuasion gained it from them,
and buried it under their house.

THE KUSHITA SETTLE IN NORTHERN APPALACHEE LANDS

As a general practice, the Muskogee peoples would establish red (war) towns near the white (peace) towns which they had conquered. These "red towns" would control the area conquered, and rely for their existence on tribute exacted from the white towns.

"The Apalichicola people gave them white feathers (peace feathers),
and asked to have a chief in common.
Ever since we have lived together."

At this point, the Kushita established the center of their "kingdom" at Cosa in the northern Appalachee lands, which is where DeSoto discovered them in 1540. The Ruler of Cosa would offer DeSoto his choice of Cosa lands, if he would help him against his enemies. The Kushita would later continue their wars against the Mississippian peoples, first allying with the Spanish, and then with the English.

446

THE WALUM OLUM:
THE ANCIENT HISTORY OF THE LENAPE

Preserved by Constantin Rafinesque

Brought into modern usage by E.P. Grondine
©Copyright 2004-2005 E.P. Grondine

INTRODUCTION

The ancient history of the Lenape survives today in a much abridged form which was preserved by Constantin Rafinesque. The Lenape [Delaware] recounted their migration cycle at their annual Big House Festival, and Rafinesque first acquired painted wooden sticks which served as a mnenoic aid for this performance, only later acquiring a phonetic record of the legend. As Rafinesque put it:

"These actual olum were at first obtained [by me] in 1820, as a reward for a medical cure; [they were] deemed a curiousity, and were unexplicable. In 1822 were obtained from another individual [not identified] the songs annexed thereto in the original language, but no one could be found by me able to translate them.

" I had therefore to learn the language since [afterwards], by the help of Zeisburger [dictionary and grammar], Heckewelder [dictionary and grammar], and a manuscript dictionary [the source of which is unidentified], on purpose to translate them, which I only accomplished in 1833."

Constantin Rafinesque, Ancient Nations, page 151.

The text here has been adapted to modern usage from the translation of Daniel Brinton, with major corrections made for substantial errors in identification.

THE CREATION

Line Numbers as assigned by Brinton, Part I.

1. In the Beginning, the Great Mind was there in the heavens,
in that place, at all times, above the Earth,
2. and the Earth itself was like an extended fog.

3. In the Beginning, the Great Mind was forever, everywhere in space.
4. Then the Great Mind made the extended land and the sky.
5. Then the Great Mind made the Sun, the Moon, and the Stars;
6. and he made them all move evenly.

7. Then the wind blew violently, and the fog of Earth [it] cleared,
and the water flowed off far and strong,
8. and groups of islands grew anew, and they remained there.

9. The Great Mind spoke anew, a Mind to minds:
10. He spoke to the beings [lesser minds],
to the mortals, to the souls, and to all.
11. And ever after he was the Great Mind to men,
and their Grandfather.

12. The Great Mind gave the First Mother, the mother of beings.
13. He gave the fish, he gave the turtles,
he gave the beasts, he gave the birds.

14. However, the Evil Mind made evil beings only: he made monsters;
15. the Evil Mind made the flies, he made the gnats.

16. All the beings were friendly then:
17. Truly the Minds were active and kindly.
18. To those very first men, and to those first mothers,
they fetched them wives,
19. And they fetched them food, when the first men first desired it.

20. All had cheerful knowledge, all had leisure,
and all thought in gladness.

21. But very secretly an Evil Being [an Evil Lesser Mind],
a mighty magician, came on the Earth:
22. and with him he brought badness, quarreling, unhappiness,
23. bad weather, sickness, and death.

24. All this took place of old on the Earth,
beyond the Great Tide-Water,
in the Beginning.

From this and other mentions later below, "The Great Tide-Water" must be Hudson's Bay. Certainly at this time the Lenape were located in a region in the extreme north.

THE HOLOCENE START IMPACT
Brinton's Part II

1. Long ago there was a Mighty Snake [comet], and beings evil to men.

2. This Mighty Snake [comet] hated those who were there,
(and) he greatly disquieted those whom he hated.

3. He harmed all things, he injured all things,
and all were not in peace.

4. Driven from their homes, the men fought with this murderer.

5. The Mighty Snake [comet] firmly resolved to harm the men.

6. The Mighty Snake [comet] brought three persons [fragments?],
he brought a monster [impact],
he brought rushing water [an impact mega-tsunami].

7. Between the hills the water rushed and rushed,
dashing through and through, destroying much.

8. Nanabush, the Strong White One, Grandfather of beings, Grandfather of men,
was on [Sea] Turtle Island.

"Turtle Island" here must refer to sea turtles.

Turtles are reptiles, and for the most part are unable to generate internal heat to warm their bodies. This limits their range to temperate climates, and there are and were none of these in the far north.

The exception to this could only have been sea turtles, who thrive in warm water. During the last ice age, the Japanese Current must have provided warm water to the north west coast of North America, while the Gulf Stream would have been inadequate to the task of warming the esat coast. From this, and the general track of the Lenape migration given below, it would appear that "Turtle Island" must refer to the north west coast of North America before the end of the last Ice Age.

9. There he was walking and creating:
and as he passed by,
he created the turtle [skin boats].

10. Beings and men all went forth,
they walked in the floods and shallow waters,
down-stream there in the turtle [skin boats].

A MIGHTY SNAKE (COMET) APPEARS

11. There were many monster fishes, which ate some of them.

12. The Great Mind's daughter came,
and helped with her canoe [wooden boat]:
she helped all, as they came and came.

13. Thus Nanabush, Nanabush, the Grandfather of all,
the Grandfather of beings, the Grandfather of men,
became the Grandfather of the turtle [skin boats].

14. The men were then together on the Great Turtle [the Earth],
like turtles.

15. Frightened on the Great Turtle [the Earth],
they prayed that what was spoiled should be restored.

16. The water ran off, the earth dried, the lakes were at rest,
all was silent, and the Mighty Snake [comet] departed.

CLIMATE COLLAPSE, AND EMIGRATION
Line numbers after Brinton's Part III.

1. After the rushing waters [had finished],
 the Lenape of the [Sea] Turtle were close together,
living together there in hollow houses.

2. It froze where they lived, it snowed where they lived,
it stormed where they lived, it was cold where they lived.

3. At this northern place they spoke favorably
of mild, cool (lands), with many deer and buffaloes.

4. As they journeyed, some being strong, and others rich,
they separated into house-builders and hunters;

5. The strongest, the most united, the purest, were the hunters.
6. The hunters showed themselves at the north, at the east,
at the south, at the west.

ATTACK ON THE SNAKES [MISSASAUGA]

7. In that ancient country, in that northern country,
in that [Sea] Turtle Country,
the best of the Lenape were the men of the Turtle Clan.

The Turtle Clan were the skin boat builders.

8. All the cabin fires of that land were disquieted,
and all said to their priest, "Let us go."

9. They went forth to the Snake [Missasauga] Land to the east,
going away earnestly grieving.

*Snakes, like turtles, are also reptiles, and for the most part are also unable to generate internal heat
to warm their bodies. This also limits their range to temperate climates, and there are and were none
of these in the far north. The northern-most range of snakes, and in particular of the poisonous
Missasauga rattlesnake, would appear to be along the Saint Lawrence at its junction with Lake Erie.*

10. Split asunder, weak, trembling, their land burned,
they went, torn and broken, to the Snake [Missasauga] Land.

11. Those from the north being free, without care,
they went forth from the land of snow, in different directions.

12. The fathers [ancestors]
of the Bald Eagle [band] and the White Wolf [band]
remained along the sea, rich in fish and muscles.

13. Floating up the streams in their canoes, our fathers were rich,
they were in the light, when they were at those islands.

14. Head Beaver and Big Bird [Head Eagle] said,
"Let us go to the Snake [Missasauga] Land,"
they said.

15. All said they would go along to destroy all the land.

16. Those of the north agreed, Those of the east agreed.
They went over the water, the frozen sea, to enjoy it.

17. On the wonderful slippery water,
On the stone-hard water [ice], all went,
On the Great Tidal Sea, the muscle-bearing sea.
They walked and walked, all of them.

From this and its earlier mention, the "Great Tidal Sea" would appear to be Hudson's Bay.

18. Ten thousand at night, All in one night,
To the Snake [Missasauga] Land, to the east, at night,
They walked and walked, all of them.

19. The men from the north, the east, the south:
The Eagle clan, the Beaver clan, the Wolf clan;
The best men, the rich men, the head men:
Those with wives, those with daughters, those with dogs,

THE SUBARTIC:
THE LAND OF THE SPRUCE PINES

20. They all came, they tarried at the Land of the Spruce Pines;
Those from the west came with hesitation,
as they highly esteemed their old home in the Turtle Land.

Line numbers after Brinton's Part IV.

1. Long ago the fathers of the Lenape
were living in the Land of Spruce Pines.

2. Hitherto the Bald Eagle band had been their pipe bearer,

3. while they were searching for the Snake [Missasauga] Land,
that great and fine land.

4. The Bald Eagle Band having died,
the hunters, about to depart, met together.

5. All of them said to Beautiful Head, "Be thou chief."

*A ceremonial pipe, commonly known today as the calumet, was carried by embassies to other peoples,
and used in peace ceremonies with them. Thus for the Lenape, "bearing the pipe", indicates a
diplomatic role. The use of pipes may either be an intrusive element or it may serve to date this
movement.*

ATTACK ON THE SNAKES [MISSASAUGA]

6. They came to the Snakes [Missasauga],
and slaughtered them at the Snake hill,
so that the Snakes [Missasauga] would leave it."

7. All of the Snake [Missasauga] tribe were weak,
and they hid themselves in the Swampy Vales.

8. After Beautiful Head was chief,
White Owl was chief in the Land of Spruce Pines.

9. After White Owl was chief,
the Man-Who-Kept-Guard was chief of that people.

A DECISION TO MIGRATE

10. After the Man-Who-Kept-Gaurd was chief, Snow Bird was chief;
Chief Snow Bird spoke of the south,
11. that our fathers should possess it by scattering abroad.

12. Chief Snow Bird went south,
while Chief White Beaver [baby seal] went east.

13. The Snake [Missasauga] Land was in the south,
the Great Spruce Pine Land was toward the shore
(of the Great Tidal Sea, [Hudson's Bay], in the north);

14. To the east was the Fish Land [coastal Atlantic],
toward the [Great] Lakes [in the west] was the buffalo land.

CONQUEST OF MISSASAUGA

15. After Snow Bird was chief, the Man-Who-Seized was chief,
and all [of these] were killed:
16. the robbers (Chikonapi), the Snakes (Akhonapi) [Missasauga],
the Evil Men (makatapi), the Stone Men (Assinapi).

The "Stone Men" referred to here may possible have been armored trans-Atlantic traders residing along the Saint Lawrence River.

17. After the Man-Who-Seized was chief,
 there were ten chiefs,
and there was much warfare in the south and east.

18. After the ten chiefs, the Peaceable-Man was chief
in Snake [Missasauga] land.

19. After the Peacable-Man was chief,
the Not-Black-Man was chief, who was a straight man.

20. After the Not-Black-Man was chief,
the Much-Loved-Man was chief, who was a good man.

21. After the Much-Loved-Man was Chief,
the No-Blood was chief, who walked in cleanliness.

22. After the No-Blood was chief,
Snow-Father was chief, he of the big teeth.

453

23. After Snow-Father was chief,
the Tally-Maker was chief, who made records.

CONQUEST OF AZTALAN, WISCONSIN

24. After the Tally-Maker was chief,
the Man-Who-Shivered-with-Cold was chief,
who went south to the corn land.

25. After the Man-Who-Shivered-with-Cold was chief,
the Corn-Breaker was chief, who brought about the planting of corn.

26. After the Corn-Breaker was Chief,
the Strong-Man was chief, who was useful to the chieftains.

27. After the Strong-Man was chief, the Salt-Man was chief,
and after him the Little-One was chief

MOVE TO THE UPPER MISSISSIPPI RIVER VALLEY

28. There was no rain, and no corn, so they moved further seaward [south - the earlier direction of the lakes].

29. At the place of caves, in the buffalo land,
they at last had food, on a pleasant plain.

THE LENAPE SPLIT:
ONE PART MOVE SOUTH

30. After the Little-One (came) the Fatigued-One;
after him, the Stiff-One.

This most likely refers to the appearance of some new disease, an influenza, or a plague.

31. After the Stiff-One was chief, the Man-Who-Reproved was chief;
some disliked him, and [became] unwilling [to remain];
32. becoming angry, they went off secretly, moving east.

33. The wise ones who remained made the Loving-One chief.

34. They settled again on the Yellow River,
and had much corn on stoneless soil.

35. All being friendly, the Affable-Man was chief, the first of that name.
36. He was very good, this Affable-Man,
and he came as a friend to all the Lenape.

37. After this good one, Strong-Buffalo was chief and pipe-bearer.

Again, the pipe referred to here is the calumet, and these lines may indicate that Strong-Buffalo entered into peace agreements.

38. Then Big-Owl was chief; then White-Bird was chief.

39. The Willing-One was [both] chief and priest, and he made festivals.

ALLIANCE WITH MENGWE;
WAR WITH MISSASAUGA, NORTHERNERS,
TOWO [TWAKANHAH, CAHOKIA]

40. Rich-Again was chief; the Painted-One was chief.

41. White-Fowl was chief;
and again there was war, in both the north and the south.

42. The Wolf [Minsi or Mengwe, Monacans] Wise-in Counsel was chief.

43. He knew how to make war on all; he slew Strong-Stone.

44. The Always-Ready-Man was chief;
he fought against the Snakes [Missasauga].

These most likely were the Missasauga who were located in the area of what is today Sandusky, Ohio. From David Cusick's Ancient History of the Six Nations, we know that these were in alliance with the Twakanha [Cahokians].

45. The Strong-Good-Man was chief,
he fought against the northerners.

46. The Lean-Man was chief;
he fought against the Towakon [Twakanhah- Cahokia] people.

[This "leaness" may indicate starvation.]

THE LENAPE HELD BY THE TOWAKON [TWAKANHAH, CAHOKIA];
ATTEMPT FLANKING MANUEVER TO THE SOUTHEAST
BY ATTACKING TALEGEWI [THILIGOTHE, CHILICOTHE, SHAWNEE]

47. The Opossum-Like-Man was chief; he fought in sadness.

The pictograph here seems to indicate that the Lenape divided, rather than opposum. See the fragment from the Sutton account given in Additional Fragments below.

48. And he said, "They are many:
let us go together to the east, to the sunrise."

49. They separated at the Fish River [Mississippi River];
the lazy ones remained there.

TALLIGEWI [THILIGOTHE, CHILICOTHE]
ALLOW LENAPE TO PASS, AND THEN ATTACK

50. The Cabin-Man was chief [of the Talligewi]:
the Talligewi [Thiligothe, Chilicothe, Shawnee] possessed the east.

51. The Man-Who-Was-a-Strong-Friend was chief,
and he desired the eastern land.

52. Some passed on east;
the Talegewi [Thiligothe, Chilicothe, Shawnee] ruler killed some of them.

53. All said in unison, "War, war."

THE TALAMATAN [NEUTRALS] ARRIVE

54. The Talamatan [Neutrals], friends from the north, came,
and they all went together.

Brinton identified the Talamatan as the Huron nation, and he appears to have been close to right. Most likely the Talamatan were the "Neutrals", as later below the Lenape speak of their driving the Talamatan to the north of Lake Erie. At this time the "Neutrals" occupied the area around today's Toledo, Ohio, and the Shawnee lived to their south.[1]

Ca 1250 CE, the Missasauga people held both the area of the junction of the Saint Lawrence with Lake Erie, and the area around Sandusky, Ohio, which controlled the rivers going inland. The Missasauga were in alliance with the people of Twakanhah, (i.l "Cahokia") and they are referred to as being their allies by the Five Nations. The Ottawa held the areas between the Eries and the Missasauga along the south shore of Lake Erie.

Between 1200-1300 CE the "Neutrals" were driven from the Toledo area by the Missasauga of the Sandusky area. The Five Nations warred with the Missasauga ca 1200 CE. Cusick claims that the Eries emerged from the Seneca about this time, and this increase may be another part of the Iroquoian retreat from the Toledo area. The Erie had their home near Buffalo, New York, and the Erie Confederation appears to have included those Iroquoian nations which were not in the confederation of the Five Nations. ca. 1250 CE the Five Nations attacked the Eries.

At this time, ca. 1250 CE, the Missasauga were warring with the Five Nations, and the Five Nations attacked the Erie Confederacy. Hence the Talmatan may possibly be identified with the Neutrals. (It has been mentioned that the Lenape knew the Hurons as the Delamattens.)

For the archaeology of western Lake Erie, see David M. Stothers and James R. Graves, Cultural Continuity and Change: The Western Basin, Ontario Iroquois, and Sandusky Traditions, A 1982 Perspective, Archaeology of Eastern North America, Volume 11, 1983, p. 109-142.

55. The Sharp-One was chief, he was the pipe-bearer beyond the river.

56. They [the Talamatan [the Neutrals and the Lenape] rejoiced greatly
that they should fight and slay
the Talegewi [Thiligothe, Chilicothe, Shawnee] towns.

*Again, the "pipe" referred to here is the calumet, and these lines indicate that Sharp-One entered into
diplomatic agreements – in this case a military alliance with the Talamatan, the new allies of the
Lenape.*

FIRE USED AS A WEAPON AGAINST STOCKADES:
THE TALEGAWE [THILIGOTHE, CHILICOTHE] SURRENDER

57. The Stirrer was chief;
the Talegawe [Thiligothe, Chilicothe, Shawnee] towns were too strong.

58. The Man-Who-Built-Fires was chief:
they all gave to him many towns.

59. The Man-Who-Broke-in-Pieces was chief:
all the Talegewi [Thiligothe, Chilicothe, Shawnee] went south.

60. He-Who-Had-Pleasure was chief: all the people rejoiced.

THE TALAMATAN [NEUTRALS] DRIVEN TO
THE NORTH SHORE OF LAKE ERIE

61. They stayed south of the lakes;
while their Talamatan friends stayed north of the lakes.

62. When the Long-and-Mild-Man was chief,
those who were not his friends [the Talamatan] conspired.

63. The Truthful-Man was chief: the Talamatans made war.

64. The Just-and-True-Man was chief: the Talamatans trembled.

VICTORY
Line numbers after Brinton's Part V.

1. All were peaceful, long ago,
there in the Talega [Thiligothe, Chilicothe, Shawnee] lands:

2. The Man-Who-Bore-the-Pipe was chief at the White River.

*Again, the "pipe" referred to here is the calumet, and these lines probably indicate the complete
surrender of the Lenape's enemies .The absolute location of "White River" is unknown.*

3. White-Lynx was chief, and much corn was planted.

457

4. The Good-and-Strong-Man was chief: the people were many.

5. The Recorder was chief: he painted the records.

6. Pretty-Blue-Bird was chief, there was much fruit.

7. Always-There-Man was chief: the towns were many.

THE LENAPE ATTACK UP THE OHIO RIVER:
THE NANTICOKES AND SHAWNEE FORCED TO LEAVE

8. The Man-Who Paddled-up-Stream was chief:
he was much on the rivers.

9. Little-Cloud was chief; many departed,
10. the Nanticokes and the Shawnees going to the south.

THE LENAPE REACH YOUNGSTOWN, OHIO

11. Big-Beaver was chief,
at the White Salt Lick [Youngstown, Ohio].

The area of the Beaver River, which connects with the Ohio River west of today's Pittsburgh, was rich in beaver. The Beaver River connects with the Mahoning River, which flows through Youngstown, Ohio; Youngstown's salt licks were well known in colonial times, and led to the first European settlement there.

12. The Seer, the praised one, went to the west:
13. he went to the west, to the southwest, to the western villages.

THE LENAPE ATTACK TWAKANHAH [CAHOKIA] AGAIN;
TWAKANHAH [CAHOKIA] FALLS Ca 1300 CE

14. The Man-Who-Was-Rich-Down-River was chief,
on the Talega [Thiligothe, Chilicothe, Shawnee] River [Ohio River].

15. The Man-who-Walked was chief, and there was much war:
16. War again with the Towako [Twakanhah, Cahokia] people,
war again with the Stone [Sinako] people,
war again with the northern people [Lowako].

THE LENAPE ATTACK NORTH ACROSS LAKE ERIE

17. The Grandfather-of-the-Boats was chief: he went to lands in boats.

18. The Man-Who-Hunted-In-The-Snow was chief:
he went to the north land.

THE LENAPE ATTACK THE CHEROKEE

19. The one who Looked-About was chief,
he went to the Talega [Tsulagi-Cherokee] Mountains.

[At a very distant time the Tsulagi [Cherokee] were related to the Thiligothe [Chilicothe], who were conquered by the Algonquin Shawnee ca. 850 CE, who subsequently adopted their name.]

LENAPE CAPITOL MOVED TO THE EAST

20. The East-Villager was chief:
he was east of the Talega [Tsulagi-Cherokee].
21. A great land and a wide land was the east land:
22. a land without snakes, a rich land, a pleasant land.

THE LENAPE HAVE THREE FACTIONS

23. The Great Fighter was chief, toward the north.

24. At the Straight River, the River-Loving-Man was chief.

25. The Man-who-was-Becoming-Fat was chief at Sassafras Land.

26. All the hunters made wampum again
at the Great Sea [Atlantic Ocean].

27. Red-Arrow was chief at the stream again.

28. The Painted-Man was chief at the Mighty Water.

LENAPE THREATEN MOHONGWI [MOHICANS]
AND NUNGWI [?]; ENTER INTO PEACE AGREEMENT

29. The Easterners and the Wolves went northeast.

30. The Man-Who-Was-A-Good-Fighter was chief,
and he went to the north.

31. The Mohongwe [Mohicans], and the Lynxes, all trembled.

32. Again an Affable-Man was chief, and he made peace with all:
33. under this great chief, all were friends, all were united,

THREE PART DIVISION CONTINUES

36. Great-Beaver was chief, remaining in Sassafras Land.

37. White-Body was chief on the sea shore.

38. The Peace-Making-Man was chief: he was friendly to all.

THE VIKING ARRIVAL ca 1325 CE

39. He-Who-Made-Mistakes was chief, coming hurriedly.

40. At this time the white men came
on the Eastern Sea [Atlantic Ocean].

41. The-Much-Honored-Man was chief: he was prosperous.

WAR WITH THE CHEROKEE AND KOWETA

42. The Well-Praised-Man was chief. He fought on the south:
43. he fought in the land of the Talega [Tsulagi-Cherokee]
and the Koweta.

These last, the Koweta, are the southern Iroquois nation of Kauwetseka, who were allied with the
Kautanohakau nation and Tuscarora nation in the south.

About 1300-1350 CE this federation came into conflict with the Nanticokes, who the Lenape had
just driven into their lands. This war would last until 1450 CE, when the Five Nations came to the
aid of the Tuscarora. The Lenape likely joined with the Talmatan [Neutrals], in this attack.

44. White-Otter was chief;
he was a friend of the Talamatans [Neutrals].

45. White-Horn was chief;
he went to the Talega [Tsulagi-Cherokee],
46. and to the Illinois [Hilini],
and to the Shawnees,
and to the Kanawhas.

These Kanawas must have lived in the area
where the Kanawa River joins with the Ohio River.

47. The Man-Who-Came-as-a-Friend was chief:
he went to the Great Lakes,
48. visiting all his children, all his friends.

49. The Cranberry-Eater was chief, who was a friend of the Ottawas.

The Ottawas lived on the south shore of Lake Erie between the Erie and Missasauga at Sandusky.

50. North-Walker was chief, he made festivals.

51. Slow-Gatherer was chief at the shore.

52. As the people desired three [nations],
there were three [nations] who grew forth:
52. The Unami, the Minsi, and the Chikini.

WAR WITH THE MOHONGWI [MOHICANS]

53. Man-Who-Fails was chief; he fought the Monhongwi [Mohicans].

54. He-is-Friendly was chief; he scared the Monhongwi [Mohicans].

THE SHAWNEE REGROUP

55. Saluted was chief; there,
56. over there on the Scioto River, he had foes.

As the Lenape moved east, the Shawnee who had fled to the south after their defeat now managed to return and reclaim their lands on the Scioto River in Ohio.

57. White-Crab was chief, a friend of the shore.

THE FRENCH AND DUTCH ARRIVE

58. The Man-who-Watched was chief: he looked toward the sea.
59. At this time, from the north and the south, the white men came.

FAMOUS LAST WORDS:

60. They are peaceful; they have great things; who are they?

ADDITIONAL FRAGMENTS OF THE HISTORY

SUTTON'S ACCOUNT

Adapted from the account of some Lenape elders, acquired by Benjamin Sutton, a captive for some years among the Lenape; acquired from Sutton by the missionary Charles Beatty during his trip of 1767; preserved by Beatty in his work Journal of a Two Months Tour, London, 1768; and cited by Daniel Brinton, The Lenape and their Legends, Philadelphia, 1885, page 138.

"Of old time the people were divided by a river; nine parts of ten passed over the river, with one part remaining behind.

"A king of the nation, where they formerly lived, far to the west, left his kingdom to his two sons. The one son making war upon the other, the later son thereupon determined to depart and seek some new habitation. Accordingly he set out, accompanied by a number of his people.

"After wandering to and fro for the space of 40 years, they at length came to the Delaware River, where they settled 370 years ago. The way they keep an account of this is by putting a black bead of wampum every year on a belt they keep for this purpose. "

Sutton heard this account some time before the year 1767 CE, the year he met Beatty. Taking 370+ years from 1767 CE, we arrive at a date of 1397 CE or so; moving back another 40 year, we arrive at a date of 1357 CE, which is close to dates established by archaeological means for the final fall of the city of Twakanha (Cahokia), ca. 1310 CE. These dates correspond to the period of the Maunder Minimum, one of the cyclic climate collapses most likely caused by the regular fluctuation in the Sun's internal fusion reaction due to the effects of Jupiter's gravity.

HECKEWELDER'S ACCOUNT

A late and highly modified version of part of the Lenape history was preserved by the Moravian missionary John Heckewelder in his Account of the History, Manners, and Customs of the Indian Nations.

Heckewelder's recording was often quoted in part by various early European authors to create a mythical people, the Allegewi, separate from the first peoples, to whom these authors ascribed the creation of any advanced ritual center. The Tallegewi, or Tsulagi, as was seen above, were an ancient people who had migrated from the Gulf of Mexico around 4,000 BCE. Their name was preserved by the Cherokee (Tsuragi), and by the Shawnee as Chilicothe (Thiligothe). The Thiligothe were one of the nations the algonquin Shawnee conquered and absorbed around 850 CE during their migration into the south.

Heckewelder's version was late, and Lenape claims of tribal affiliation as given by Heckewelder in this account are also known to be incorrect. In particular, as the Lenape used "Mengwe" to refer to Iroquoian peoples, and Heckewelder identified these as the Five Nations, as he had no knowledge of other Iroquoian peoples living at this earlier period in today's lower Michigan.

What follows has been adapted from that preserved in the Transactions of the American Philosophical Society, Volume III, page 388, and cited by Daniel Brinton, The Lenape and their Legends, Philadelphia, 1885, pages 140-144

The Lenni Lenape resided many hundreds of years ago in a very distant country in the western part of the American continent.

They determined on migrating eastward, and accordingly set out together in a body.

After a very long journey, and many encampments along the way, they at last arrived on the Na Maesi-Sipu [Mississippi River], where they fell in with the Mengwe, who had likewise emigrated from a distant country, and had struck upon the Mississipi River higher up. The Mengwe's object was the same as that of the Lenape: they were proceeding on eastward, until they should find a country that pleased them.

The spies who the Lenape had sent forward for the purpose of reconnoitering had discovered long before their arrival there that the country east of the Mississippi River was inhabited by a very powerful nation, who had many large towns built on the great rivers flowing through their lands. Those people called themselves the Talligeu or Talligewi...

When the Lenape arrived on the banks of the Mississippi River, they sent a message to the Tallegewi [Thiligothe, Shawnee] to request permission to settle themselves in their neighborhood. This was refused them, but they received leave to pass through the country and seek a settlement further to the eastward.

As was seen above in the Walum Olum, this is the flanking maneuver which the Lenape undertook in response to their defeat by the Twakanha (Towakon, "Cahokia").

They accordingly began to cross the Na Maesi Sipu [Mississippi River], when the Tallegewi [Thiligothe, Shawnee], seeing that their numbers were so very great, and in fact they consisted of many thousands, made a furious attack on those who had crossed, threatening them all with destruction if they dared to persist in coming over to their side of the river.

Having united their forces, the Lenape and Mengwi declared war against the Tallegewi [Thiligothe, Shawnee], and great battles were fought, in which many warriors died on both sides. The enemy fortified their large towns and erected fortifications, especially on the large rivers and near lakes, where they were successively attacked and sometimes stormed by the allies.

An engagement took place in which hundreds fell, who were afterwards buried in holes or laid together in heaps and covered over with earth.

No quarter was given, so that the Tallegewi, at last, finding that their destruction was inevitable if they persisted in their obstinacy, abandoned the country to the conquerors, and fled down the Mississippi River, from whence they never returned.

While the Chilicothe would flee south, they did return – this must refer to the Towako, the Twakanhah of "Cahokia".

In the end the conquerors divided the country between themselves. The Mengwe made their choice of the lands in the vicinity of the Great Lakes and on their tributary streams, and the Lenape took possession of the country to the south. For a long period of time the two nations resided peaceably in this country, and increased very fast.

Some of their most enterprising huntsmen and warriors crossed the great swamps, and falling on streams running to the eastward, followed them on down to the Great Bay River, thence into the Bay itself.

Heckewelder understood the "Great Bay River" as the Potomac River, and the "Bay" as the Chesapeake Bay, but perhaps the "Great Bay River" is today's Delaware River, and the "Bay" is Delaware Bay.

As they pursued their travels, partly by land, and partly by water, sometimes near and at other times on the Great Salt-Water Lake [the Atlantic Ocean], they discovered the Great River [the Delaware River]; and from there exploring still eastward, in the Scheyichbi country [New Jersey], they arrived at another great stream [the Hudson River].

At last they settled on the four great rivers, which you call the Delaware River, the Hudson River, the Susquehanna River, and the Potomac River, and made the Delaware River, which they called the Lenape whittuck, (the Lenape River) the center of their possessions.

The whole of the nation did not reach this country; many remained behind, in order to assist that great body of people who had not crossed the Na Maesi-Sipu [Mississippi River], but instead had retreated into the interior of the country on the other side.

The nation finally became divided into three separate bodies: the larger body, one half of the whole, settled on the Atlantic Ocean; the other half was again divided into two parts, the strongest one of which remained beyond the Mississippi River; and the remainder are where we left them, on the east side of that river.

Those of the Lenape who made their houses on the shores of the Atlantic Ocean divided themselves into three tribes. Two of these tribes, the Undmi (Turtle) and the Unalachigo (Turkey), chose those grounds to settle on which lay nearest to the ocean, between the coast and the high mountains.

As they multiplied, their settlements extended from the Mohicanittuck (the River of the Mohicans, [Hudson River]), to the Potomac River.

This line refers to the war with the Mohicans which the Walum Olum testified to above.

The third tribe, the Minsi [the Wolf, (Monseys)], chose to live back of the other two… They extended their settlements from the Minisink, a place named after them, where they had their council seat or fire, up to the Hudson River on the east, and to the west or southward far beyond the Susquehanna River.

From the above three tribes, the Undmi (Turtle), Unalachiga (Turkey), and the Minsi (Wolf),
sprang many others...

The Mahicanni, or Mohicans, who spread themselves over all that country which now composes the eastern states...and the Nanticokes, who proceeded far to the south, in Maryland and Virginia...

These last two claims are most likely spurious.

FRAGMENTS OF THE BIG HOUSE CEREMONY:
ANOTHER VERSION?

This late fragment of the legend is given in "Native American Spirituality of the Eastern Woodlands" edited by Elizabeth Tooker, who refers to "A Study of the Delaware Indian Big House Ceremony" by Frank G. Speck, which is unavailable to me. This may possibly contain other parts of the entire migration oral cycle, or it may contain parts of one Lenape variant of it.

"The first beginning of this Big House was the beginning long ago of that worship by the Lenape, now called ngammin, when there was a quaking of the Earth throughout where the Lenape lived."

I apologize to the reader for what little of this fragment is given here. The earthquakes continued, with crevices opening, and dust and smoke and then a tar like substance coming out of the ground, which the Lenape called the Breath of the Evil Creator. This may refer to an eruption of crude oil along the Pacific coast.

(Footnotes)
[1] For the archaeology of western Lake Erie, see David M. Stothers and James R. Graves, *Cultural Continuity and Change: The Western Basin, Ontario Iroquois, and Sandusky Traditions, A 1982 Perspective*, Archaeology of Eastern North America, Volume 11, 1983, p. 109-142.